CELL BIOLOGY

F O U R T H   E D I T I O N
O F
G E N E R A L   C Y T O L O G Y

E. D. P. De ROBERTIS, M.D.

Professor and Director of the Institute
of General Anatomy and Embryology,
Faculty of Medicine,
University of Buenos Aires

WIKTOR W. NOWINSKI
Ph.D. (Cantab.), Dr. Phil. (Berne)

Research Professor of Biochemistry,
Director of the Cell Biology Unit,
Department of Surgery,
University of Texas Medical School

FRANCISCO A. SAEZ, Ph.D.

Head of the Department of Cytogenetics,
Institute for the Investigation of
Biological Sciences,
Montevideo, Uruguay

W. B. SAUNDERS COMPANY
Philadelphia and London 1965

1st Spanish Edition   1946
2nd Spanish Edition   1952
3rd Spanish Edition   1955
1st Japanese Edition   1956
2nd Japanese Edition   1958
4th Spanish Edition   1960
1st Russian Edition   1962
5th Spanish Edition   1963
6th Spanish Edition   1965

Cell Biology

PREFACE
TO THE
FOURTH EDITION

In the preface to the first Spanish edition of this book—then entitled *General Cytology*—published in 1946 by El Ateneo of Buenos Aires, we stated:

"This book originally arose from the need for a synthesis in the Spanish language of the most important aspects of modern cytology.

"In recent years this branch of biology has shown rapid progress and has become fundamental to the study of the structure and function of living organisms. The cell can be regarded as the vital unit of organisms and the anatomic and physiologic substrate of biologic phenomena. In its morphologic aspect, modern cytology has gone beyond simple description of structures visible to the light microscope; by the application of new methods, an analysis has been begun of submicroscopic organization—the architectural arrangement of the molecules and micelles composing living matter. In this functional aspect, it has transcended the stage of pure description of physiologic changes, and seeks an explanation of them in the intimate physicochemical and metabolic processes of protoplasm. Finally, modern cytology, based on the nuclear structures, has tried to interpret and explain the phenomena of heredity, sex, variation, mutation and evolution of living organisms."

Through the two decades that have elapsed, these postulates have been valid, but progress has been so rapid and revolutionary that we revised each edition extensively and now, in this fourth edition, have revised the book entirely. We have adopted the new title *Cell Biology* not only to stress the profound changes that have been introduced, but to emphasize the cell as a fundamental unit in biology.

While in recent years we have been spectators of the extraordinary development of molecular biology, which stresses the fundamental role of macromolecules such as the proteins and nucleic acids, it is again evident that these advances should be integrated within the framework of the cell as the true structural and functional organization of living matter.

In this book, the cell is analyzed at all levels of organization using the various optical instruments (e.g., light and electron microscopes, x-ray diffraction) that are able to reveal its subcellular, macromolecular and molecular architecture. At the same time the chemical composition and metabolism of the cell are studied cytochemically and functionally by analyzing the most important manifestations of cellular activity, such as contractility, excitability, permeability, nutrition and secretion. This integration is further stressed in the study of the macromolecules that carry biologic information, of the chromosomes, cell division and the cytologic and molecular bases of genetics.

This book is intended primarily for college courses in cytology, cell biology, general biology, general physiology, general zoology, general botany and cytogenetics, and for students who, for purposes of teaching or investigation in other fields of biology such as medicine, genetics, physiology, agronomy or veterinary medicine, wish to gain a general view of modern cytology.

The content of the book has been organized in a manner that is most useful to the student, going from simple to more complex matters. Thus chapters that review the chemistry of the cell, the enzymes and metabolism are at the beginning of the book, and the study of elementary macromolecular structures and membrane models introduces the study of the structural aspects of the cell. To keep the book within reasonable limits, we have incorporated the new material at the expense of older, less essential material. Most figures are new, and numerous tables and diagrams serving as teaching aids have been added.

The material is now divided into 23 chapters instead of 17 as in the last edition. Following two introductory chapters, the other 21 are organized into seven parts entitled: Molecular Components of the Cell, Methods for the Study of the Cell, Structural Bases of the Cell, The Cytoplasm and Cytoplasmic Organoids, Cellular Bases of Cytogenetics, Molecular Bases of Cytogenetics, and Cell Physiology. The entirely new chapters are concerned with the elementary structures, human cytogenetics, molecular genetics, membrane permeability, nerve conduction and synaptic transmission.

Because of the nature of the present book, only a few references are given at the end of each chapter and these are divided into two groups. Under General References is a list of books or general review articles that can be used for supplementary reading or as a guide to more specific literature. No attempt has been made to cover the literature extensively, and the few Cited References mentioned by number in the text should also be considered as keys to recent information in cell biology.

We are indebted to numerous of our colleagues for their help in the improvement of this edition. We would like to mention particularly Dr. Amanda Pellegrino de Iraldi for helping with the electron micrograph illustrations; Prof. José L. Reissig, Prof. Hersch M. Gerschenfeld and Dr. Carlos Tandler, for critically reading the chapters on molecular genetics, synaptic transmission and cytochemistry of the nucleus, respectively; and Drs. José A. Zadunaisky and Arnaldo Lasansky for their contributions to the chapters dealing with the cell membrane and cell permeability.

We would like to thank the many colleagues who have contributed tables and figures to enrich the value of this book.

In the preparation of the manuscript Misses Alicia Fernández Cowper, Julia Elena Connaughton, and Susana Mansfield and Mr. Walter Ludwig were most helpful. We are very much indebted to the W. B. Saunders Company for the excellent editorial work and presentation of this new edition.

We were stimulated in our task by the good reception this book has received in its several English, Spanish and Japanese editions and also the recent Russian edition. We have received numerous suggestions and criticisms from our colleagues and students of many countries. We cannot enumerate these here, but all of them have contributed to the improvement of this edition. We want to thank particularly Professors George E. Palade, Elof Carlson, Donald R. Ritchie and Miriam Schurin for critically reading the former edition and for numerous valuable suggestions. We are especially grateful to Prof. Warren Andrew, whose excellent translation of the first English edition became a starting point for the success of our book in the English speaking countries.

A book that tries to interpret and translate into didactic terms the extraordinary advances made by modern cytology is possible only with the unselfish collaboration of all who contribute to the permanent progress of this field of biologic knowledge.

E. De Robertis
W. W. Nowinski
F. A. Saez

CONTENTS

PART ONE. MOLECULAR COMPONENTS OF THE CELL

PART FIVE. CELLULAR BASES OF CYTOGENETICS

GENERAL INTRODUCTION TO THE STUDY OF THE NUCLEUS AND
CHROMOSOMES 205

    The Nucleus 205
            Morphology 205
            General Structure of the Interphase Nucleus 207
        Mitosis and Meiosis 207
    Chromosomes 210
            Morphology 210
            Chromonema and Chromonema Cycle 213
            Euchromatin, Heterochromatin and Chromomeres 217
        Special or Giant Chromosomes 219
            Polytene Chromosomes 219
            Lampbrush Chromosomes 221
        References 223

CHAPTER 14

CELL DIVISION: MITOSIS AND MEIOSIS 224

    Mitosis 225
        Analysis of Mitosis 225
        The Cell Center and Mitotic Apparatus 229
            Centriole and Pericentriolar Structures 229
            Centriole Cycle during Mitosis 231
            Centrioles and Cilia 233
        Mitotic Apparatus 233
            Isolation and Biochemical Studies of the Mitotic
                Apparatus 234
            Mitotic Apparatus and Anaphase Movements 236
            Cytokinesis (Cell Cleavage) 236
    Meiosis 237
            Germ Cells of Animals 237
            Germ Cells of Flowering Plants 237
        Analysis of Meiosis 238
            Meiotic Division I 239
            Meiotic Division II 244
        References 245

CHAPTER 15

CYTOGENETICS. CHROMOSOMAL BASES OF GENETICS 247

    Laws of Heredity 247
        Law of Segregation 247
            Genotype and Phenotype 249
        Law of Independent Assortment 249
    Linkage and Crossing Over 250

PART SIX. MOLECULAR BASES OF CYTOGENETICS

CHAPTER 1

INTRODUCTION. HISTORY AND GENERAL CONCEPTS OF CELL BIOLOGY

structure. The cell can be considered as an organism in itself, often very specialized and composed of many elements, the sum of which not only constitutes the cellular unit, but has particular significance in the organism as a whole. If by mechanical or other means cellular organization is destroyed, cellular function is likewise altered, and although some vital functions may persist (such as enzymic activity), the cell becomes disorganized and dies.

The development and refinement of microscopic techniques made it possible to obtain further knowledge of cellular structure, not only as it appears in the cell killed by fixation, but also as seen in the living state. Biochemical studies have demonstrated that the products of living matter, and even the living matter itself, are composed of the same elements that make up the inorganic world. Biochemists have isolated from the complex mixture of cell constituents not only inorganic components but much more complex molecules such as proteins, fats, polysaccharides and nucleic acids.

Ancient philosophers and naturalists, particularly Aristotle and Paracelsus, arrived at the conclusion that "All animals and plants, however complicated, are constituted by few elements which are repeated in each one of them." They were referring to the macroscopic structures of an organism, such as roots, leaves and flowers common to different plants or segments and organs that are repeated in the animal kingdom. Many centuries later, owing to the invention of magnifying lenses, the world of microscopic dimensions was discovered. In the 19th century, the *cell* came to be regarded as "the unit of living matter" (Herbert Spencer) or "the primary representative of life" (Claude Bernard). It also was found that a single cell can constitute an entire organism, as in Protozoa, or it can be one of many cells that are grouped and differentiated into tissues and organs, forming a multicellular organism.

The cell is thus a fundamental structural and functional unit of living organisms, just as is the atom in chemical

LEVELS OF ORGANIZATION IN BIOLOGY

The advance of knowledge concerning the composition of the cell—particularly that resulting from the application of modern physical methods of investigation, such as polarization optics, x-ray diffraction and electron microscopy—has produced a fundamental change in the interpretation of cellular structures. For example, it has been demonstrated that beyond the organization visible with the light microscope are a number of more elementary structures at the macromolecular level that constitute the "ultrastructure" of the cell. We find ourselves in the era of *molecular biology*, that is, the study of the shape, aggregation and orientation of the molecules and of the intramolecular structure of the essential constituents that compose the cellular system as a unit. Discovery of this submicroscopic world is of basic importance, because among the elements that compose it, such as macromolecules, enzymes, substrates and metabolites, all

1

the chemical and energy transformations that characterize vital phenomena are produced.

Modern studies on living matter demonstrate that there is a combination of levels of organization which are integrated and that this integration results in the vital manifestations of the organism. The concept of levels of organization as developed by Needham[1] and others implies that in the entire universe—in both the nonliving and living worlds—there are such various levels of different complexity that "The laws or rules that are encountered at one level may not appear at lower levels." One must remember that the whole is more than a sum of its parts; e.g., sodium chloride has characteristics that neither sodium nor chlorine has. Similarly, the properties of large molecules (e.g., glycogen) cannot be predicted from those of their components. This concept can be applied to the different structural constituents of a cell or to the association of numerous cells in a tissue.

Although matter is similar in these respects, there are fundamental differences between organic and inorganic matter. According to our present concepts, while in the nonliving world there is a continuous tendency toward reaching a thermodynamic equilibrium with a random distribution of matter and energy, in the living organism a high degree of structure and function is maintained by a method of energy transformation based on continuous input and output of matter and energy.[2]

LIMITS AND DIMENSIONS IN BIOLOGY

Table 1–1 shows the limits that separate the study of biologic systems at different dimensional levels. In this classification, the boundaries between different levels of organization are imposed artificially by the resolving power of the instruments employed, and it can be seen that a great deal of overlapping exists. The human eye cannot resolve (discriminate) two points separated by less than 0.1 mm (100 μ). Most cells, in general, are much smaller and must be studied under the full resolving power of the light microscope (0.2 μ). However, most cellular components are even smaller and require the resolution of the electron microscope.

From a morphologic point of view, all these fields of biology fall within the discipline of *anatomy* (Gr. to cut apart), which etymologically implies the separation of the different components in such a way as to identify and study them both as isolated parts and as integrated parts of the whole organism. Bennett,[3] in a lucid interpretation of these concepts, says that "the operational approaches to all branches of anatomy have essential features in common." Whether working in the field of gross, microscopic or molecular anatomy, one generally proceeds by separating the objects of interest. The methodological approach is the same whether a scalpel is used to dissect the cadaver or sections are made for the light microscope or the electron microscope or whether subcellular components are separated by homogenization and centrifugation. Also into this category falls the resolution of different structures into their molecular or atomic elements by means of optical instruments using different electromagnetic waves (Fig. 1–1). (For further discussion of this problem, the reader is referred to the article by Weiss, 1962.)

In order to build up an image of the molecular organization of a biological system, one should start with knowledge of the main constituent molecules, particularly those of high molecular weight such as nucleic acids, proteins and polysaccharides. Lipids, although of smaller molecular size, also play an important role as structural components of the cells. In order to understand their organized structure in relation to that of water and small molecules, these components must be studied from the point of view of their size, shape, charge, stereochemical characteristics and main reacting groups. Such a study is difficult when the molecules are isolated or distributed at random. Frequently, however, the molecules arrange themselves into repetitive periodic structures, which can be analyzed with crystallographic techniques. Of these, the most precise

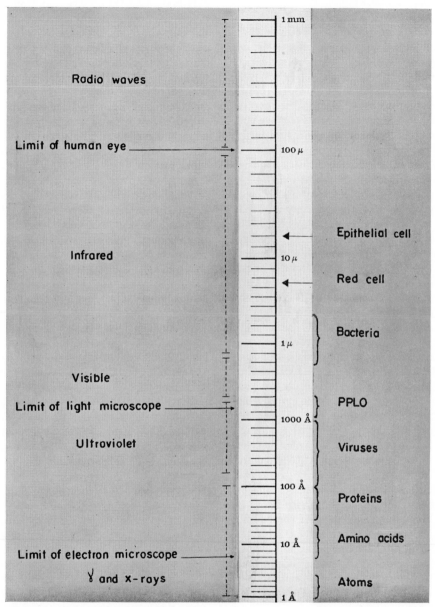

FIGURE 1–1. Logarithmic scale of microscopic dimensions. Each main division represents a size ten times smaller than the preceding one. *To the left,* the position of the different wavelengths of the electromagnetic spectrum and the limits of the human eye, the light microscope and the electron microscope. *To the right,* the sizes of different cells, bacteria, PPLO (the smallest living organism), viruses, molecules and atoms. (Modified from M. Bessis.)

and of highest resolution are the x-ray diffraction techniques, which permit determination of not only the molecular configuration of the crystal but also the three-dimensional disposition of the atoms within the molecule. Recently great advances have been made in the detailed analysis of the molecular configuration of proteins, nucleic acids and even of larger molecular complexes, such as certain viruses. This important field, which started to flourish only in the last decade, is now called *molecular biology* (Table 1–1).

At a cytologic level, *ultrastructure* or *submicroscopic morphology* is more concerned with the larger repeating units that can be analyzed with microscopic techniques. The first technique to be applied, about a century ago, was *polarization microscopy.* German workers, starting with Nägeli and Ballentine, first recognized ordered structures within biologic systems. Later these studies became quantitative and considerably extended by the work of W. J. Schmidt. In this technique use is made of the effect that anisotropic structures have on polarized light (see Chap. 4).

Finally, the most important tool in the study of submicroscopic morphology is the *electron microscope.* With this instrument, direct information can be obtained about structures ranging between 10 and 2000 Å or more, thus bridging the gap between observations with the light microscope and the world of macromolecules. Results obtained by application of electron microscopy have changed the field of cytology so much that a large part of the present book discusses the achievements obtained by this technique.

In Figure 1–1 the sizes of different cells, bacteria, viruses and molecules are indicated in a logarithmic scale and compared with the wavelengths of various radiations as well as the limits of resolution of the eye, the light microscope and the electron microscope. Notice that the light microscope (limit of resolution 2000 Å) introduces a 500-fold increase in resolution over the eye (10^6 Å), and the electron microscope (10 Å) a 200-fold increase over the light microscope.

Some cytologic structures, such as mitochondria, centrioles, chromosomes and nucleoli, can be resolved with the optical microscope, but many more, such as ribosomes, the plasma membrane, myofilaments, chromosomic microfibrils, neurotubules and synaptic vesicles, which are studied in different parts of

this book, can be resolved only with the electron microscope. On the other hand, most molecular dimensions are much smaller than these limits. For example, a molecule of glucose has a diameter of only 5 Å. One billion of these molecules would be necessary to make up the smallest particle visible with the light microscope. A million particles the size of a protein molecule (100 Å) would be needed to form one mitochondrion.

In several chapters of this book examples are given of the different levels of organization of biologic structures through the use of different magnifying instruments, but from the very start the reader must become aware of the importance of these concepts and be able to visualize the proper level of organization that is being considered, i.e., anatomic, histologic, cytologic, ultrastructural or molecular (Table 1–1).

Table 1–2 shows the general relationships between some of the linear dimensions used in cytology and the weight of material used in different fields of chemical analysis of living matter. Familiarity with these relationships is essential to the study of cell biology. The weight of the important components of the cell is expressed in picograms (1 pg $= 1 \mu\mu$g or 10^{-12} gm).

The Smallest Mass of Living Matter

The typical cell, with the nucleus and cytoplasm and all the cellular organoids, which is described in this book, is not the smallest mass of living matter or protoplasm (Gr. *protos* first + *plasma* formation); simpler or more primitive

TABLE 1–1. DIFFERENT FIELDS OF BIOLOGY

DIMENSION	FIELD	STRUCTURE	METHOD
0.1 mm (100 μ) and larger	anatomy	organs	eye and simple lenses
100 μ to 10 μ	histology	tissues ⎱	various types of light microscopes,
10 μ to 0.2 μ (2000 Å)	cytology	cells, bacteria ⎰	x-ray microscopy
2000 Å to 10 Å	submicroscopic morphology ultrastructure molecular biology	cell components, viruses	polarization microscopy, electron microscopy
smaller than 10 Å	molecular and atomic structure	arrangement of atoms	x-ray diffraction

units of life exist. Thus, unlike the higher types of cells which have a true nucleus (eukaryotic cells), prokaryotic cells (Gr. *karyon* nucleus), which comprise most viruses, bacteria and some algae, lack a nuclear envelope, and the nuclear substance is mixed or is ·in direct contact with the rest of the protoplasm. From the historical viewpoint, it is interesting to recall that in 1868 Haeckel postulated as the most primitive form of organized substance the so-called "*Monera*," i.e., "masses of homogeneous proteins, structureless and amorphous," which he thought to be formed directly from inorganic substance.

The discovery of the *viruses* at the end of the 19th century shed a new light on knowledge of the more primitive organisms. Known at first by the property of passing through pores of porcelain filters and by the pathologic changes which they produce in cells, all viruses are now within the range of the electron microscope and can be recognized morphologically and studied in their macromolecular organization. Although viruses have properties common to living organisms, such as autoreproduction, heredity and mutation, they are dependent on the energy and substrates of the living cells they enter. For this reason they can hardly be considered the most primitive organisms.

Among agents that have the smallest living mass, the best suited for study are microbes of the so-called pleuropneumonia group which produce infectious diseases in different animals and which can be cultured in vitro like any bacteria. These agents range in diameter from 0.25 μ (the limit of resolution of the optical microscope) to 0.1 μ; thus

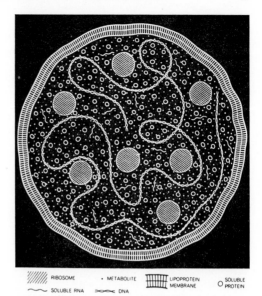

FIGURE 1–2. Schematic representation of a single cell of the pleuropneumonia organism (PPLO), the smallest living cell. Deoxyribonucleic acid (DNA), ribonucleic acid (RNA), soluble protein, lipoprotein membrane, ribosomes and metabolites are represented schematically. (From H. J. Morowitz and M. E. Tourtellotte.[4])

their size corresponds to that of some of the large viruses. This microbe is of general biological interest because it is a living mass a thousand times smaller than the average size bacterium (diameter $= 1 \mu$) and a million times smaller than a cell, and approaches the order of magnitudes found in molecular dimensions.

Figure 1–2, taken from the interesting article of Morowitz and Tourtellotte,[4] is a diagram of the probable molecular structure of such a primitive organism. As in all cells, a lipoprotein membrane constitutes a molecular barrier with the surrounding medium and, by controlling the entrance and exit of smaller mole-

TABLE 1–2. RELATIONSHIPS BETWEEN LINEAR DIMENSIONS AND WEIGHTS IN CYTOCHEMISTRY*

LINEAR DIMENSION	WEIGHT	TERMINOLOGY
1 cm	1 gm	conventional biochemistry
1 mm	1 mg or 10^{-3} gm	microchemistry
100 μ	1 μg or 10^{-6} gm	histochemistry ⎰ ultramicrochemistry
1 μ	1 $\mu\mu$g (or 1 picogram or 10^{-12} gm)	cytochemistry ⎱

* From Engström, A., and Finean, J. B. (1958) *Biological ultrastructure.* Academic Press, New York.

cules, contributes to the establishment of a special internal milieu for the protoplasm. In the interior are: long, double-stranded molecules of deoxyribonucleic acid (DNA), which contain the genetic information that governs the synthesis of other components of the cell; ribonucleic acid molecules, lying free or forming part of small particles or *ribosomes;* and soluble, spherical proteins, which form more than 40 different enzymes.

The study of this elementary organization of living matter is of paramount importance to cell biology because it is the extreme simplification of the various patterns of structure and function that are found in higher cells.

EARLY HISTORY OF CYTOLOGY

Cytology (or, as it is called today, cell biology) is one of the youngest branches of the life sciences. It was recognized as a separate discipline by the end of the last century. The early history is intimately bound to the development of optical lenses and to their combination in the construction of the compound microscope (Gr. *mikros* small + *skopein* to see, to look).

The term *cell* (Gr. *kytos* cell; L. *cella* hollow space) was first used by Robert Hooke (1665) in describing his investigations on "the texture of cork by means of magnifying lenses." In these observations, repeated by Grew and Malpighi in different plants, only the cavities ("utricles" or vesicles") of the cellulose wall were recognized. In the same century and the beginning of the next, Leeuwenhoek (1674) discovered free cells as opposed to the "walled in" cells of Hooke and Grew and observed some organization within cells, particularly the nucleus in some erythrocytes. For more than a century afterwards, this was all that was known about the cell.

Cell Theory

More directly related to the origin of cell biology was the establishment of the *cell theory*, probably the broadest and most fundamental of all biologic generalizations. It states in its present form that all living beings—animals, plants or protozoa—are composed of cells and cell products. This theory resulted from numerous investigations that started at the beginning of the 19th century (Mirbel, 1802; Oken, 1805; Lamarck, 1809; Dutrochet, 1824; Turpin, 1826), and finally led to the studies of the botanist Schleiden (1838) and then to the zoologist Schwann (1839), who established it in a definite form.

The cell theory has illuminated all the fields of biological research. As an immediate consequence it was established that every cell is formed by division of another cell. Much later, with the progress of biochemistry, it was shown that there are fundamental similarities in the chemical composition and metabolic activities of all cells. The function of the organism as a whole was also recognized to be a result of the sum of the activities and interactions of the cell units.[2]

The cell theory was soon applied to pathology by Virchow (1858). Kölliker extended it to embryology after it was demonstrated that the organism develops from the fusion of two cells, the spermatozoon and the ovum.

A more general and biologic approach was reached at the same time by investigators such as Brown (1831), who established that the nucleus is a fundamental and constant component of the cell, and by Wagner (1832), who discovered the nucleolus. Others (Dujardin, Schultze, Purkinje, von Mohl) concentrated on the description of the cell content, termed the protoplasm.

Thus the primitive concept of *cell* was transformed into that of a mass of protoplasm limited in space by a cell membrane and possessing a nucleus. The protoplasm surrounding the nucleus became known as the *cytoplasm* to distinguish it from the *karyoplasm*, the protoplasm of the nucleus.

Once these fundamental theories and concepts were established, the progress of cytologic knowledge was extremely rapid. The extraordinary changes produced in the nucleus at each cell division attracted the attention of a great number of investigators. For example, the phenomenon of *amitosis*, or direct division (Remak), and of indirect division were discovered by Flemming in animals and by Strasburger in plants. Indirect division was also called *karyokinesis* (Schleicher, 1878) or *mitosis* (Flemming, 1880). It was proved that fundamental to mitosis is the formation of the nuclear filaments, or *chromosomes* (Waldeyer, 1890), and their equal division between the nuclei (daughter cells). Other discoveries of importance were the fertilization of the ovum and the fusion of the two pronuclei (O. Hertwig, 1875). In the cytoplasm the cell center (van Beneden, Boveri), the mitochondria (Altmann, Benda) and the reticular substance (Golgi) were discovered.

While studying tissues as cellular aggregates, biologists concentrated more and more on the cell as a fundamental unit of life. In 1892, O. Hertwig published his monograph *Die Zelle und das Gewebe* in which he attempted a general synthesis of biological phenomena, based on the characteristics of the cell, its structure and function. In this book he showed that the solution of biological problems is to be found in cellular processes, thus creating cytology as a separate branch of biology. It is characteristic that the later editions of his book were changed to *General biology.* (For details of the development of cytology, see reference 5.)

RECENT PROGRESS IN CELL BIOLOGY

Although scientific progress is essentially evolutionary and advances are continuously made on the bases of previous achievements, the rate of progress varies at different times. If one follows the development of cell biology in the present century it is evident that cytologic knowledge has advanced for two reasons: (1) the resolving power of instrumental analysis, essentially the introduction of electron microscope and x-ray diffraction techniques, and (2) the convergence with other fields of biologic research, especially with genetics, physiology and biochemistry. This has resulted in the application of combined physical and chemical methods to the study of the cell and in an integration of their concepts, which finally broke the artificial boundaries between these sciences. As a direct consequence, biological knowledge has been more firmly established on the basis of the cell and of its molecular constitution.

In the following sections we present in general terms the results of the impact that the convergence of these fields has had in the modern aspects and orientation of cell and molecular biology.

Cytology and Genetics: Cytogenetics

By the middle of the 19th century the universality of cell division as the central phenomenon in the reproduction of organisms was established, and Virchow expressed it in the famous aphorism *"Omnis cellula e cellula."* From this time on the study of cells and that of heredity and evolution converged, as was well stated by Wilson: "Heredity appears as a consequence of the genetic continuity of the cells by division."

Observations on the germ cells made by van Beneden, Flemming, Strasburger, Boveri and others gave support to the theory of the continuity of the germ plasma proposed by Weissmann in 1883 to explain the transmission mechanism of hereditary characters. This theory stated that the carrier of hereditary factors from one generation to the next takes place through the continuity of what he called *germ plasm,* located in the sex elements (spermatozoon and ovum), and not through somatic cells.

The discovery of fertilization in animals, foreseen by O. Hertwig but observed directly by H. Fol (1879), and in plants, by Strasburger, led to the theory that the cell nucleus is the bearer of the physical basis of heredity. Furthermore, Roux postulated that chromatin, the substance of the nucleus that constitutes the chromosomes, must be aligned, and Weissmann stated that the hereditary units are disposed along the chromosomes in an orderly manner.

The fundamental laws of heredity were discovered by Gregor Mendel in 1865, but at that time the cytologic changes produced in the sex cells were not sufficiently known to permit an interpretation of the independent segregation of hereditary characters (see Chap. 15). For this and other reasons, Mendel's work fell into oblivion until the botanists Correns, Tschermack and De Vries in 1901 independently rediscovered Mendel's laws. At this time cytology was advanced enough so that the mechanism of distribution of the hereditary units postulated by Mendel could be understood and explained. It was known that the sex cells have a double, or *diploid,* hereditary constitution, whereas in the reproductive cells or gametes this constitution is single, or *haploid.* In addition, cytologists had observed that the cycle that the chromosomes undergo in *meiosis* of germ cells was related to hereditary phenomena.

In direct accord with these findings, McClung (1901–1902) suggested that sex determination was related to some special chromosomes, and this theory was later corroborated by Stevens and Wilson (1905). The experimental demonstration of the chromosome theory of heredity was finally established by Boveri and Baltzer, but it was Morgan and his collaborators, Sturtevant and Bridges, who assigned to the *genes* (Johannsen) or hereditary units, definite loci within the chromosomes. Thereafter experimental research on heredity and evolution became a separate branch of biology, which Bateson in 1906 called *genetics.* However, almost from the beginning the science of genetics maintained a close relationship with cytology, and from the convergence of both originated cytogenetics (see Chap. 15). In the past decade the study of genetics has become linked to biochemistry and reached the molecular level, and thus the new fields of biochemical and molecular genetics have been established.

Cytology and Physiology: Cell Physiology

Most of the early cytologic knowledge was based on observations of fixed and stained cells and tissues; this led to the formation of different theories regarding the physicochemical structure of protoplasm. By 1899, interest shifted toward the study of living cells mainly owing to the work of Fischer and Hardy who showed that several of the structures observed in fixed cells could be reproduced by the action of fixatives on colloidal models. Various types of movements, such as cyclosis (cytoplasmic streaming), ameboid motion, and ciliary, flagellar and muscular contraction, were studied at a cellular level.

At the end of the 19th century, Overton advanced the theory that the cell membrane was a lipoidal film. Michaelis made membrane models to study the passage of substances and did the first vital staining of mitochondria. However, the actual technique of vital staining (methylene blue) was introduced by Ehrlich in 1881. The basic concepts of cell irritability and nerve function were established by the middle of the 19th century by Du Bois-Reymond, and physiological techniques were then developed for the study of these cells and to measure action potentials and nerve currents.

An important avenue to the study of the living cell was opened in 1909 by Harrison, who demonstrated that nerve cells from an embryo could grow and differentiate in vitro. This gave rise to the technique of *tissue culture,* which together with the work of Carrel had a great impact upon cytology. This technique is still used, and has been developed into many different aspects. One of the main results of this technique was the demonstration that, as in Protozoa (Maupas, Woodruff and others), the cells of Metazoa are potentially immortal. (In fact, Carrel's culture of the embryonic heart has been kept since 1912 through thousands of cell generations.) With the isolation of pure strains of cells, tissue culture became an ideal technique for the study of structure and behavior of living cells. This analysis was greatly improved by the introduction of phase contrast microscopy and by the use of vital staining and microcinematography.

Another method for the study of the physicochemical properties of the living cell—*microsurgery*—came from the field of bacteriology. At the beginning of this century, Schouten and Barber used fine micropipets moved by precision instruments to isolate and culture single bacteria. In 1911, Kite adapted this method to cytology. By introducing a microneedle between the two pronuclei of a recently fertilized egg, he observed that they acted as if attempting to overcome the interposed resistance and complete the conjugation. Levi, Peterfi, Chambers and others have perfected techniques of intracellular operations and have obtained data on the viscosity, hydrogen concentration, redox potential, nucleocytoplasmic relation and similar physicochemical problems.

Among the important phenomena studied in this branch of cell biology are: the nature of the cell membrane and of active transport across membranes, the reaction of cells to changes in environment, and the basic mechanism of cell excitability and contraction, cell nutrition, growth, secretion and other manifestations of cellular activity.

Cytology and Biochemistry: Cytochemistry

Another modern branch of cell biology is *cytochemistry*, which is the result of the convergence of methods and sciences devoted to the chemical and physicochemical analysis of living matter. Among many outstanding biochemical studies were those of Fischer and Hofmeister in 1902, who independently recognized that the protein molecule consists of a small number of amino acids united by the peptide bond. Of similar or even more importance to cell biology were the earlier investigations of Miescher (1869) and Kossel (1891), who, by the analysis of cells of pus, spermatozoa, hemolyzed erythrocytes of birds and other cell types, isolated the nucleic acids, whose basic role in heredity and protein synthesis has been recognized only recently.

Another great advancement was the introduction into biologic thinking of the concept of catalytic activity by Ostwald and the discovery that enzymes are the molecular entities used by the cell to produce the various types of energy transformations necessary for maintenance of living activities. The

main types of cellular oxidations were discovered by Wieland (1903) and by Warburg (1908), but the final mechanism was discovered much later by Keilin (1934). It is interesting to recall that Altmann predicted the relation between mitochondria and cellular oxidations. Batelli and Stern (1912) and Warburg (1913) observed that respiratory enzymes were present in some cytoplasmic particles.

Because of the emphasis on morphology, cytologists were at first very slow in grasping the importance of the biochemical approach; on the other hand, biochemists, because of the emphasis on organic chemistry, had no interest in cell structure and mainly were busy isolating chemical components and studying elementary enzyme reactions. The point of convergence can be traced back to 1934, when Bensley and Hoerr isolated mitochondria from cells by homogenization and differential centrifugation in large enough quantities to permit analysis by chemical and physicochemical methods.

This direction was followed with great success by Claude, Hogeboom and others, and led to the conclusion that mitochondria are centers of cellular oxidations. The isolation of other cellular fractions followed these pioneering studies. Advances in cell fractionation have been of the greatest importance to biology and biochemistry, especially with the development of radioactive tracer techniques which permit a dynamic approach to the study of cell metabolism. Similarly, a great advance was the use of the electron microscope for the observation and characterization of cell fractions. These advances have recently led to the isolation from many different cells not only of mitochondria, but also of chloroplasts, the nucleolus, nerve endings, the Golgi complex, nuclei, chromosomes, ribosomes, the mitotic apparatus and other cell components all of which are described in different chapters of this book.

Modern cytochemistry has also developed along the lines of microchemical and ultramicrochemical analysis with the use of techniques for assay of minute quantities of material and the isolation of single cells and even of parts of cells (see Table 1–2). Chemical analysis can be carried out by cytophotometry, which permits study of the localization of nucleic acids and proteins within parts of a single cell. Other techniques based on physical properties, i.e., fluorometry and x-ray absorption, have given interesting and important results.

Another important branch of cytochemistry arose from the application of numerous enzyme reactions, which could then be observed under the light microscope and, recently, even with the electron microscope. This last approach is of particular interest since it permits the combination of cytochemistry and ultrastructure and thus study of the localization of enzymes at the level of resolution of the electron microscope. Of similar importance have been the radioautographic studies on the localization of radioactive tracers in different cellular structures.

Ultrastructure and Molecular Biology

In studying the limits and dimensions in biology (see Tables 1–1 and 1–2), the impact of instrumental analysis was mentioned and the modern fields of ultrastructure and molecular biology were delineated. These are the most advanced branches of biology in which the merging of cytology with biochemistry, physicochemistry and especially macromolecular and colloidal chemistry becomes increasingly close. Knowledge of the submicroscopic organization or ultrastructure of the cell is of fundamental importance because practically all the functional and physicochemical transformations take place within the molecular architecture of the cell and at a molecular level.

On the other hand, as was so well stated by Heller et al.,[6] molecular biology cannot be considered as something separate from biochemistry and biophysics. There is no problem in molecular biology that is not a problem of biophysics and biochemistry and that would not require biophysical or biochemical methods for its solution. However, the following are having an extraordinary impact on biology: the finding that in

the structure of a protein molecule the exact sequence of amino acids and the three-dimensional arrangement of the polypetide chain go hand in hand with definite biological properties, the studies of active groups in different enzymes, the molecular model of DNA suggested by Watson and Crick in 1953, as well as all the recent knowledge on the stereochemistry of macromolecules. Molecular biology is thus illuminating the fields of genetics (through molecular genetics), biochemistry and even pathology—the latter with establishment of molecular diseases.

Both in ultrastructure and molecular biology the integration between morphology and physiology becomes so intimate that it is impossible to separate them, and the concepts of *form* and of *function* fuse into an inseparable unity.

In summary, it can be said that modern cell biology approaches the problems of the cell at all levels of organization from molecular structure on. It is therefore the common ground where the convergence of genetics, physiology and biochemistry takes place. Modern cytologists, without losing sight of the study of the cell as a morphologic and functional unit within the organism, must be prepared to use all the methods, techniques and concepts of the other sciences and to study biological phenomena at all levels. This is a great challenge, but there is no other way if the life of the cell and of the organism is to be interpreted mechanistically, i.e., on the bases of combinations and associations of atoms and molecules.

LITERARY SOURCES IN CELL BIOLOGY

The preceding considerations on the present scope of cell biology explain why the sources of literature are wide and multidisciplinary. Current studies are presented at scientific meetings and published in specialized periodicals. Of the long list of literary sources that could be made, let us mention only a few of the more specific ones: *Journal of Cell Biology, Experimental Cell Research, Journal of Molecular Biology, Journal of Ultrastructure Research, Zeit-*

schrift für Zellforschung, Journal de Microscopie, Quarterly Journal of Microscopical Science, Journal of Cellular and Comparative Physiology, Journal of General Physiology, Chromosoma, Cytogenetics, Heredity and Hereditas. Papers on cell biology are frequently published in more general periodicals such as Nature, Science, Proceedings of the Royal Society, Proceedings of National Academy of Sciences (Wash.), Comptes Rendus de l'Académie des Sciences and Naturwissenschaften, or even in such specialized publications as Biochemica et Biophysica Acta, Biochemical Journal or Journal of Biological Chemistry.

Reviews of recent advances are found in the International Review of Cytology, Quarterly Review of Biology, Physiological Reviews, Biological Reviews, Advances in Genetics, Plant Physiology, etc.

For compiling a bibliography, special journals which give titles of papers or abstracts of the literature such as Biological Abstracts, Index Medicus, Excerpta Medica, Chemical Abstracts and Berichte über die Wissenschaftliche Biologie are most useful. Journals such as Current Contents or Bulletin Signaletique du Conseil des Recherchés publish titles of all papers which appear in various journals.

In addition there are many monographs, compendia and textbooks that cover different specialized subjects of cell biology, and which will be mentioned in the different chapters of this book. The most recent and of widest coverage is The cell, in six volumes, edited by Brachet and Mirsky.

GENERAL REFERENCES

Alexander, J. (1948) Life: its nature and origin. Reinhold Publishing Corp., New York.

Baker, J. R. Five articles evaluating the cell theory. Quart. J. Micros. Sci., 1948, 89:103; 1949, 90:87; 1952, 93:157; 1953, 94:407; 1955, 96:449.

Bayliss, L. E. (1959–1960) Principles of general physiology. I. The physicochemical background. II. General physiology. Longmans, Green and Co., New York.

Bertalanffy, L. von. (1952) Problems of life. John Wiley & Sons, New York.

Brachet, J., and Mirsky, A. E. (1959–1961) The cell. 6 volumes. Academic Press, New York.

Burnet, F. M. F. (1946) Virus as organism. Harvard University Press, Cambridge, Mass.

Commoner, B. (1961) In defense of biology. Science, 133:1745.

Conklin, E. G. (1940) Cell and protoplasm concept. In: The cell and protoplasm. Amer. Assn. Advance. Sci., Washington, D.C.

Davson, H. (1959) A textbook of general physiology. 2nd Ed. Little, Brown and Co., Boston.

Dawes, B. (1952) A hundred years of biology. The Macmillan Co., New York.

Driesch, H. (1921) Philosophie der Organischen. 2nd Ed. Englemann, Leipzig.

Heilbrunn, L. V. (1952) An outline of general physiology. 3rd Ed. W. B. Saunders Co., Philadelphia.

Heilbrunn, L. V., and Weber, F., eds. (1953–1959) Protoplasmatologia, Handbuch der Protoplasmaforschung. Springer, Vienna.

Hober, R., et al. (1945) Physical chemistry of cells and tissues. The Blakiston Co., New York.

Hughes, A. (1952) Some historical features in cell biology. Internat. Rev. Cytol., 1:1.

Hughes, A. (1959) History of cytology. Abelard-Schuman, London and New York.

Mitchell, P. H. (1956) A textbook of general physiology. McGraw-Hill Book Co., New York.

Needham, J. (1936) Order and life. Yale University Press, New Haven, Conn.

Needham, J. (1942) Biochemistry and morphogenesis. Cambridge University Press, London.

Singer, C. (1931) A short story of biology. Oxford University Press, London.

Singer, C. (1950) A history of biology. Henry Schuman, New York.

Stanley, W. M. (1940) The structure of viruses. In: The cell and protoplasm. Amer. Assn. Advance. Sci., Washington, D.C.

Wald, G. (1955) The origin of life. In: The physics and chemistry of life. Simon and Schuster, New York.

Weiss, P. (1962) From cell to molecule. In: Molecular control of cell activity. (Allen, J. M., ed.) McGraw-Hill Book Co., New York.

Wilson, E. B. (1925) The cell in development and heredity. 3rd Ed. The Macmillan Co., New York.

CITED REFERENCES

1. Needham, J. (1936) Order and life. Yale University Press, New Haven, Conn.

2. Bertalanffy, L. von. (1952) Problems of life. John Wiley & Sons, New York.

3. Bennett, H. S. (1956) Anat. Rec., 125:2. Proc. Amer. Assn. Anatomists, p. 327.

4. Morowitz, H. J., and Tourtellotte, M. E. (1962) Scient. Amer., 206(3):117.

5. Hughes, A. (1959) History of cytology. Abelard-Schuman, London and New York.

6. Heller, J., Mochancka, I., Szafranzki, P., and Szarkowski, J. W. (1962) Molecular biology (Polish). Kosmos, Ser. A., 11:305.

GENERAL
STRUCTURE
OF THE CELL

OBSERVATION OF THE LIVING CELL

The cell, a definite unit of living substance, consists of a small mass of protoplasm, the cytoplasm, containing a nucleus and surrounded by the plasma membrane. The cells of a multicellular organism vary greatly in shape and structure, and are conditioned mainly by adaptation to their specific function in the different tissues and organs. Because of this functional specialization, all cells acquire special characteristics. However, general characteristics common to all cells invariably persist, and, for example, can be found in the following: cells that are slightly differentiated, such as the blastomeres or germinative cells, meristematic cells of plants, and others having a relatively simple organization, such as some of the epithelial or connective tissue cells. These common characteristics are dealt with preferentially in this book.

Shape

Some cells, such as amebae and leuko-

cytes, have a variable shape. Other cells always have a typical shape, more or less fixed, which is specific for each cell type, e.g., the spermatozoids, infusoria, erythrocytes, epithelial cells, nerve cells and most plant cells.

The shape of cells depends mainly on functional adaptations and partly on the surface tension and viscosity of the protoplasm, the mechanical action exerted by the adjoining cells and the rigidity of the cell membrane. When isolated in a liquid, many cells become spherical, obeying the laws of surface tension. For example, leukocytes in the circulating blood are spherical, but in extravascular milieu they emit pseudopods (ameboid movement) and become irregular in shape.

The cells of many plant and animal tissues have a constant polyhedral shape, determined principally by reciprocal pressures. The original spherical form of these cells has been modified by contact with the other cells, just as each bubble in soap foam is pressed by its neighbors.

Individual cells in a large mass appear to behave like polyhedral solids of minimal surface that are packed without interstices. Although regular polyhedra of four, six and twelve sides can be packed without interstices, the fourteen-sided polyhedron (tetrakaidecahedron) satisfies most closely the conditions of minimal surface. The study of bubbles in soap foam by Plateau and Lord Kelvin showed that these conditions of minimal surface exist, and that the average bubble has 14 sides (Fig. 2–1A, B).

In observing cells under the microscope, the student should always think in terms of three dimensions and observe sections of varied orientations. The best way to learn about the actual shape of cells is by making serial sections of known thickness, drawing all of them and making reconstructions in wax, a procedure similar to that used in anatomic reconstructions.

Figure 2–1C–H shows some reconstructions of different cell types. The ideal tetrakaidecahedron has rarely been encountered in cells, but making reconstructions and counting the surfaces of a considerable number of different animal

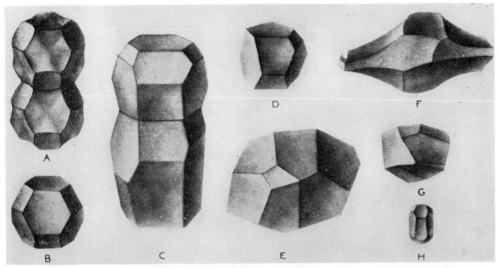

FIGURE 2–1. Three-dimensional reconstructions of: **A** and **B**, Kelvin's minimal tetrakaidecahedron. **C–H**, wax plate reconstructions of different cell types: **E**, human fat cell; **F**, **G** and **H**, outer, middle and basal cells of a stratified epithelium of the mouth of a five month human embryo. Approximate magnifications: C, ×170; D, ×150; E, ×300; F, G, H, ×750. (From F. T. Lewis.)

and plant cells in appropriate masses have revealed an average very close to 14 faces.

Size

The size of different cells varies within broad limits. Some plant and animal cells are visible to the naked eye. For example, the eggs of certain birds have a diameter of several centimeters and are composed, at least at first, of a single cell. However, this is an exception; the great majority of cells are visible only with the microscope, since they are only a few microns in diameter (Fig. 1–1). The smallest animal cells have a diameter of 4 μ.

In the tissues of the human body, with the exception of some nerve cells, the volume of cells varies between 200 μ^3 and 15,000 μ^3. In general, the volume of the cell is fairly constant for a particular cell type and is independent of the size of the organism. For example, kidney or hepatic cells have about the same size in the bull, horse and mouse; the difference in the total mass of the organ is due to the number and not the volume of cells. This is sometimes called the *law of constant volume*.

Structure

Living cells can be studied only with light microscopes, since in electron microscopy the tissue must be in a vacuum. Many animal cells can be observed isolated in an isotonic liquid, such as blood serum, aqueous humor or Ringer's solution, or in tissue culture. They appear as irregular, translucent masses of cytoplasm containing a nucleus. In Figure 2–2 most cells are in interphase, the nondividing stage (see Chap. 13), and show a clear nucleus having one or more nucleoli and separated from the cytoplasm by the nuclear membrane (or envelope). When cells are about to divide, several refractile bodies, the *chromosomes*, appear in the nucleus.

The cytoplasm appears as a translucent, amorphous, homogeneous substance, the ground cytoplasm, containing refractile particles of various sizes, among which the mitochondria are the most conspicuous (Fig. 2–2). Frequently the peripheral layer of the cytoplasm, the *ectoplasm*, is relatively more rigid and devoid of granules. (This region is also called the *plasmagel*, or *cortex*, although some persons reserve the term cortex for the most peripheral birefringent, jelly-like layer of cytoplasm.) The ectoplasm often behaves as a colloid and undergoes reversible gelation and solation. This transformation, which is very evident in amebae during the extension of pseudopods, is a general mechanism in all cells. The internal cy-

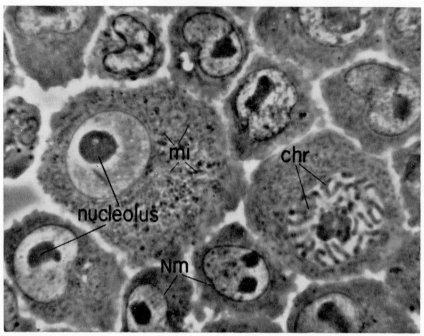

FIGURE 2–2. Photomicrograph in phase contrast of the living cells from an ascitic tumor. *chr,* chromosomes; *mi,* mitochondria; *Nm,* nuclear membrane. (Courtesy of N. Takeda.)

toplasm, the *endoplasm,* which contains different granules, is less viscous than the ectoplasm.

The living cell can be centrifuged and the effect on the cell components can be observed in a special centrifuge microscope. For example, if a sea urchin egg is subjected to intense and prolonged centrifugation, the different components of the endoplasm become stratified in accordance with their densities, and the ground cytoplasm is separated, although not completely, from the other components (Fig. 2–3). The egg elongates and then becomes constricted in the center. The fat droplets accumulate at the centripetal pole. Beneath this is a clear, wide zone, the ground cytoplasm, which contains the nucleus. The mitochondria form the next layer, and the yolk bodies the next. Pigment granules accumulate at the centrifugal pole. The ectoplasm, owing to its greater viscosity and rigidity, is not displaced by centrifugation; this property appears to depend on the presence of calcium ions, since the cortex liquefies when eggs are treated with an oxalate.

Interesting studies on the colloidal properties of cytoplasm and on the physicochemical forces involved have been made (see Chap. 21). By increasing the hydrostatic pressure, the cortex can be liquefied and the cell no longer can change in shape. This effect is reversible within certain limits. The ground cytoplasm behaves in general as a reversible sol-gel colloid system (see Chap. 9). This change can be produced sometimes by mechanical action, a property generally called *thixothropism.* (Gr. *thixis* touch + *trope* a change).

In addition to mitochondria, other particles observed in the cell, such as highly refractile lipid droplets (Fig. 10–1), yolk bodies and pigment and secretion granules, are products elaborated by the cell and are found in varying amounts. These are called *inclusions,* or *deutoplasm* (Gr. *deuteros* second), or *paraplasm.* In plant cells, in addition to mitochondria various granules called *plastids* can be observed. Among these are the *chloroplasts,* which contain a green pigment—chlorophyll. The function of chlorophyll is *photosynthesis,* a process of immense importance in the biologic world. In addition there are *leukoplastids* (colorless plastids), which under certain conditions can be converted into chloroplasts or into plastids of other colors (chromoplasts), or which may store starch (amyloplasts)

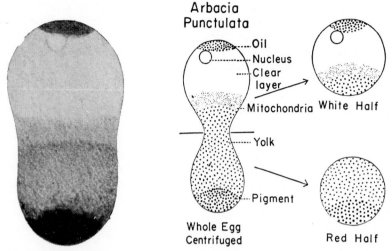

FIGURE 2–3.   **Left,** sea urchin egg (*Arbacia*) submitted to the action of centrifugal force. The egg has elongated and is being divided into two halves. The cellular materials become stratified (see description in the text). (Courtesy of Costello.) **Right,** diagram of the stratification of the egg and its division into two halves. (From E. B. Harvey.)

or oils or perform other functions (see Chap. 12).

In both animal and plant cells, but more commonly in the latter, fluid vacuoles surrounded by a membrane may be found. When vacuoles, plastids or mitochondria are isolated from the cell, they expand or shrink in accordance with changes in osmotic pressure (Boyle's law). These phenomena depend on the existence of interface membranes, which regulate osmotic interchanges.

Mitochondria and chloroplasts (in plant cells) are considered cell *organoids,* or *organelles,* because of their general presence and their important function in cells. Some other cell organoids, such as the *Golgi substance* and the *centrioles,* are observed less often in living cells. Some organoids cannot be resolved with the light microscope, and therefore cannot be observed in living cells.

OBSERVATION OF THE FIXED CELL

As mentioned, the examination of the living cell is limited to the light microscope and is based mainly on the differences in refractive index of the different cell components. Sometimes the use of stains that act on the living organism (*vital staining*) facilitates observation of the living cell. However, more important in the morphologic study of the cell are *methods of fixation,* by which cell death results in such a way that physiologic structure and chemical composition are preserved as much as possible (see Chap. 6). The skepticism about fixation that was started at the end of the last century by work on colloidal models (see Chap. 1) has passed, and it is now recognized that the examination of fixed cells can give most important data on cellular structure. Furthermore, electron microscope observation can be carried out only after the cells and tissues have been fixed.

In describing the general morphology of the fixed cell, we will no longer indicate the instrument used for particular observations. The student should be able to analyze the structures at the proper level of organization. He has to know that all the parts observed with the light microscope can be seen in greater detail with the electron microscope, which in addition shows structures that cannot be seen with the light microscope.

In observing a cell of the higher plants or animals, one is impressed by the complexity of structural organization. However, although there are great differences between the primitive forms of life, such as that illustrated in Figure 1–2, and the higher plant and animal cells, the similarities between primitive and advanced cells are also notable. Eukaryotic cells are characterized by a true nucleus with a *nuclear membrane* or *envelope* which divides the cell into two main compartments: nucleus and cytoplasm. The cytoplasm in turn is limited from the environment by the *plasma membrane*. In a plant cell (Fig. 2–4), the plasma membrane is covered and protected on the outside by a thicker cell wall through which there are tunnels, the *plasmodesmata*, which communicate with the neighboring cells. In animal cells (Fig. 2–5), parts of the plasma membrane are covered by a thin layer of material,

which is generally described as the *extraneous coat* of the plasma membrane (see Chap. 8). The so-called basement membranes shown in Figure 2–5 correspond to this extraneous coat.

In Figure 2–4 the nucleus is in the nondividing stage (interphase). The *chromatin substance* (so-called because of its strong staining properties), which during division constitutes the different chromosomes, appears irregularly distributed in flakes or filaments through the *nuclear sap*. Some of the larger flakes of chromatin are called *chromocenters, karyosomes* or false nucleoli because they are morphologically similar to some

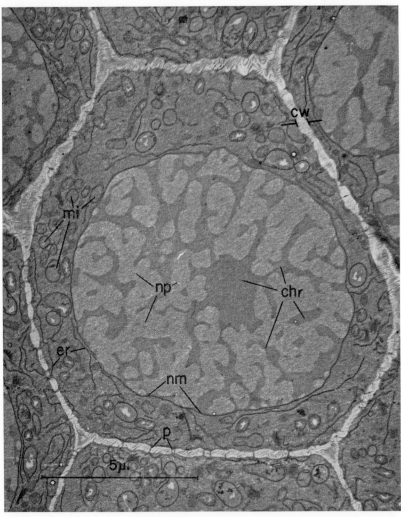

FIGURE 2–4. Electron micrograph of a promeristematic cell of the root of *Allium sativum*. Fixation in KMnO₄. The large central nucleus shows dense accumulations of chromatin (*chr*) between the nucleoplasm (*np*). The nuclear membrane (*nm*) and the endoplasmic reticulum (*er*) are clearly seen. *mi*, mitochondria and protoplastids; *p*, plasmodesmata that go through the cell wall (*cw*). ×8800. (Courtesy of R. D. Machado and K. R. Porter.)

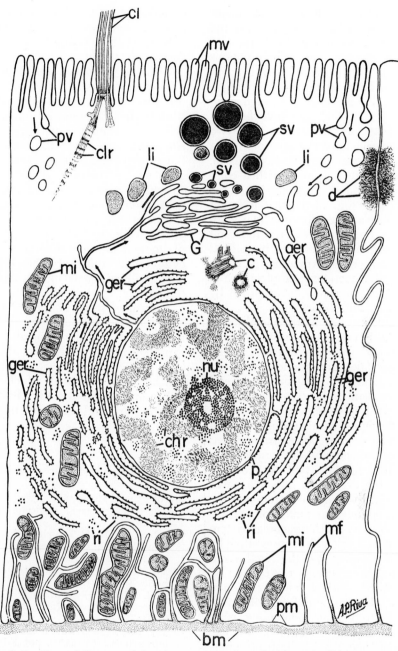

Figure 2–5. General diagram of the ultrastructure of an ideal animal cell. *aer,* agranular endoplasmic reticulum; *bm,* basal membrane; *c,* centriole; *chr,* chromosome; *cl,* cilium; *clr,* cilium root; *d,* desmosome; *G,* Golgi complex; *ger,* granular endoplasmic reticulum; *li,* lysosome; *mf,* membrane fold; *mi,* mitochondria; *mv,* microvilli; *nu,* nucleolus; *p,* pore; *pm,* plasma membrane; *pv,* pinocytic vesicle; *ri,* ribosome; *sv,* secretion vesicle. (From E. De Robertis and A. Pellegrino de Iraldi.)

nucleoli. In addition to these two components, there are one or more spherical bodies, the *nucleoli,* which differ from the chromocenters in some staining properties and in chemical composition (Fig. 2–2).

The outer, or cytoplasmic, compartment of the cell has the most complex structural organization and is described in detail in several chapters of this book. In observing a cell under the electron microscope, one is particularly struck by the enormous development of membranes. These membranes constitute the outer limiting membrane with the numerous infoldings and differentiations (Fig. 2–5) and the nuclear envelope. In addition, a basic membranous organization is found in cell organoids, such as *lysosomes* (Fig. 2–5*li*) and *mitochondria* (Fig. 2–5*mi*), in which one and two membranes separate the interior matrix from the surrounding ground cytoplasm. *Chloroplasts* are organoids with a complex, multilayered organization (see Chap. 12 and Fig. 12–8), that is found in animal cells, e.g., the myelin sheath and the outer segments of the rods and cones which are also formed by packed membrane systems. Numerous vesicles, vacuoles and secretory droplets found in the cytoplasm are also surrounded by membranes (Fig. 2–5*sv*).

A complex system of membranes, which varies in development in different cell types and according to cell differentiation, pervades the ground cytoplasm, forming numerous compartments and subcompartments. This system is so polymorphic that it is difficult to describe and to encompass within a single denomination. The term *vacuolar system* seems to us the most general and appropriate to describe the fact that it generally separates the cytoplasm into two parts, one contained within the system and the other, the *cytoplasmic matrix* proper, remaining outside. To this vacuolar system belongs a cell organoid represented by the *Golgi complex* and the *nuclear envelope*, but the major part is formed by the so-called *endoplasmic reticulum*, which may in turn be differentiated into a *granular reticulum*, containing ribosomes, and an *agranular reticulum*. The diagram of Figure 2–5 indicates the possible continuities and functional interconnections of these different portions of the cytoplasmic vacuolar system.

Other cell organoids, the *centrioles*, are involved in cell division. During cell division a centriole is contained in a clear, gel-like zone, the *centrosphere*, from which radiations of fibrillar cytoplasm extend, the *astrosphere*. At this stage of maximal development this organoid can also be called a *cell center*. Centrioles are also related to the differ-

entiation of *cilia* and *flagella*, which are motile appendixes of the cell (Fig. 2–5*cl*).

In spite of this complex structural organization, the most important constituents of the cytoplasm are in the *matrix* (ground cytoplasm), which lies outside the vacuolar system. This matrix constitutes the true internal milieu of the cell, and contains the following: the *ribosomes*, which are the main part of the biosynthetic machinery of the cell, glycogen particles, soluble enzymes, structural proteins and all the components found in a primitive organism, excluding DNA. In addition, it is the site of the colloidal activity of the protoplasm and of the production of many cytoplasmic differentiations, such as keratin fibers, myofilaments and neurotubules.

A detailed study of the vacuolar system, the cytoplasmic organoids and differentiations and the cytoplasmic matrix is presented in later chapters of the book, after the chemical organization of the cell has been discussed, which is essential to an integrated study of the different structural and functional parts of the cell.

GENERAL REFERENCES

Brachet, J., and Mirsky, A. E., eds. (1959–1961) *The cell.* 6 volumes. Academic Press, New York.

Chambers, R. (1924) The physical structure of protoplasm. In: *General cytology.* University of Chicago Press, Chicago.

Fischer, A. (1946) *Biology of tissue cells.* Cambridge University Press, London.

Gaillard, P. J. (1953) Growth and differentiation of explanted tissues. *Internat. Rev. Cytol.,* 2:331.

Harvey, E. B. (1950) *McClung's handbook of microscopical technique.* 3rd Ed., Paul B. Hoeber, New York.

Runnström, L. (1952) The cytoplasm, its structure and role in metabolism, growth and differentiation. In: *Modern trends in physiology and biochemistry.* (Barrón, E. S. G., ed.) Academic Press, New York.

Seifriz, W. (1936) *Protoplasm.* McGraw-Hill Book Co., New York.

White, P. R. (1959) The cell as organism, tissue culture, cellular autonomy and cellular interrelations. In: *The cell,* Vol. 1, p. 291. (Brachet, J., and Mirsky, A. E., eds.) Academic Press, New York.

Wilson, E. B. (1937) *The cell in development and heredity.* The Macmillan Co., New York.

PART ONE

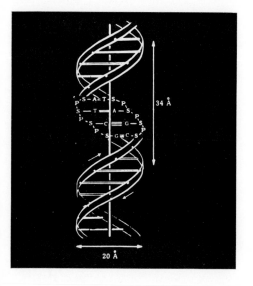

34 Å

20 Å

MOLECULAR
COMPONENTS
OF THE CELL

The general organization of the cell presented in the two introductory chapters may be interpreted best upon chemical and physicochemical bases. The reader should review his previous studies of inorganic and organic chemistry and especially those on proteins, carbohydrates, lipids and nucleic acids, which are the main molecular components of the cell.

The next part of the book is a general discussion of these cell components, mainly from the stereochemical viewpoint. It introduces the concept of enzymes as molecular machines used by the cell to produce all chemical transformations. In addition, this part of the book discusses the main metabolic pathways utilized to obtain chemical energy from the different foodstuffs, energy that is then used for the synthesis of new products that increase the proper mass of the cell or are eliminated to the environment, as in secretion. Without knowledge of the fundamental principles, one could not make progress in cell biology.

CHAPTER 3

CHEMICAL
COMPONENTS
OF THE CELL

In order to comprehend the organization of biologic systems, one should first become familiar with the main constituent molecules, particularly those of high molecular weight, such as proteins, nucleic acids, polysaccharides and lipids. Also, one should know the general molecular constitution of the smallest mass of living matter (Fig. 1–2).

According to Hofmeister, a rough calculation of the number of molecules in a single hepatic cell is:

Proteins	53,000	$\times 10^6$
Lipids	166,000	$\times 10^6$
Small molecules	2,900,000	$\times 10^6$
Water	225,000,000	$\times 10^6$

These figures show that the cell has an extremely large molecular population, but they do not indicate the high degree of complexity of cell organization at a molecular level, nor the functional changes that take place in the cell.

The cell has been compared to a minute laboratory capable of carrying out the synthesis and breakdown of numerous substances at normal body temperature. These chemical reactions are carried out with the intervention of *enzymes* (biologic catalysts), which

speed up the different chemical reactions. Enzymes, which are special proteins or have protein components, can be compared to molecular machines capable of performing in a most efficient way all kinds of chemical transformations (see Chap. 4).

MOLECULAR POPULATION OF THE CELL

An early approach to the study of the chemical composition of the cell was the biochemical analysis of whole organs and tissues, such as the liver, brain, skin or plant meristem. This method had limited cytologic value, because the material analyzed was generally a mixture of different cell types and in addition contained extracellular material. In recent years the development of cell fractionation methods and of various micromethods has led to the isolation of different subcellular particles and thus to more important and precise information about the molecular architecture of the cell (Chap. 6).

The chemical components of the cell can be classified as *inorganic* (water and mineral ions) and *organic* (proteins, carbohydrates, nucleic acids, lipids and so forth). Some organic components, such as enzymes, coenzymes and hormones, that have specific activities are mentioned in Chapter 4 and should be studied in detail in biochemistry textbooks.

The protoplasm of a plant or animal cell contains 75 to 85 per cent water, 10 to 20 per cent protein, 2 to 3 per cent lipid, 1 per cent carbohydrates and 1 per cent inorganic material. Although the most abundant cellular component is water, from the structural viewpoint the proteins and other substances of large molecular weight, which readily form macromolecules or molecular complexes, are more abundant.

Table 3–1 gives approximate figures of the relative amounts of the main inorganic and organic compounds found in active protoplasm. The relative number of molecules is roughly estimated by using definite percentages and average molecular weights for the different com-

[see Chap. 17].

TABLE 3–1. RELATIVE NUMBER OF
MOLECULES OF VARIOUS TYPES
OF CELLULAR MATERIALS*

SUBSTANCE	PER CENT	AVERAGE MOLECULAR WEIGHT	NUMBER OF MOLECULES PER MOLECULE OF DNA
Water	85	18	1.2×10^7
Protein	10	36,000	7.0×10^2
DNA	0.4	10^6	1.0
RNA	0.7	4.0×10^4	4.4×10^1
Lipid	2	700	7.0×10^3
Other organic materials	0.4	250	4.0×10^3
Inorganic	1.5	55	6.8×10^4

* Data on all but nucleic acids from Sponsler and Bath. DNA and RNA data on rat liver cell taken from Euler and Hahn. (From Giese, A. C. (1962) *Cell Physiology*. 2nd Ed. W. B. Saunders Co., Philadelphia.)

pounds. Although these figures are only approximate, they give an interesting picture of the relative molecular population of protoplasm. Arbitrary molecular weights have been assigned to deoxyribonucleic acid (*DNA*), ribonucleic acid (*RNA*) and protein. (In studying these calculations, bear in mind from the very beginning that DNA is the molecule that contains the genetic information for the formation of specific cellular proteins. It is the least changeable cellular component and is present in a fixed amount in each cell type of an individual [see Chap. 17].) The number of other molecules relative to one DNA molecule is indicated. For example, there are about 44 RNA, 700 protein and 7000 lipid molecules per molecule of DNA. Remember that nucleic acids (DNA + RNA), though consisting of only about 1 per cent of the wet weight of the cell, are among the most important molecules in cellular activity.

Water, Free and Bound

With few exceptions, such as bone and enamel, water is the most abundant cellular component. It serves as a natural solvent for mineral ions and other substances and also as a dispersion medium of the colloid system of protoplasm. For instance, from microinjection experiments it is known that water is readily miscible with protoplasm. Furthermore, water is indispensable for metabolic activity, since physiologic processes occur exclusively in aqueous media. Water molecules also participate in many enzymatic reactions of the cell and can be formed as a result of metabolic processes.* Furthermore, water furnishes hydrogen ions in photosynthesis.

Water in the cell is in two forms: *free* and *bound*. *Free water* represents 95 per cent of the total cellular water and is the part mainly used as a solvent for solutes and as a dispersion medium of the colloid system of protoplasm. *Bound water*, which represents only 4 to 5 per cent of the total cellular water, is loosely held to the proteins by hydrogen bonds and other forces (see the following diagram). It includes the so-called *unmobilized* water contained within the fibrous structure of macromolecules. Because of the asymmetric distribution of charges, a water molecule acts as a *dipole* as shown in the following diagrams:

Because of this property, water can be bound electrostatically by both positively and negatively charged groups in the protein. Thus each amino group in a protein molecule is capable of binding 2.6 molecules of water.

In addition to these functions of water, i.e., as a solvent and as a dispersion medium, and in metabolic reactions, water is used also for the elimination of substances from the cell and to absorb heat —by virtue of its high specific heat coefficient—and thus to prevent drastic temperature changes in the cell.

The water content of an organism is

* The production of water by this mechanism is insufficient for the needs of the cell, and therefore water has to be supplied by the extracellular fluids.

related to the organism's age and metabolic activity. For example, it is highest in the embryo (90 to 95 per cent) and decreases progressively in the adult and in the aged. Water content also varies in the different tissues in relation to metabolism. For example, the water content of the gray matter of the brain is 85 per cent whereas that of the white matter is 78 per cent. Tissues with low water content are bone (20 per cent) and enamel (10 per cent).

The time required for complete turnover of an amount of water equal to the body weight varies according to the environment to which an organism has adapted itself. The following are examples: ameba, seven days; man, four weeks; camel, three months; tortoise, one year; cactus, a desert plant, as long as 29 years. In the camel, large quantities of water are obtained by oxidation of the fat contained in the hump.

Salts and Mineral Components

Inorganic and mineral constituents of the cell are found in the form of salts or combined with proteins, carbohydrates and lipids. Salts dissociated into anions (e.g., Cl^-) and cations (e.g., Na^+ and K^+) are important in maintaining *osmotic pressure* (see Chap. 20) and the *acid-base equilibrium* of the cell. Retention of ions produces an increase in osmotic pressure and thus the entrance of water.

The concentration of various ions in the intracellular fluid differs from that in the interstitial fluid (Chap. 20; see Table 20–1). For example, the cell has a high concentration of K^+ and Mg^{++}, while Na^+ and Cl^- are mainly localized in the interstitial fluid. The dominant anion of cells is phosphate, and some bicarbonate is also present. Figure 3–1 compares the ion content of a cell with that of serum. The most pronounced difference is in Na^+ and K^+, which are the most important ions in such tissues as muscle and nerve that have action potentials.

Characteristics of Mineral Components. *Calcium ions* are found in the circulating blood and in cells. In bone

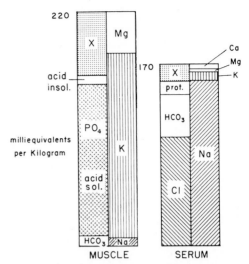

FIGURE 3–1. Comparison of ion content in milliequivalents per kilogram in muscle and serum. (After O. Lowry, 1943.)

they are combined with phosphate and carbonate ions and form a crystalline arrangement.

Phosphate occurs in the blood and tissue fluids as free ions, but much of the phosphate of the body is bound in the form of phospholipids, nucleotides, phosphoproteins and phosphorylated sugars. As primary phosphate ($H_2PO_4^-$) and secondary phosphate (HPO_4^{--}), phosphate contributes to the buffer mechanism, stabilizing the pH of the blood and tissue fluids.

Other ions found in tissues are sulfate, carbonate, bicarbonate, magnesium and amino acids.

Certain mineral components are found in a nonionized form. For example, *iron*, bound by metal-carbon linkages, is found in hemoglobin, ferritin, the cytochromes and some enzymes (such as catalase and cytochrome oxidase).

Manganese and *copper* are found in small amounts (less than 0.05 per cent), and *vanadium, zinc, nickel, molybdenum* and *tin* are present in minute quantities, but even these traces are indispensable for maintenance of the normal cellular activities.

For normal function a cell requires a medium with well balanced equilibrium of different ions. For instance, if the heart of a frog is perfused with a saline solution containing only one salt (e.g.,

Na^+ Cl^-), it stops beating after a short time; if, however, other salts are present in physiologic amounts, the beating persists for a prolonged period. For these reasons, artificial physiologic solutions (such as Ringer's or Tyrode's solution), are not only isotonic (have an osmotic pressure identical to that of the blood and tissues), but have a proper ionic balance.

Macromolecules. Monomers and Polymers

The structural properties of the cell are intimately related to long molecules made of repeating units linked by covalent bonds. These units are called *monomers*, and the resulting macromolecule is called a *polymer*. The three main examples of polymers in biology are as follows: (a) *Nucleic acids* result from the repetition of four different units called *nucleotides*. Chains of deoxyribonucleic acid of molecular weight ranging in the millions and as long as a millimeter or more can be found in nature forming the chromosome of a bacterium (see Fig. 17–8). (b) *Polysaccharides* can be polymers of monosaccharides forming starch, amylose or glycogen, or may also involve the repetition of other molecules, forming more complex polysaccharides. (c) *Proteins* and *polypeptides* consist of the association in various proportions of some 20 different amino acids linked by peptide bonds. The order in which these 20 monomers can be linked may give rise to an astounding number of combinations in various protein molecules. This can determine not only their specificity, but in certain cases their biologic activity. Also the repetition of four nucleotides in the DNA molecule is the primary source of biologic information as is explained in detail in the chapter on molecular genetics.

Amino Acids and Proteins

The building blocks of proteins are 20 different amino acids, which the reader should remember from studies of biochemistry (see Table 3–2). Essentially an amino acid is derived from an

TABLE 3–2. TYPES OF NATURAL AMINO ACIDS AND ABBREVIATIONS USED FOR THEM*

Monoamino-monocarboxylic
  Glycine (Gly)
  Alanine (Ala)
  Valine (Val)
  Leucine (Leu)
  Isoleucine (Ileu)
Monoamino-dicarboxylic
  Glutamic acid (Glu)
  Aspartic acid (Asp)
Diamino-monocarboxylic
  Arginine (Arg)
  Lysine (Lys)
  Hydroxylysine (Hlys)
Hydroxyl-containing
  Threonine (Thr)
  Serine (Ser)
Sulfur-containing
  Cystine (Cys or Cy-S)
  Methionine (Met)
Aromatic
  Phenylalanine (Phe)
  Tyrosine (Tyr)
Heterocyclic
  Tryptophan (Tryp)
  Proline (Pro)
  Hydroxyproline (Hpro)
  Histidine (His)

* From Giese, A. C. (1962) *Cell physiology*. 2nd Ed. W. B. Saunders Co., Philadelphia.

organic acid in which the hydrogen in the alpha position (i.e., the carbon next to the —COOH group) is replaced by an amino group (—NH₂). For example, acetic acid gives *glycine* and propionic acid, *alanine*. Because of the simultaneous presence of acidic carboxyl (—COOH) and of basic amino (—NH₂) groups, such molecules are called amphoteric.

The free amino acids present in a cell may result from the breakdown of proteins or from absorption from the serum surrounding the cell. Free amino acids constitute the so-called *amino-acid pool*, from which the cell draws its building blocks for the synthesis of new proteins (see Chap. 18).

The condensation of amino acids to form a protein molecule occurs in such a way that the acidic group of one amino acid combines with the basic group of the adjoining one, with the simultaneous loss of one molecule of water.

$$
\begin{array}{ccc}
 & R' & \\
 & C & H_2N \quad COOH \\
 & {}^{/}H\diagdown & {}^{\diagdown}H{}^{/} \\
H_2N & CO(OH) & C \\
 & & R''
\end{array}
$$

$$
\begin{array}{cccccc}
H & O & R' & H & O & R''' \\
N & C & C & N & C & C \\
{}^{/} \diagdown H{}^{/} & \diagdown & {}^{/}H\diagdown & {}^{/} & \diagdown H{}^{/} & \diagdown \\
C & N & C & C & N & C \\
R & H & O & R'' & H & O
\end{array}
$$

In this chain, R′, R″ and so forth represent radicals of different amino acids. The linkage R—NH—CO—R is known as the *peptide linkage* or *peptide bond* (Emil Fischer). The formed molecule preserves its amphoteric character, since an acidic group is always at one end and a basic group is at the other, in addition to the lateral residues (radicals) that can be either basic or acidic. A combination of two amino acids is a *dipeptide;* of three, a *tripeptide.* When a few amino acids are linked together, the structure is an *oligopeptide.* A *polypeptide* contains a large number of amino acids.

The distance between two peptide links is about 3.5 Å, and the average volume of an amino acid is $3.5 \times 4.6 \times 10$ Å, or 161 Å.[3] From these figures one can calculate that a protein of a molecular weight 30,000 consisting of 300 amino acid residues, if fully extended, should have a length of 1000 Å, a width of 10 Å and a thickness of 4.6 Å.

Table 3–3 is a list of the molecular weights of different proteins. The term *protein* (Gr. *proteuo* I occupy first place) indicates that all basic functions in biology depend on specific proteins. It is certain that life cannot exist without proteins. They are present in every cell and cell organoid; they constitute the enzymes and the contractile machinery of the cell, and are present in the blood and other intercellular fluids. Some long-chain proteins, such as *collagen* and *elastin,* play an important role in the organization of tissues that form the extracellular framework.

For details of the classification of the proteins, the reader is referred to biochemistry textbooks; however, we wish to emphasize here that the properties of proteins on which the classification is based vary considerably. For instance, the *scleroproteins,* e.g., *keratin* and *collagen,* are insoluble and fibrous; the *globular proteins,* e.g., egg albumin and serum proteins, are soluble in water or salt solutions and are spherical rather than thread-like molecules.

There are also *conjugated proteins,* which are attached to a nonprotein moiety, the so-called *prosthetic group.* To such a group belong the *nucleoproteins* associated with nucleic acids, the *glycoproteins* (in which the prosthetic group may be chondroitin sulfate), *lipoproteins* (e.g., blood lipoproteins), and *chromoproteins* that have a pigment as the prosthetic group, such as hemoglobin, hemocyanin and the cytochromes. Figure 3–2 presents the molecular dimensions of some globular proteins from the blood.

Primary Structure of Proteins. The straight polypeptide chain built of amino acids is known as the *primary structure* of the protein molecule. It is the most important and specific structure, and to a certain extent determines the so-called *secondary* and *tertiary* structures.

Determination of the sequence of amino acids has been made possible by the development of a series of methods

TABLE 3–3. MOLECULAR WEIGHTS OF SOME PROTEINS

Cytochrome	15,000
Trypsin	24,000
Pepsin	35,500
Egg albumin	43,800
Insulin (tetramer)	47,800
Hemoglobin (human)	68,000
Albumin (human)	69,000
γ-Globulin (human)	156,000
Catalase	224,000
Collagen	280,000
Thyroglobin (pig)	650,000
Thymonucleohistone	2,150,000
Tobacco mosaic virus	40,000,000

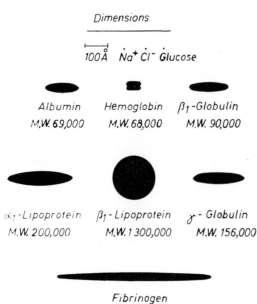

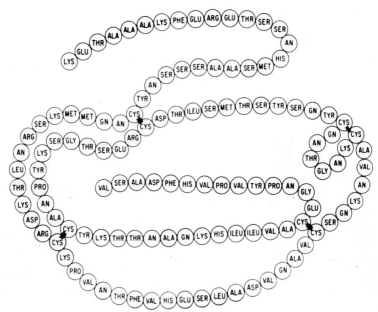

FIGURE 3–2. Molecular dimensions and shapes of serum proteins. (From P. Karlson, 1963.)

FIGURE 3–3. The primary structure of bovine pancreatic ribonuclease. Notice the position of the four disulfide bridges between cystine residues. (From C. B. Anfinsen, 1959.)

for the degradation of proteins, which finally gave the first complete analysis of *insulin* (Sanger, 1954). This molecule is composed of two chains: the A-chain consists of 21 amino acids and the B-chain, of 30. Both chains are linked by two —S—S— bonds. Figure 3–3 shows the whole sequence in *ribonuclease,* an enzyme that consists of 124 amino acid residues. Other proteins whose structure has been studied are those of the tobacco mosaic virus, hemoglobin and cytochrome.

In the protein molecule, amino acids are arranged like beads on a string (Fig. 3–3), and their sequence is of great biologic importance. For example, the enzymic properties of certain proteins are determined by a special sequence of amino acids, such as in the *active center* of the enzyme (see Chap. 4). In the hemoglobin molecule a change in a single amino acid produces profound biologic changes (see Chap. 18 and Table 18–1). A fully extended polypeptide chain is shown in Figure 3–4, with the exact dimensions and bond angles as determined by x-ray diffraction.

Secondary Structure of Proteins. In a protein formed by several hundred amino acids, the chain may sometimes be linear, but more frequently it assumes different shapes that constitute the so-called *secondary structure*. Fibrous proteins (scleroproteins) are often arranged in an orderly manner that can be analyzed by x-ray diffraction methods, which give different identity periods (see Chap. 6). According to this technique, proteins are classified into:

silk, fibroin, β-keratin group
α-keratin, myosin, fibrinogen group
collagen group.

The β-keratin type has an identity period of about 7.2 Å (Fig. 3–4), but the adjacent chains are disposed in a *pleated sheet structure* as shown in Figure 3–5, in which the side-chains of the

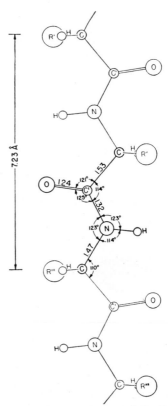

FIGURE 3–4. Dimensions and angles in a polypeptide chain that is totally extended. (From Corey and Pauling.)

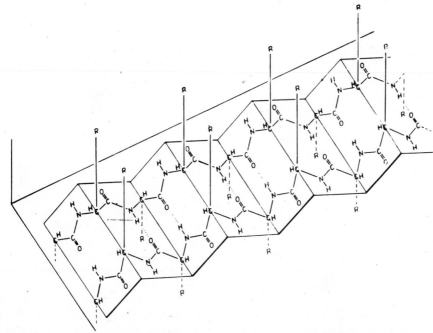

FIGURE 3–5. Pleated sheet structure of β-protein chains. (See the description in the text.) (From P. Karlson, 1963.)

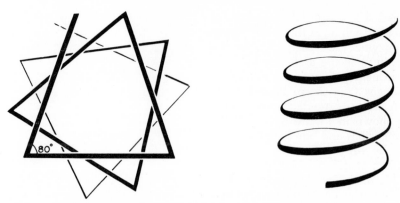

FIGURE 3–6. An α-helix polypeptide chain. **Left,** top view. **Right,** side view. (From C. M. A. Kuyper, 1962: *The organization of cellular activity.* Elsevier, Amsterdam.)

amino acid residues stick out perpendicular to the plane of the chain. The individual chains are held together by hydrogen bonds, forming a "peptide grid."

The *α-helix structure* found in α-keratin is produced when the polypeptide chain forms a helical structure, like a winding spiral around an imaginary cylinder, in such a way that hydrogen bonds are established within the molecule and not with an adjacent molecule. Figure 3–6 shows a top view and a side view of the α-helix configuration. The turn of the α-helix contains 3.7 amino acid residues and the identity period is 5.4 Å. In the *collagen group,* a model made of three helical chains has been proposed (see Fig. 7–1).

Tertiary Structure of Proteins. In the so-called *globular proteins* the polypeptide chain is held together in a definite way to form a compact structure. The disposition in space of such chains is very complex and has been resolved by x-ray diffraction only in hemoglobin and myoglobin. (In Chapter 5 more details of the technique used are given [see also Fig. 5–9].) The spatial arrangement is to some extent predetermined by the sequence of amino acids in the primary structure and by the bonds that can be established among some of the residues. A series of the biologic properties of proteins, such as enzyme activity and antigenicity, is related to the tertiary structure.

Bonds in the Protein Molecule. Different types of bonds are involved in the structure of proteins. The primary struc-

ture (peptide bond) is fully determined by *chemical or covalent bonds.* —S—S— bonds of the same nature can be established between cystine residues, as in insulin and ribonuclease (Fig. 3–3). The secondary and tertiary structures are determined by a series of weaker bonds, which are illustrated in Figure 3–7. These bonds can be classified as:

Ionic or electrostatic, which bind positive and negative ions that are in close range of 2 to 3 Å (Fig. 3–7a).

Hydrogen bonds, with a range between 2.5 and 3.2 Å and weaker than ionic bonds. These are essentially electrostatic bonds that form a kind of bridge between two strongly negative atoms such as C, N or O (Fig. 3–7b).

Weaker bonds produced by interaction of *nonpolar side-chains* and caused by mutual repulsion of the solvent (Fig. 3–7c).

van der Waals forces produced by interaction between polar side-chains (Fig. 3–7d).

Electric Charges of Proteins. All amino acids are amphoteric (zwitterions), having both positively and negatively charged groups (—NH_2 and —COOH). Since these groups are used in the peptide bond, if it were not for the presence of dicarboxylic and diamino acids, only the free terminal —COOH and —NH_2 would remain (see Table 3–2). These special amino acid residues dissociate as follows:

1. The acidic groups may lose protons and become negatively charged. This type is found in the dicarboxylic amino acids, such as aspartic and glutamic

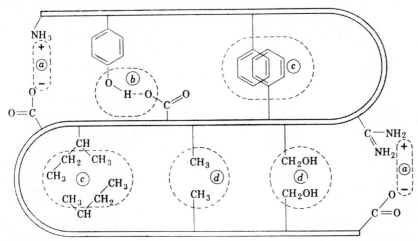

FIGURE 3–7. Types of noncovalent bonds that stabilize protein structure. (See description in the text.) (From C. B. Anfinsen, 1959.)

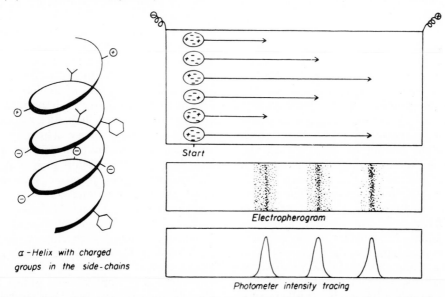

Start

Electropherogram

α-Helix with charged
groups in the side-chains

Photometer intensity tracing

FIGURE 3–8. Schematic representation of electrophoresis. **Left,** a segment of an α-helix that shows the location of certain charged groups. **Right,** three proteins with different charges are applied to the supporting medium; these proteins migrate within a given time (e.g., 15 hours) as far as the arrows indicate. The "electropherogram" is made visible by staining and evaluating quantitatively by photometry. (From P. Karlson, 1963.)

acids, in which the free carboxyl group dissociates into $-COO^- + H^+$.

2. The basic groups, by gaining protons, become positively charged $-NH_2 + H^+$. This type is found in amino acids with two basic groups, such as lysine or arginine, in which the free amino groups and the guanidine group in arginine may become ionized and get positive charges. All these so-called *ionogenic groups,* together with the terminal free carboxyl and amino groups, contribute to the acid-base reactions of pro-

teins and to the electrical properties of protein molecules. Figure 3–8 shows an α-helix of a protein molecule with various types of charges on the side-chains in addition to other noncharged residues.

Because of the presence of these ionogenic groups, proteins such as free amino acids are amphoteric and form *zwitterions.* The actual charge of a protein molecule is the result of the sum of all single charges at the lateral residues. Because dissociation of the different acidic and basic groups takes place at different hydrogen ion concentrations of the medium, pH greatly influences the total charge of the molecule. In an acid medium, amino groups capture hydrogen ions and react as bases ($-NH_2 + H^+ \rightarrow -NH_3^+$); in an alkaline medium the reverse takes place and carboxylic groups dissociate ($-COOH \rightarrow COO^- + H^+$). For every protein there is a definite pH at which the sum of positive and negative charges is zero. This pH is called the *isoelectric point* (pI). At the isoelectric point, proteins placed in an electric field do not migrate to either of the poles, whereas at a lower pH they migrate to the cathode and at a higher pH to the anode; this migration is called *electrophoresis* (Fig. 3–8). At the isoelectric point many of the physicochemical properties of the proteins are changed. For instance, their viscosity, solubility, hydration, osmotic pressure and conductivity are at a minimum.

Every protein has a characteristic isoelectric point, which depends on the type and number of ionogenic groups contained in the molecule. For example, in histones and protamines, which are found mainly in the nucleus, the isoelectric point is high (pI 10 to 12). This is because of the presence of numerous diamino-monocarboxylic amino acids. The isoelectric point of gelatin is 4.7 because of the predominance of monoamino-dicarboxylic amino acids.

The acid-base binding capacity resulting from the presence of positive and negative charges in proteins and in other compounds can be studied cytologically by staining sections with acidic or basic dyes in appropriate ranges of pH under standard conditions (Fig. 6–3). This method has been used to determine the isoelectric point of different parts of the cell and to characterize different compounds present in cells and tissues (see Chap. 6).

Carbohydrates

Carbohydrates, composed of carbon, hydrogen and oxygen, are sources of energy for animal and plant cells; in many plants they also form important constituents of cell walls and serve as supporting elements for the whole cell or plant. Plants possess the capacity for synthesizing a great variety of carbohydrates directly from carbon dioxide and water in the presence of light. Animal tissues have fewer carbohydrates, of which the most important are glucose, galactose, glycogen and amino sugars and their polymers.

Carbohydrates of biologic importance are divided into three classes: monosaccharides, disaccharides and polysaccharides. The first two, commonly referred to as *sugars,* are readily soluble in water, can be crystallized and pass easily through dialyzing membranes. Polysaccharides, on the other hand, do not crystallize and do not pass through membranes.

Monosaccharides. Monosaccharides are simple sugars with the empirical formula $C_n(H_2O)_n$. They are classified in accordance with the number of carbon atoms, e.g., trioses and hexoses. The pentoses *ribose* and *deoxyribose* are found in the molecules of nucleic acids. The pentose *ribulose* is important in photosynthesis (see Chap. 12). Glucose, a hexose, is the primary source of energy for the cell. Other important hexoses are: *galactose,* found in the disaccharide lactose, and *fructose* (*levulose*), which forms part of sucrose.

Disaccharides. Disaccharides are sugars formed by the condensation of two monomers of monosaccharides with the loss of one molecule of water. Their empirical formula is therefore $C_{12}H_{22}O_{11}$. The most important of this group are *sucrose* and *maltose* in plants and *lactose* in animals. Sucrose (saccharose), the sugar of cane or beets, is a combination of one molecule of glucose and one molecule of fructose. Lactose, the sugar of milk, is composed of glucose and galactose. Maltose is made from glucose and glucose.

Polysaccharides. Polysaccharides result from the condensation of many molecules of monosaccharides with a corresponding loss of water molecules. Their empirical formula is $(C_6H_{10}O_5)_n$. Upon hydrolysis they yield molecules of simple sugars. The most important polysaccharides in biology are: *starch* and *glycogen,* which are reserve substances in cells of plants and animals respec-

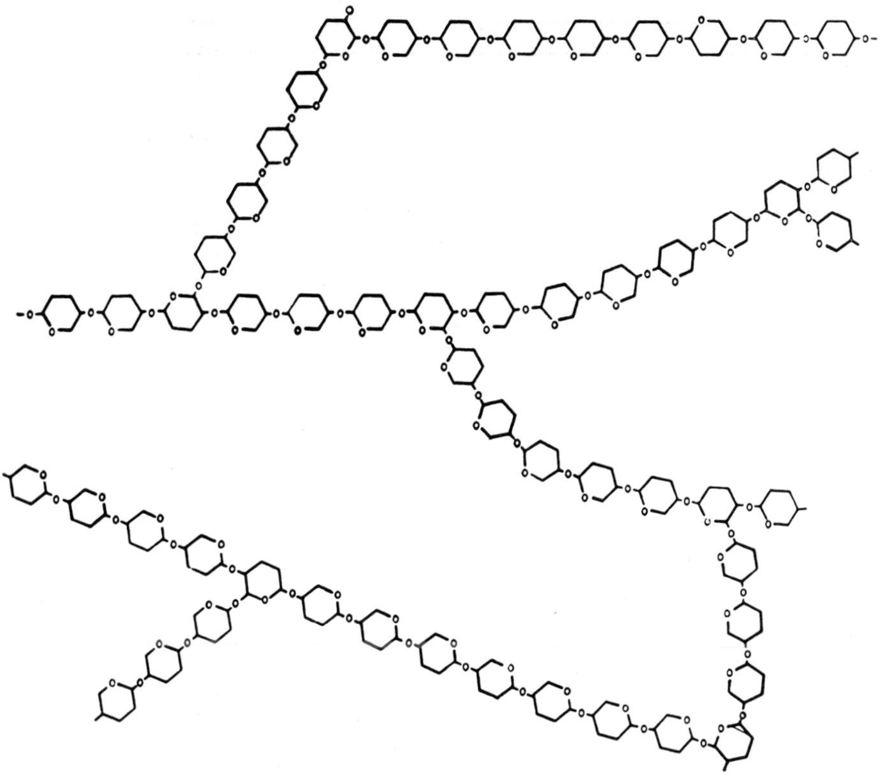

FIGURE 3–9. Molecular representation of part of a macromolecule of amylopectin. (From J. L. Oncley, 1959: *Biophysical science*. John Wiley & Sons, New York.)

tively, and *cellulose,* the most important structural element of the plant cell.

Starch is a combination of two long polymer molecules: *amylose,* which is linear, and *amylopectin,* which is branched. Both are composed of D-glucose; amylose gives the familiar blue color with Lugol reagent, whereas amylopectin gives red. The amylopectin molecule consists of a chain of approximately 200 to 500 units (Fig. 3–9).

Glycogen may be considered as the starch of animal cells. It is a polymer composed of many molecules of glucose and thus is an important reserve of energy in the body. It is found in numerous tissues and organs, but the greatest proportion is contained in liver cells and muscle fibers. In the living cell it is invisible, but on treatment with various fixatives is precipitated in the form of very small granules (Fig. 6–1), which can be demonstrated histochemically by means of the iodine reaction which gives a reddish brown color. (See also Chapter 6 for histochemistry and Chapter 7 for electron microscopy of glycogen.)

Cellulose constitutes a part of the wall of plant cells and also of a series of other structures that form the supporting skeleton of plants. Cellulose is composed of units of cellobiose ($C_{12}H_{22}O_{11}$). On hydrolysis, cellobiose yields glucose.

Besides cellulose, plant tissues contain structural components, such as xylan (composed of xylose units), alginic acids (in algae) and pectic acid (see Table 12–1).

Complex Polysaccharides, Mucopolysaccharides, Mucoproteins and Glycoproteins

In addition to the polysaccharides made of hexose monomers mentioned in the preceding section, are many more complex long molecules that contain amino nitrogen (e.g., glucosamine) or that can in addition be acetylated (e.g., acetylglucosamine). Still more complex are those that have a substitution of sulfuric or phosphoric acid. All these polymers are important in molecular organization, particularly as intercellular substances. These polysaccharides may exist either free or combined with proteins. The most important are:

Neutral polysaccharides, which contain only acetylglucosamine. The main example is *chitin,* a supporting substance found in insects and crustacea.

Neutral mucopolysaccharides are more complex molecules containing also other monosaccharides, such as galactose and rhamnose. They constitute the walls of bacteria and are involved in the determination of the blood groups.

Acidic mucopolysaccharides, which contain sulfuric or other acids in the molecule. Because of the acid component, these molecules are strongly basophilic (i.e., they stain with basic dyes; see Chap. 6). To this group belong: *heparin,* an anticoagulant substance; *chondroitin sulfate,* which contains acetylgalactosamine, glucuronic acid and sulfuric acid; and *hyaluronic acid,* which contains acetylglucosamine and glucuronic acid.

Mucoproteins (also called mucoids) and *glycoproteins* are complexes of acetylglucosamine and other carbohydrates with proteins. Among mucoproteins are substances secreted in saliva and in the gastric mucosa, the ovomucoid and so forth; among glycoproteins are ovalbumin and serum albumin.

Of this heterogeneous group of substances, acidic polysaccharides and, particularly, hyaluronic acid, chondroitin-sulfuric acid and mucoitin-sulfuric acid, are important in cytology. All three compounds are found in the ground substance of connective tissue, where they probably act as binding and protective agents. All three are also found in the umbilical cord.

Hyaluronic acid is present in synovial fluids, vitreous humor, aqueous humor and probably in other tissues. It is a binder of cells, and it can be easily hydrolyzed by the action of *hyaluronidases,* enzymes that attack hyaluronic acid specifically. Similar to other high polymers, hyaluronic acid produces very viscous gels even at low concentrations.

(For the histochemistry of these substances, see Chapter 6.)

Lipids

This large group of compounds is characterized by their relative insolubility in water and solubility in such organic solvents as benzene, petroleum ether and chloroform. This general property of lipids and related compounds is caused by the predominance of long aliphatic hydrocarbon chains or of benzene rings. Such structures are nonpolar and hydrophobic. In many lipids these chains may be attached at one end to a polar group, which makes it hydrophilic, and capable of binding water by hydrogen bonds.

Lipids can be classified as:

Simple Lipids. Simple lipids are alcohol esters of fatty acids. Among these are:

Natural fats (glycerides), often called triglycerides (Fig. 3–10a), are triesters of fatty acids and glycerol. These are sometimes further divided into fats and oils. At 20°C. fats are solid, whereas oils are liquid. Some common fats are tallow, lard, human fat and cocoa butter. Among oils are fish oils and castor oil.

Waxes have a higher melting point than natural fats, and are esters of fatty acids with alcohols other than glycerol, such as beeswax.

Steroids. These lipids are characterized by the cyclopentano-perhydrophenanthrene nucleus (Fig. 3–10e). This is an aliphatic ring system that may have one or more unsaturated double bonds as well as various side-chains. The steroids include a series of highly important substances in the body, such as the sex hormones (Fig. 3–10f), adrenocortical hormones, vitamin D and bile acids. Steroids that possess an —OH group are called *sterols. Cholesterol* is a widely distributed sterol, which, as cholesterol palmitate, is the principal constituent of lanolin (wool fat), and is found also in bile, the brain, the adrenal glands and other organs. It often occurs in ester linkage with some fatty acids.

Stereochemically, sterols form complex ring systems that are rather flattened.

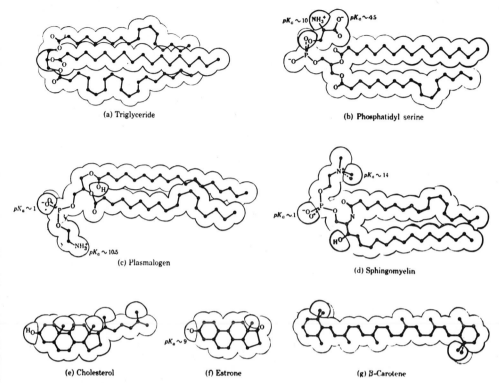

Figure 3–10. Some lipid molecules, showing the three-dimensional array and relative size. (From J. L. Oncley, 1959: *Biophysical science.* John Wiley & Sons, New York.)

The cholesterol molecule is about 20 Å long, 7 to 7.5 Å wide, and 5 Å thick. A polar —OH group is at one end and a nonpolar hydrocarbon residue is at the other (Fig. 3–10e).

Compound (Conjugated) Lipids. On hydrolysis these lipids yield other compounds in addition to alcohol and acids. Together with sterols they are called *lipoids* (fatlike) because of the solubility properties. Lipoids serve mainly as structural components of the cell, particularly in cell membranes (see Chaps. 7 and 8). Among these compounds are:

Phosphatides (phospholipids) are diesters of phosphoric acid that can be esterified with: either glycerol, sphingosine or choline; ethanolamine; serine; or inositol. This group includes the lecithins, cephalins, inositides and plasmalogens (acetyl phosphatides) (see Fig. 3–10 and Table 3–4).

Glycolipids and *sphingolipids* are characterized by the fact that glycerol is replaced by the amino alcohol *sphingosine.* To these groups belong: the *sphingomyelins* (Fig 3–10d), present mainly in the myelin sheath of nerves; the *cerebrosides,* which are characterized by the presence of galactose or glucose in the molecule; the *sulfatides,* which contain sulfuric acid esterified to galactose; and the *gangliosides* (Table 3–4).

The gangliosides deserve special mention because of their presence in cell membranes and of their possible role as receptors of virus particles and in the transport of ions across membranes (see Chap. 20). As shown in Figure 3–11, a ganglioside is a complex molecule that contains sphingosine, fatty acids, carbohydrates (lactose + galactosamine) and neuraminic acid. This is a long and highly polar molecule.

Carotenoids. These are animal and plant pigments that belong chemically to the hydrocarbons and whose general formula is $C_{40}H_{56}$. These compounds consist of two aliphatic rings connected by a chain. Carotenes isolated from carrots are responsible for the orange-yellow color of the vegetable. In the animal body, carotenes are often deposited in the skin cells, giving the skin a deep coloring. They are widely distributed pigments in the plant kingdom and they exist in three forms: α, β and γ-carotenes. It is from these substances, particularly the β-carotenes, that animal tissues synthesize vitamin A.

Directly related to vitamin A is retinene; it differs only in that the alcohol group of the vitamin is converted into an aldehyde group. Retinene, with a pro-

tein component, forms the visual purple, which is localized in the terminal segment of the rods in the retina.

Another common pigment belonging to the carotenoids is *lycopene;* it is present in ripe tomatoes and is responsible for their red color.

Chemically related to the carotenoids are the *xanthophylls,* an example of which is *lutein,* a pigment found in the

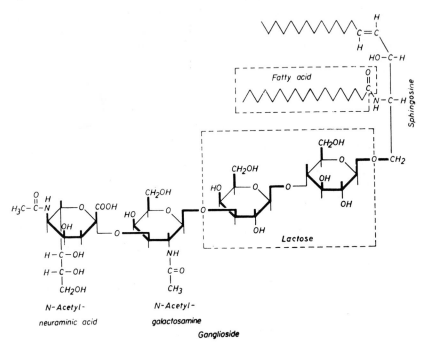

Figure 3–11. Molecular structure of a ganglioside. (From P. Karlson, 1963.)

Table 3–4. Classification of Phosphatides and Glycolipids[*]

NAME	MAIN ALCOHOL COMPONENT	OTHER ALCOHOL COMPONENTS	P :N RATIO
I. Glycerophosphatides			
1. Phosphatidic acids	Diglyceride (= glycerol diester)		1:0
2. Lecithins	Diglyceride (= glycerol diester)	Choline	1:1
3. Cephalins	Diglyceride (= glycerol diester)	Ethanolamine, serine	1:1
4. Inositides	Diglyceride (= glycerol diester)	Inositol	1:0
5. Plasmalogens ("acetyl phosphatides")	Glycerol ester and enol ether	Ethanolamine, choline	1:1
II. Sphingolipids			
1. Sphingomyelins	N-Acylsphingosine	Choline	1:2
2. Cerebrosides	N-Acylsphingosine	Galactose,[a] glucose[a]	0:1
3. Sulfatides	N-Acylsphingosine	Galactose[a]	(1 H_2SO_4)
4. Gangliosides	N-Acylsphingosine	Hexoses,[a] hexosamine,[a] neuraminic acid[a]	no P

[a] These components are present as glycosidic linkage, and thus are called glycolipids.
[*] From P. Karlson, 1963.

chloroplasts of green leaves, but over-shadowed by the presence of chlorophyll. As soon as chlorophyll diminishes, when the leaves dry in autumn, lutein becomes manifest.

Other biologically important pigments besides the carotenoids and the porphyrins (such as chlorophyll and hemoglobin), are the flavins. In aqueous solutions they have a yellow color and a yellowish-green fluorescence. The flavins include the lactoflavins in milk and riboflavin (vitamin B_2). As flavoproteins they form important enzymes or their prosthetic groups, such as succinic dehydrogenase, alcohol dehydrogenase, xanthine oxidase and amino acid oxidases.

Some other *lipoidal substances* are the xanthocyanins, which are plant pigments; certain melanin-like phenolic polymers, which are soluble in organic solvents; the tocopherols, e.g., antisterility vitamin E; the *phylloquinones*, e.g., anticoagulant vitamin K; and *ubiquinone* (*coenzyme Q*), which is present in the respiratory chain of mitochondria.

Lipids in Cytology. The lipids of primary cytologic interest include *triglycerides* composed of glycerol and fatty acids. Glycerol is a trihydric alcohol of the following formula:

$$CH_2OH$$
$$|$$
$$CHOH$$
$$|$$
$$CH_2OH$$

Its three hydroxyl groups can be substituted by three molecules of fatty acids to form a triester (triglyceride). In animals the most frequent fatty acids combined with glycerol are palmitic, stearic and oleic. All these acids are monovalent; three of them combine with one molecule of glycerol, forming tripalmitin, tristearin and triolein, respectively. There are also triglycerides that have two or more fatty acids bound to the same glycerol residue. The fat of adipose tissue is largely a mixture of these esters in variable proportions.

Stereochemically, fatty acids are composed of long hydrocarbon chains (generally containing fourteen to eighteen carbons) with a polar —COOH group at one end. This particular disposition of the end groups makes fatty acids and other lipid substances highly polarized and explains the particular orientation of these substances in the presence of polar or nonpolar solvents (see Chap. 7).

In the organism the role of lipids varies greatly according to their location and distribution. Glycerides serve as stores of energy, and in some aquatic animals, such as whales and seals, provide protection against cold and injury. Phospholipids and cerebrosides are found principally in nervous tissue as constituents of myelin. Of the steroids, the bile acids serve as protein emulsifiers to aid digestion; cholesterol is important in the mechanical functions of epidermis and hair, and the steroid hormones regulate a number of essential metabolic and reproductive processes. Common components of tissues are the *lipoproteins,* i.e., lipids linked to a protein molecule. They also occur in cell membranes and in cell nuclei, as well as in the blood.

From a cytologic point of view it is important to differentiate the "visible" lipids, those easily demonstrable in the cells by common methods of histochemical analysis, and the invisible or "masked" lipids. The former generally are visible directly in the form of refractile droplets which readily give the typical reaction for lipids, such as blackening with osmium tetroxide or staining with Sudan III. "Masked" lipids, however, can be demonstrated indirectly by chemical analysis. (For the histochemistry of lipids, see Chapter 6.)

Nucleic Acids

Nucleic acids are chemical compounds of the utmost biologic importance. All living organisms contain nucleic acids in the form of *deoxyribonucleic acid* (DNA) and *ribonucleic acid* (RNA). Some viruses may contain only RNA, e.g., tobacco mosaic and poliomyelitis virus, and others only DNA, e.g., bacteriophages, vaccinia and adenoviruses. In bacteria and higher cells both types of nucleic acids are found. DNA is mainly present in the nucleus and forms part of the *chromosomes* when the cell is dividing; during interphase, DNA is in the *chromatin.* In the nucleus, DNA is combined with proteins—histones or protamines — forming nucleoproteins. RNA is found both in the nucleus and in the cytoplasm; in the nucleus it is present in the nucleolus and in small amounts in the chromosomes and chromatin; in the cytoplasm it forms a large part of the ribosomes (Table 3–5).

The histochemistry of nucleic acids is studied in Chapter 6. A large part of Chapter 17 is dedicated to the physiological importance of nucleic acids and in Chapter 18 their role in genetics and protein synthesis is described. Only an introductory section on their chemical structure is presented here.

Components of Nucleic Acids. Nucleic acids have a complex chemical structure. They are formed from a sugar moiety (pentose or deoxypentose), nitrogenous bases (purines and pyrimidines) and phosphoric acid. Nucleic acids are long polynucleotides, resulting from the linkage of many units called *nucleotides* (Fig. 3–12).

Table 3–5 lists the location of nucleic acids, their chemical composition and the specific enzymes that hydrolyze them. In addition to nucleic acids, several simpler nucleotides of biologic importance such as adenylic, guanylic and inosinic acids have been isolated from tissues. Nucleotides that play a role as important coenzymes are mentioned in Chapter 4.

Each monomer of the nucleic acid is thus a *nucleotide* and results from the combination of one molecule of phosphoric acid, one of pentose and one of purine or pyrimidine. Within the nucleotide the combination of a pentose with a base constitutes a *nucleoside*. For instance, deoxythymidine is the nucleoside of thymine.

PHOSPHORIC ACID. Phosphoric acid links the nucleotides by joining the pentose of two consecutive nucleosides with an ester-phosphate bond. These bonds link carbon 3′ in one nucleoside with carbon 5′ in the next (Fig. 3–13). In this way phosphoric acid uses two of the three acid groups. The remaining acid group enables the molecule to form ionic bonds with basic proteins (i.e., histones and

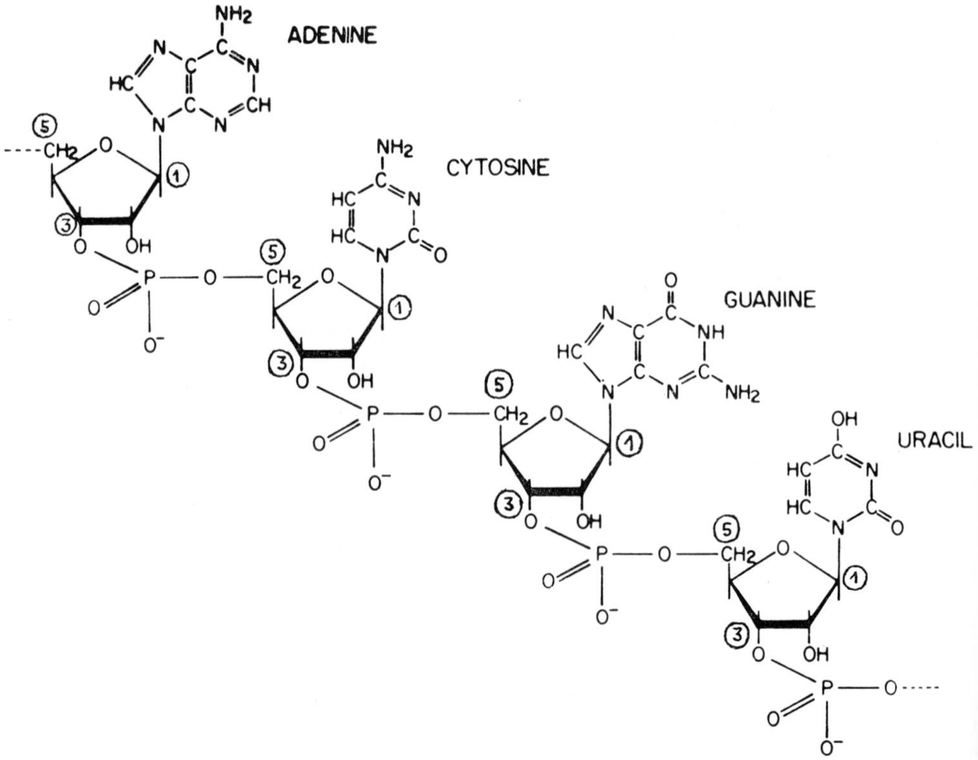

FIGURE 3–12.   Chemical structure of a polynucleotide chain of ribonucleic acid. Notice the four nucleotides.

TABLE 3–5. NUCLEIC ACIDS: STRUCTURE, REACTIONS AND ROLE IN THE CELL

	DEOXYRIBO- NUCLEIC ACID	RIBONUCLEIC ACID
Location	in nucleus	in cytoplasm, nucleolus and chromosomes
Pyrimidine bases	cytosine thymine	cytosine uracil
Purines	adenine guanine	adenine guanine
Pentose	deoxyribose	ribose
Reaction	Feulgen	basophilic dyes after ribonuclease treatment
Hydrolyzing enzyme	deoxyribonuclease	ribonuclease
Role in cell	genetic information	synthesis of proteins

PENTOSES. There are two pentoses, one for each type of nucleic acid: *ribose* in RNA and *deoxyribose* in DNA. In the latter, the oxygen in the second carbon $(2')$ is lacking. Both ribose and deoxyribose have a pentagonal ring with five carbons, two of which $(3'$ and $5')$ are linked to phosphoric acid and a third one (carbon $1'$) to the base. Deoxyribose is responsible for the Feulgen reaction, which is specific for DNA (Chap. 6).

PYRIMIDINE BASES. Pyrimidine bases, so-called because they are derived from pyrimidine, comprise mainly *cytosine, thymine* and *uracil*. Cytosine is found in both DNA and RNA while thymine is characteristic of DNA and uracil of RNA. In much smaller amounts 5-methylcytosine may be found in DNA and 5-hydroxymethylcytosine in DNA of bacteriophages.

An important point to remember is that DNA and RNA differ not only in the structure of pentose but also in the pyrimidine base. In Chapter 6 it will be shown that this fact is basic to the cytochemical study of nucleic acids. Radioactive *thymidine* is used to label DNA specifically, and radioactive *uracil* can be used for RNA.

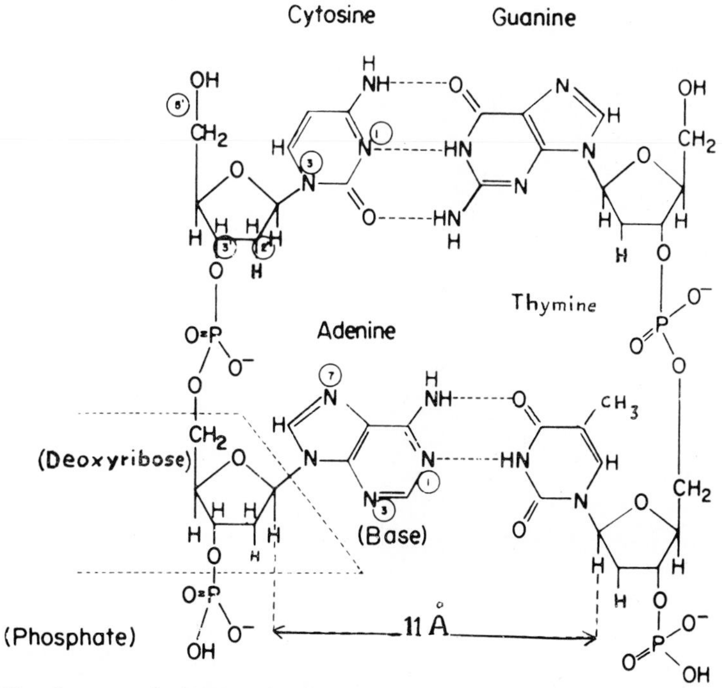

protamines). This group makes nucleotides highly basophilic, i.e., they stain readily with basic dyes (see Chap. 6 and Table 6–1).

FIGURE 3–13. Segment of a DNA molecule, showing two complementary pairs of bases (cytosine-guanine, adenine-thymine) with the hydrogen bonds in between.

PURINE BASES. Purine bases comprise mainly *adenine* and *guanine,* which are common to both DNA and RNA.

In certain RNA molecules, particularly the so-called *soluble (transfer) RNA,* a large proportion of bases are methylated (i.e., contain methyladenine, methylguanine or methylcytosine). (See Chapters 17 and 18.)

All nitrogenous bases have double bonds between the carbons that alternate with single bonds. These bonds can interchange continuously, producing the phenomenon known as *resonance,* and enable the bases (and thus the nucleic acids) to absorb ultraviolet light of 2600 Å (see Chap. 6 and Table 6–1). A cell photographed at this wavelength is shown in Figure 3–14. The nucleolus, the chromatin and all the RNA-containing regions of the cytoplasm absorb the ultraviolet light intensively.

MOLAR RATIO OF THE BASES. While in the past it was thought that the four bases in nucleic acids were in equimolecular amounts that formed a *tetranucleotide* structure, subsequent and more accurate studies have demonstrated that

this is not so. The proportion of bases in RNAs from different species varies, as does that in DNA.

An important observation is that the sum of purine nucleotides in DNA (adenine, A + guanine, G) is equal to the sum of pyrimidine nucleotides (cytosine, C + uracil, U). In addition, the molar ratio $\frac{A}{T} = 1$ and $\frac{C}{G} = 1$ also. It has also been shown that in some DNA molecules AT predominates and in others CG predominates. (Chapter 15 presents data suggesting that some chromosome zones may be rich in AT and others rich in CG.) It follows that the ratio $\frac{A + T}{C + G}$ varies from one species to another: for example, it is 0.42 in avian tubercle bacillus and 1.53 in man.

The Watson-Crick Model of DNA. Biologists became especially interested in DNA structure when, after the x-ray diffraction studies of Wilkins and Franklin in 1953, Watson and Crick proposed a spacial molecular model. Such a model is important because it explains better the physicochemical and biologic properties of DNA and especially its duplication in the cell (see Chap. 17). The essential characteristics of the model are (Fig. 3–15): (a) Each DNA molecule is composed of two long polynucleotide chains that run in opposite directions, forming a double helix around a central axis. (b) Each nucleoside is disposed in a plane that is perpendicular to that of the polynucleotide chain. (c) The two chains are held by *hydrogen bonds* established between the pair of bases (Fig. 3–13). (d) The pairing is highly specific. Because there is a fixed distance of 11 Å between the two sugar moieties in the opposite nucleotides, one purine base can pair only with a pyrimidine base (Fig. 3–15). Thus A—T, C—G, T—A and G—C pairs are the only ones that can be formed. Figure 3–15 shows that two hydrogen bonds are formed between A and T and three hydrogen bonds are formed between C and G. This hydrogen bond formation prevents A—C or G—T from pairing. (e) The *axial sequence* of bases along *one* polynucleotide chain may vary considerably, but on the other

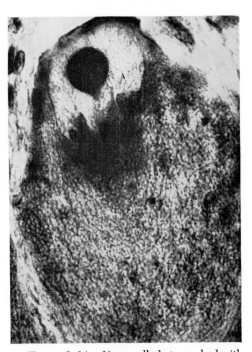

FIGURE 3–14. Nerve cell photographed with ultraviolet light at 2600 Å. The regions in the nucleus and cytoplasm that absorb the ultraviolet light contain nucleic acid. (From H. Hydén.)

chain the sequence must be complementary as in the following example:

1st chain: T, G, C, T, G, T, G, G, T, A

2nd chain: A, C, G, A, C, A, C, C, A, T

Because of this property, given an order
of bases in one chain, the other chain is
exactly complementary.

During DNA duplication, the two
chains dissociate and each one serves as

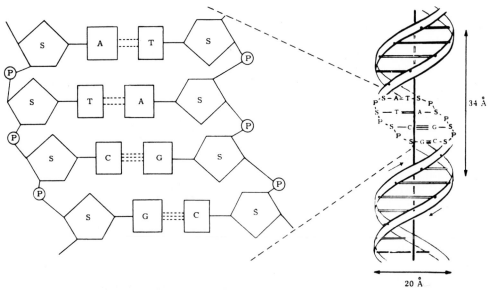

FIGURE 3–15.   The Watson-Crick model of DNA. (See the description in the text.)

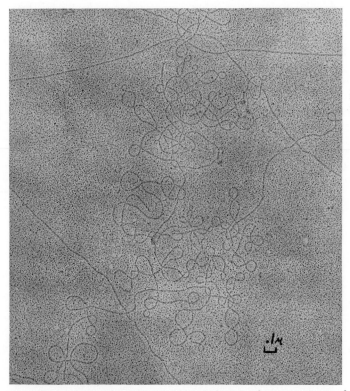

FIGURE 3–16.   Demonstration that DNA is a long polymer. Electron micrograph of DNA molecules extracted from a spermatozoon. Notice the continuity of the long molecules in spite of the
numerous loops. Shadowcast with platinum. ×40,000. (Courtesy of A. J. Solari and D. Mazia.)

a template for the synthesis of two complementary chains (Chap. 17). In this way two DNA molecules are produced which have exactly the same molecular constitution (Fig. 17–9).

The significance of DNA in heredity is explained in Chapter 18, but the reader should note from now on that the varying sequence of the four bases along the DNA chain forms the basis for genetic information. Four bases can produce thousands of different hereditary characters, because DNA molecules are long polymers (Fig. 3–16). For example, in a chain that has 1000 nucleotides, the number of combinations produced are 4^{1000}, which is larger than the number of atoms in the entire solar system.

Other important properties of DNA are explained by the Watson-Crick model. For example, by heating DNA it is possible to break the hydrogen bonds and to separate the individual chains (the so-called "melting effect"). Upon slow cooling, the bonds form again between the complementary chains. With fast cooling the chains remain separated and can be isolated by other methods. Hybrid molecules with DNA and RNA can also be produced (see Chapters 17 and 18).

Structure of Ribonucleic Acids

The primary structure of RNA is similar to that of DNA except that RNA contains ribose and uracil instead of thymine. The molecular arrangement of RNA is less known than that of DNA, but some RNA molecules may possibly be two-stranded, as in DNA. Three classes of RNA are now recognized on the basis of molecular weight and other properties: ribosomal, messenger and soluble (transfer) RNA. These three types of RNA are derived from the nucleus and are used in protein synthesis. (In Chapters 9, 17 and 18 much more is said about RNA.)

GENERAL REFERENCES

Anfinsen, C. B. (1959) *The molecular basis of evolution.* John Wiley & Sons, New York.

Bernal, J. D. (1958) Structure arrangements of macromolecules. *D. Faraday Soc.,* 25:1.

Bier, M. (1959) *Electrophoresis.* Academic Press, New York.

Bull, H. B. (1951) *Physical biochemistry.* 2nd Ed. John Wiley & Sons, New York.

Cantarow, A., and Schepartz, B. (1962) *Biochemistry.* 3rd Ed. W. B. Saunders Co., Philadelphia.

Chargaff, E. E. (1958) Of nucleic acids and nucleoproteins. *Harvey Lect.,* ser. 52 (1956–1957).

Crick, F. H. C. (1957) Nucleic acids. *Scient. Amer.,* 197:188.

Davidson, J. N. (1960) *The biochemistry of the nucleic acids.* 4th Ed. John Wiley & Sons, New York.

Fieser, L. F., and Fieser, M., eds. (1959) *Steroids.* Reinhold Publishing Corp., New York.

Fox, S. W., and Foster, J. R. (1957) *Introduction to protein chemistry.* John Wiley & Sons, New York.

Karlson, P. (1963) *Introduction to modern biochemistry.* Academic Press, New York.

Pauling, L. (1952) The hemoglobin molecule in health and disease. *Proc. Amer. Phil. Soc.,* 96:556.

Sanger, F. (1956) The structure of insulin. In: *Currents in biochemical research.* (Green, D. E., ed.) Interscience Publishers, New York.

CHAPTER 4

ENZYMES

AND

CELL METABOLISM

The cell can be compared to a minute laboratory capable of carrying out the synthesis and breakdown of numerous substances. In this chemical "factory" the work is done isothermally at body temperature, low ionic strength and a narrow range of pH. The "machines" used in this energy transformation are at the molecular level. In fact, they are the so-called *enzymes.*

The enzymes are not randomly distributed within the cell but are located in various cell compartments and frequently are disposed in an orderly fashion within the macromolecular framework of the cell and cell organoids to form what is called a *multienzyme system.* Knowledge of the localization and grouping of enzymes within the cell structure is essential and is emphasized throughout several chapters of this book. In Chapter 18 is a discussion of the genetic determination of enzymes. Then the one-gene–one-enzyme concept is considered as well as the fact that the genetic change of one or more enzymes may produce errors in enzymatic reactions (metabolism), leading to true *molecular diseases,* i.e., ailments due to abnormalities in a molecule.

Metabolism can be defined as the sum of all chemical transformations in the cell. It comprises both the processes of *catabolism* by which substances are broken down and *anabolism* by which new products are synthesized. Catabolic reactions are mostly *exergonic,* i.e., they liberate energy; anabolic reactions are *endergonic,* i.e., they consume energy. For example, the different substrates taken by the cell as foodstuffs, such as glucose, amino acids and lipids, are broken down into smaller molecules with liberation of energy. This energy in turn is utilized by the cell in the synthesis of new and more complex molecules.

The following brief introduction to the study of enzymes explains their cytochemistry and function in the different cell organoids. Then cell metabolism is discussed in order to prepare the student for more specific topics, such as the function of mitochondria and chloroplasts and active transport, which are presented in other chapters. This general introduction should be supplemented by reference to biochemistry and enzymology textbooks.

ENZYMES

Enzymes are the biologic catalysts that accelerate chemical reactions inside the cell. They are proteins with one or more definite adsorption loci (active centers) on the molecules to which are attached the substrate, i.e., the substance upon which the enzyme acts. The substrate (S) is modified and converted into one or more products (P). Since this is in general a reversible reaction, it can be written as follows:

$$S \underset{\longleftarrow}{\overset{\longrightarrow}{enzyme}} P$$

The direction of the reaction is determined by an equilibrium constant. Enzymes accelerate the reaction until the equilibrium of the reversible reaction is reached.

Nomenclature

The present terminology of enzymes is based on their specificity. The suffix "ase" is added to the name of the substrate. For example, enzymes that break down polypeptides (proteins) to oligopeptides or to amino acids are called *proteinases;* those that act on phosphoric esters are called *phosphatases.* In other cases, enzymes are classified by their general activity. For example, *dehydrogenases* are a number of enzymes capable of separating hydrogen from various substrates, e.g., succinic and glutamic dehydrogenases, which transfer hydrogen from succinic and glutamic acids respectively. *Hydrolases* (hydrolytic enzymes) comprise a large group of enzymes that split the substrate by addition of one or more molecules of water.

Several hundred enzymes are known by their action, and over 150 enzymes have been isolated and crystallized, thus allowing estimation of their molecular weight, which ranges from 12,700 for ribonuclease to 1,000,000 for glutamic dehydrogenase.

Specificity

The preceding terminology also embodies the concept that enzymatic activity, unlike inorganic catalysis, is *specific,* i.e., each enzyme is capable of acting on a predetermined substrate. There are, however, different degrees of specificity. The specificity is *absolute* when only one substrate is attacked (e.g., succinic dehydrogenase); *stereochemical* when the action depends on stereochemical configuration; or *relative*

when a variety of compounds of one type are split.

One example of enzyme specificity of different proteinases is shown in Figure 4–1. Aminopeptidase and carboxypeptidase will split the terminal amino- and carboxyl groups of the protein. *Pepsin* is specific for the amino side of tyrosine (or phenylalanine); *chymotrypsin* is specific for the carboxyl side of such residues; and *trypsin* is specific for the carboxyl side of arginine and lysine residues.

Chain Reaction

Although enzymes can be isolated and studied within the living cell, they do not work independently. In most cases there are chains of chemical reactions that are catalyzed by a series of enzymes. In these chains the product of one reaction acts as the substrate of the following and so forth. It is said that chemical reactions are "coupled" within the chain or with other chains of reactions. There are numerous chain reactions in the cell. For example, the Krebs cycle in mitochondria is a chain of reactions, which in turn is "coupled" to the respiratory chain, the electron transport system.

Factors That Affect Enzymatic Activity

Numerous factors may affect the activity of enzymes. As in all chemical reac-

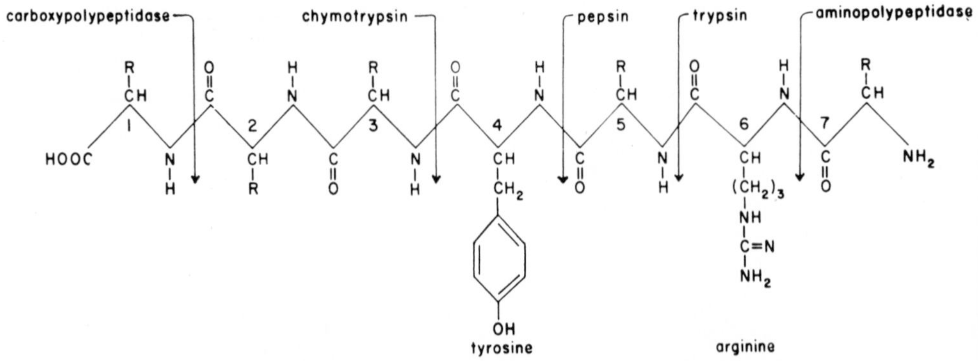

FIGURE 4–1. A diagram to indicate the specificity of various proteolytic enzymes. The numbers refer to the amino acid residues, of which only two, tyrosine and arginine, are labeled below. The polypeptidases are specific, one to the free carboxyl end (left) of a protein molecule or peptide, the other to the free amino end (right) of such molecules. Pepsin is specific to the amino side of tyrosine (or phenylalanine) residues inside a protein molecule; chymotrypsin is specific to the carboxyl side of such residues; and trypsin is specific to the carboxyl side of arginine or lysine residues. (From Giese, A. C., 1962: *Cell physiology.* 2nd Ed.)

tions, enzyme activity depends on the number of contacts, or *collisions*, between the molecules of the enzyme and the substrate. The number of enzyme molecules is in general very small compared to that of the substrate, and any factor that increases the rate of collision with the substrate (such as temperature) will speed up the reaction. Other factors that act directly on the enzyme are the following:

pH. Enzymes, like all proteins, are zwitterions and have an isoelectric point. They are very sensitive to variations of hydrogen ion concentration (pH). There is an optimum pH for each enzyme at which the activity is maximal. For example, for alkaline phosphatase the optimal pH is 8.5 to 10; for acid phosphatase it is 4.5 to 5.

Temperature. There is also an optimum of temperature, which in homothermal organisms is generally the normal body temperature. At temperatures that are above the optimum for activity, the enzyme may be rapidly inhibited and destroyed by protein denaturation. Temperatures beyond 56° C. inactivate enzymes in the majority of cases; however, some enzymes, such as ribonuclease, do not become inactive even if heated to 80° C. The majority of enzymatic reactions are reversible according to thermodynamic conditions; however, the rate of activity is seldom the same in both directions.

Substrate and Enzyme Concentration. The velocity of reaction is dependent upon the relative concentrations of the enzyme and its substrate. If the enzyme concentration is great, the initial velocity of the reaction increases proportionately. If the substrate is increased, the activity may be speeded up until a certain concentration is reached. Then the enzyme becomes saturated and there is no more effect.

Activation. Some enzymes exist in the cell in an inactive form called a *zymogen*. Zymogens are activated by the so-called *kinases*. For example, trypsinogen, produced by pancreatic cells, is activated in the intestine by enterokinase. *Pepsinogen*, secreted by the chief cells of the stomach, is activated by hydrochloric acid (hydrogen ions) secreted by the

parietal cells. In this case the activation is caused by the splitting off of a small polypeptide, which probably masks the active center of the enzyme (see below).

Other hydrolytic enzymes that require free sulfhydryl groups (—SH), e.g., *papain* and *cathepsin*, need reducing agents such as glutathione to be activated.

Coenzymes, Prosthetic Groups and Activators

Some enzymes are conjugated proteins that have a *prosthetic group*. For example, the *cytochromes*, enzymes that transfer electrons between the substrate and atmospheric oxygen, have a metalloporphyrin complex.

Other enzymes cannot function without the addition of small molecules called *coenzymes*, which become bound during the reaction. Such an inactive enzyme, also called an *apoenzyme*, plus the *coenzyme*, forms the active *holoenzyme*. For example, *dehydrogenases* utilize either di- or triphosphopyridine nucleotide (DPN or TPN) (now also called nicotinamide-adenine dinucleotide [NAD] and nicotinamide-adenine dinucleotide phosphate [NADP], respectively). The function of these coenzymes is that of accepting hydrogen ions from the substrate, activated by dehydrogenase, thus passing into a reduced form (DPNH or TPNH). In the following reaction, H_2 is transferred between two enzymes with an intervening coenzyme (P and Q are enzymes and CoH_2 is the reduced coenzyme):

$$PH_2 + Co \rightleftarrows P + CoH_2$$
$$CoH_2 + Q \rightleftarrows Co + QH_2$$

DPN and TPN are nucleotides having adenine, nicotinamide, two molecules of D-ribose and two or three phosphoric acids (see Chap. 3). Coenzymes are closely related to some *vitamins*. For example, *nicotinamide* is a vitamin of the B-group and *pyridoxal*, or vitamin B_6, is a cofactor in transaminases and decarboxylases.

It is valuable to remember that other components of the vitamin B complex are part of the prosthetic groups of different enzymes. For example, *thiamine*, vitamin B_1, is part of cocarboxylase, an important enzyme in the metabolism of pyruvic acid; *pantothenic acid* is part of coenzyme A, and *riboflavin*, vitamin B_2, is the prosthetic group of flavoprotein enzymes.

Other enzymes are influenced by metallic ions. For example, certain important adenosinetriphosphatases are activated by Na^+ and K^+. Oxidative enzymes generally use a metal in their reaction. For example, carbonic anhydrase contains zinc in its reactive group; the cytochromes and catalase, iron; and tyrosinase, laccase and ascorbic acid oxidase, copper.

Active Center of the Enzyme

According to the present concept of enzymatic activity, the substrate attaches itself to the protein component of the enzyme, which has on its molecule a place of specific configuration for this purpose. This is also called an *active center*. Those parts of the substrate upon which an enzyme acts link themselves to this active center, thus forming a lock and key relationship. This concept explains the specificity of enzymatic activity in a simple way.

An excellent example of the present ideas concerning such enzyme-substrate interaction is shown in Figure 4–2, which represents the mechanism of splitting off a compound consisting of sugar and alcohol. The upper part of the compound is the sugar; the lower, the alcohol. On the left side is the protein part of the enzyme with two indentations, which represent the adsorption loci (active centers). The compound (substrate) orients itself along the active centers (1). In the next step, according to the lock and key theory, the sugar moiety fits the upper locus, and the alcohol moiety the lower one (2); a molecule of water is attached so that at the side where the alcohol is linked to sugar (3), one hydrogen atom is fixed to the oxygen of the sugar moiety, and the hydroxyl group (OH) becomes fixed to the first carbon atom of the alcohol (4). The bond between the two moieties breaks and the sugar is thus separated from the alcohol (5). The substrate molecule is attached to the active center by the various types of bonds that have already been discussed.

The lock and key theory also explains the inhibition of an enzyme by a competitor. A substance that has the same configuration as the substrate can fit the active center and thus block it (Fig. 4–3).

The active center of an enzyme is directly related to the primary structure of the protein, since it corresponds to a special amino acid sequence, but also depends on the secondary and tertiary configuration studied in Chapter 2. The

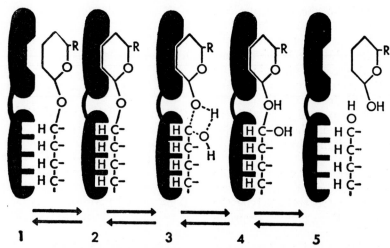

Figure 4–2. Diagram of the active centers of an enzyme. The enzyme, drawn in black, has two active centers which fit the molecule on which they act (**1**). When they combine with the molecule (**2**), they deform it in such a way (**3, 4**) that it is broken down (**5**) into two molecules, in this case sugar and alcohol. (After J. E. Pfeiffer, *Sci. Amer.*, 1953.)

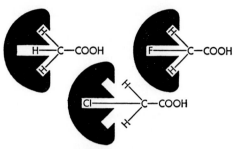

FIGURE 4–3. The lock and key theory explains why enzymes are specific to certain compounds and how their action can be inhibited by similar compounds. **Left,** Acetic acid fits an enzyme (black) and the reaction works. **Right,** When a fluorine atom is substituted for a hydrogen atom, forming monofluoroacetate, the fit is close enough to occupy the enzyme and to block its reaction with acetic acid. **Middle,** However, when a chlorine atom replaces the fluorine atom (monochloroacetate) the key fits so poorly that the enzyme does not accept it. (After J. E. Pfeiffer, *Sci. Amer.*, 1953.)

study of the molecular nature of the active centers is one of the most fundamental problems of molecular biology.

CELL METABOLISM

Energy Cycle

The ultimate source of energy in living organisms comes from the sun. The energy carried by photons of light is trapped by the pigment *chlorophyll*, present in the chloroplasts of green plants, and accumulates as chemical energy within the different foodstuffs. Without the sun, there would be no life on this planet.

All cells and organisms can be grouped into two main classes, differing in the mechanism of extracting energy for their own metabolism. In the first, called *autotrophic* (i.e., green plants), CO_2 and H_2O are transformed by the process of *photosynthesis* into the elementary organic molecule of *glucose* from which the more complex molecules are then made.

The second class of cells, called *heterotrophic* (i.e., animal cells), obtain energy from the different foodstuffs (i.e., carbohydrates, fats and proteins), that were synthesized by autotrophic organisms. The energy contained in these organic molecules is relased mainly by combustion with O_2 from the atmosphere (i.e., oxidation) in a process called *aerobic respiration*. The release of H_2O and CO_2 by heterotrophic organisms completes this cycle of energy.

The diagram of Figure 4–4 shows that plant cells also may derive energy by respiration of the foodstuffs that were synthesized in their own chloroplasts. Both autotrophic and heterotrophic processes take place in plant cells.

There is a small group of bacteria that is able to obtain energy from inorganic molecules, a process called *chemosynthesis*. For example, the bacteria of genus *Nitrobacter* oxidate nitrites to nitrates

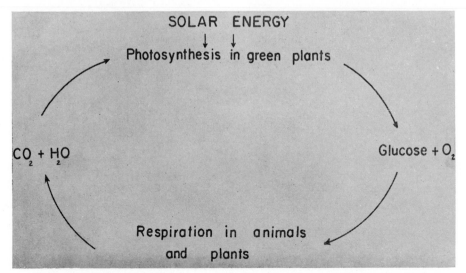

FIGURE 4–4. Diagram of the energy transformations in green plants and animals.

$(NO_2^- + \frac{1}{2} O_2 \rightarrow NO_3^-)$. Other bacteria transfer ferrous into ferric oxides and some oxidize SH_2 to sulfate.

Energy Transformation

The *chemical* or *potential* energy of foodstuffs is locked in the different covalent bonds between the atoms of a molecule. For example, during hydrolysis of a chemical bond (such as a peptide or an ester bond), about 3000 calories per mol is liberated. In *glucose*, between the atoms of C, H and O there is an amount of potential energy of about 680,000 calories per mol (i.e., per 180 grams of glucose) which can be liberated by combustion, as in the following reaction:

$$C_6H_{12}O_6 + 6O_2 \rightarrow$$
$$6H_2O + CO_2 + 680,000 \text{ calories}$$

Within the living cell this enormous amount of energy is not released suddenly as in the combustion in a flame. It proceeds in a stepwise and controlled manner, requiring dozens of oxidative enzymes that finally convert the fuel into CO_2 and H_2O.

In the heat engine of a car there are great changes in temperature; within the cell this does not occur. Only a part of the energy liberated from the foodstuff is dissipated as heat; the rest is recovered as new chemical energy. The energy liberated in the exergonic reactions resulting from the oxidation of foodstuffs is used in the different cellular functions. As shown in Figure 4–5, the energy may be used: (a) to synthesize new molecules (i.e., proteins, carbohydrates and lipids) by means of *endergonic* reactions. These molecules can then be used to replace others or for the natural growth of the cell; (b) to perform mechanical work as in cell division, cyclosis (cytoplasmic streaming), or the muscle contraction; (c) to produce *active transport* against an osmotic or ion gradient; (d) to maintain membrane potentials as in nerve conduction and transmission or to produce electric discharges (e.g., in electric fish); (e) in cell secretion; or (f) to produce radiant energy as in bioluminescence. Only in the reactions of group (a) is the energy provided by the foodstuff transformed into chemical bond energy. In all the other reactions chemical energy is transformed into other forms of energy.

High Energy Bonds. Figure 4–5 shows that in between all these transformations is a common link, namely, the molecule of *adenosine triphosphate* (ATP). This is a compound found in all cells. Its main characteristic is two terminal bonds with a potential energy much higher than all the other chemical bonds. As shown in Figure 4–6, ATP is composed of the purine base *adenine*, of ri-

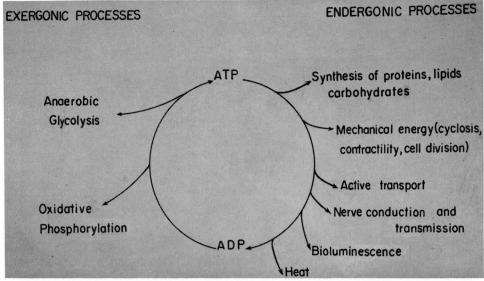

FIGURE 4–5. Energy wheel of Baldwin, showing the relationship between exergonic and endergonic processes through ATP.

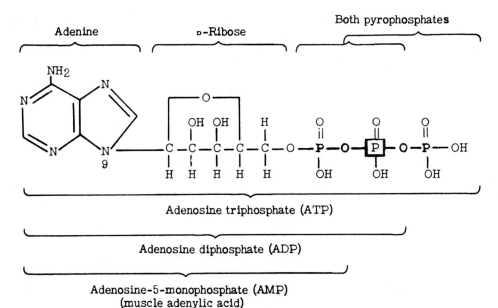

FIGURE 4–6. Diagram showing the molecules of ATP, ADP and AMP. (From Harper, H. A. 1963. *Review of physiological chemistry.* Lange Med. Pub., Cal.)

bose and of three molecules of *phosphoric acid*. Adenine plus ribose forms the nucleoside *adenosine;* this in turn with the first phosphate forms adenosine monophosphate, *adenylic acid*. The most important compounds in energy transformation are however adenosine diphosphate (ADP) and adenosine triphosphate. If we represent adenosine by A and phosphate by P, the simplified formula of ATP and its transformation into ADP is as follows:

$$A—P \sim P \sim P \rightleftharpoons A—P \sim P$$
$$+ \text{ Pi} + 8000 \text{ calories}$$

This reaction indicates that the release of the terminal phosphate of ATP produces about 8000 calories instead of the 3000 calories from common chemical bonds. In Figure 4–5 the reaction ATP ⇌ ADP plays the central role between the exergonic processes that liberate energy and those that store or transform energy in the different cellular functions.

The high energy ~P bond enables the cell to accumulate a great amount of energy in a very small space and to keep it ready to be used as soon as it is needed. The presence of ATP explains why some important cellular functions such as nerve conduction can go on for some time even with complete inhibition of respiration.

In recent years it has been discovered that other nucleotides having high energy bonds, such as cytosine triphosphate (CTP), uridine triphosphate (UTP) and guanosine triphosphate (GTP), are involved in biosynthetic reactions. High energy phosphate bonds are also found in phosphocreatine, acetylphosphate and phosphoenolpyruvic acid.

ATP is a polyelectrolyte having five negative charges, and is normally bound to bivalent cations such as Ca^{++}, Mg^{++} and Mn^{++}. The terminal phosphate bond is liberated by the enzyme adenosinetriphosphatase (ATPase). For example, in muscle, myosin has ATPase activity and can release Pi from ATP (see Chap. 21). The mechanochemical conversion in muscle is as follows:

$$\text{ATP} + \text{muscle fiber} \rightarrow \text{ADP} \sim \text{muscle fiber} + \text{Pi}$$
$$\text{(extended)} \qquad\qquad \text{(contracted)}$$

$$\text{ADP} \sim \text{muscle fiber} + H_2O \rightarrow \text{muscle fiber} + \text{ADP}$$
$$\text{(contracted)} \qquad\qquad \text{(extended)}$$

$$\overline{\text{ATP} + H_2O \rightarrow \text{ADP} + \text{Pi}}$$

This is an excellent example of how structure and function are coupled at the molecular level (see Chap. 22).

Concept of Oxidation and Reduction

The study of biologic oxidation began with Lavoisier in 1780 when he demonstrated that animals use oxygen from the air and produce carbon dioxide. *Oxidation* was then considered as the process by which oxygen combines with a substance—*reduction* being the opposite phenomenon, i.e., that of removal of oxygen. Later on the term oxidation was applied to the process by which hydrogen is removed—reduction being the process by which hydrogen is accepted by a substrate. Finally the same terminology was applied to reactions in which there is an electron transfer, e.g., a ferrous ion is converted to a ferric ion by loss of an electron.

$$Fe^{++} \rightarrow Fe^{+++} + e^-$$

At present, loss of electrons is considered the most important characteristic of oxidation. This may or may not be accompanied by addition of oxygen and loss of hydrogen.

Oxidation reactions are catalyzed by enzymes generically called *oxidases*. Reactions involving electron transfer—the most frequent biologic oxidations—are catalyzed by *dehydrogenases,* enzymes that remove hydrogen from the substrate. Both *oxidases* and *dehydrogenases* may be contained in mitochondria, and by their coordinated work they bring about the different steps of the respiratory chain (Chap. 9).

Dehydrogenases remove hydrogen from substrates in the presence of DPN or TPN, which acts as a carrier. The action of these enzymes can be easily studied by the technique devised by Thurnberg with methylene blue. If this dye is put in contact with a cell suspension, the suspension becomes colorless, being transformed into a leucobase by the addition of H_2. The dye acts in this case as a *hydrogen acceptor.* That this action is caused by dehydrogenases is demonstrated by heating the tissue. As soon as the enzyme is destroyed, there is

no more bleaching of the methylene blue. At present, the reduction of DPN or TPN is studied spectrophotometrically.

Many dehydrogenases can function only in the presence of coenzymes. The hydrogen detached from the substrate is transferred to *either* of the coenzymes DPN$^+$ or TPN$^+$.

Dehydrogenases operating through DPN$^+$ or TPN$^+$ are in general *flavoproteins (yellow enzymes),* the prosthetic group of which is a vitamin: riboflavin. Flavoproteins act as hydrogen transfer agents to an acceptor. Most dehydrogenases do not need oxygen for their activity and do not transfer hydrogen from the substrate directly to O_2. For this part of the oxidative chain other enzyme systems that couple with molecular oxygen are required. This function is performed by the *cytochromes,* which are iron-containing hemoproteins widely distributed in nature. As demonstrated by Keilin, cytochromes a, b and c can be distinguished spectroscopically in the living cell by their different absorption bands, which represent the substance in the oxidated or in the reduced form. Cytochrome a_3 is probably identical with the enzyme *cytochrome oxidase,* which contains copper and was known for a long time by its property of forming indophenol blue in the presence of the Nadi reagent of Ehrlich (α-naphthol and paraphenylene diamine) (Chap. 6).

As shown in Figure 4–7, the respiratory chain is based on the transport of electrons along the successive cytochromes with change of the reduced form, ferrocytochrome (Fe^{++}), into the oxidized form, ferricytochrome (Fe^{+++}).

Cell Respiration

It is now possible to understand better the exergonic processes produced in the living cell by which organic substances are oxidized and chemical energy is released. All these processes are grouped under the name of *cell respiration.* We have already seen that to dismantle an organic molecule, cells undergo mainly dehydrogenations, which can be carried

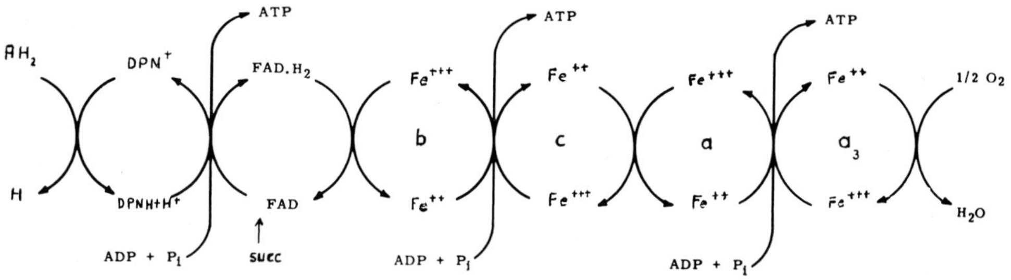

FIGURE 4–7.   Diagram of a respiratory chain AH_2 substrate. A, oxidized substrate; FAD, flavo-enzyme; b, c, a, series of cytochromes; a_3, cytochrome oxidase. Most substrates are dehydrogenated by DPN^+ or TPN^+ dependent dehydrogenases. Notice that succinate (succ) goes directly to the cytochrome by way of succinate dehydrogenase. The three points along the chain at which phosphorylation with formation of ATP is probably produced are indicated. The entire respiratory chain is coupled to the left to the Krebs cycle and receives the H^+ and electrons produced in it through the specific dehydrogenases.

out in the presence or absence of atmospheric O_2. There are thus two types of respiration: aerobic respiration and anaerobic respiration. Anaerobic respiration is also called fermentation (Table 4–1).

Anaerobic Respiration (Fermentation). This denomination is applied to exergonic reactions by which complex molecules can be degraded without participation of molecular oxygen. The best known example is that of the degradation of glucose, also called *anaerobic glycolysis*. The term *fermentation* is used more in reference to microorganisms and plants.

The six-carbon chain of glucose can be degraded by glycolysis into different smaller molecules. For example, in muscle, each molecule of glucose is converted into two of lactic acid. In yeast, the main products are ethanol and CO_2, as in the following general reaction which is called *alcoholic fermentation*.

$$C_6H_{12}O_6 \rightarrow 2C_2H_5OH + 2CO_2$$
$$\text{glucose} \qquad \text{ethanol}$$

In other microorganisms the products of fermentation may be: butanol, acetone, acetic acid and so forth.

In 1861, Pasteur demonstrated that yeast can produce alcohol in complete absence of oxygen. He postulated that living cells can derive energy either from the use of oxygen, i.e., *aerobiosis*, or by the mechanism of fermentation, i.e., *anaerobiosis*.

In muscle, the general reaction of glycolysis is:

$$C_6H_{12}O_6 \rightarrow 2C_3H_6O_3 + 58{,}000 \text{ calories}$$
$$\text{lactic acid}$$

This reaction shows that hexose is broken down into two trioses with liberation of less than 10 per cent of the energy contained in glucose (i.e., 680,-000 cal.). The most important product of glycolysis is *pyruvic acid*, which can be converted into lactic acid in anaerobic conditions or in the presence of oxygen

TABLE 4–1.   SOME DIFFERENCES BETWEEN AEROBIC AND ANAEROBIC RESPIRATION

AEROBIC RESPIRATION (OXIDATIVE PHOSPHORYLATION)	ANAEROBIC RESPIRATION (FERMENTATION)
Uses molecular O_2	Does not use O_2
Degrades glucose to CO_2 and H_2O	Degrades glucose to trioses and other complex organic compounds
Exergonic	Exergonic
Recovers almost 50 per cent of chemical energy	Recovers less chemical energy
Present in most organisms	Present in some microorganisms and important in embryonic and neoplastic cells
Enzymes localized in mitochondria	Enzymes localized in the cytoplasmic matrix

may enter the aerobic cycle of respiration (see Aerobic Respiration, which follows). (For a detailed study of all the steps of glycolysis, the student is referred to biochemistry and enzymology textbooks.) Essentially in glycolysis (also called the Embden-Meyerhof pathway), the glucose molecule is submitted to a series of phosphorylations before being degraded into two molecules of triose. In the simplified diagram of Figure 4–8, notice that the six-carbon molecule of glucose undergoes two phosphorylations by ATP, followed by rupture into two molecules of triose, which will finally be converted into pyruvate or lactate. Notice that for each molecule of glucose, two ATP molecules are used and four ATP molecules are produced with a positive balance of two new ATP molecules.

In Figure 4–8 the sequence of chemical events, the enzymes and the cofactors involved are also listed. Remember that in the entire glycolytic chain molecular oxygen is not used. Pyruvate may enter into the aerobic or Krebs cycle to complete the oxidation of the molecule to CO_2 and H_2O.

If the carbohydrate source is glycogen, glycolysis starts by depolymerization with direct incorporation of phosphate, giving glucose-1-phosphate which is converted into glucose-6-phosphate, and then the cycle follows (Fig. 4–8). In this case one molecule of ATP is saved and the final balance is 3 ATP molecules per each glucose molecule.

In glycolysis, as in other biochemical pathways, there is a series of reactions in which the changes are gradual and even reversible. The energy is thus released in small amounts at a time and, through the many intermediary compounds, new synthetic chains can be initiated. Since in the series of reactions of glycolysis two or three new ATP molecules are formed, it is easily understood that from the 58,000 calories liberated from each glucose molecule, about 30 per cent is accumulated into high energy bonds. Most of the enzymes involved in glycolysis are localized in the cytoplasmic matrix of the cell (Chap. 8). Anaerobic glycolysis is the main exergonic pathway in some microorganisms and is important in embryonic and neoplastic (e.g., cancer) cells. Anaerobic respiration also takes place in higher cells, but normally it is less important than aerobic respiration (see Table 4–1).

Aerobic Respiration, Krebs Cycle and Oxidative Phosphorylation

Aerobic respiration is the group of reactions by which organic substances are degraded to CO_2 and H_2O with intervention of molecular oxygen. (This process takes place in mitochondria, and in intimate relationship with their macromolecular structure [Chap. 11; see Table 4–1].) Aerobic respiration is directly related to anaerobic glycolysis. After the degradation of glucose to pyruvic acid, this metabolite may enter the aerobic cycle to be finally degraded to CO_2 and H_2O.

The various reactions involved constitute the *citric acid cycle*, also called *Krebs cycle* or *tricarboxylic acid cycle*. This series of reactions is of fundamental importance not only for the degradation of carbohydrates but also for the metabolism of proteins and fats. In fact, the Krebs cycle is not only used for the oxidation of the products of glycolysis but of fatty acids and amino acids as well. In other words, the citric acid cycle is a final common pathway in metabolism, where the substrates are being burned to CO_2 and H_2O (see Chap. 11 and Fig. 11–11).

The pyruvate molecule is first decarboxylated; it loses CO_2 and is converted by oxidation into acetate. This molecule combined with coenzyme A actually enters into the citric acid cycle.

The first step of the Krebs cycle is the condensation of acetate with *oxaloacetate* (a four-carbon compound) to produce *citrate* with six carbons. To this a series of reactions follow in the course of which the molecule of acetate is degraded to CO_2 and H^+ (with electrons). The molecule of oxaloacetate is regenerated to start a new cycle. The series of reactions, enzymes and cofactors involved in the Krebs cycle are indicated in Table 4–2.

Krebs Cycle and Respiratory Chain. The Krebs cycle is normally coupled to

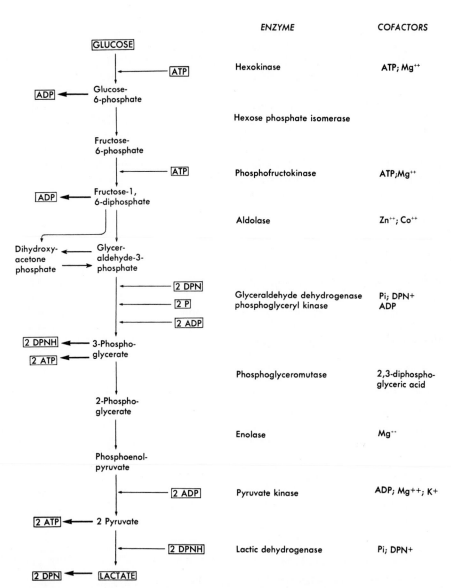

FIGURE 4–8. Diagram of the different steps of anaerobic glycolysis, starting with the glucose molecule. *To the left,* the different reactions are shown together with the sites of penetration, an exit of ATP. Notice that there is a net gain of 2ATP in this process. The different enzymes and cofactors involved are also indicated.

the respiratory chain or electron transport system. In all dehydrogenations occurring with pyruvic acid and then with acetic acid within the Krebs cycle, the hydrogen ions and electrons that have been separated by the specific dehydrogenase are taken by the coenzymes DPN+ and TPN+. These H+ and e⁻ are then transported through the chain formed by the flavoprotein (yellow enzyme of Warburg) and the different cytochromes and cytochrome oxidase just studied (Fig. 4–7). Along this chain a series of oxidations and reductions occurs and the energy released at each step is locked in the high energy bonds of ATP. Finally the H+ transported combines with the activated ½ O₂ to form water.

At three points along the respiratory chain ADP and P enter to form ATP, a process known as phosphorylation (Fig. 4–7). Because of this, aerobic respiration is also called *oxidative phosphorylation*.

Normally the Krebs cycle and phosphorylation are coupled within the structure of the mitochondria. These two processes can be uncoupled under certain conditions (Chap. 11). In this case the ratio between inorganic phosphate, which is transferred to organic ATP, and O₂ consumed (the so-called P:O ratio) falls.

It is interesting to consider also the yield of energy from oxidative phosphorylation and to compare it with that of anaerobic glycolysis. For each glucose molecule (i.e., two of pyruvate), the Krebs cycle yields about 30 high energy ATP bonds. In comparison only 2 or 3 ATP molecules are produced by fermentation. We can conclude that oxidative phosphorylation yields 10 to 15 times more chemical energy than glycolysis. The thermodynamic efficiency of oxidative phosphorylation is about 50 per cent. This means that the other half of the energy present in the glucose molecule dissipates in the form of heat.

It is interesting that from the phylogenic viewpoint the lowest forms of life get their energy by fermentation. In higher forms oxidative phosphorylation appears, and in the highest organisms this is preceded by fermentation and coupled to it. The first gives the lowest supply of energy, the second is intermediary and the third is the most efficient.

For other alternative pathways of glu-

TABLE 4–2. REACTION SEQUENCE OF THE TRICARBOXYLIC ACID CYCLE*

	REACTION	ENZYME	COFACTORS
1	pyruvate ⇌ acetyl CoA	pyruvic dehydrogenase	DPN+; TPP; Mg++ lipoic acid; CoA
2	acetyl CoA + oxaloacetate ⇌ citrate + CoA	condensing enzyme	Mg++
3	citrate ⇌ isocitrate	aconitase	—
4	isocitrate ⇌ oxalosuccinate	isocitric dehydrogenase	TPN+; Mg++
5	oxalosuccinate ⇌ α-ketoglutarate + CO₂	oxalosuccinate decarboxylase	Mn++
6	α-ketoglutarate ⇌ succinyl CoA	α-ketoglutaric dehydrogenase	DPN+; TPP; Mg++ lipoic acid; CoA
7	succinyl CoA ⇌ succinate	(several)	GDP; ADP; Mg++; CoA
8	succinate ⇌ fumarate	succinic dehydrogenase	FAD
9	fumarate + H₂O ⇌ malate	fumarase	—
10	malate ⇌ oxaloacetate	malic dehydrogenase	DPN+

* From Kuyper, C. M. A. (1962) *The organization of cellular activity.* Elsevier, Amsterdam.

cose, such as the pentose shunt, and for the metabolism of proteins, amino acids and lipids, the reader is referred to biochemistry textbooks.

GENERAL REFERENCES

Baldwin, E. (1957) *Dynamic aspects of biochemistry*. 3rd Ed. Cambridge University Press, London.

Boyer, P. D., Lardy, H., and Myrback, K. (1959–1963) 2nd Ed. *The enzymes*. 8 volumes. Academic Press, New York.

Bradfield, J. A. G. (1950) The localization of enzymes in cells. *Biol. Rev., 25:*113.

Dixon, M. (1951) *Multi-enzyme systems.* Cambridge University Press, London.

Dixon, M., and Webb, E. C. (1958) *Enzymes.* Longmans, Green and Co., New York.

George, P., and Rutman, R. J. (1960) The high energy bond concept. *Progr. Biophys., 10:*2.

Greenberg, D. M. (1961) *Metabolic pathways.* 2 volumes. Academic Press, New York.

Krebs, H. A. (1950) The tricarboxylic acid cycle. *Harvey Lect.,* ser. *44* (1948–1949) p. 165.

Lehninger, A. L. (1961) How cells transform energy. *Sci. Amer., 205:*62.

Lipmann, F. (1941) Metabolic generation and utilization of phosphorus bond energy. *Advanc. Enzymol., 1:*99.

Lipmann, F. (1953) On the chemistry and function of coenzyme A. *Bact. Rev., 17:*1.

McElroy, W. D. (1961) *Cellular physiology and biochemistry.* Prentice-Hall, Englewood Cliffs, New Jersey.

Racker, E. (1961) Mechanism of synthesis of ATP. *Advanc. Enzymol., 23:*323.

Sumner, J. B., and Somers, G. F. (1953) *Chemistry and methods of enzymes.* 3rd Ed. Academic Press, New York.

PART TWO

METHODS
FOR THE STUDY
OF THE CELL

The recent extraordinary progress in cell biology has resulted from the development of new methods for the study of the cell and of its molecular and macromolecular components. In the following chapters the two main groups of techniques employed in cytology are studied in a simplified way.

Chapter 5 includes all the methods that employ electromagnetic waves. These may be visible or ultraviolet radiations, electrons or x-rays. In studying these methods, review the chapters of physics textbooks that deal with reflection, refraction, interference and diffraction of electromagnetic waves in order to understand better the series of instruments used for the analysis of cellular and subcellular structure, which includes molecular biology. The importance of electron microscopy and x-ray diffraction are emphasized. The images given by the light, phase, interference, polarization, and electron microscopes are discussed in relation to the different physical principles involved.

This study of instruments is complemented by Chapter 6, which is a brief discussion of the main methods of cytologic and cytochemical analysis used for observation and experimentation. Since the number of techniques surpasses by far the limits of this book, only a few selected examples are mentioned. The methods for study of living cells, the process of fixation for the preparation of cells and tissues and the mechanism of staining are considered. At present the cytochemical techniques for the identification and localization of substances within cells are of paramount importance. Only a few examples are mentioned, pointing mainly to the mechanism of cytochemical analysis and to the problems that can be tackled.

CHAPTER 5

INSTRUMENTAL ANALYSIS OF BIOLOGIC STRUCTURES

In studying this chapter, the student should be familiar with the limits and dimensions in biology presented in Chapter 1 and with the optical laws and principles on which the ordinary light microscope is based (Fig. 5–1).

Observation of biologic structures is difficult because cells are in general very small and are transparent to visible light. The search continues for new instruments designed to provide better definition of cell structure down to the molecular level by an increase in *resolving power* and to counteract the transparency of the cell by an increase of *contrast*.

Resolving Power of the Microscope

In the light microscope, as in any other type of microscope, the power of resolution, which is the instrument's capacity for giving distinct images of points very close together in an object, depends upon the wavelength (λ) and the numerical aperture (NA) of the objective lens. The *limit of resolution,* which can be defined as the minimum distance between two points in order that they may be discriminated as such, is:

$$\text{Limit of resolution} = \frac{0.61\lambda}{\text{NA}} \quad (1)$$

The numerical aperture is: $\text{NA} = \text{n} \cdot \sin \alpha$. Here α is the refractive index of the medium and sin α the sinus of the semi-angle of aperture. Remember that the limit of resolution (minimal distance) is inversely related to the resolving power (maximal capacity); the higher the resolving power the smaller the limit of resolution.

Since the sin α cannot exceed 1, and the refractive index of most optical material does not exceed 1.6, the maximal NA of lenses, using oil immersion, is about 1.4. With these parameters it is easy to calculate from formula (1) that the limit of resolution of the light microscope cannot surpass 1700 Å (0.17 μ) using monochromatic light of $\lambda = 4000$ Å (violet). With white light the resolving power is about 2500 Å = 0.25 μ. Since in formula (1) the NA is limited, it is evident that the only way to increase the resolving power (that is, to reduce the limit of resolution) is to use smaller wavelengths. In this case glass lenses are not transparent any longer and one should introduce other refractive media. For example, with ultraviolet radiation of 2000 to 3000 Å, quartz lenses or reflecting optical instruments should be used, and the resolution is increased only by a factor of two, reaching 1000 Å (0.1 μ). By similar reasoning, a microscope using infrared radiation of $\lambda = 8000$ Å would have a limit of resolution of 0.4 μ.

METHODS FOR INCREASING CONTRAST

Phase Microscopy

The eye detects variations in wavelength (color) and in intensity of visible light. The majority of cell components are essentially transparent to the visible region of the spectrum, except

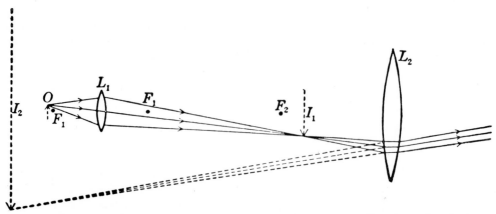

FIGURE 5–1.   Light path in the ordinary light compound microscope. The group of ocular lenses is diagrammatically represented by L_2, the group of objective lenses by L_1. The object (O) on a microscope slide is placed just outside the principal focus of the objective lens (L_1), which has a short focus. This lens produces a real image at I_1, which is formed inside the principal focus of the eyepiece lens (L_2). The eye, looking through the lens L_2, sees a magnified virtual image (I_2) of the image I_1. The eyepiece lens is thus used as a magnifying glass to view the real image (I_1).

for some pigments (more frequent in plant cells) that absorb light at certain wavelengths (colored substances). The low light absorption of the living cell is caused largely by its high water content, but even after drying, cell components show little contrast.

One way of overcoming this limitation is by the use of dyes that selectively stain different cell components and thus introduce contrast by light absorption. However, in most cases, staining techniques cannot be used in the living cell. The tissue must be fixed, dehydrated, embedded and sectioned prior to staining, and all these procedures may introduce morphologic and chemical changes.

In recent years remarkable advances have been made in the study of living cells by the development of special optical techniques, such as *phase contrast* and *interference microscopy*. These two techniques are based on the fact that although biologic structures are highly transparent to visible light, they cause phase changes in transmitted radiations. These phase differences, which result from small differences in the refractive index and thickness of different parts of the object, can now be made more clearly detectable.

Figure 5–2 indicates the effects on a light ray of a nonabsorbent transparent material (A) and an absorbent transparent material (C). In A the wave im-

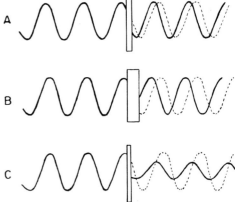

FIGURE 5–2.   Diagram showing: **A**, the effect of a transparent and nonabsorbent material of higher reactive index than the medium, which introduces a phase change (retardation). **B**, the same but thicker object. The retardation or phase change is more pronounced. **C**, effect of a transparent and absorbent object. There is a retardation but also a decrease in amplitude (intensity).

pinges on a material that has a refractive index different from that of the medium. In traversing the object, the amplitude of the wave is not affected, but the velocity is changed. If the refractive index of the material is higher than that of the medium, there is a *delay* or *retardation*, which is also called a *phase change*. After the wave emerges from the object, its original velocity is re-established, but retardation is maintained. This retardation implies a phase change, which can be measured in fractions of a wavelength. The phase change increases in direct proportion to the difference between the refractive indices of the object and the surrounding medium and to the thickness of the object (Fig. 5–2B).

To understand the phase microscope better, it is necessary to analyze first the behavior of a ray of light that traverses a thin, transparent particle that has a refractive index very close to that of the surrounding medium, as is the case with the living cell. The particle represents an obstacle. While a portion of the light ray traverses the particle without deviation, maintaining the same amplitude and wavelength, the other portion of the light ray (wave D in Fig. 5–3B), is diffracted and deviates with respect to the rays that do not traverse the object (wave S in Fig. 5–3B).

It is interesting to remember that in biologic materials the phase difference between the S and D waves is approximately ¼ wavelength (Fig. 5–3B). These two rays (S and D) penetrate the objective lens and undergo interference. The resulting ray has the same wavelength and amplitude as the one that traverses the medium, but has a small phase retardation. This is not sufficient to produce a change in amplitude, and thus is not detectable with an ordinary light microscope in which these phenomena also take place.

In the phase contrast microscope, originally developed by Zernike as a method for testing telescope mirrors, the small phase differences are amplified (and thus intensified) so that they are detected by the eye or the photographic plate. In the phase microscope, the most lateral light passing through the objective of the microscope is advanced or retarded by ¼ wavelength (¼ λ) with respect to the central light passing the object. An annular phase plate that introduces this ¼ wavelength variation is put in the back focal plane of the objective. In addition, an annular diaphragm is placed in the substage condenser (Fig. 5–3). The phase plate is a transparent disk containing an annular groove or elevation of a shape and size that coincide with the direct image of the substage condenser. The phase effect results from the interference between the direct geometric image given by the central part of the objective and the lateral diffracted image, which has been retarded or advanced to ¼ wavelength. In *bright*, or *negative*, *contrast* the two sets of rays are added (Fig. 5–3D) and the object appears brighter than the surroundings; in *dark*, or *positive*, *contrast* the two sets of rays are subtracted (Fig. 5–3C), making the image of the object darker than the surroundings (Fig. 2–2). Because of this interference, the minute phase changes within the object are amplified and translated into changes of amplitude (intensity). The transparent object thus appears in shades of gray, depending on the product of the thickness and the difference in refractive index of the object with the medium. (For further details on this technique and its application to the ultraviolet and infrared spectrums and the use of polarized light, see references 1 to 6 and the general references.)

Phase microscopy is now used routinely to observe living cells and tissues. Extraordinary cytologic detail can be observed in tissues that are simply excised and studied in a physiologic fluid (Fig. 2–2). Phase microscopy is particularly valuable in the observation of cells cultured in vivo (see Fig. 10–1). In these, using time-lapse motion pictures, one can easily record and study the following phenomena: the different nuclear and cytoplasmic changes occurring during cell division and cell movement; the continuous flow of mitochondria, watery vacuoles (pinocytosis) and inclusion bodies; the formation of fine membranes and fibrillar expansions; and so forth.

Phase microscopy is used to study the effect of different chemical and physical agents on the living cell and to examine the artifacts introduced by different methods of fixation and staining.

Interference Microscopy

The interference microscope is based on principles similar to those of the phase microscope, but has the advantage of giving quantitative data. With this instrument it is possible to determine the optical-phase difference for

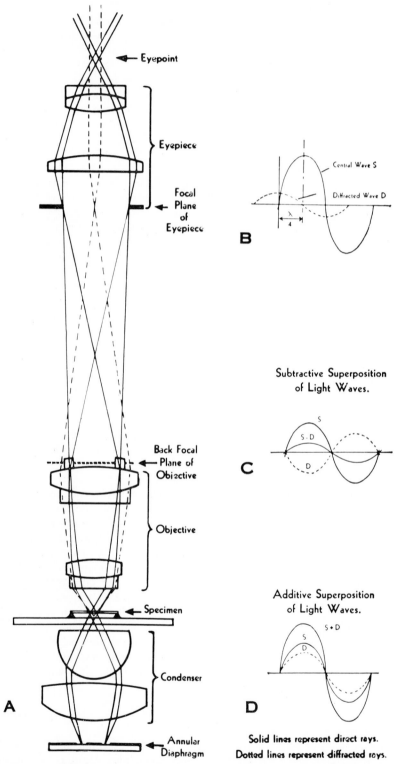

FIGURE 5–3.   **A,** the light path in a phase microscope. **B,** the normal retardation by ¼ wavelength of light diffracted by an object, and its difference in phase from the light passing through the surrounding medium. By phase optics the two waves are superimposed to reinforce each other in bright contrast phase as shown in **D** or to subtract from each other as in dark contrast phase shown in **C.** (From the American Optical Company.)

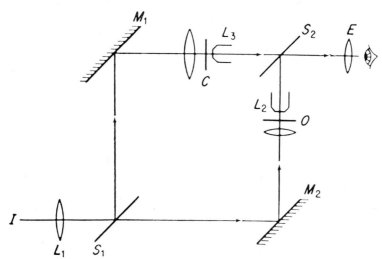

FIGURE 5–4. Schematic representation of an "ideal" interference microscope system: S_1 and S_2, semireflecting mirror surfaces; M_1 and M_2, fully reflecting mirror surfaces; L_2 and L_3, microscope lenses; O, object slide; C, comparison or "blank" slide. (From R. Barer.[2])

the various cellular structures and, as a consequence, to measure their dry weight. Furthermore, it is possible to detect small, continuous changes in refractive index, whereas the phase microscope reveals only sharp discontinuities. The variations of phase can be transformed into such vivid color changes that a living cell may resemble a stained preparation. (A description of the different interference microscopes and of the theoretical principles on which they are based is beyond the scope of this book. See references 7 to 9.)

A schematic representation of an interference microscope system is shown in Figure 5–4, in which the light emitted by a single source is split into two beams: one is sent through the object; the other bypasses the object. The two beams are then recombined and interfere with one another as in the phase microscope. In comparison with the direct beam, the beam that has crossed the object is retarded, which means that it has undergone a phase change. As in the polarizing microscope, this retardation is determined by the thickness of the object (t) and the difference between the refractive indices of the object (no) and of the surrounding medium (nm).

$$no - mn = \frac{\Gamma}{t} \qquad (2)$$

If nm is known, no can be determined.

By use of the interference microscope it is possible to measure the dry weight of the object, because this is related to the refractive index. When the object is measured in water, the following relationship applies:

$$Co = \frac{100\,(no - nw)}{X} \qquad (3)$$

Co is the percentage concentration of dry material in the object; nw is the refractive index of water; X is a constant that equals $100\,\alpha$ (α is the specific refractive increment of the material in solution). X is about 0.18 for the major substances of the cell—proteins, lipoproteins and nucleic acids.[10]

Interference microscopy permits the simultaneous determination of the thickness of the object (t), the concentration of dry matter and the water content by

TABLE 5–1. MEASUREMENT OF DRY MATTER (Co) IN CELLS*

	NO — NW	Co† FOR X = 0.165
Cytoplasm	0.036	25.5
Nucleus	0.021	16.4

* From Michison and Swann.

† $Co = \dfrac{100\,(no - nw)}{X}$

successive measurements of the optical phase difference in two media of known refractive indices. An example of the application of this method to the study of the sea urchin oöcyte is illustrated in Table 5–1. In this material the nucleus may appear red in contrast to the blue cytoplasm or vice versa. The sequence of colors indicates the difference in refractive index (RI). In the sea urchin oöcyte the nucleus has a lower RI than the cytoplasm and the nucleolus a much higher RI than the cytoplasm. Changes in RI have been observed during fertilization and cleavage of the egg. Table 5–1 indicates some of the measurements of dry matter in the cytoplasm and the nucleus. These show that the percentage concentration of dry matter is much lower in the nucleus (at this stage of cell development) than in the cytoplasm.

Interference microscopy has been used to determine the lipid, nucleic acid and protein content of the cell. The dry mass is first determined and then the tissue is extracted with lipid solvents and with trichloroacetic acid. The differences in measurement before and after extraction give the content of lipid and nucleic acid.

Darkfield Microscopy

Darkfield microscopy, also called *ultramicroscopy,* is another method used for the study of living cells. It is based on the fact that light is scattered at boundaries between phases having different refractive indices. The instrument is a microscope in which the ordinary condenser is replaced by one that illuminates the object obliquely. With this darkfield condenser, no direct light enters the objective; therefore, the object appears bright owing to the scattered light, and the background remains dark. In a living cell in a tissue culture, for example, the nucleolus, nuclear membrane, mitochondria and lipid droplets appear bright and the background of cytoplasm is dark.

In the darkfield microscope objects smaller than those seen with the ordinary light microscope can be detected but not resolved.

Polarization Microscopy

This method is based on the behavior of certain components of cells and tissues when observed with polarized light. If the material is *isotropic,* polarized light is propagated through it with the same velocity, whatever may be the impinging direction. Such substances or structures are characterized by having the same *index of refraction* in all directions. On the other hand, in *anisotropic* material the velocity of propagation of polarized light varies. Such material is also called *birefringent* material because it presents two different indices of refraction corresponding to the respective different velocities of transmission.

Birefringence may be expressed quantitatively as the difference between the two indices of refraction ($N_e - N_o$) associated with the fast and slow ray. In practice, with the polarization microscope one measures the retardation (Γ) of the light polarized in one plane relative to that of light polarized in another perpendicular plane. The retardation depends on the thickness of the specimen (d) in this way:

$$\text{Birefringence (B)} = N_e - N_o = \frac{\Gamma}{d} \quad (4)$$

Measurement of the retardation is carried out by the use of some sort of compensator introduced into the optical system. The measurement is in $m\mu$ or in fractions of a wavelength (λ).

The birefringence of biologic material is generally very small (0.01 to 0.001). Measurement of small retardations requires very sensitive compensators.

The *polarizing* microscope differs from the ordinary one in that two polarizing devices have been added: the *polarizer* and the *analyzer,* which can be made from a sheet of polaroid film or with Nicol prisms of calcite. The polarizer is mounted below the substage condenser and sends only plane polarized light into the object. The analyzer, a similar system, is placed above the objective lens. When the analyzer is rotated 360 degrees, the visual field alternates between bright and dark at every 180 degree turn. The two positions of maximal light transmission are obtained when the analyzer is set parallel to the polarizer.

In the crossed position (at a 90 degree angle), polarized light is not transmitted. Under this last condition, if a birefringent specimen is placed on the stage, the plane of polarization will deviate according to the retardation introduced by the object. The usual test with the polarizing microscope consists of rotating the specimen (on a special rotating stage) to find the points of maximal and minimal brightness. Maximal brightness is obtained when the axis of the object makes a ± 45 degree angle with those of the polarizer and analyzer (Fig. 5–5).

When the birefringence has been demonstrated and the retardation has been measured, the axis and sign of birefringence must be determined. In most biologic fibers birefringence is *uniaxial*. It is *positive* if the index of refraction is greater along the length of the fiber than in the perpendicular plane, and is *nega-*

tive in the opposite case. The sign can be determined by interposing a birefringent material whose slow and fast axes are known. With the improved methods of polarization microscopy now available, retardations of 0.1 mμ (1 Å) with a resolution of 0.3 μ can be measured (Fig. 14–5).

Since birefringence depends on structural properties that are much smaller than the wavelength of light, polarization microscopy has been a method for analyzing indirectly cell ultrastructure. This was the only method for almost a century, but electron microscopy is of greatest importance now. However, it is important for the student to know that in biologic systems birefringence depends on different intrinsic properties that are related to molecular and macromolecular organization.

The main types of birefringence are:
Crystalline (Intrinsic) Birefringence. Crystalline bifringence is found in systems in which the bonds between molecules or ions have a regular asymmetrical arrangement. This birefringence is independent of the refractive index of the medium. In structures composed of pro-

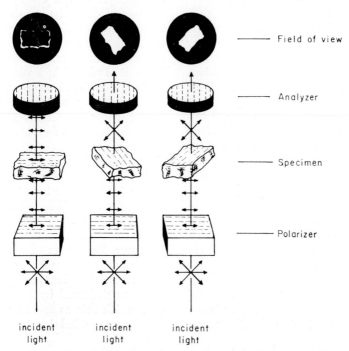

	Field of view
	Analyzer
	Specimen
	Polarizer

incident light   incident light   incident light

FIGURE 5–5. Schematic drawing showing variations in darkness and brightness of an anisotropic object when placed between crossed polarizer and analyzer and rotated ± 45°. (Extracted from Wilson and Morrison's *Cytology,* 1961, with the permission of Reinhold Publishing Corporation.)

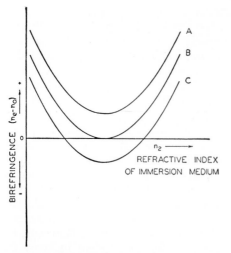

FIGURE 5–6. Method of determining the sign and relative amount of form and crystalline birefringence by the immersion technique. *A* indicates positive form and positive crystalline birefringence. *B* indicates positive form and no crystalline birefringence. *C* indicates positive form and negative crystalline birefringence. (From Schmitt, 1944–1945.)

teins or lipids, a certain degree of crystalline birefringence may appear, which in both cases is positive uniaxial. On the other hand, fibers of nucleoprotein have a negative uniaxial birefringence.

Form Birefringence. This is produced when submicroscopic asymmetrical particles are oriented in a medium of a different refractive index. In this case, the birefringence is changed when the refractive index of the medium varies (Fig. 5–6).

According to the Wiener theory, if the particles are cylinders oriented with their long axes parallel to the axis of the fiber, the birefringence is positive. If they are platelets with their axes oriented perpendicular to the fiber, the birefringence is negative. By immersing a structure in media of different refractive indices, one can construct curves in which birefringence is plotted against the index of refraction. The position of the minimum of these curves indicates whether the form birefringence is pure or, as is generally the case, is combined in greater or lesser degree with crystalline birefringence (Fig. 5–6).

Strain Birefringence. Certain isotropic structures show strain birefringence when subjected to tension or pressure. It occurs in muscle and in embryonic tissues.

Dichroism. This type of birefringence occurs when the absorption of a given wavelength of polarized light changes with the orientation of the object. In dichroism the changes are in amplitude, that is, in the intensity of the transmitted light. Dichroism is seldom found with visible light in biologic objects. However, it can be induced in tissues by some staining procedures. For example, organic dyes, such as congo red or thionine, can produce dichroism in certain structures by the special orientation of the dye molecules. Precipitation of colloid metallic particles within the oriented framework of a structure can also produce dichroism. (For more details of these techniques, see references 11 and 12.)

Electron Microscopy

The electron microscope is the only instrument that permits a direct study of biologic ultrastructure. Its resolving power is much greater than that of the light microscope. In the electron microscope streams of electrons are deflected by an electrostatic or electromagnetic field in the same way that a beam of light is refracted when crossing a lens. If a metal filament is placed in a vacuum tube and heated, it emits electrons, which can be accelerated by an electrical potential. Under these conditions the stream of electrons tends to follow a straight path and has properties similar to those of light. Like light, it has a corpuscular and vibratory character but the wavelength is much shorter (i.e., $\lambda = 0.05$ Å for electrons and 5500 Å for light).

In the electron microscope the filament or cathode emits the stream of electrons. By means of a magnetic coil, which acts as a condenser, electrons are focused in the plane of the object, and then are deflected by another magnetic coil, which acts as an objective lens and gives a magnified image of the object. This is received by a third magnetic "lens," which acts as an ocular or projection lens and magnifies the image from the objective. The final image can

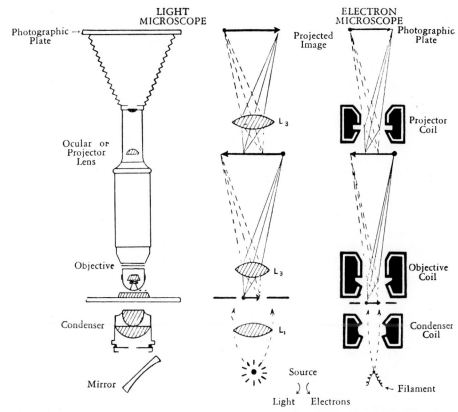

FIGURE 5–7. Comparison between the optical microscope and the electron microscope. (From G. Thompson.)

be visualized on a fluorescent screen or recorded on a photographic plate (Fig. 5–7).

In spite of the apparent similarities shown in Figure 5–7, there are great differences between the light and the electron microscope, some of which refer to the mechanism of image formation. Whereas in the light microscope image formation depends mainly on the degree of light absorption in different zones of the object, in the electron microscope image formation is mainly due to electron scattering. The electrons colliding against atomic nuclei in the object are often dispersed in an elastic manner, so that they fall outside the aperture of the objective lens. In this case the image on the fluorescent screen results from the absence of the electrons that were stopped by the aperture. Dispersion may be also due to multiple collisions, which diminish the energy of the passing electrons. In this case, chromatic effects occur. Electron dispersion is in turn a function of the thickness and molecular packing of the object and depends especially on the atomic number of its atoms. The higher the atomic number, the greater is the dispersion caused. Most of the atoms that constitute biologic structures (e.g., C, H, O, N) are of low atomic number and contribute little to the image. For this reason, heavy atoms should be added to the molecular structure.

The greatest advantage of the electron microscope is its high resolving power, which depends on the same variants as does the light microscope.

The wavelength of a stream of electrons is a function of the acceleration voltage to which the electrons are subjected, and can be calculated by the formula of De Broglie:

$$\lambda = \frac{12.2}{\sqrt{V}} \text{Å} \qquad (5)$$

For example, in one current model of the electron microscope, V = 50,000 volts and λ = 0.0535 Å.

Owing to the great aberration of the

magnetic lenses, the actual numerical aperture of the electron microscope is small and the limit of resolution is theoretically 3 to 5 Å (Fig. 1–1). In practice, the limit of resolution for biologic specimens is now about 10 Å.

In the light microscope, magnification is largely determined by the objective, and a maximum magnification of 100 to 120× can be reached. Since the ocular lens can increase this image 5 to 15 times, a total useful magnification of 500 to 1500× can be achieved.

In the electron microscope the resolving power is so high that the image from the objective can be greatly enlarged. For example, with an initial magnification by the objective of 100×, the image can be magnified 200× with the projector coil, achieving a total magnification of 20,000×.

In the more recent instruments a wide range of magnifications can be reached by introducing an intermediate lens. Direct magnifications as high as 160,000× may thus be obtained, and the micrographs may be enlarged photographically to 1,000,000× or more, depending on the resolution achieved (see Fig. 11–5).

Preparation of Biologic Material for Electron Microscopy

Because of its extraordinary resolving power, the electron microscope seems to be an ideal instrument for the study of cellular ultrastructure. Nevertheless, its usefulness is reduced by a number of technical difficulties and limitations.

One limitation is the low penetration power of electrons. If the specimen is more than 5000 Å (0.5 μ) thick, it appears almost totally opaque. The specimen must be deposited on an extremely fine film (75 to 150 Å thick) of collodion, carbon or other substance that supports the specimen and must be supported by a fine metal grid.

Another limitation is that the specimen must be dehydrated to be placed in a vacuum. Therefore, electron microscopy of living cells is almost impossible.

Techniques for preparing specimens vary considerably. Two main types are used in biology: suspensions of small particles and thick objects. In studying *particle suspensions,* such as viruses and macromolecules, one of the difficulties arises from the tendency of the particles to clump together upon drying on the supporting film. A better dispersion can be obtained by spraying the liquid into small droplets with an atomizer.[13] Submicroscopic droplets can also be produced by transforming the suspension into an aerosol (colloid of liquid in air) and then depositing the charged droplets by electrostatic means on the grid.[14]

Biologic materials, such as thin membranes, filaments or macromolecules (having a diameter of 100 Å or less), have a very low power of electron dispersion because they are uniformly thin and light atoms are involved. Special methods have been devised to overcome these difficulties by increasing the *contrast* and by defining details on the surface of objects. One technique called *"shadow casting"* consists of placing the specimen in an evacuated chamber and in evaporating at an angle a heavy metal such as chromium, palladium, platinum or uranium from a filament of incandescent tungsten.[15] The material is thus deposited on one side of the surface of the elevated particles; on the other side a shadow forms, the length of which allows one to ascertain the height of the particle. Photomicrographs made of such specimens have a three-dimensional aspect, which otherwise is lacking (Fig. 5–8).

One of the most important and recent techniques in the study of viruses and macromolecules is *"negative staining,"* in which the specimen is embedded within a droplet of a dense material, such as phosphotungstate, which penetrates into all the empty spaces between the macromolecules. These spaces appear well defined in negative contrast. With this technique the number of protein molecules (capsomeres) of different viruses have been determined and interesting observations on cellular structures have been made (see Figs. 11–5 and 22–19).

A positive increase of contrast in biologic structures has been obtained by the use of substances containing heavy atoms, such as osmic tetroxide, uranyl, and lead ions, which, under certain con-

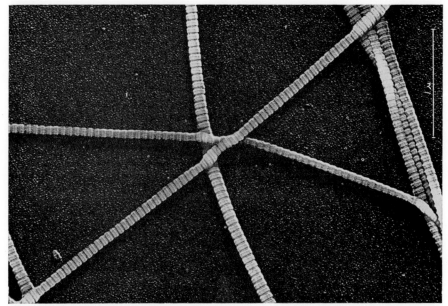

FIGURE 5–8.   Electron micrograph of collagen fibers from human skin, shadowed with chromium. Bands with a period of 640 Å are seen. ×28,000. (Courtesy of J. Gross.)

ditions, act as *"electron stains,"* comparable to histologic stains, by combining selectively with certain regions of the specimen. Electron stains have given excellent results in the visualization of the fine ultrastructure of collagen fibers and muscle fibers. Some electron stains are used as fixatives.

Thick specimens can be disintegrated by mechanical means, such as homogenizers, sonic or supersonic waves, and so forth. The material is thus divided along natural cleavage planes into fragments thin enough to be partially transparent to the electron beam.

Study of cells and tissues can be achieved only by the use of *thin sections*. This technique is essentially similar to that used for making preparations for the optical microscope, but the requirements are more exact. To be sectioned, a tissue must first be *fixed and embedded*. (The problem of fixation is discussed in Chapter 6.)

The tissue is embedded after dehydration, although new water-soluble plastics are now being studied. The need for thinner sections has been satisfied by the use of hard embedding media. The most often used are acrylic monomers or epoxy resins that impregnate the tissue and then are polymerized by proper catalysts.

In recent years methods of *sectioning*

have improved considerably. Several microtomes have been designed that have a thermal or a mechanical advance. With both types the thinnest sections that can be made are of the order of 200 Å. The limiting factors seem to be proper embedding and the sharpness of the cutting edge. Glass and diamond knives are now in general use.

X-ray Diffraction

This technique is based on the diffraction of radiations when they encounter small obstacles. If a ray of white light (λ averaging 0.5 μ) impinges upon a diffraction grating that has 1000 lines per millimeter (1 μ spacing), it will be diffracted, giving the various bands of the spectrum. If the wavelength of the light is known, the spacing can be calculated from the diffracted angles and vice versa. This type of grating would be too wide for x-rays and no diffraction would be produced.

Laue suggested that gratings of much smaller dimensions, such as are found in natural crystals, would be necessary for the diffraction of x-rays. The atoms, ions or molecules in crystals constitute a true lattice of molecular dimensions capable of diffracting radiations of this wave-

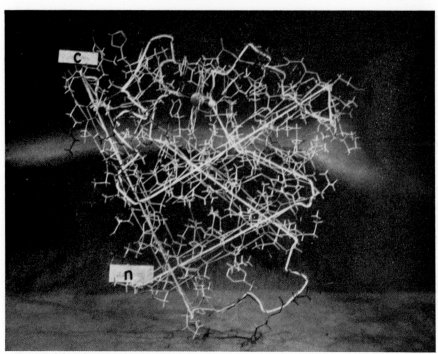

Figure 5–9. Model of the myoglobin molecule. The white cord represents the course of the polypeptide chain. The iron molecule is indicated by a grey sphere. c and n, the two terminals of the protein molecule. (From J. C. Kendrew, 1963.)

length (see Fig. 1–1). This technique has its widest application in the study of inorganic and organic crystals, in which it is possible to determine the precise spacial relationships between the constituent atoms. An analysis of the structure of complex biologic molecules, such as proteins and nucleic acids, is much more difficult because of the great number of atoms involved in a single molecule and the irregularities in three-dimensional architecture that most of these large and complex molecules have (Fig. 5–9). However, as shown in Chapter 3, this configuration of molecules is so vitally important to the understanding of biologic function that a great deal of work by Perutz, Kendrew, Wilkins and others has been carried out to elucidate it. The study of the molecular structure of hemoglobin, myoglobin, DNA, collagen and so forth has been of fundamental importance in the recent development of molecular biology.

In essence, the technique of x-ray diffraction consists of making a beam of collimated x-rays traverse the material that is to be analyzed (e.g., crystal of hemoglobin, DNA or collagen fiber), and placing beyond this a photographic plate, which records the diffraction pattern (Fig. 5–10).

A series of concentric spots or bands may appear on the plate, which cause interference between the different diffracted rays (Fig. 5–10). The distance between these spots and the center of the pattern depends upon the spaces between the regularly repeating units or *periods of identity* in the specimen that produce the diffraction. The smaller the angle of diffraction, the greater the distance between the repeating units; the sharper the spots, the more regular the spacing (Fig. 5–11).

A crystal structure can be considered as a three-dimensional lattice in which the atoms are regularly spaced along the three principal axes. The so-called *unit cell* is a solid parallelepiped that represents the minimal repeating unit within the crystal. In practice it is simpler to think of the crystal as made of sets of superimposed lattice planes such as indicated in Fig. 5–12. In this, d is the spacing of the diffracting planes and θ the angle of incidence.

According to Bragg's law, d can be

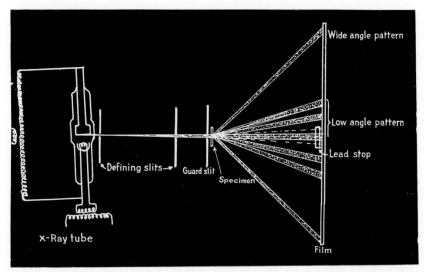

FIGURE 5–10.   Diagram of the x-ray diffraction set-up for biologic specimens. Two defining slits collimate a fine beam of x-rays. The specimen is put behind the guard slit and the film at a distance varying between 3 to 30 cm. A lead plate stops the undiffracted beam. The position of the wide-angle and small-angle pattern on the film is indicated. (Courtesy of R. S. Bear and O. Bolduan.)

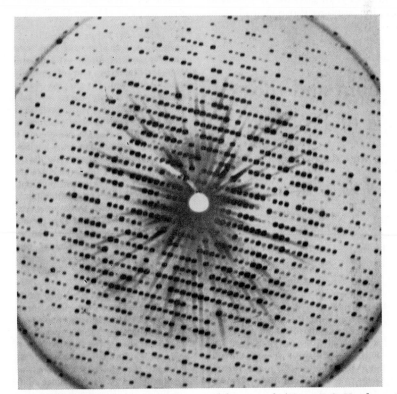

FIGURE 5–11.   X-ray diffraction pattern of a myoglobin crystal. (From J. C. Kendrew, 1963.)

calculated as follows (n is an integer corresponding to the diffraction order):

$$n\lambda = 2d \sin \theta \qquad (6)$$

Knowing the wavelength and the angle of incidence of a definite spot in the dif-fraction pattern, the spacing producing the diffraction can be calculated. A wavelength frequently used in diffraction is the $K\alpha$ line of Cu (1.54 Å).

In biologic specimens (e.g., collagen, keratin, muscle, myelin), the degree of

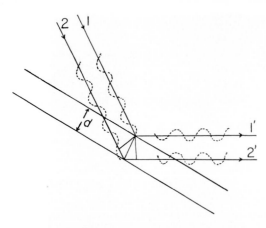

FIGURE 5–12. Diagram showing the effect of an x-ray beam incident upon two parallel planes in a crystal lattice that are separated by a distance, d. Incident rays 1 and 2 make an angle with these planes and two secondary or diffracted rays are produced ($1'$ and $2'$). By simple geometrical considerations, Bragg's law ($n\lambda = 2d \sin \theta$) can be deduced and the distance (d) calculated.

molecular orientation is shown by the nature of the interference patterns. When the particles are unoriented, concentric rings are found; orientation in fibers generally gives arcs or sickles; a perfect orientation (as in crystals) is indicated by spots (Fig. 5–11). In general, in oriented protein chains, such as those that characterize many biologic fibers, the equatorial points are thought to indicate the lateral separation between the individual chains; the meridional points, in certain cases, represent the distance between the amino acid residues.

As indicated, the distance between the spots or bands and the center of the diffraction pattern is smaller for diffraction effects, owing to longer spacings in the material. These long spacings, which may range from 25 Å to 1000 Å in high polymers, are of great importance in biologic material. In wide-angle patterns they appear as small meridional spots close to the center and thus are not clearly resolved. This difficulty has been overcome by using special technical refinements that permit one to obtain small-angle patterns and thus a much better resolution of the long spacings.

In the more refined methods of x-ray analysis of biologic molecules, such as myoglobin, hemoglobin and DNA, not only is the distance within the unit cell calculated, but also the *scattering power* of the individual atoms. This is similar to electron microscopy in that this is related to the atomic number, but in this case the electron density (number of electrons) of the atoms is the most important factor. To carry this similarity further, by introducing heavy atoms

(such as mercury) into known points of the biologic molecule, it is possible to increase their scattering power. The heavy atom serves as a landmark for the reconstruction of the molecule. This is done by a very complex process that involves plotting the electron density and the Fourier synthesis of all the component waves or diffraction orders. This sort of analysis is then carried out into the different axes, and thus two- and three-dimensional Fourier projections are produced. This is carried out by complex calculations, which at present are done with high-speed computers. From this mathematical synthesis a three-dimensional representation of the object can be constructed and models of the entire molecule made (Fig. 5–9).

X-ray diffraction is one of the most important methods in molecular biology and ultrastructure because it permits us not only to determine the orientation of the molecules, but also to measure exactly the distances that separate them and even to recognize their atomic organization (Table 1–1).

GENERAL REFERENCES

Bennett, H. S. (1948) The microscopical investigation of biological material with polarized light. In: *Handbook of microscopical technique.* 3rd Ed. (McClung, C. E., ed.) Paul B. Hoeber, New York.

Burton, E. F., and Kohl, W. H. (1942) *The electron microscope.* Reinhold Publishing Corp., New York.

Chambers, R., and Chambers, E. (1961) *Explorations into the nature of the living cell.* Parts *I* and *III.* Harvard University Press, Cambridge, Mass.

Clark, G. L. (1940) *Applied x-ray*. 3rd Ed. McGraw-Hill Book Co., New York.

Cosslett, V. E. (1951) *Practical electron microscopy*. Academic Press, New York.

Dalton, A. J. (1953) Electron microscopy of tissue sections. *Internat. Rev. Cytol.*, 2:103.

Engström, A., and Finean, J. B. (1958) *Biological ultrastructure*. Academic Press, New York.

Kendrew, J. C. (1963) Myoglobin and the structure of proteins. *Science, 139:*1259.

Kopac, M. J. (1959) Micrurgical studies on living cells. In: *The cell*, Vol. 1, p. 161. (Brachet, J., and Mirsky, A. E., eds.) Academic Press, New York.

Oster, G. (1956) X-ray diffraction and scattering. In: *Physical techniques in biological research*, Vol. 2, p. 441. (Oster, G., and Pollister, A. W., eds.) Academic Press, New York.

Osterberg, H. (1955) Phase and interference microscopy. In: *Physical techniques in biological research*, Vol. 1, p. 378. (Oster, G., and Pollister, A. W., eds.) Academic Press, New York.

Pease, D. C. (1960) *Histological techniques for electron microscopy*. Academic Press, New York.

Ruch, F. (1956) Birefringence and dichroism of cells and tissues. In *Physical techniques in biological research*, Vol. 3, p. 149. (Oster, G., and Pollister, A. W., eds.) Academic Press, New York.

Schmitt, F. O. (1944–1945) Ultrastructure and the problem of cellular organization. *Harvey Lect.*, 40:249.

Shillaber, C. P. (1959) *Photomicrography in theory and practice*. 5th Printing. John Wiley & Sons, New York.

Sjöstrand, F. S. (1956) The ultrastructure of cells as revealed by the electron microscope. *Internat. Rev. Cytol.*, 5:455.

CITED REFERENCES

1. Barer, R. (1951) *J. Roy. Micr. Soc.*, 307.
2. Barer, R. (1956) In: *Physical techniques in biological research*, Vol. 3, p. 30. (Oster, G., and Pollister, A. W., eds.) Academic Press, New York.
3. Bennett, A. H., et al. (1951) *Phase microscopy. Principles and application.* John Wiley & Sons, New York.
4. Zernike, F. (1955) *Science, 121:*345.
5. Richards, O. W. (1954) *Science, 120:*631.
6. Blout, E. R. (1953) *Advanc. Biol. Med. Phys.*, 3:286.
7. Engström, A., and Finean, J. B. (1958) *Biological ultrastructure.* Academic Press, New York.
8. Hale, A. J. (1958) *The interference microscope in biological research.* E. & S. Livingstone, Edinburgh.
9. Mellors, R. C., ed. (1959) *Analytical cytology.* 2nd Ed. McGraw-Hill Book Co., New York.
10. Davies, H. G., and Wilkins, M. H. F. (1952) *Nature, 189:*541.
11. Schmidt, W. J. (1937) *Die Doppelbrechung von Karyoplasma, Zytoplasma und Metaplasma.* Gebrüder Borntraeger, Berlin.
12. Frey-Wyssling, A. (1953) *Submicroscopic morphology of protoplasm and its derivatives.* Elsevier Pub. Co., New York.
13. Backus, R. C., and Williams, R. C. (1950) *J. Appl. Physiol.*, 21:2
14. De Robertis, E., Franchi, C. M., and Podolsky, M. (1953) *Biochim. Biophys. Acta.* 11:507.
15. Williams, R. C., and Wyckoff, R. W. G. (1946) *J. Appl. Physiol.*. 17:23.

CHAPTER 6

METHODS FOR CYTOLOGIC AND CYTOCHEMICAL ANALYSIS

Cells and tissues must be specially prepared for instrumental analysis and for the study of their chemical organization. As is indicated throughout this book, in cell biology many different types of specimens and techniques are used.

In general, for each particular problem one or a few types of cells are best suited. Sometimes an entire branch of cytology has developed from the discovery or accurate choice of a special material or the development of a certain technique. A few examples are as follows: The chromosomes and their behavior during mitosis and meiosis are best studied in the sex glands of insects and in meristems of roots and stems or the pollen mother cells of plants; mitochondrial movements, in tissue cultures; cell permeability, in erythrocytes; pinocytosis, in ameba; and protein synthesis, in reticulocytes. Cytogenetics is best studied in *Drosophila*, neurospora and human chromosomes; molecular genetics, in bacteria and viruses.

The two main procedures of instrumental analysis are: (1) direct observation of living cells within the organism (*vital examination*) or after fresh removal from it (*supravital examination*) and (2) observation after killing cells by procedures that preserve morphology and composition, i.e., *fixation*.

EXAMINATION OF LIVING CELLS

Vital or supravital examination can be made of free cells in a liquid medium, cells isolated from tissue fragments, transparent membranes, transparent parts of animals (e.g., larvae of urodeles) and even opaque organs. This type of observation can be improved by the use of dyes that have little or no noxious effect on cells, e.g., neutral red, Janus green, Trypan blue and methylene blue. Janus green is particularly interesting because it stains mitochondria in the living cell.

Tissue Culture

One of the methods that permit the observation of living cells under favorable conditions is *tissue culture*. The technique consists of explanting small portions of different tissues, preferably embryonic, i.e., placing them in a suitable medium where cells can adapt and grow autonomously. This generally consists of one drop of plasma and another of embryonic fluid, which are deposited on a coverglass. The coverglass is then inverted, placed on a special slide that has a spherical concavity, and sealed with paraffin. In this closed space, incubated at the normal body temperature of the organism from which the specimen was taken, the cells have the nutritive elements and the oxygen necessary for development. The cells grow and spread over the coagulum of plasma and emigrate from the explant to form the *zone of growth,* which, owing to its thinness, lends itself admirably to phase microscopy.[1–3]

In the last few years, with the development of synthetic media, important advances have been made in the use of tissue culture techniques for studying the nutritional requirements for cell growth. Furthermore, small organs, such as growing bones and endocrine glands, have been kept alive and studied under different experimental conditions, e.g., the action of hormones.

One of the most interesting developments from the cytologic viewpoint has been the establishment of pure cell strains. Research in this field has been greatly advanced by the use of enzymes (e.g., trypsin) and other means by which the individual cells of the explant may be separated and mass cultures of cells made. By this method, tissue cells can be disaggregated and cultured in suspension[4] or on Petri dishes, as is done with bacteria.[5] Colonies, or *clones*, of cells can be obtained from the division of a single cell, and then, by proper isolation, pure strains of cells can be separated.[6-9]

Microsurgery

This is another method that has contributed considerably to the knowledge of the living cell.[10-11] Instruments such as micropipets, microneedles, microelectrodes and microthermocouples are introduced into cells with the aid of a special apparatus that controls the movement of these instruments under the field of the microscope. Examples of microsurgical procedures are the following: the dissection and extraction of parts of cells or tissues, the injection of substances, the measurement of electrical variables and the grafting of parts from cell to cell.

Figure 10–8 shows an example of the application of microsurgery to the study of electrical potentials at the plasma and nuclear membranes.

FIXATION

Fixation brings about the death of the cell in such a way that the structure of the living cell is preserved with a minimal addition of artifacts. Some fixation methods, at the same time, attempt to keep the chemical composition of the cell as intact as possible.

The choice of a suitable fixative is dictated by the type of analysis desired. For example, for studying the nucleus and chromosomes, *acid fixatives* are frequently used (e.g., *Carnoy's solution:* 3 parts absolute ethanol, 1 part glacial acetic acid; or *Bouin's fluid:* 5 parts saturated picric acid, 5 parts 40 per cent formaldehyde [formalin], 1 part glacial acetic acid). Acetone, formaldehyde or gluteraldehyde, which produce minimal denaturation and preserve many enzyme systems, are used for the study of enzyme activity.

The majority of fixatives are solutions that act essentially upon the protein part of the cell. In fixation there is a separation of the solid phase (dispersed phase) of the colloid from the liquid (dispersing phase).[12-14] The colloid precipitates in the form of granules, nets, flakes and so forth. In selecting a cytologic fixative one should seek the one that precipitates protein in the finest form and, if possible, in ultramicroscopic aggregates so that the appearance of the cell is not modified.

Some fixing agents, such as formaldehyde, dichromate and mercuric chloride, that are used in well known mixtures (e.g., *Zenker's, Helly's, Flemming's* and *Regaud's* solutions[15, 16]) produce strong cross linkages between protein molecules. For example, formaldehyde reacts with the amino, carboxyl and indole groups of a protein and then produces methylene bridges with other protein molecules. The two-step reaction is as follows:

$$-\overset{\displaystyle |}{\underset{\displaystyle H}{N}}-H \quad + \quad HCHO \quad \rightarrow \quad \text{———}NH \cdot CH_2OH$$

amino group   formaldehyde   methylol

$$-NH \cdot CH_2OH \quad + \quad -\overset{\displaystyle |}{\underset{\displaystyle H}{N}}-H \quad \rightarrow \quad -NH-CH_2-HN + H_2O$$

methylol   amino group   methylene bridge

Chromium salts (e.g., potassium dichromate) produce oxidation and chromium linkages between proteins. They also bind the phospholipids. Mercuric chloride acts on sulfhydryl, carboxyl and amino groups of proteins, producing mercury linkages between molecules.

When a piece of tissue is immersed in a fixing liquid, cellular death does not occur instantaneously, and "post mortem" alterations due to anoxia, changes in the concentration of hydrogen ions and enzymatic action (autolysis) may occur. The fixative penetrates the tissue by diffusion in such a way that the most external cells are fixed more rapidly and better than the central ones. For this reason, every fixed tissue has a *gradient of fixation,* which depends upon the *penetrability* of the fixative and its progressive *dilution* with the liquid of the cells. The rate of fixative penetration does not appear to depend so much upon its coefficient of diffusibility as upon the protein barrier of precipitation produced at the periphery of the tissue. For example, with osmium tetroxide the precipitation is very fine, and a barrier preventing further passage of the fixative is produced. For this reason only very thin pieces (0.5 to 1.0 mm thick) are fixed in osmic liquids.

Diffusion currents that displace the soluble components, such as glycogen, may be observed (Fig. 6–1A). Fixatives may also extract soluble substances, such as electrolytes, soluble carbohydrates and even some lipids. It has been demonstrated that 10 to 14 per cent of mineral substances in the cells are extracted by fixation.

Fixation for the Electron Microscope

Osmium Tetroxide

Osmium tetroxide (OsO_4) is one of the most frequently used fixatives for investigation of cell structure under the electron microscope. The well known reaction that this fixative has with lipids is probably due to double bonds that form unstable osmium esters, which decompose to deposit osmium oxides or hydroxides. The fixative causes proteins to gel initially, giving a homogeneous structure under the electron microscope, whereas with other fixatives the coagulation is evident. This initial gelation may then be followed by further oxidation and solubilization of some products that can be washed out of the cell.[17]

The binding of osmium tetroxide by different chemicals of the cell has been studied.[18] It is interesting that nucleic acids do not bind OsO_4. Osmium fixation has been improved by introducing buffer solutions at physiologic pH,[19] maintaining osmotic pressure, adding calcium ions[20] and maintaining a temperature of about 0° C.

Extensive studies have been made to demonstrate that this fixing technique does not introduce artifacts. Down to the microscopic level this can be seen by comparing the image of a living cell with that observed after fixation. Beyond that the problem can be approached only on certain biologic materials that have a degree of orderly organization high enough to give birefringence under polarized light and definite x-ray diffraction patterns in the living cell. A correlative study of this type has been done on natural lipoprotein systems, such as the myelin sheath.[21, 22]

The degree of organization at the macromolecular level is of great importance in the preservation of the structure by fixation. In a well organized structure, such as a chromosome, a mitochondrion or a chloroplast, a great number of interacting forces hold the molecules together, and the action of the fixative is insufficient to break structural relationships. However, less organized regions of the cell, such as the cytoplasmic matrix, are more difficult to preserve and the production of fixation artifacts is more probable.

Freezing-Drying

This method consists of rapid freezing of the tissue and then dehydrating it in a vacuum at a low temperature. The initial freezing is generally accomplished by plunging small pieces of tissues in a bath of liquid nitrogen cooled at a temperature of —160° to —190° C. Fixation

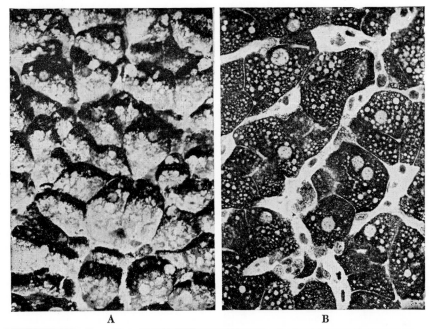

A   B

FIGURE 6–1. A, liver cells of *Ambystoma* fixed in Zenker-formol. The diffusion current produced by the chemical fixative (from the lower to the upper part of the figure) displaces the glycogen of the cell. B, liver cells of *Ambystoma* fixed by freezing-drying. The glycogen appears to be distributed homogeneously in the cytoplasm. Spheroid nuclei and lipid droplets are distinguishable. Stain: Best's carmine. (From preparations of I. Gersh.)

in liquid helium near the absolute 0° (Kelvin) has also been used. The drying is done in a vacuum at —30° to —40° C. Under these conditions the water of the tissues is changed directly into a gas and dehydration is achieved.

The advantages of this method are obvious. The tissue does not shrink; fixation is homogeneous throughout; soluble substances are not extracted; the chemical composition is maintained practically without change; and the structure, in general, is preserved with very few modifications produced by the ice crystals (Fig. 6–1B). Also, fixation takes place so rapidly that cell function is arrested at critical moments, such as when kidney cells are excreting colored material or when thyroid cells are extruding colloid droplets into the follicular cavity.

The freezing-drying technique should be considered as intermediary between the examination of fresh and fixed tissues, since many of the cellular components are preserved in the same soluble form as in the living state. Since some cells can resist rapid freezing, this pro-

cedure is commonly used to keep them alive (e.g., spermatozoa).

Freezing-Substitution

In the freezing-substitution method, the tissue is rapidly frozen and then kept frozen at a low temperature (—20° to —60° C.) in a reagent that dissolves the ice crystals (e.g., ethanol, methanol or acetone). The advantages of this method are somewhat similar to those just mentioned for fixation by freezing-drying.

Embedding and Sectioning

Tissues should be conveniently sectioned before they are observed under the microscope. For this purpose, *freezing microtomes* cooled with liquid carbon dioxide are frequently used. Several instruments consisting of a microtome enclosed in a chamber at low temperature, the so-called *cryostat*, can make sections of fixed or fresh tissue for cytochemical purposes (Fig. 6–2).

In the most frequently used sectioning

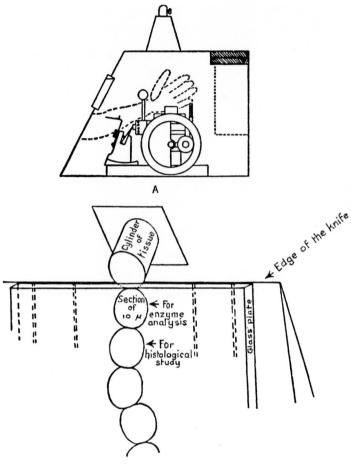

A

B

FIGURE 6–2. A, microtome for frozen sectioning. The apparatus is kept in a refrigerated container that keeps the tissue and the sections frozen. **B,** scheme of sectioning with the freezing microtome. The cylinder of tissue is sectioned and the sections are collected so that each alternate piece is used for enzymatic analysis and the others for histologic control. (After Linderstrom-Lang.)

techniques the tissue is *embedded* with a material that imparts the proper consistency for the section. For sections to be observed under the light microscope, *paraffin* or *celloidin* is generally used. The fixed tissue is dehydrated and then penetrated by the embedding material. This requires a proper intermediary solvent (e.g., xylene or toluene for paraffin; ethanol-ether for celloidin). Because electron microscopy requires thinner sections, harder embedding media must be used. Most often used are acrylic monomers that impregnate the tissue and are then polymerized by proper catalysts. Epoxy resins are most used at present.

Because some plastics are water-soluble, the tissue is not dehydrated before being embedded. This method is used for some histochemical studies under the electron microscope.[23]

CYTOLOGIC STAINING

Many staining procedures are used to demonstrate the various parts of the cell or the intercellular substances. Most cytologic stains are solutions of organic aromatic dyes.

Since Ehrlich, two types of dyes are recognized: basic and acid. In a basic dye the *chromophoric group,* which imparts the color, is basic (cationic). For example, methylene blue is a chlorhydrate of tetramethylthionine, in which the acid part (HCl) is colorless. Eosin is generally used as potassium eosinate, in which the base is colorless. Sometimes the two components of the salt are chromophoric, e.g., eosinate of methylene blue. The most used chromophores for acid dyes contain nitro ($-NO_2$) and quinoid ($O=\langle\overline{\quad}\rangle=O$) groups. Basic chromophores contain azo ($-N=N-$) and indamin ($-N=$) groups. For example, picric acid has three nitro groups (chromophores) and one OH group, also called *auxochrome,* by which the dye combines with the tissue:

$$\text{OH}$$
$$NO_2 \bigcirc NO_2$$
$$NO_2$$

Acid dyes combine with the protein structure of the cell by either hydroxyl ($-OH$), carboxyl ($-COOH$) or sulfonic ($-SO_3H$) groups; basic dyes usually bind by amino ($-NH_2$) groups.

Mechanism of Staining

It is important to learn the mechanism of action of different dyes. The properties that proteins, certain polysaccharides and nucleic acids have of ionizing either as bases or acids should be remembered (Chap. 3). For example, a protein molecule is amphoteric and may behave as a zwitterion, dissociating as an acid or a base.

Acid ionization may be produced by carboxyl ($-COOH$), hydroxyl ($-OH$), sulfuric ($-HSO_4$) or phosphoric ($-H_2PO_4$) groups. Basic ionization results from amino ($-NH_2$) and other basic groups in the protein. The ionization of a protein depends on the pH of the medium. At pH values that are above the isoelectric point, acid groups become ionized; below the isoelectric point, basic groups dissociate (see Chap. 3). Because of this property, at a pH above the isoelectric point proteins will react with basic dyes (e.g., methylene blue, crystal violet or basic fuchsin) and below it, with acid dyes (e.g., orange G, eosin or aniline blue). The intensity of staining with basic or acid dyes depends on the degree of acidity or alkalinity of the medium, because when more basic or acid groups dissociate, more dye will be bound to the protein by salt linkages (Fig. 6–3). By measuring the dye bound as a function of the pH of the medium, curves can be obtained that are typical for different proteins, nucleic acids and mucopolysaccharides.[24, 25]

The net charge of nucleic acids is determined primarily by the dissociation of the phosphoric acid groups, and the isoelectric point is very low (pH 2 or less). For this reason, staining with basic dyes (e.g., toluidine blue or azure B) at low pH values is selective for nucleic acids. Toluidine blue is used frequently to stain ribonucleic acid, and its specificity can be demonstrated by previous hydrolysis with ribonuclease (Fig. 6–4).

Because of different isoelectric points, the staining affinities of cellular components may be markedly different. For example, the background cytoplasm, certain secretion granules and the erythrocytes stain with acid dyes at the ordinary pH of staining (about pH 6). The nucleus and the ribonucleoprotein, mucus and mucoprotein of the cytoplasm stain with basic dyes.

Basophilic and acidophilic properties of cell components depend also on the

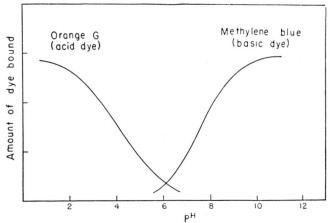

FIGURE 6–3. Curves indicating the amount of stain fixed by a protein at different pH values. Both the acid and the basic staining show a minimum fixation at the isoelectric point of the protein. (From Singer and Morrison.[24])

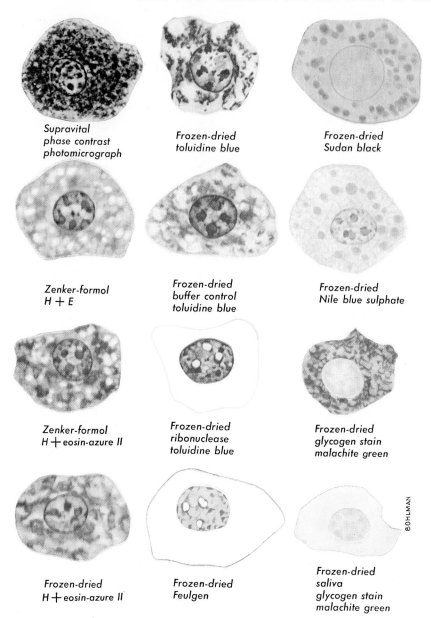

Supravital phase contrast photomicrograph

Frozen-dried toluidine blue

Frozen-dried Sudan black

Zenker-formol H + E

Frozen-dried buffer control toluidine blue

Frozen-dried Nile blue sulphate

Zenker-formol H + eosin-azure II

Frozen-dried ribonuclease toluidine blue

Frozen-dried glycogen stain malachite green

Frozen-dried H + eosin-azure II

Frozen-dried Feulgen

Frozen-dried saliva glycogen stain malachite green

FIGURE 6–4. Mouse liver cells fixed and stained by a variety of cytochemical procedures to show distribution of deoxyribonucleic acid, ribonucleic acid, glycogen and lipid droplets. Since these tests were all done on material fixed by freezing and drying, some of the sections are compared with similarly stained sections fixed by Zenker-formol. For further orientation, the fixed cell stained by hematoxylin and eosin and the unfixed cell photographed by phase contrast are also shown. ×1500. (Courtesy of I. Gersh. In Bloom and Fawcett: *Textbook of histology*, 8th Ed.)

previous treatment of the tissue, particularly on the kind of fixation. For example, formaldehyde fixation increases the basophilic properties of a protein because of its property of combining with free amino groups. On the contrary, heavy metal cations, such as Hg^{++}, Al^{+++} and Cu^{++}, combine with carboxyl groups, thus increasing the acidophilic properties of proteins. Some histochemical methods based on these staining properties of proteins are now in use. One of the best known is the fast green method for the detection of basic proteins and, especially, of histones.[26]

Metachromasia

Some basic dyes of the thiazine group, especially thionine, azure A and toluidine blue, stain certain cell components a different color than the original one of the dye. This property, called *metachromasia*, has interesting histochemical and physicochemical implications.[27] This reaction occurs in substances of high molecular weight having free anionic (acid) groups, which include the mucopolysaccharides and, to a lesser extent, the nucleic acids and some acid lipids. This reaction is strong in cells that contain sulfate groups (such as chondroitin sulfate), e.g., cartilage and connective tissue.

In cells that contain mucoproteins, e.g., mucus-secreting cells, basophilic leukocytes and mast cells, the mucoproteins are not stained the ordinary color of the dye, but acquire a red-violet tint (metachromatic reaction). Some of the intercellular substances that take a similar stain are the matrix of cartilage, tendons and cornea and the gelatinous substance of the umbilical cord.

Some investigators believe that metachromasia depends on the formation of dimeric and polymeric molecular aggregates of dye upon these high molecular weight compounds.[28] The same basic dyes do not form polymers when acting upon nucleic acid. In this case each cation of the dye combines with one acidic side-chain of the nucleic acid to form a stoichiometrically well-defined saltlike compound. A distance of about 5 Å between the anionic groups appears to be necessary for metachromatic staining.[29]

HISTOCHEMISTRY AND CYTOCHEMISTRY

The immediate goal of *cytochemistry* is the identification and localization of the chemical components of the cell. As R. R. Bensley, one of the founders of modern cytology, once said: The aim of cytochemistry is the outlining "within the exiguous confines of the cell of that elusive and mysterious chemical pattern which is the basis of life." This aim is quantitative as well as qualitative, and once achieved the next step is to study the dynamic changes in cytochemical organization taking place in different functional stages. In this way it is possible to discover the role of different cellular components in the metabolic processes of the cell.

Cytochemistry is included within the more general subject of *histochemistry*, which deals with the chemical characterization and localization of substances or groups of substances in the cells and intercellular materials of a tissue.

The main results of the application of cytochemical methods are discussed throughout different chapters. In the present chapter some general and methodological considerations are made and some specific material not included elsewhere is mentioned. Consideration of the many cytochemical techniques used and of the results obtained exceeds the limits of this book. For this purpose the student should consult the specialized monographs in histochemistry. (See references 30 to 34.)

Modern cytochemistry has followed three main methodological approaches. Of these, only one can be considered strictly microscopic, because it comprises a series of chemical and physical methods used to detect or measure different chemical components within the cell. In this type of cytochemistry the structure of the cell is maintained and the cytochemical results can be observed with the different types of instrumental analysis mentioned in Chapter 5.

The other two methods are more related to biochemistry and microchemistry, since they involve the development of techniques for the assay of small quantities of material. (In Chapter 1 and Table 1–2 we indicated the relationships existing between linear dimensions, weights and the fields of chemical analysis. The table shows that substances in cells are measured in picograms [1 pg = 10^{-12} gm].) Of these two methods one uses the more conventional biochemical techniques upon subcellular fractions that are isolated and studied. The other—that of *microchemistry* and *ultramicrochemistry*—is applied to minute quantities of material, which may comprise a few cells, single cells or even parts of a cell.

Cell Fractionation Methods

These methods essentially involve the

homogenization or destruction of cell boundaries by different mechanical or chemical procedures followed by the separation of the subcellular fractions according to mass, surface and specific gravity. The different cell fractions are then analyzed by biochemical or microchemical methods.

These techniques have been important in the study of the chemical constitution of the different cell components, such as nuclei (Fig. 17–2), nucleoli (Fig. 17–2), chromosomes, mitochondria (Fig. 11–13), the Golgi complex (Fig. 10–12),

microsomes, the mitotic apparatus (Fig. 14–9), asters, ribosomes, nerve endings (Fig. 22–18), synaptic vesicles (Fig. 22–19), secretion granules and lysosomes (Fig. 20–12). The results of these studies are of particular interest when based on accurate and precise cytologic analysis of the cell fraction, preferably by electron microscopy.

Many different methods of cell fractionation are in use. Most of them are based on the homogenization or mechanical disintegration of the cell in aqueous media, usually sucrose solutions in vari-

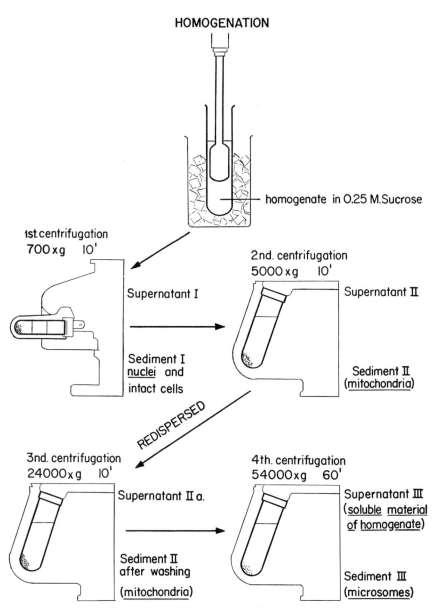

FIGURE 6–5.   Diagram of a cell fractionation.

ous concentrations (Fig. 6–5). Cell fractionation also can be carried out in nonpolar media, as in Behrens' method for the separation of nuclei. This method has the advantage of reducing the loss of soluble substances, such as proteins and certain enzymes.

A standard cell fractionation procedure is diagrammatically shown in Figure 6–5. The liver of an animal is first perfused with an ice cold saline solution, followed by cold 0.25 M sucrose to eliminate blood. The tissue is then forced through a perforated steel disk and homogenized in 0.25 M sucrose. This classical type of cell fractionation is directed toward the subdivision of the cell components into four morphologically distinct fractions (nuclear, mitochondrial, microsomal and soluble fractions). In some glandular tissue a fifth fraction containing secretory granules may be obtained.

A word of caution is necessary regarding the purity of fractions and the use of nomenclature. It is necessary to differentiate clearly between *fractions* and the parts of the cell (*organoids*) they contain. For example, the mitochondrial fraction of the liver contains mainly mitochondria, but the "mitochondrial fraction" of the brain is very heterogeneous and contains nerve endings and myelin besides free mitochondria.[35] One fraction that is a greater problem is the so-called "microsomal" fraction. As will be shown in Chapter 11, "microsomes" do not exist as such in the cell and this fraction comprises mainly broken parts of the endoplasmic reticulum including the ribosomes, the Golgi complex and other membranes.

As mentioned, the separability of the different cell components depends on the differences in the coefficient of sedimentation. This is in itself determined by the size, shape and density of the particle and the density and viscosity of the medium. This last variable can also be controlled. For example, some methods of differential centrifugation are based on a density gradient. In these, the homogenate is put in a centrifuge tube on top of a stratified sucrose solution that increases in density toward the bottom. In another method, rather than a step variation in density, there is a continuous gradient.[36, 37]

Recent improvements in the fractionation technique are the use of heavy water, macromolecular substances and media that have different partition coefficients.[38] Also, this technique has been employed extensively to separate macromolecules into different molecular components. Using different types of *preparative* and *analytical ultracentrifuges* and proper suspending media, one can isolate and determine the molecular weight of macromolecular components, such as protein molecules, viruses and nucleic acids. For example, as mentioned in Chapter 17, if a gradient of cesium chloride is used, the two strands of a DNA molecule can be separated when one of them is marked with N^{15}.[39]

Microchemistry and Ultramicrochemistry

This cytochemical approach is essentially *microchemical* and *ultramicrochemical*. In recent years many ingenious methods have been devised for the quantitative analysis of extremely small quantities of substances (see Table 1–2). For details of these techniques, see the specialized monographs.[33, 40–43]

Such micromethods are particularly illuminating when chemical analysis or enzymatic determinations are combined with cytologic methods so that the correlation between cell function and chemical topography can be studied. For example, if freshly frozen tissue is sectioned in a *cryostat* (Fig. 6–2), some sections can be weighed on a balance made of a fine *quartz fiber* and then enzymatic determinations can be carried out using ultramicropipets and burets and microcolorimetric or microspectrophotometric methods. Of even higher sensitivity are *microfluorimetric* methods, which can be applied to the determination of different enzymes and coenzymes.

Also of considerable interest are *micromanometric* methods. One of these employs the Cartesian diver microrespirometer, which is 1000 times more sensitive than the classic Warburg manometer. With this instrument the oxygen consumption of a single sea urchin egg can be measured during short intervals. Based on similar principles is the *Cartesian diver balance* of Zeuthen,[44] by which a single ameba can be weighed with great accuracy. With this sensitive method, weight changes in the ameba during its life cycle, during starvation and in correlation with the metabolism of the cell have been studied.[45]

With the use of *microchromatographic* and *microelectrophoretic* methods the ribonucleic acid content of a single nerve cell has been determined.[46, 47] Individual cells are dissected with a micromanipulator and the ribonucleic acid extracted and hydrolyzed. The extract is then absorbed on a cellulose fiber and the mononucleotides separated by ionophoresis. The nucleotides are then detected and estimated by spectrophotometric absorption in ultraviolet light.

Cytochemical and Histochemical Staining Methods

This cytochemical approach comprises all the *chemical* or *physical* methods by which direct visualization of different cell substances can be made microscopically. This is histochemistry or cytochemistry in a restricted sense. Most of these methods are qualitative, but some, particularly the physical methods (e.g., fluorescence, cytophotometry and x-ray absorption) can be quantitative.

For the cytochemical determination of a substance several conditions must be fulfilled:

The substance must be immobilized at its original location. It is relatively easy to immobilize nondiffusible components, such as proteins, nucleoproteins or lipids, but immobilization of diffusible substances, such as sugars and ions, is difficult. The importance of freezing-drying and freezing-substitution for this purpose was mentioned.

The substance must be identified by a procedure that is specific for it or for the chemical group to which it belongs. This identification can be made by: (1) chemical reactions similar to those used in analytical chemistry but adapted to tissues, (2) reactions that are specific for certain groups of substances and (3) physical methods.

To demonstrate proteins, nucleic acids, polysaccharides and lipids within the cell structure, some chromogenic agents that bind selectively to some specific groups of these substances may be used. The best reactions generally involve the formation of covalent bonds. In each case the specificity can be improved by the use of collateral methods involving the extraction, blockade or enzymatic digestion of the nonspecific components. Only a few cytochemical stainings that are widely used in cytology are mentioned here.

Detection of Proteins

Millon Reaction. A nitrous-mercuric reagent applied to the tissue reacts with the tyrosine groups present in the sidechains of the protein, forming a red precipitate.

Diazonium Reaction. The chromogenic agent, a diazonium hydroxide, reacts with tyrosine, tryptophan and histidine groups, forming a colored complex.[48]

Detection of —SH Groups. Certain reagents bind —SH by a mercaptide covalent linkage. A red sulfhydryl reagent, 1-(4-chloromercuri-phenylazo)-naphthol-2, was first used for this purpose.[49] The —SH content of the cell can be measured quantitatively by photometric analysis of tissues stained by this technique.[50] One example of the application of this method to the important study of the —SH groups in mitosis is shown in Figure 14–11.[51] Other methods for —SH groups are also widely used.[52–54]

Detection of Arginine. The Sakaguchi test for arginine has been introduced in histochemistry. A reddish color is produced when the tissue sections are treated with an alkaline mixture of α-naphthol and sodium hypochlorite. A high concentration of arginine in a tissue is indicative of basic proteins, such as histones.

Detection of Aldehydes

Some other widely used cytochemical

staining reactions are based on the formation and subsequent reaction of aldehyde groups. For example, deoxyribonucleic acid, certain carbohydrates and lipids can be demonstrated with a single reagent for aldehyde groups, the so-called *Schiff's reagent*. This reagent is made by treating basic fuchsin, which contains parafuchsin (triaminotriphenylmethane chloride), with sulfurous acid. Parafuchsin is converted into the colorless compound bis-N aminosulfonic acid (Schiff's reagent), which is then "recolored" by the aldehyde groups present in the tissue.

In the histochemical tests involving Schiff's reagent, two types of aldehydes may be involved: *free aldehydes,* which are naturally present in the tissue, such as those giving the plasmal reaction and *aldehydes produced by selective oxidation* (which give the PAS reaction) or by *selective hydrolysis* (which give the Feulgen nucleal reaction).

Detection of Nucleic Acids

Cytochemical staining methods for nucleic acids depend on the properties of the three components of the nucleotide (phosphoric acid, carbohydrate and purine and pyrimidine bases [Chap. 3]). They may also depend on the degree of polymerization of the polynucleotide chain.

Both DNA and RNA absorb ultraviolet light at 2600 Å, owing to the presence of nitrogenous bases. The deoxyribose present in DNA is responsible for the Feulgen reaction, which is specific for this type of nucleic acid (Table 6–1).

The phosphoric acid residue is responsible for the basophilic properties of both DNA and RNA, which can be observed even with common basic histologic stains, such as hematoxylin. Among the basic stains, azure B gives a specific reaction with DNA and RNA.[55, 56] Another stain for DNA, based on the use of methyl green, also depends on the phosphoric acid residues.[57]

Feulgen Nucleal Reaction. DNA can be topographically located within the cell by means of the *nucleal reaction,* a technique developed in 1924 by Feulgen and Rossenbeck. In this method sections of fixed tissue are first submitted to a mild acid hydrolysis and then treated with Schiff's aldehyde reagent. This hydrolysis is sufficient to remove RNA but not DNA. This reaction takes place in the following stages: (1) The acid hydrolysis removes the purines at the level of the purine-deoxyribose glucosidic bond of DNA, thus unmasking the aldehyde groups of deoxyribose. (2) The free aldehyde groups react with Schiff's reagent (Fig. 6–6).[58, 59]

Acid hydrolysis should be done under carefully controlled conditions, since, if allowed to progress too far, it may lead to depolymerization of DNA.[58] The results should always be checked using nonhydrolyzed samples.

TABLE 6–1.   SOME SPECIFIC REACTIONS USED IN CYTOPHOTOMETRIC ANALYSIS*

SUBSTANCE TESTED FOR	REACTION OR TEST	MAXIMUM ABSORPTION (WAVELENGTH IN Å)
Total nucleotides	Natural absorption of purines and pyrimidines	2600
Soluble nucleotides	"	"
Ribonucleic acid (RNA)	"	"
Deoxyribonucleic acid (DNA)	"	"
"	Feulgen nucleal reaction for deoxyribose	5500–5750
"	Methyl green	6450
(phosphoric acid groups)		
Nucleic acids (phosphoric acid groups)	Azure A	5900–6250
Protein (free basic groups)	Fast green	⁓6300
Protein (tyrosine)	Millon reaction	⁓3550
Polysaccharides with 1,2-glycol groupings	Periodic acid–Schiff reaction (PAS)	~5500

* From Moses, M. J. (1952) *Exp. Cell Res.,* suppl. 2:76.

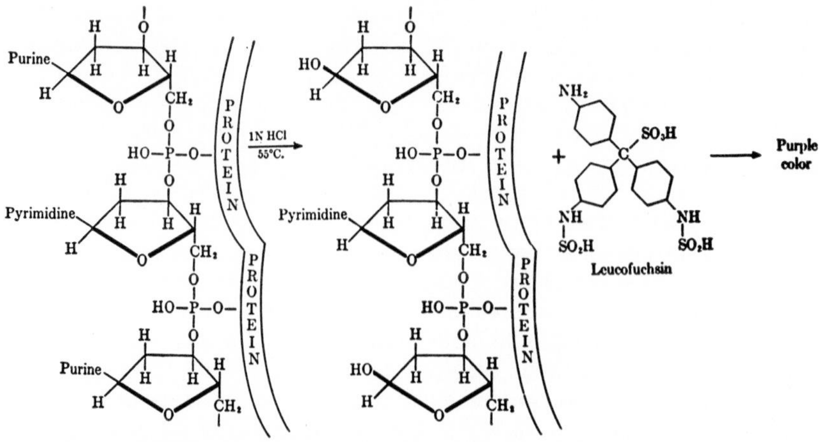

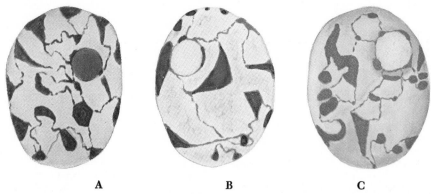

FIGURE 6–6.   Chemistry of the Feulgen reaction. Acid hydrolysis removes the purines and liberates the aldehyde groups, which react with leucofuchsin (Schiff's reagent), resulting in a purple color. In the diagram the size of deoxypentose is greatly exaggerated in relation to the protein. (From Lessler.[59])

A	**B**	**C**

FIGURE 6–7.   Interphase nuclei of pancreatic cells fixed by freeze-drying. **A,** Azan staining: the nucleolus (in red), the chromonemic filaments with their enlarged portions (chromocenters) and the nuclear sap are visible. **B,** Feulgen reaction: the nucleolus gives a negative reaction; in the nuclear sap the reaction is slightly positive. **C,** action of ribonuclease and staining with Azan. The nucleolus does not stain, owing to the digestion of the ribonucleic acid. (De Robertis, Montes de Oca and Raffaele, 1945: *Rev. Soc. Arg. Anat. Normal Patol.*)

The specificity of the reaction can be confirmed by treating the sections with deoxyribonuclease, which removes DNA.[59–61]

The quantitative applications of the Feulgen reaction are discussed later. When applied to the cell, the reaction is positive in the nucleus and negative in the cytoplasm (Fig. 6–4). In the nucleus, the chromonemata and particularly the chromocenters are intensely positive; the nucleolus is Feulgen-negative (Fig. 6–7).

Periodic Acid–Schiff (PAS) Reaction

McManus[62] devised a reaction based on the oxidation with periodic acid of the "1,2-glycol" group of polysaccharides with liberation of aldehyde groups, which give a positive Schiff reaction (Fig. 6–8). This test is done on plant cells for starch, cellulose, hemicellulose and pectins; and on animal cells for mucin, mucoproteins and probably also for hyaluronic acid and chitin.

Another reaction is based on a similar mechanism but employs sodium tungstate in an acid medium as an oxidizer followed by irradiation with ultraviolet light. All glycol-containing components appear blue after the reaction has taken place.[63]

The development of these and other histochemical techniques has opened a wide field for the study of this large

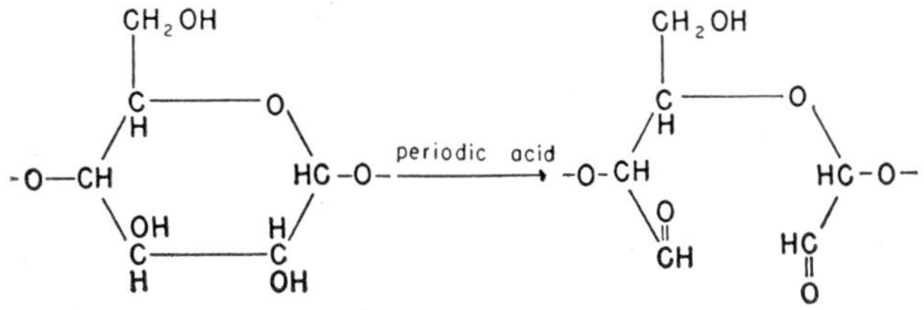

FIGURE 6–8. Chemical diagram of a polysaccharide, showing the action site of periodic acid in the PAS reaction of Mc-Manus. The resulting aldehydes react with Schiff's reagent.

group of compounds that are very important in the metabolism of cells and intercellular substances. Since the PAS reaction is given by a number of substances, different tests can be applied to improve its specificity. For example, enzymes, such as ptyaline present in saliva or amylase, can be used to remove glycogen (Fig. 6–4); hyaluronidase can be used to remove hyaluronic acid. Similarly, some extraction or blocking procedures serve this purpose.

Detection of Lipids

Fat droplets can be demonstrated by osmium tetroxide, which stains them black by reacting mainly with unsaturated fatty acids. Staining with Sudan III or Sudan IV (scarlet red) has a greater histochemical value. These stains act by a simple process of diffusion and solubility and in this way are accumulated in the interior of the lipid droplets. Sudan black B has the advantage of being dissolved also in phospholipids and cholesterol, and of producing greater contrast (Fig. 6–4).[64] Nile blue sulfate is used to detect acidic lipids, which include fatty acids and phospholipids. A test for phospholipids is treatment with chromium salts followed by acid hematein.[65]

Plasmal Reaction. Among other lipid substances that can be studied histochemically are long-chain aliphatic aldehydes occurring in plasmalogens, which give the so-called *plasmal reaction* upon direct treatment of the tissue with Schiff's reagent. Since the substances giving the plasmal reaction are soluble in organic solvents, the tissue is not embedded in the usual way but is studied in frozen sections. The compounds may be free aldehydes, such as *palmitaldehyde*, $CH_3(CH_2)_{14}CHO$, and *stearaldehyde*, $CH_3(CH_2)_{16}CHO$, corresponding to palmitic and stearic acids respectively,

which together constitute the so-called *plasmal.*[66]

Detection of Enzymes

The identification and localization of enzymes is one of the most recent and rapidly developing fields of cytochemistry. Until recent years, the oxidative enzymes were practically the only enzymes that could be investigated (dehydrogenases, oxidases, dopa-oxidase, amine oxidase). In 1939, the demonstration of alkaline phosphatase in tissue sections opened a new chapter in enzyme cytochemistry, permitting the cytologic localization of a number of other hydrolytic enzymes, such as acid phosphatase, lipase, esterase, cholinesterase and aminopeptidase.[67]

Because of the inactivating action of most fixatives, special preparation of tissues for enzyme chemistry is necessary. To detect some enzymes, unfixed frozen sections are made in a cryostat; in other cases, the enzyme resists a brief fixation in cold acetone, formaldehyde, gluteraldehyde and other dialdehydes.[12]

Techniques for identifying and localizing enzymes are based on the incubation of the tissue sections with an appropriate substrate. For example, in the Gomori method for alkaline phosphatase, phosphoric esters of glycerol are used as the substrate. The phosphate ion liberated by hydrolysis is converted into an insoluble metal salt (generally in the presence of Ca^{++}), and the metal in turn is visualized by conversion into metallic silver, lead sulfide, cobalt sulfide or other colored compounds. In another method, first used for alkaline phosphatase[68, 69] and applied to tissues, a phosphoric ester of β-naphthol is used as the substrate. The hydrolysis liberates β-naphthol, which, in the presence of a diazonium salt, couples immediately, giving a colored azo component at the site

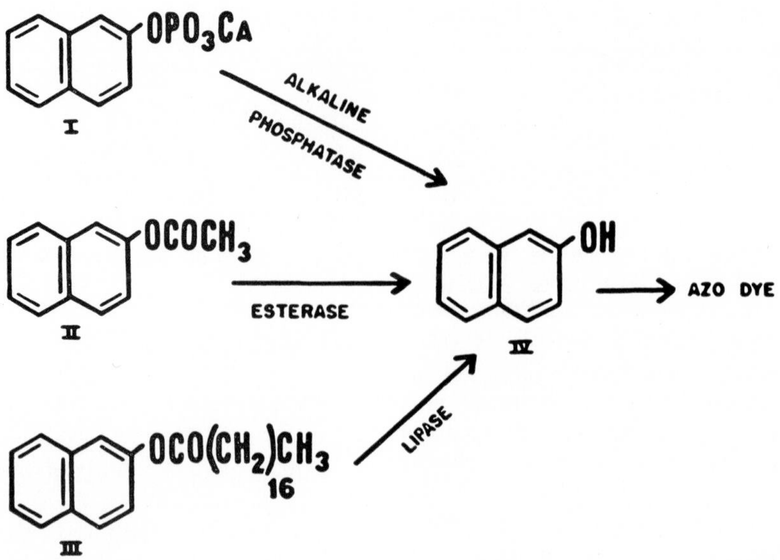

FIGURE 6–9. Diagram showing the cytochemical steps in the methods used to demonstrate hydrolytic enzymes. (See the description in the text.) (From Seligman et al.[69])

of enzymatic activity. Figure 6–9 illustrates the principles involved in this method. Other hydrolytic enzymes, such as esterase, lipase, acid phosphatase, sulfatase and β-glucuronidase, can be detected by this method by changing the conditions and substrate.

Phosphatases. Phosphatases are enzymes that liberate phosphoric acid from many different substrates. A number of phosphatases are known, and they differ with respect to substrate specificity, optimum pH and the action of inactivators and inhibitors. The best known are the *phosphomonoesterases*, which hydrolyze simple esters held by P—O bonds, and the *phosphamidases*, which hydrolyze P—N bonds. Table 6–2 indicates some of the most common enzymes studied histochemically and some of the substrates used. An example of the alkaline phosphatase reaction is given in Figure 6–10.

Esterases. Esterases are enzymes that catalyze the following reversible reaction:

$$-COOR + HOH \leftrightarrows R-COOH + R'OH$$

Esterases have been divided into *simple esterases* (*aliesterases*), which hydrolyze short chain aliphatic esters; *lipases,* which attack esters with long carbon chains; and *cholinesterases,* which act on esters of choline.[34]

In the three main methods for detecting simple esterases and lipases the substrates used are: water-soluble fatty acid esters (Tweens),[67] azo dyes, such as β-naphthyl acetate,[70] and indoxyl acetate.[71] Cholinesterases are usually subdivided into "true" (specific), which hydrolyze acetylcholine, and "pseudo" (nonspecific), which act on other choline esters. Important advances have been

TABLE 6–2. SOME PHOSPHATASES STUDIED CYTOCHEMICALLY

TYPE	SUBSTRATE
Phosphomonoesterases	
Alkaline phosphatase	α- or β-glycerophosphate
Acid phosphatase	Naphthylphosphate
Adenosine triphosphatase (ATPase)	Adenosine triphosphate
5-Nucleotidase	5-Adenylic acid
Phosphamidase	Phosphocreatine Naphthyl phosphoric acid diamines
Glucose-6-phosphatase	Glucose-6-phosphate
Thiamine pyrophosphatase	Thiamine pyrophosphate
Pyrophosphatase	Sodium pyrophosphate Dinaphthyl pyrophosphate
Phosphodiesterases	
Ribonuclease	Ribonucleic acid (RNA)
Deoxyribonuclease	Deoxyribonucleic acid (DNA)

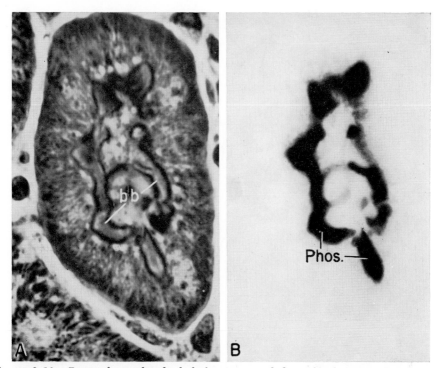

FIGURE 6–10. Proximal convoluted tubule from a mouse kidney after freezing-substitution. **A**, observation in phase contrast with a medium of refractive index n = 1460. *bb*, brush border. **B**, observation with transmitted light (*Phos.*, alkaline phosphatase reaction). (Courtesy of B. J. Davies and L. Ornstein.)

made since acetylthiocholine was introduced as a histochemical substrate for cholinesterases.[72]

Other *hydrolytic enzymes* studied histochemically are β-D-glucuronidase, β-D-galactosidase, aryl sulfatase and aminopeptidase. Figure 6–11B shows an example of the reaction of aminopeptidase, a proteolytic enzyme that can attack peptide bonds adjacent to a terminal α-amino group (Fig. 4–1).

Oxidases. Oxidases are enzymes that catalyze the transfer of electrons from a donor substrate to oxygen (Chap. 4). They usually contain iron, e.g., peroxidase and catalase, or copper, e.g., tyrosinase and polyphenol oxidase. Another enzyme of this series is monoamine oxidase, which is involved in the metabolism of indole and catecholamines.

Colorless substrates, such as benziline, are used to detect peroxidases. These substrates are transformed into stained dyes by H_2O_2 in the presence of the enzyme. *Cytochrome oxidase* gives the so-called *Nadi* reaction. It oxidates the Nadi reagent, a mixture of α-naphthol and dimethyl paraphenylene dia-

mine (Fig. 6–12). The well-known stain Janus green is also related to the oxidase activity in mitochondria. This dye is reduced and becomes colorless as soon as it enters the cell, but then it is reoxidized specifically by mitochondria[73] (see Chap. 11).

Dehydrogenases. Most oxidation reactions that are catalyzed by enzymes are dehydrogenations, i.e., transfer of electrons from the substrate (proton donor) to the oxidizing agent or electron acceptor (see Chap. 4).

Dehydrogenases represent the first components of the chain of enzymes that, in successive steps, are able to transfer hydrogen from the substrate to molecular oxygen, for example, succinic dehydrogenase and the numerous pyridine nucleotide–linked dehydrogenases (see Fig. 11–11), which require the coenzyme DPN or TPN (di- or triphosphopyridine nucleotide). Another group of dehydrogenase reactions are catalyzed by a flavin nucleotide system.

Among the best known DPN enzymes are lactic acid dehydrogenase, which converts lactic acid into pyruvic acid,

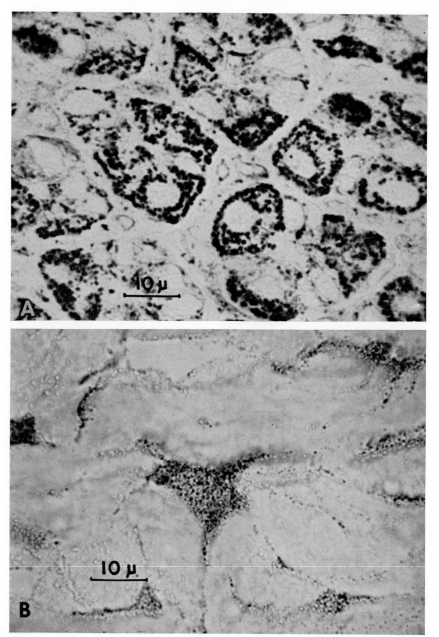

FIGURE 6–11. A, cytochemical demonstration of lactic acid dehydrogenase in parietal cells o the rat stomach. The insoluble formazan produced by the reaction delineates the mitochondria. I aminopeptidase activity in fibroblasts of the rat dermis. × 1500. (Courtesy of B. Monis.)

dimethyl-*p*-phenylene diamine   *α*-naphthol   indophenol blue

FIGURE 6–12. Nadi reaction for cytochrome oxidase.

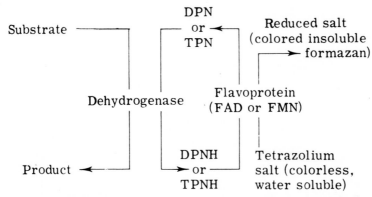

FIGURE 6–13.   Schematic representation of the transfer of electrons to tetrazolium salt. *FAD,* flavin adenine dinucleotide; *FMN,* flavin mononucleotide; *DPN,* diphosphopyridine nucleotide; *TPN,* triphosphopyridine nucleotide.

and malic acid dehydrogenase, which converts malic acid into oxaloacetic acid. Among the TPN enzymes are isocitric acid dehydrogenase and the malic enzyme (malate → pyruvate + CO_2).[34] From the histochemical standpoint, tellurite, triazole and tetrazolium have been used, but of these only the last two, which produce an insoluble chromogenic formazan dye, have been successful.

Figure 6–13 represents the mechanism of action of these histochemical reactions, and Figure 6–11A illustrates the detection of lactic acid dehydrogenase in parietal cells of the stomach. Several of the enzyme reactions studied in these sections have been adapted for the use with the electron microscope, and examples are given in other chapters.

Histochemical Methods Based on Physical Determinations

Cytophotometric Methods

Several cell components can absorb ultraviolet light specifically. For example, the absorption range of nucleic acids is 2600 Å while that of proteins is mainly 2800 Å (Fig. 6–14). Also, some histochemical staining reactions give specific absorption in the visible spectrum and can be analyzed quantitatively by appropriate instruments called *cytophotometers.*

A typical apparatus for absorption cytophotometry is represented in Figure 6–15. By changing the light source and

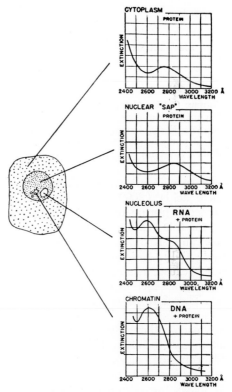

FIGURE 6–14.   Ultraviolet absorption spectrum of the cytoplasm, nuclear "sap," nucleolus and chromatin. The extinction at different wavelengths is indicated. (Courtesy of T. Caspersson.)

the optical system, this instrument can be used for either the ultraviolet or the visible spectrum. The absorption is measured directly by means of a photomultiplier or by densitometry on calibrated photographic plates. Table 6–1 indicates some of the histochemical reactions that can be analyzed by cytophotometric analysis.

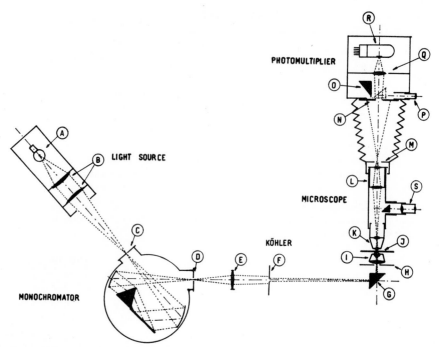

Figure 6–15. Cytophotometer used at the Instituto de Anatomía General y Embriología. A light source of a tungsten light; B, condenser lens; C and D, entrance and exit slits of the monochromator; E, lens; F, diaphragm; G, prism; H, diaphragm; I, condenser; J, slide; K, objective; L, ocular; M and N, diaphragms; O, prism for observation of the final image; P, to displace prism; Q, lens; R, photomultiplier; S, lateral view. (Courtesy of A. O. Pogo and J. Cordero Funes.)

The specific ultraviolet absorption of nucleic acids (2600 Å) is due to the presence of purine and pyrimidine bases, and, for this reason, is 2600 Å in both DNA and RNA and in nucleotides (Table 6–1). This is of particular interest because, as already said, the Feulgen nucleal reaction is positive only for DNA. Therefore, absorption cytophotometry and the nucleal reaction complement each other. By ultraviolet cytophotometry the two types of nucleic acids can be localized but not distinguished (Fig. 6–14). The nucleal reaction shows the presence of DNA (Fig. 6–4). By comparing the results from each method, the distribution of RNA can be determined.

The nucleal reaction can be adapted to quantitative determinations of DNA in tissue sections. Monochromatic light of 5500 Å corresponding to the maximum absorption of this stain is used for this purpose.[58-61] Under certain conditions the results can be given in absolute values, but the method generally measures relative amounts of DNA. The classic Millon reaction can be used to determine the protein content (Table 6–1).

Microincineration (Spodography)

This method has been used in the study of the mineral components of the cell. It consists simply of heating the slice of tissue to about 525° C. and then observing the ashes under a darkfield microscope. The iron oxides, which give a reddish color, are the only mineral components that can be identified. Sometimes some silica particles can be studied with the polarizing microscope. The spodograms show that structures containing nucleic acids also have large amounts of ash, which has been attributed to the phosphate content.

Microincineration has also been applied to electron microscopy. In some cases the specimen has been incinerated by bombardment with the electron beam; in others it has been put directly on the cathode and an emission image has been recorded. Additional information about the chemical composition of the ash is obtained by electron diffraction.

Fluorescence Microscopy

In this method the tissue sections are examined under ultraviolet light, near the visible spectrum, and the components are recognized by the fluorescence they emit in the visible spectrum. Two types of fluorescence can be studied: natural fluorescence (*autofluorescence*), which is produced by substances normally present in the tissue, and secondary fluorescence, which is induced by staining with fluorescent dyes called *fluorochromes.*

The most important advantage of fluorescence microscopy is its great sensitivity. Since the emitted light has a different wavelength from that absorbed, it can be observed more readily, and the contrast given is high. This is particularly important for vital studies, since only a low concentration of fluorescent dye is necessary and therefore there is minimum interference with the normal physiology of the tissue.

Fluorescence often gives specific cytochemical information because some of the normal components of the tissue have a typical fluorescent emission. Thus vitamin A, thiamine, riboflavin and other substances can be detected. The cytochemical value of the method can be increased considerably by spectrographic analysis of the radiation.[74] Sometimes certain substances incorporated in cells, e.g., sulfonamides, can be localized.[75]

The most common pattern of autofluorescence is a weak, diffuse, bluish fluorescence of the cytoplasm, with a yellow and stronger fluorescence of the granules; usually the nucleus is not fluorescent. Mitochondria of the liver and kidney give a strong fluorescence, calcium deposits appear yellow-white, and free porphyrins have a strong red fluorescence. An important application concerns the so-called lipogenic pigments, which are found in numerous cells and which increase with age. It is thought that these pigments represent different degrees of oxidation and polymerization of unsaturated fatty acids. By fluorescence two types of pigments, the so-called *lipofuscin* and the *ceroid,* can be determined.[75]

Vitamin A gives a green or yellow fluorescence, which rapidly disappears upon irradiation. Fluorescence has also been used for the detection of other vitamins and some hormones.[75]

Histoimmunology

The use of fluorescence microscopy in cytochemistry has been widely extended by Coon's technique, which employs fluorescein-marked antibodies to localize antigens in tissues.[76] Antibodies present in the serum are coupled with fluorescein isocyanate. The tissues are frozen and sectioned in a cryostat (see Fig. 6–2), and then the sections are attached to slides, dried at room temperature, and stained with the coupled antiserum. This method has been widely used for the localization of viruses and bacterial antigens. It has been also possible to localize antibodies at the sites of formation within plasma cells. An important simplification of this technique consists of the use of an ordinary antiserum to react with the antigen. Antibodies are then localized by a second coupled antiserum in general use.[76] Among findings of cytochemical interest are those that demonstrated that the pituitary hormone ACTH is localized in the basophilic cells of the pituitary gland.[77] Several of the enzymes produced by the pancreas have also been localized by this technique.[78, 79] Figure 6–16 gives an example of the degree of localization that can be achieved with Coon's technique in muscle and spermatozoa. The myofibril shown in the figure has been stained with an antibody against myosin, and it demonstrates that this protein is strictly localized in the A-bands (see also Chap. 21).

Different proteins can be tagged with fluorescent dyes without denaturing the molecule. These fluorescent proteins may then be injected into the animal and localized in sections. By this method the reabsorption of homologous and heterologous serum proteins by the kidney can be studied, along with the general distribution of these proteins outside the circulatory system.[80]

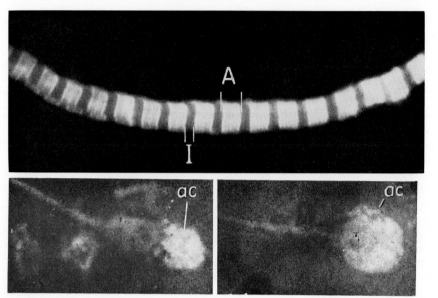

FIGURE 6–16.   **Above,** striated myofibril isolated and stained with a fluorescent antibody against myosin. Notice that the antigen (myosin) is located exclusively in the A-bands. Observation made with the fluorescence microscope. (Courtesy of H. Marshall.) **Below,** bull spermatozoon (*left*) and guinea pig spermatozoon (*right*) incubated with the corresponding hyaluronidase antibody. Notice that in both cases the bright fluorescence is localized at the acrosome (*ac.*) ×1250. (Courtesy of R. E. Mancini.)

The histoimmunologic methods have recently been brought to the level of electron microscopy. By coupling the antibody with ferritin molecules, the sites of antibody-antigen reaction can be observed under the electron microscope.[81] This method has been used to localize viruses and to detect the secretion of gamma globulin into the endoplasmic reticulum of plasma cells (see Chap. 10 and Fig. 10–19).

Radioautography in Cytochemistry

One of the most important modern cytochemical methods is based on the use of substances marked (tagged) with radioisotopes. The tagged substance is incorporated in the cell by one of several different ways and then localized by using a photographic emulsion.

Radioautography is based on the property of radioisotopes of acting on the silver bromide crystals of the emulsion. The tissue section is put in contact with the photographic emulsion for a certain period; then the radioautograph is developed as an ordinary photograph. By comparing the radioautograph with the

cells in the tissues seen under a microscope, the radioisotope can be localized fairly accurately.

Radioisotopes used in radioautography may emit one or more of three types of radiation: α- and β-particles and γ-rays. α-Particles are positively charged helium nuclei, which produce straight tracks in the emulsion; they can easily be traced back to the point of origin. Resolution is highest with these emitters, but they have limited use in biologic work because they are produced mainly by heavy metals. β-Particles are electrons, which may have different energy levels. Their tracks are tortuous and may vary in length from a few microns to a millimeter, depending on their energy. γ-Rays are not important in radioautography. Most of the isotopes used are β-emitters.[82–85]

In the most commonly used *stripping film* technique, a 5 μ emulsion on a gelatin base of 10 μ is used.[86] The film is stripped off the glass plate and floated on a water bath. Then the section mounted on a glass slide is immersed beneath the floating film. Upon withdrawal of the specimen, the emulsion covers the preparation tightly. After exposure for different lengths of time according to the isotope used, which may be for several weeks or months, the radioautograph is developed. Quantitative results can be obtained by determining the density in the radioautographs by various optical methods,[87] or by counting the grains.[84]

Substances marked with the β-emitter C^{14} have been widely used in radioautography. With such an emitter, *track radioautography* can also be used.[88] This consists of applying a liquid emulsion instead of a photographic film. With this technique the contact is even more intimate, and it is possible to follow and count the single tracks of β-emission coming out from a definite area, thus providing a quantitative estimation. The resolution of this method is of the order of 1 to 2 μ.

Indirect chemical determination of the substances tagged by the isotope can be made by extraction or by specific enzyme methods. For example, ribonuclease and hyaluronidase may be used for studies in which nucleic acids and acid polysaccharides are tagged.

Tritium (H^3), which is a soft β-emitter, has helped in a finer localization of the isotope. With this isotope the resolution may be of the order of 1 μ. For the study of deoxyribonucleic acid (DNA) metabolism of the cell, tritiated thymidine is now being widely used (Fig. 17–8) and is specific for this type of nucleic acid. Important studies of the mechanism of DNA replication (see Chap. 17) and the RNA metabolism have been made with appropriate precursors (Figs. 17–17 and 17–23). In the example shown in Figure 6–17, the nuclei tagged with tritiated thymidine and present at the bottom of the intestinal crypts are found after 36 hours near the tip of the villus. This result indicates in a graphic manner the life cycle of the cell. After a division at the bottom of the crypt, the cell ascends along the epithelium until, after a few hours, it is destroyed at the tip of the villus. (For other examples of nucleic acid metabolism in mitosis and meiosis, see Chapter 17.)

Recently a two-emulsion radioautography that can distinguish β-particles emitted from C^{14} and H^3 atoms has been developed. With this a tritiated precursor of DNA and C^{14}-labeled precursor of RNA or of a protein can be used simultaneously.[89]

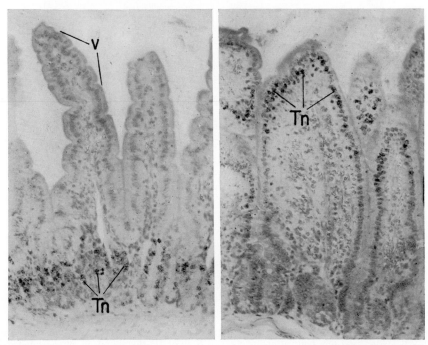

FIGURE 6–17.   Section of intestine of a mouse injected with tritiated thymidine. **Left,** animal killed eight hours after injection; **right,** 36 hours after injection. *Tn,* tagged nuclei; *V,* villus. (See the description in the text.) (Courtesy of C. P. Leblond.)

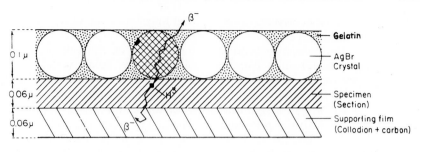

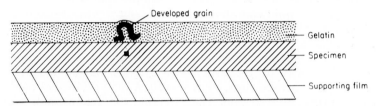

FIGURE 6–18. Diagrammatic representation of an electron microscope autoradiograph preparation. **Top,** *during exposure:* The silver halide crystals, embedded in a gelatin matrix, cover the section. A beta particle, from a tritium point source in the specimen, has hit a crystal (cross-hatched), causing the appearance of a latent image on the surface (black speck on upper left region of crystal). **Bottom,** *during examination and after processing:* The exposed crystal has been developed into a filament of silver; the nonexposed crystals have been dissolved. The total thickness has decreased because the silver halide occupied approximately half the volume of the emulsion. (Courtesy of L. G. Caro.)

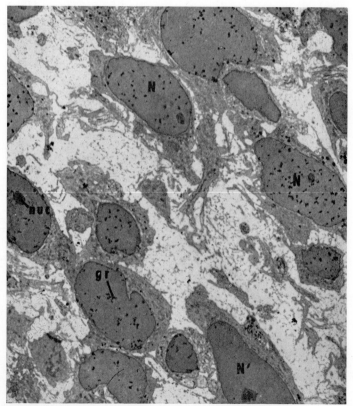

FIGURE 6–19. Low power electron micrograph of blastema cells from a regenerating limb of a salamander. Tissue fixed one hour after injection of 5 μc of H³-thymidine. *N*, nuclei labeled by the developed silver grains (*gr*). Some nuclei (*N′*) are not labeled; *nuc*, nucleolus. ×2000. (Courtesy of E. D. Hay and J. P. Revel.)

In recent years the technique of radioautography with tritiated substances has been brought to the electron microscope level. Special liquid emulsions are applied on thin sections forming a monolayer of silver halide crystals (Fig. 6–18). After proper development, the silver grains that were hit by the β-emulsion stand up upon the electron microscope image (Fig. 6–19). A resolution of about 0.1 μ (1000 Å) has been achieved.[85, 90]

GENERAL REFERENCES

Allfrey, V. G. (1959) The isolation of subcellular components. In: *The cell,* Vol. 1, p. 193. (Brachet, J., and Mirsky, A. E., eds.) Academic Press, New York.

Boyd, G. A. (1955) *Autoradiography in biology and medicine.* Academic Press, New York.

Brachet, J. (1957) *Biochemical cytology.* Academic Press, New York.

Burstone, M. S. (1962) *Enzyme histochemistry and its application in the study of neoplasms.* Academic Press, New York.

Coons, A. H. (1956) Histochemistry with labeled antibody. *Internat. Rev. Cytol.,* 5:1.

Danielli, J. F. (1953) *Cytochemistry, a critical approach.* John Wiley & Sons, New York.

Deane, H. W. (1958) Intracellular lipids: their detection and significance. In: *Frontiers in cytology.* (Palay, S. L., ed.) Yale University Press, New Haven, Conn.

Engström, A. (1956) Historadiography. In: *Physical techniques in biological research,* Vol. 3, p. 489. (Oster, G., and Pollister, A. W., eds.) Academic Press, New York.

Ficq, A. (1959) Autoradiography. In: *The cell,* Vol. 1, p. 67. (Brachet, J., and Mirsky, A. E., eds.) Academic Press, New York.

Glick, D. (1949) *Techniques of histo- and cytochemistry.* Interscience Publishers, New York.

Glick, D. (1959) Quantitative microchemical techniques of histo- and cytochemistry. In: *The cell,* Vol. 1, p. 139. (Brachet, J., and Mirsky, A. E., eds.) Academic Press, New York.

Gomori, G. (1952) *Microscopic histo-chemistry.* University of Chicago Press, Chicago.

Gomori, G. (1952) The histochemistry of esterases. *Internat. Rev. Cytol.,* 1:335.

Hale, A. J. (1957) The histochemistry of polysaccharides. *Internat. Rev. Cytol.,* 6:194.

Lison, L. (1960) *Histochimie et cytochimie animale.* 3rd Ed. Gauthier-Villars, Paris.

Pearse, A. G. E. (1960) *Histochemistry, theoretical and applied.* 2nd Ed. J. & A. Churchill, London.

Price, G., and Schwartz, S. (1956) Fluorescence microscopy. In: *Physical techniques in biological research,* Vol. 3, p. 91. (Oster, G., and Pollister, A. W., eds.) Academic Press, New York.

Singer, M. (1952) Factors which control the staining of tissue sections with acid and basic dyes. *Internat. Rev. Cytol.,* 1:211.

Swift, H. (1953) Quantitative aspects of nuclear nucleoproteins. *Internat. Rev. Cytol.,* 2:1.

Taylor, J. H. (1958) The duplication of chromosomes. *Scient. Amer., 198*(No. 6):36.

CITED REFERENCES

1. Rinaldini, L. M. J. (1958) *Internat. Rev. Cytol.,* 7:587.
2. Parker, P. C. (1961) *Methods of tissue culture.* 3rd Ed. Paul B. Hoeber, New York.
3. Cameron, G. (1950) *Tissue culture technique.* Academic Press, New York.
4. Moscona, A. (1952) *Exp. Cell Res.,* 3:535.
5. Dulbecco, R. (1952) *Proc. Nat. Acad. Sci.* (*Wash.*), 38:747.
6. Earle, W., Evans, V., and Schilling, E. (1950) *J. Nat. Cancer Inst.,* 10:943.
7. Puck, T. T., and Marcus, P. I. (1956) *J. Exp. Med., 103*:653.
8. Puck, T. T., Marcus, P. I., and Cieciura, S. J. (1956) *J. Exp. Med., 103*:273.
9. Sato, G., Fisher, H. W., and Puck, T. T. (1957) *Science, 126*:961.
10. Chambers, R. (1940) *J. Roy. Micr. Soc., 60*:113.
11. Chambers, R. (1949) *Biol. Rev.,* 24:2346.
12. Sabatini, D. D., Bensch, K. G., and Barrnett, R. J. (1962) New fixatives for cytological and cytochemical studies. In: *Fifth international congress on electron microscopy,* Vol. 2, L-3. Academic Press, New York.
13. Wolman, M. (1955) *Internat. Rev. Cytol.,* 4:79.
14. Gersh, I. (1959) Fixation and staining. In: *The cell,* Vol. 1, p. 21 (Brachet, J., and Mirsky, A. E., eds.) Academic Press, New York.
15. McClung, C. E., ed. (1950) *Handbook of microscopical technique.* 3rd Ed. Paul B. Hoeber, New York.
16. Bensley, R. R., and Bensley, S. A. (1941) *Handbook of histological and cytological technique.* University of Chicago Press, Chicago.
17. Porter, K. R., and Kallman, F. (1953) *Exp. Cell Res.,* 4:127.
18. Bahr, G. F. (1954) *Exp. Cell Res.,* 7:457.
19. Palade, G. E. (1952) *J. Exp. Med.,* 95:285.
20. De Robertis, E. (1956) *J. Biophys. Biochem. Cytol.,* 2:785.
21. Fernández-Morán, H., and Finean, J. B. (1957) *J. Biophys. Biochem. Cytol.,* 3:725.
22. Engström, A., and Finean, J. B. (1958) *Biological ultrastructure.* Academic Press, New York.
23. Bernhard, W., and Leduc, E. (1962) In: *Fifth international congress on electron microscopy,* Vol. 2, L-4. Academic Press, New York.
24. Singer, M., and Morrison, P. R. (1948) *J. Biol. Chem., 175*:1, 133.

25. Singer, M. (1954) *J. Histochem. Cytochem.*, 2:5, 322.
26. Alfert, M., and Geschwind, I. I. (1953) *Proc. Nat. Acad. Sci.* (Wash.), 39:991.
27. Schubert, M., and Hamermann, D. (1956) *J. Histochem. Cytochem.*, 4:158.
28. Michaelis, L., and Granick, S. (1945) *Amer. Chem. Soc.*, 67:1212.
29. Sylvén, B. (1954) *Quart. J. Micr. Sci.*, 95: 327.
30. Lison, L. (1960) *Histochimie et cytochimie animale.* 3rd Ed. Gauthier-Villars, Paris.
31. Casselman, W. G. B. (1959) *Histochemical technique.* Butler & Tanner, London.
32. Pearse, A. G. E., (1960) *Histochemistry: theoretical and applied.* J. & A. Churchill, London.
33. Glick, D. (1959) Quantitative microchemical techniques of histo- and cytochemistry. In: *The cell*, Vol. 1, p. 139. (Brachet, J., and Mirsky, A. E., eds.) Academic Press, New York.
34. Burstone, M. S. (1962) *Enzyme histochemistry.* Academic Press, New York.
35. De Robertis, E., Pellegrino de Iraldi, A., Rodriguez de Lores Arnaiz, G., and Salganicoff, L. (1962) *J. Neurochem.*, 9:23.
36. Kuff, E. L., Hogeboom, G. H., and Dalton, A. J. (1956) *J. Biophys. Biochem. Cytol.*, 2:1, 33.
37. Anderson, N. G. (1956) Techniques for the mass isolation of cellular components. In: *Physical techniques in biological research*, Vol. 3, p. 300. (Oster, G., and Pollister, A. W., eds.) Academic Press, New York.
38. Albertsson, P. (1960) *Partition of cell particles and macromolecules.* John Wiley & Sons, New York.
39. Messelson, M., and Stahl, F. W. (1958) *Proc. Nat. Acad. Sci.* (*Wash*), 44:671.
40. Holter, H., and Linderström-Lang, K. (1940) Enzymatische Histochemie. In: *Handbuch der Enzymologie.* (Nord and Weidenhagen, eds.) Akademische Verlagsgesellschaft, Leipzig.
41. Kirk, P. L. (1950) *Quantitative ultramicroanalysis.* John Wiley & Sons, New York.
42. Eränko, Q. (1955) *Quantitative methods in histology and microscopic histochemistry.* Little, Brown and Co., Boston.
43. Lowry, O. H. (1957) Micromethods for the assay of enzymes. In: *Methods in enzymology*, Vol. 4. (Colowick, S. P., and Kaplan, N. O., eds.) Academic Press, New York.
44. Zeuthen, E. (1946) *Comp. Rend. Lab. Carlsberg, série chim.*, 25:191.
45. Holter, H., and Zeuthen, E. (1948) *Comp. Rend. Lab. Carlsberg, série chim.*, 26: 7, 243.
46. Edström, J. E., and Hydén, H. (1954) *Nature*, 174:128.
47. Edström, J. E. (1956) *Biochim. Biophys. Acta*, 22:378.
48. Danielli, J. F. (1953) *Cytochemistry, a critical approach.* John Wiley & Sons, New York.
49. Bennett, H. S. (1951) *Anat. Rec.*, 110:231.
50. Bennett, H. S., and Watts, R. M. (1958) The cytochemical demonstration and measurement of sulfhydryl groups by Azo-Aryl mercaptide coupling, with special reference to mercury orange. In: *General cytochemical methods*, Vol. I, p. 317 (Danielli, J. F., ed.) Academic Press, New York.
51. Kawamura, N., and Dan, K. (1958) *J. Biophys. Biochem. Cytol.*, 4:5, 615.
52. Barrnett, R. J., and Seligman, A. M. (1954) *J. Nat. Cancer Inst.*, 14:769.
53. Barrnett, R. J., and Seligman, A. M. (1955) *J. Histochem. Cytochem.*, 3:406.
54. Cafruny, E. J., Di Stefano, H. S., and Farah A. (1955) *J. Histochem. Cytochem.*, 3. 354.
55. Flax, M. H., and Himes, M. H. (1952) *Physiol. Zool.*, 25:297.
56. Saez, F. A. (1951) *Anat. Rec.*, 113:306.
57. Kurnick, N. B. (1950) *Exp. Cell Res.*, 1:151
58. Di Stefano, H. (1948) *Chromosoma*, 4:282.
59. Lessler, M. A. (1953) *Internat. Rev. Cytol.* 2:231.
60. Brachet, J. (1957) *Biochemical cytology* Academic Press, New York.
61. Stowell, R. E. (1946) *Stain Technol.*, 21. 137.
62. McManus, F. A. (1946) *Nature*, 158:202.
63. Etcheverry, M. A., and Mancini, R. E (1948) *Rev. Soc. Argent. Biol.*, 48:136
64. Baker, J. R. (1944) *Quart. J. Micr. Sci.*, 85:1
65. Baker, J. R. (1946) *Quart. J. Micr. Sci.*, 87. 441.
66. Danielli, J. F. (1949) *Quart. J. Micr. Sci.* 90:67.
67. Gomori, G. (1952) *Microscopic histochemistry.* University of Chicago Press, Chicago.
68. Menten, M. L., Junge, J., and Green, M. H (1944) *Proc. Soc. Exp. Biol. Med.*, 57. 82.
69. Seligman, A. M., et al. (1949) *Ann. Surg.* 130:333.
70. Nachlas, M. M., and Seligman, A. M. (1949) *J. Nat. Cancer Inst.*, 9:415.
71. Barrnett, R. J., and Seligman, A. M. (1951) *Science*, 114:579.
72. Koelle, G. B., and Friedenwald, J. S. (1949) *Proc. Soc. Exp. Biol. Med.*, 70:617.
73. Lazarow, A., and Copperstein, S. J. (1953) *J. Histochem. Cytochem.*, 1:234.
74. Sjöstrand, F. S. (1946) *Acta Physiol. Scand.* 8:42.
75. Price, G., and Schwartz, S. (1956) Fluorescence microscopy. In: *Physical techniques in biological research*, Vol. 3, p 91. (Oster, G., and Pollister, A. W., eds.) Academic Press, New York.
76. Coons, A. H. (1956) *Internat. Rev. Cytol.* 5:1.
77. Marshall, J. M., Jr. (1951) *J. Exp. Med.*, 94. 21.

78. Marshall, J. M., Jr. (1954) *Exp. Cell Res.,* 6:240.
79. Holter, H., and Marshall, J. M., Jr. (1954) *Comp. Rend. Lab. Carlsberg, série chim.,* 29:7.
80. Mancini, R. E. (1963) *Internat. Rev. Cytol.,* 14:193.
81. Singer, S. J. (1959) *Nature, 183*:1523.
82. Gross, J., Bogoroch, R., Nadler, N. J., and Leblond, C. P. (1951) *Amer. J. Roentgenol., 65*:3, 420.
83. Boyd, G. A. (1955) *Autoradiography in biology and medicine.* Academic Press, New York.

84. Taylor, J. H. (1956) Autoradiography at the cellular level. In: *Physical techniques in biological research,* Vol. 3, p. 546. (Oster, G., and Pollister, A. W., eds.) Academic Press, New York.
85. Caro, L. (1962) *J. Cell Biol., 15*:189.
86. Howard, A., and Pelc, S. R. (1951) *Exp. Cell Res.,* 2:178.
87. Mazia, D., Plaut, W. S., and Ellis, G. W. (1955) *Exp. Cell Res.,* 9:305.
88. Ficq, A. (1955) *Exp. Cell Res.,* 9:286.
89. Baserga, R., and Nemeroff, K. (1962) *J. Histochem. Cytochem., 10*:628.
90. Caro, L. G., and van Tubergen, R. P. (1962) *J. Cell Biol., 15*:173.

PART THREE

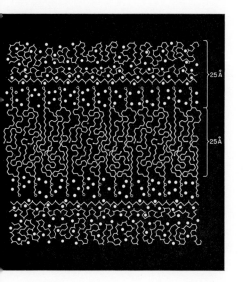

STRUCTURAL
BASES
OF
THE CELL

The following chapters are a general discussion of the processes by which molecular components become organized into complex structures. The passage from the molecular to the subcellular level may thus be better interpreted as well as the images given by the different optical instruments.

In speaking of the elementary structures (i.e., macromolecular, fibrous and membranous) it is possible to see how they can be formed by the interaction of different molecules. The use of molecular models has been of great importance in interpreting the image given by the electron microscope.

The cell membrane is studied in relation to elementary structures because it has macromolecular dimensions. Starting with lipoprotein artificial models it is possible to reach a better understanding of the structure and properties of biologic membranes. The numerous differentiations of the cell membrane in the various cell types are discussed. (Only in Chapter 20 is the physiology of the cell membrane considered under the name of cell permeability.)

CHAPTER 7

ELEMENTARY UNITS

OF STRUCTURE

IN

BIOLOGIC SYSTEMS

The molecular constituents of the cell that were described in Chapter 3 can interact among themselves and become organized into supramolecular units, which in turn are part of structures recognizable within the cells by means of the electron microscope. These *elementary units* of structure are difficult to study because of their small size. Frequently their organization can be discovered by several indirect methods and sometimes from molecular models made with pure substances.

These elementary units are primarily: *unilinear* (fibrous), when the molecules are associated linearly; *two-dimensional*, when they are extended in two dimensions forming thin membranes; or *three-dimensional*, when they are crystalline or amorphous particles. All these molecular organizations are maintained by physicochemical forces of interaction, which are of great interest to biology.

In certain systems these elementary structures may aggregate to form higher types of organization visible in the light microscope and even to the naked eye.

In animal and plant tissues there are a series of components with this type of organization. They can be classified into three categories: *subcellular*, which comprise parts of cells, such as membranes, cilia and chromosomes; *extracellular*, such as collagenous and elastic fibers, membranes of cellulose or chitin situated outside the cells; and *supracellular*, which are macroscopic structures, such as hair, bone and muscle, also with a similar supramolecular organization.

Several of the molecules described in Chapter 3 are very thin (10 to 30 Å) and highly elongated (1000 to 5000 Å). Among them are some fibrous proteins (e.g., collagen, myosin, actin and fibrin), the nucleic acids (DNA and RNA) and the polysaccharides (e.g., cellulose, hyaluronic acid and chondroitin sulfate). Many of these components are polymers in themselves (e.g., proteins are polymers of amino acids), but in turn, are monomers of larger units and can polymerize end to end or can interact laterally to form the fibrous, membranous or crystalline structures.

FUNCTION OF ELEMENTARY STRUCTURES

The function of these elementary structures in biologic systems is mentioned throughout this book, but from the very beginning the student should recognize their importance. Several of these molecular systems are involved in *mechanical functions;* for example: collagen fibers that form a tendon, fibrin fibers used in blood clotting to prevent bleeding or muscle proteins that interact to produce shortening during contraction. Several of these supramolecular complexes have *enzymatic properties* that are involved in these mechanical functions; for example, one part of the myosin molecule (meromyosin) has ATPase activity, which is involved in contraction.

Another important function of these complexes is that of storing (coding) and transmitting *genetic information* (DNA and RNA systems, Chap. 18). Most of the fundamental functions of biologic systems, such as osmotic work, association of cells, permeability and oxidations are intimately related to these basic structures.

Collagen as an Example of a Fibrous Unit

In order to understand better the principles involved in the formation of large molecular complexes let us take collagen as an example. Collagen is one of the most abundant proteins in the animal kingdom. It is synthesized primarily by the fibroblasts and is an important part of major fibrous components of the body, such as skin, tendon, cartilage and bone. The large aggregates are visible to the naked eye and under the light microscope, but the intimate structure down to the molecular level can be studied only by combining electron microscopy, x-ray diffraction, chemical analysis and other techniques. One important advance has been the discovery that collagen fibers can be dissociated into smaller and smaller units by several treatments (such as the action of acids), and then can be reassembled.

The basic collagen molecule has a weight of 360,000,[1] a length of about 2800 Å and a width of 14 Å. It consists of three chains coiled together in a helical fashion as shown schematically in Figure 7–1.[2, 3] It is interesting to recall that collagen has a rather simple amino acid constitution: about one third is glycine, another third is proline and hydroxyproline and the rest is other amino acids.

This molecular unit of collagen—also called "tropocollagen"—can be considered as a macromolecular monomer,[4–6] because it is capable by interaction of "turning into" or forming different collagen structures. The tropocollagen molecule with the dimensions just given is thought to be asymmetrical or polarized in the sense of having a definite linear sequence of the amino acid residues in the intramolecular strands. In fact, in relation to its interaction, the tropocollagen molecule behaves as if it has a "head" and "tail" (Fig. 7–2).

The study of native *collagen fibers* with x-ray diffraction and electron microscopy has shown that they are com-

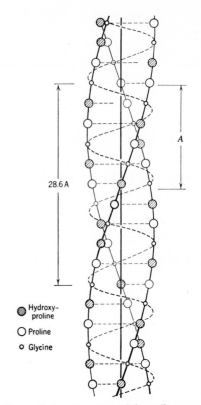

FIGURE 7–1. Structure of the collagen molecule with the three-stranded helix. (From A. Rich, 1959: *Biophysical science.* John Wiley & Sons, New York.)

posed of *fibrils* that have a repeating period of 700 Å, which is reduced to 640 Å after drying (Fig. 5–8). At first it was difficult to discover the relationship of the tropocollagen molecule of 2800 Å to this period of the fibrils. This has been clarified by reconstituting collagen in the presence of some glycoproteins or of ATP. This results in the formation of two other types of fibers (Fig. 7–3): one is composed of long fibrils having a spacing of 2800 Å; the other contains short segments having a similar period, but showing no polymerization. The most probable explanation for these findings is illustrated in Figures 7–2 and 7–3: native collagen fibrils—with a period of 700 Å—result from the lateral association of tropocollagen molecules, which overlap at intervals of one fourth their length. It is assumed that in this case the molecules are longitudinally associated "heads" with "tails" (Fig. 7–2).

In the case of fibrous collagen with long spacing, resulting from interaction with glycoprotein, there is no lateral

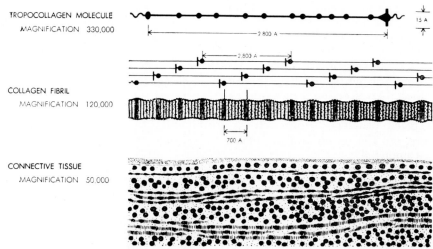

FIGURE 7–2.   Schematic representation of the organization of collagen at different magnifications. **Above,** tropocollagen molecule with the "head and tail" structure. **Middle,** collagen fibril with the 700 Å period and the molecular explanation for it. **Below,** the organization of collagen fibrils in a dense connective tissue. (Courtesy of J. Gross, 1961.)

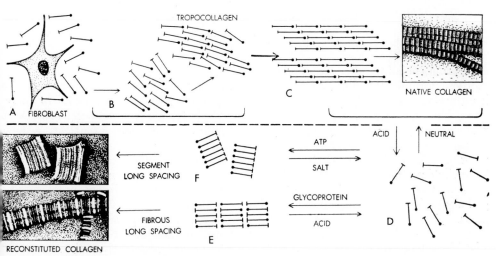

FIGURE 7–3.   Diagram of the formation and reconstitution of collagen. A fibroblast (**A**), manufactures *tropocollagen* molecules (**B**), which form *native collagen* (**C**). Collagen fibrils are solubilized in acid (**D**) and the resulting tropocollagen, in the presence of glycoprotein, produces *fibrous long spacing* (**E**) and, with addition of ATP, *segment long spacing* collagen (**F**). The long spacing of 2800 Å results from the lateral aggregation of the tropocollagen molecules without overlapping. The 700 Å spacing of native collagen fibrils is due to the overlapping of the tropocollagen molecule. (Courtesy of J. Gross, 1961.)

overlapping, and the tropocollagen molecules are assembled side by side and randomly linked in a linear direction. In the segments with long spacing resulting from interaction with ATP, it is supposed that the tropocollagen molecules do not overlap laterally, and, because they are all in phase, they cannot link longitudinally (Fig. 7–3).[7]

This mechanism of macromolecular interaction of collagen is of great biologic interest because it probably also occurs in other protein systems. In fact, similar findings have been obtained for some proteins of muscle, such as paramyosin and tropomyosin.[8]

Blood Clotting

The important process of *blood clotting* is another mechanical function of molecular complexes. The fibrinogen molecule is elongated and has a weight of 340,000. Under the action of thrombin, which splits off a small peptide from fibrinogen, fibrinogen is activated and starts to interact with other monomers. The end-to-end association forms long fibrin fibrils,[9] but apparently there is also some lateral staggering and cross linking with other fibers, forming a network. As clotting progresses, under the influence of the blood platelets,[10] fibrin retracts, squeezing out the serum and the blood clot is completed.

Physicochemical Forces

The nature of the physicochemical forces involved in these different macromolecular interactions vary considerably. For example, the fact that collagen fibrils are soluble in weak organic acids implies that salt linkages and hydrogen bonds are involved. In blood clotting, the process of binding the molecules is more complex, since, as indicated, the interaction involves enzymatic action.

Stronger bonds, such as —S—S— linkages, are involved in other proteins, such as those forming the different types of keratin fibers. Within the cell loose and reversible aggregations of corpuscular proteins may occur. It is postulated that in some processes involving displacement of parts of the cell matrix, such as in ameboid motion, cyclosis or the formation of the mitotic apparatus, these globular-fibrous transformations take place.

The Macromolecular Organization of Particulate Glycogen

Another interesting example of molecular interaction is observed in the glycogen deposits found in liver cells, muscle and in many other tissues. The branched structure of the polysaccharides amylopectin and glycogen is based on 1,6-α-glycosidic bonds, as mentioned in Chapter 3. Electron microscopy has revealed that glycogen particles have three structural levels of organization, each with a special size and morphology.[11, 12] The largest units—called α-particles—are spheroid and measure 500 to 2000 Å with a mean of 1500 Å. These particles have a morular aspect, which indicates that

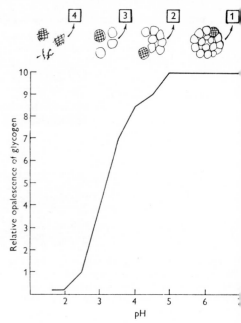

FIGURE 7–4. The structure of particulate glycogen. At decreasing pH values the glycogen particle dissociates progressively (see the text). (From P. Drochmans.[12])

they are composed of smaller units—the β-particles—which are ovoid or polyhedral and 300 Å in diameter (Fig. 7–4). Finally, within the β-particles a finer structure—the γ-particles—composed of rods of 30 × 200 Å can be observed. By the action of acid on particulate glycogen these three different units can be demonstrated (Fig. 7–4).

Ferritin molecules with their typical four subunits can be observed within many cells, particularly in those involved in the metabolism of iron-containing pigments. Crystalline arrays of proteins have been seen in different cells and cell organoids. (Other important macromolecular complexes of the cell, such as the *ribosomes*, are studied in Chapter 9.)

ELEMENTARY MEMBRANOUS STRUCTURES

Biologic membranes are known to result from interaction between lipids and proteins, but the molecular arrangement of these two components is difficult to ascertain. The use of models and artificial monomolecular films is of considerable interest.

Monolayer Films

The structural importance of certain lipids was mentioned in Chapter 3. Fatty acids, phospholipids, cholesterol and cholesterol esters can be packed in single layers of constant thickness. The orientation of the lipids within the structure depends on the dipolar constitution with a polar group and a nonpolar hydrocarbon chain (Fig. 7–5A). These properties of the lipids can be studied by forming films on the surface of water.

The technique of making *monolayer* (*monomolecular*) *films* is of considerable biologic importance. The so-called *film balance* devised by Langmuir in 1917 is still the principal instrument for the study of these films. Essentially it consists of a shallow trough filled with water on which the substance is spread. A bar or barrier can be pushed across the trough to compress the film. The surface pressure exerted by the film is measured by a sensitive floating and suspended balance. For example, if a fatty acid, such as stearic acid (sixteen carbons), is dissolved in a volatile solvent and deposited on the water, the molecules will spread until they reach an equilibrium. Upon evaporation of the solvent, a film one molecule thick is formed. Because the molecule is bipolar, the polar group (—COOH) is attracted by the water molecule and the nonpolar hydrocarbon chain tends to stand straight on the surface. At first, some molecules are not well aligned because of the ample space, but as the barrier is pushed across the trough and the surface area is reduced,

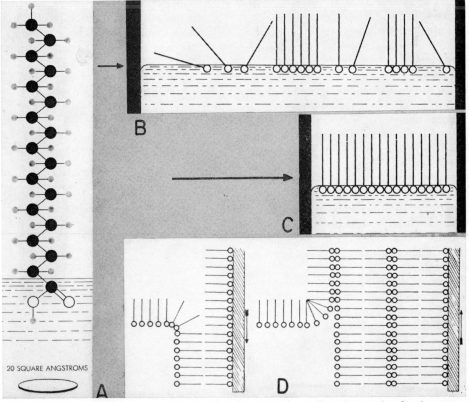

20 SQUARE ANGSTROMS

FIGURE 7–5.   Diagram of the technique of making monolayer films. **A,** a molecule of stearic acid with the polar group dipped in water. **B,** at low compression, molecules are oriented at different angles or form packed aggregates. **C,** at high compression, molecules are tightly packed and are vertical. Circles represent polar groups and straight lines the nonpolar hydrocarbon chains. **D,** method of building up molecular films at an air-water interface. *Left,* a glass slide previously coated with a monomolecular film of barium stearate (notice the polar groups attached to the glass surface) is dipped in water that has a monomolecular film at the interface. The second monomolecular layer attaches to the first by the nonpolar ends. *Right,* several bimolecular layers of barium stearate have been deposited on the glass slide by successive dips into the water. (A, B, C, from H. R. Ries; D, courtesy of D. Waugh.)

the molecules are compressed until they form a packed film (Fig. 7–5B, C). Under these conditions, because of the horizontal motion and electrical repulsion, the molecules exert a pressure that can be measured with the film balance. When the number of molecules and the total surface occupied by the film at the maximum of compression are known, the average area of each molecule can be calculated. For example, a stearic acid molecule occupies about 20 square angstrom units (Fig. 7–5A).

By this method the thickness of the monolayer can also be measured. This depends on the number of carbons (25 Å for stearic acid). The monomolecular film can be deposited on the surface of a glass slide dipped into the water. As shown in Figure 7–5D, by successive dippings bimolecular or multimolecular layers can be built. It is interesting to observe that the polar groups of the molecules attract one another, as do the nonpolar groups, so that bimolecular layers similar to biologic membranes can be produced. Such a procedure has been used in the past to measure the thickness of the red cell membrane by comparing it under reflected light with molecular layers of barium stearate of known thickness. The optical apparatus used in this procedure—the *leptoscope*[13]—is now of little use since the electron microscope gives more direct information. By similar experiments multilayered systems can be obtained which give coherent x-ray diffractions from which the distance or period between the layers can be measured.

In mixed lipid systems in water the different components, including those of weaker polarity, such as cholesterol, are integrated in a single layer. However, as soon as the system dries, the phases separate, and each one gives a different x-ray diagram.

Myelin Figures. Interpretation of the Electron Microscope Image

Other interesting models of lipid films are the so-called *myelin figures*. If phospholipids extracted from brain or other tissues are mixed with water, the water

penetrates into the polar interfaces an gives rise to wormlike, concentric, sem liquid structures, which flow from th lipid phase. These structures have strong birefringence with the radiall oriented axis. The lipid molecules ar disposed in bimolecular layers attache by their nonpolar interfaces, while th polar endings are separated by layers c water, which may be several molecule thick (Fig. 7–6).

The myelin figures can be studied b x-ray diffraction and also fixed with os mium tetroxide and observed under th electron microscope.[14] These models ar of considerable interest for the inter pretation of the electron microscop image. The micrographs show alternat parallel light and dark bands, which re peat at approximately 40 Å. Since th electron microscope image depends o the electron scattering of the heav atoms present in the structure (Chap. 5) the dark bands should be attributed t the osmium deposits in this multilame

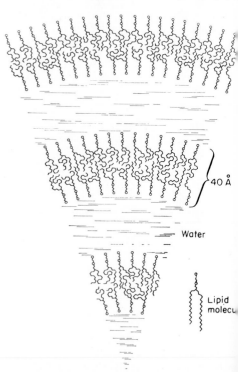

40 Å

Water

Lipid molecu

FIGURE 7–6. Molecular arrangements o lipids and water in a myelin figure. The pola groups are represented by circles. The width o the bimolecular lipid layers is approximately constant while the water layers change in widt with the degree of hydration of the specimen (Courtesy of W. Stoeckenius.)

ar structure. While it is known that OsO_4 reacts with the double bonds of insaturated lipids, evidence favors the view that most of the osmium is taken up by the polar groups of the lipids and thus the dense lines are generally interpreted as corresponding to the polar ends of these molecules.[14]

Probably the best interpretation of myelin figures comes from parallel studies with x-ray diffraction[15] and electron microscopy of phospholipid systems maintained at low water concentration and at 37° C. In this case, instead of disposing concentrically into lamellae, the lipid molecules are distributed in a hexagonal array with the small water channels forming thin cylinders. The electron microscope shows a similar pattern with the dense dots in the place of the water phase, thus indicating that osmium is bound to the polar groups.

More complex models of membrane structures can be made by incorporating some protein into the myelin figure. Under these conditions the image observed is similar, but with wider and denser bands bounding the lipid structures.

As shown in Figure 7–7B, a double layer of lipid coated on both sides with protein should give two parallel dense

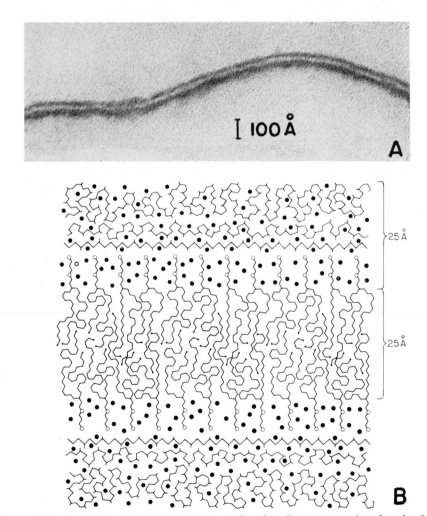

FIGURE 7–7.   **A,** electron micrograph of the smallest lamellar structure found in lipid-protein-water preparations. This is practically identical with the unit membrane structure seen in cell membranes (see Fig. 8–3). × 500,000. **B,** diagram showing the probable arrangement of lipid and protein molecules in such a membrane. Black dots indicate deposit of OsO_4, which would be mainly at the polar interfaces. (Courtesy of W. Stoeckenius.)

lines of 25 to 50 Å, separated by a lighter interspace of 20 to 25 Å, and this is actually observed (Fig. 7-7A).

Natural lipoprotein systems contain polar lipids, such as fatty acids, phospholipids, cerebrosides and gangliosides, and nonpolar lipids, such as glycerides and cholesterol esters. The association with the protein seems to be essentially with the polar lipids, which may be held by their polar groups (Fig. 7-7) forming hydrogen or ionic bonds, or by interaction of their nonpolar endings. The nonpolar lipids seem to be coordinated with the protein through their association with polar lipids.

GENERAL REFERENCES

Fernández-Morán, H. (1959) Fine structure of biological lamellar systems. In: *Biophysical science.* (Oncley, J. L., et al., eds.) John Wiley & Sons, New York, p. 319.

Frey-Wyssling, A. (1953) *Submicroscopic morphology of protoplasm and its derivatives.* Elsevier Co., New York.

Gross, J. (1961) Collagen. *Scient. Amer., 204* (5):120.

Hodge, A. J. (1959) Fibrous proteins of muscle. In: *Biophysical science.* (Oncley, J. L., et al., eds.) John Wiley & Sons, New York, p. 409.

Meyer, K. H., and Mark, H. (1950) *Makromolekularchemie.* Akademische. Verlagsgesellschaft, Leipzig.

Schmitt, F. O. (1959) Interaction properties of elongate protein macromolecules with particular reference to collagen (tropocollagen). In: *Biophysical science.* (Oncley, J. L., et al., eds.) John Wiley & Sons, New York, p. 349.

Sjöstrand, F. S. (1959) Fine structure of cytoplasm: The organization of membranous layers. In: *Biophysical science.* (Oncley, J. L., et al., eds.) John Wiley & Sons, New York, p. 301.

CITED REFERENCES

1. Doty, P., and Nishihara, T. (See Linderstrom-Lang, K. In: *Lane medical lectures,* 1951. Stanford University Press Stanford, Calif., 1952.)
2. Crick, F. H. C., and Rich, A. (1955) *Nature* 176:780.
3. Crick, F. H. C., and Rich, A. (1957) In *Recent advances in gelatine and glue research.* Pergamon Press, London, p. 20.
4. Schmitt, F. O., Gross, J., and Highberger, J. H. (1955) *Symp. Soc. Exp. Biol., 9* 148.
5. Schmitt, F. O. (1959) Interaction properties of elongate protein macromolecules with particular reference to collagen (tropocollagen). In: *Biophysical science.* (Oncley, J. L., et al., eds.) John Wiley & Sons, New York, p. 349.
6. Gross, J. (1961) *Scient. Amer., 204:*5, 120.
7. Hodge, A. J., and Schmitt, F. O. (1958) *Proc. Nat. Acad. Sci.* (*Wash.*), 44:418.
8. Hodge, A. J. (1959) Fibrous proteins of muscle. In: *Biophysical science.* (Oncley, J. L., et al., eds.) John Wiley & Sons, New York, p. 409.
9. Porter, K. R., and Hawn, C. V. A. (1949) *J. Exp. Med.,* 90:225.
10. De Robertis, E., Paseyro, P., and Reissig, M. (1953) *Blood, J. Hemat.,* 8:7.
11. Drochmans, P. (1962) *J. Ultrastruct. Res.* 6:141.
12. Drochmans, P. (1963) In: Methods of separation of subcellular structural components. *Biochem. Soc. Symp.,* 23:127.
13. Waugh, D. F., and Schmitt, F. O. (1940) *Cold Spr. Harb. Symp. Quant. Biol.,* 8. 233.
14. Stoeckenius, W. (1962) In: *The interpretation of ultrastructure.* (Harris, R. J. C. ed.) *Symp. Internat. Soc. Cell Biol.,* Vol 1, p. 349.
15. Luzzati, V. and Husson, F. (1962) *J. Cell Biol.,* 12:207.

CHAPTER 8

THE
PLASMA MEMBRANE

The cell is a unit that has a different internal milieu than that of the environment. For example, the ionic content of animal cells is very different from that of the circulating blood (Fig. 3–1). This difference is maintained throughout the life of the cell by the thin surface membrane, the *plasma membrane,* which controls the entrance and exit of molecules and ions. Other mechanisms of control involve parts of the whole protoplasm, and are particularly important in certain types of cells. The function of the plasma membrane of regulating the exchange between the cell and the medium—generally called *permeability*—is discussed in Chapter 20.

The plasma membrane is so thin that it cannot be resolved with the light microscope, but in some cells it is covered by thicker protective layers that are within the limits of microscopic resolution. For example, most plant cells have a thick cellulose wall that covers and protects the true plasma membrane (Fig. 2–4). Some animal cells are surrounded by cement-like substances that constitute visible cell walls. Such protective or adsorbed layers, also called *extraneous coats,* generally play no role in permeability, but have other important functions.

Indirect evidence of a plasma membrane in the living cell has been obtained by microsurgical experiments. If a cell that is not permeable to a dye put in the medium is injected with a dye by a micropipet, it becomes colored and the dye remains within the limits of the plasma membrane. If a cell is punctured by a microneedle, a lesion of the plasma membrane is produced, which can be repaired within certain limits. With more drastic injury, especially in the absence of calcium ions, the cytoplasm flows outside and the cell dies.

Under certain conditions a plasma membrane may readily become visible. For example, in a sea urchin egg, after penetration by a sperm, a membrane is separated from the surface, preventing other spermatozoa from penetrating the egg. By electron microscopy at this stage, numerous thin tubules have been observed in the cortical region of the egg. These tubules seem to contribute to the formation of a new plasma membrane (Fig. 8–1).[1]

THEORETICAL MOLECULAR STRUCTURE OF THE PLASMA MEMBRANE

Knowledge of the molecular structure of membranes comes mainly from the integration of data from chemical analysis; the study of different physicochemical properties of living cells; optical analysis with polarization microscopy and x-ray diffraction of multimembranous systems (e.g., myelin sheath); and electron microscopy at high resolution. Studies of monomolecular films and myelin figures have also been valuable (Chap. 7).

Theories on the molecular structure of the plasma membrane are generally based on indirect information. Since substances soluble in lipid solvents penetrate the plasma membrane easily, Overton postulated in 1902 that the plasma membrane is composed of a thin layer of lipid. In 1926, Gorter and Grendell found that the lipid content of hemolyzed erythrocytes was sufficient to form a continuous layer 30 to 40 Å thick over the entire surface, and postulated that the plasma membrane is composed of a

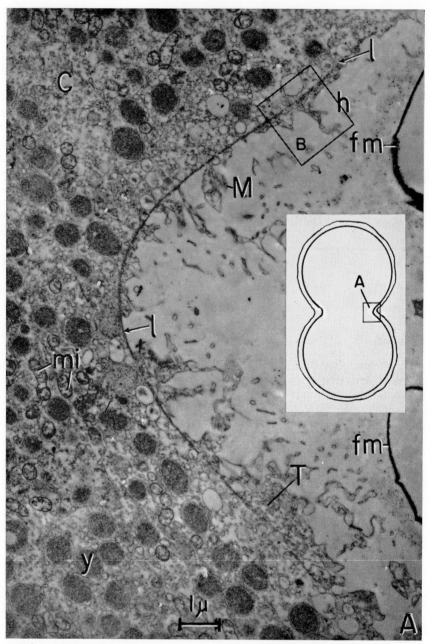

Figure 8–1. Electron micrograph of a sea urchin egg during telophase. The zone indicated in the inset corresponds to the vicinity of the dividing ring. *C*, cytoplasm of the egg with yolk granules (*y*), mitochondria (*mi*) and vacuoles; *fm*, fertilization membrane; *h*, hyaline layer; *l*, membrane formed below the plasma membrane; *M*, microvillus; *T*, tubules. (Courtesy of E. H. Mercer and L. Wolpert.)

double layer of lipid molecules. This theory was also supported by electrical measurements that indicated a high impedance at the plasma membrane.[2] For example, impedance in the squid giant axon is 1000 ohms per square centimeter. This high impedance is due to the fact that it is difficult for ions to penetrate a lipid layer. Also supporting the theory are experiments with lipolytic agents, such as lipid solvents (e.g., benzene or carbon tetrachloride), digitonin and the enzyme lecithinase, which hydrolyzes lecithin.[3]

The evidences for the presence of protein in the cell membrane are also multiple. For example, the membrane's elasticity and mechanical ability to expand and contract could be due to fibrous proteins.[4]

Other indirect information about the molecular structure of the plasma membrane comes from the study of the interfacial tension of different cells. Tension at a water-oil interface is about 10 to 15 dynes per centimeter, but the surface tension of cells is almost nil. For example, by centrifuging a sea urchin egg until the elongated cell breaks into two halves, the surface tension has been calculated to be 0.2 dyne/cm. Values of 0.1 have been found for erythrocytes and of 0.45 for a slime mold. By compressing eggs or other cells with a flat, gold ribbon, a very low surface tension (0.08 dyne/cm.) has been recorded. It has been postulated that the low tension is due to the presence of protein layers on the lipid components. In fact, when a very small amount of protein is added to a model lipid-water system, the surface tension is lowered comparably.

Other evidence comes from experiments on the action of lytic agents. For example, animal cells injected into a different species act as antigens and stimulate the production of antibodies in the serum, which can cause lysis of the cell membranes. In this case the action is against the proteins and carbohydrates in cell membranes.[5]

To explain all these facts the theory has been proposed that the membrane is composed of a *lipid layer* with protein adhering to both lipid-aqueous interfaces.[6] Figure 8–2 shows a recent model in which the existence of pores in the membrane is postulated. The lipid layer is bimolecular, with the polar groups situated at the lipid-aqueous interface, while the nonpolar groups are adjacent to each other. The polypeptide chains of the protein molecules are perpendicular to the lipid molecules. It is postulated that this protein layer is composed of a mesh of long, parallel molecules at the interface with nonpolar groups directed toward the lipid phase and polar groups directed toward the aqueous phase. Although the plasma membrane is delicate, its elasticity and relative mechanical resistance are attributed to the presence of these protein layers, which are thought to maintain the cohesion of the different parts of the plasma membrane.

The model shown in Figure 8–2 is similar to that prepared by the interaction of phospholipids and proteins (Fig. 7–7). As shown in the following section, electron microscopy has also supported this model of the plasma membrane, at least in its general architecture. How-

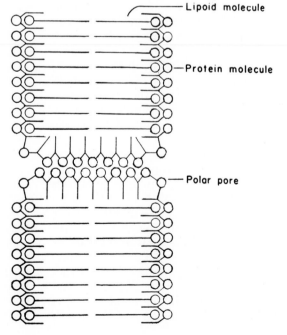

FIGURE 8–2. Diagram of the cell membrane. (From Danielli, 1954: *Colston Papers*, 7:1.)

ever, finer details of structure, such as water-filled pores, postulated to explain certain permeability properties and the exact relationship of the different lipid molecules to specific proteins is still not amenable to direct investigation.

Electron Microscopy of the Plasma Membrane

Electron microscopy has thrown some light on the fine structure of the plasma membrane and has revealed the numerous structural differentiations that this membrane and the underlying cell cytoplasm have in different cell types. In early observations of cultured cells a definite boundary at the periphery of the cytoplasm was resolved but not a particular structure (Fig. 10–1). To resolve the particular structure, extremely thin sections ($\sim$ 200 Å) must be used, otherwise one would observe different orientations of the plasma membrane with respect to the plane of section. The membrane appears most thin when it is exactly perpendicular to the plane of the section. With the increase in resolution afforded by this technique, definite plasma membranes of 60 to 100 Å have been observed at the surface of all cells. The plasma membranes of two cells that are in close contact appear as dense lines separated by a space of 110 to 150 Å, which is strikingly uniform and contains a material of low electron density. This intercellular component can be considered as a kind of cementing substance. By changing the tonicity of the medium, this space can be narrowed or widened.[7] As will be shown later, the plasma membranes of adjacent cells may be totally adherent at certain points, forming the so-called tight junctions.

With improved preparative techniques and higher microscopic resolution the plasma membrane of most types of cells appears three-layered. Each of the three layers is about 25 Å; the middle layer is less dense than the other two.[8] This structure, called the "unit membrane," is also found in most intracellular membranes.[7] This basic three-layered structure has been generally confirmed, and with improved techniques, differences in thickness and asymmetry of the layers

have been observed in various membrane types.[9] Some finer details have also become apparent, such as small discontinuities at the dense layers and, particularly, bridges across the light central layer, which suggest fine pores (Fig. 8–3).

The electron microscope image of the membrane was interpreted in Chapter 7 in relation to the study of artificial lipoprotein models. Other information regarding the molecular structure of the cell membrane comes from the study of some natural multilayered lipoprotein systems, such as the myelin sheath and outer segments of the retinal rods and cones.

The Myelin Sheath

The myelin sheath is a lipoprotein membrane that surrounds the axon, or axis-cylinder, of the nerve fiber. In peripheral nerves this sheath is formed by the Schwann cells that are found at each internode (the distance between two Ranvier nodes). In central nerves the myelin sheath is produced by the activity of the oligodendroglial cells.

It has been known for over a century that the myelin sheath has a strong birefringence, which indicates a high degree of organization at a submicroscopic level. The birefringence is radially oriented and negative with respect to the fiber axis. Studies with lipid solvents have led to the suggestion that the protein and lipid layers are wrapped concentrically around the axon. According to this concept, the myelin sheath is a liquid crystalline structure formed by bimolecular layers of lipid oriented radially and with alternating concentric layers of protein, as shown in Figure 8–4.

Further studies of the myelin sheath with x-ray diffraction have revealed a spacing of 170 Å in amphibian and 180 to 185 Å in mammalian peripheral nerves.[10] Within this period, the proportion corresponding to the lipid, protein and water content has been estimated. Several diagrams have been used to postulate the molecular arrangement. The lipid composition is represented approximately by the ratio 2:2:1 for phospholipid, cholesterol and cerebrosides.[11]

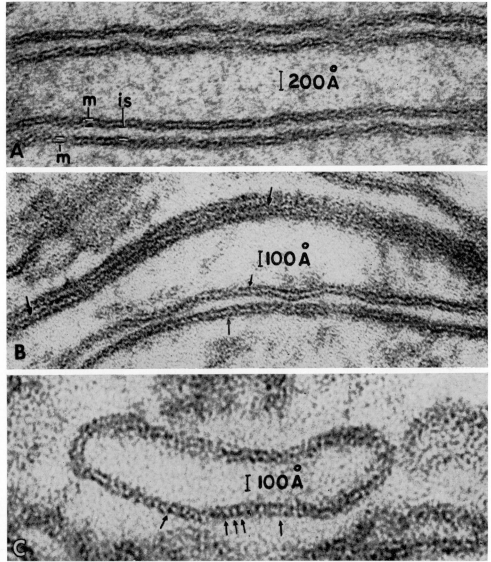

FIGURE 8–3. **A,** electron micrograph of cell membranes of intestinal cells (*m*), showing the three-layered structure (unit membrane). *is,* intercellular space. ×240,000. **B,** cell membranes in the rat hypothalamus showing the unit membrane structure and, with arrows, some finer details across the membrane. The upper arrows indicate a region in which the two cell membranes are adherent (*tight junction*) and the intercellular space has disappeared. ×360,000. **C,** the same as **B,** showing fine bridges (arrows) across the unit membrane. ×380,000. (From E. De Robertis.)

Electron microscope studies have confirmed that myelin has a multilayered membranous structure. With fixation in osmium tetroxide, a repeating period of about 120 Å has been observed. There is a very dense line of 30 Å and a thin and discontinuous band at half the period (Fig. 8–5).

The direct study of the molecular organization of myelin with the electron microscope suffers from the lack of specific methods for the demonstration of

the chemical components of the lipoprotein system. As explained, although osmium tetroxide has a very complex mechanism of action in the tissue, in the lipoprotein system it is mainly deposited at the lipoprotein boundary. Thus in the myelin sheath the heavily osmophilic band of 30 Å can be interpreted as representing a lipoprotein interface (Fig. 7–7B).

By a histochemical method based on anionic chromium, which preserves and

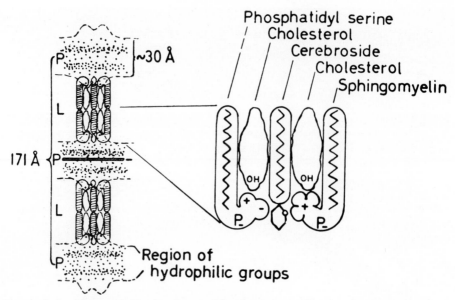

FIGURE 8–4. Diagram indicating the possible relationships of lipid molecules within the structural unit of the myelin sheath. (Courtesy of J. B. Finean.)

binds phosphatides preferentially, the chemical organization of myelin can be analyzed at a molecular level.[12] With this technique, two dense layers containing phospholipids are found within the total period. A possible molecular interpretation based on these observations is shown in Figure 8–6.

The myelin sheath in nerve conduction seems to function as an insulator, preventing the dissipation of energy into the surrounding medium. In peripheral nerve fibers it has been suggested that the nerve impulse is renewed or "boosted" at each node of Ranvier (saltatory conduction), whereas at the internode it is conducted electrotonically. The myelin sheath might act not only as a dielectric (insulating) material but also as a kind of resonant conductor in which the energy waves resonating in the lipid layers between the protein membranes could pass with maximum speed and minimum loss of energy.[13] (See Chapter 22.)

Retinal Rods and Cones

The retinal rods and cones are highly differentiated cells that have at their outermost segment a lipoprotein structure that is specialized for photoreception. Studies with the polarization microscope have revealed that the outer segments have a positive uniaxial birefringence, which changes to negative upon extraction with lipid solvents. These results suggest a submicroscopic organization consisting of transversely oriented protein layers alternating with lipid molecules arranged longitudinally along the axis of the photoreceptor. This type of layered organization has been demonstrated by electron microscopy in fragmented rod outer segments[14] and in thin sections of the retina.[15] These observations indicate that the rod consists of a pile of superimposed disks (several hundred) along the axis. These disks are really flattened sacs[16] made of two membranes 30 to 40 Å thick, which surround a thin space of 30 Å and become continuous at the edges (Fig. 8–7). The space between the rod sacs is 50 to 120 Å. The cone outer segments, with minor differences, have a similar structure.[17]

Rod sacs are highly sensitive to osmotic change. In hypotonic solutions they swell considerably, and the inner space between the membranes becomes very large.

Our knowledge of the submicroscopic structure of cones and rods is based mainly on fixation with osmium tetroxide (Fig. 8–7). The use of anionic chromium for the detection of phosphatides under the electron microscope permits the localization of the lipid layers (Fig. 8–8).

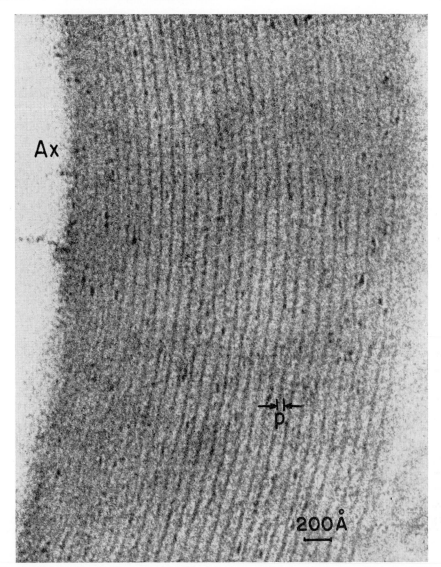

Figure 8–5. Electron micrograph of the myelin sheath of the sciatic nerve of an amphibian. The main period of 100 Å is formed by the dense line *p*. *Ax*, axon. ×340,000. (From De Robertis and Lasansky.[12])

Comparison of the electron microscope images obtained with both techniques show that they are complementary, which indicates the alternation of lipid and protein molecules within a very compact macromolecular organization. (The morphogenesis of the outer segment of the rods and cones is discussed in Chapter 21.)

Photoreceptors transform light energy into another type of energy that can be conducted as nerve impulses. This process is based on a cycle of chemical reactions, which involve the visual pigments present in the protein membranes of the rod and cone sacs. This multilayered structure is a very effective system that facilitates the maximum absorption and utilization of light by the chromophoric groups present in the visual pigments (retinenes). The acute sensitivity of the photoreceptors, which can react to a single photon, can be explained by the fact that the chances of striking a sensitive molecule is increased by a factor of hundreds or thousands by the molecular organization of the photoreceptor. As in the myelin sheath and the chloroplasts, the layers may act as resonating conductors facilitating the interaction between the chemical pigment stored in the layers and the incident radiation (Chap. 12).

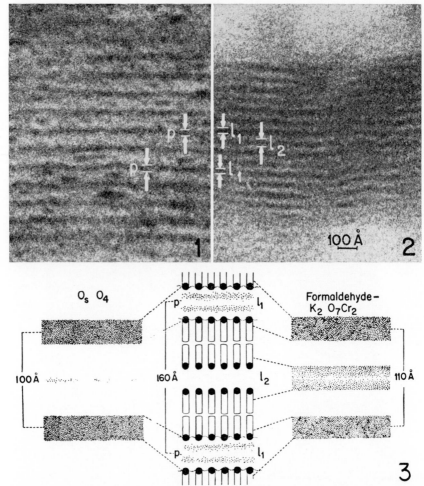

FIGURE 8–6.   Electron photomicrographs of the myelin sheath of the optic nerve of an amphibian. **1,** fixed with osmium tetroxide; **2,** fixed with formalin dichromate for the electron staining of phospholipids, ×690,000; **3,** molecular diagram interpreting these observations. (See the description in the text.) (From De Robertis and Lasansky.[12])

DIFFERENTIATIONS AT THE CELL SURFACE

Light microscope observations have revealed that parts of the cell surface of certain cells are related to absorption, secretion, fluid transport and other physiologic processes. Electron microscopy has permitted a much better analysis and interpretation of these cell differentiations and numerous specializations of the cell surface have been recognized.[18, 19] Topographically they are described as: specializations of the cell surface, specializations of contact surfaces between cells and specializations of the cell base.

Figure 8–9A is a diagram of a three-dimensional view of an epithelial cell of the proximal convoluted tubule of the kidney. All three types of differentiation can be observed. At the surface are slender processes called *microvilli,* which are the structural units of the so-called *brush* border seen in the light microscope. The left edge of the cell is in contact with another cell by means of a *terminal bar* or point of strong adhesion. At the cell base, numerous infoldings of the plasma membrane penetrate deep into the cell cytoplasm.

The so-called *striated border* of the intestine, another example of specialization at the free surface (Fig. 8–10), was described over a century ago as a homogeneous layer and regarded as a protective cuticle. Later its finely striated structure was recognized but could not be

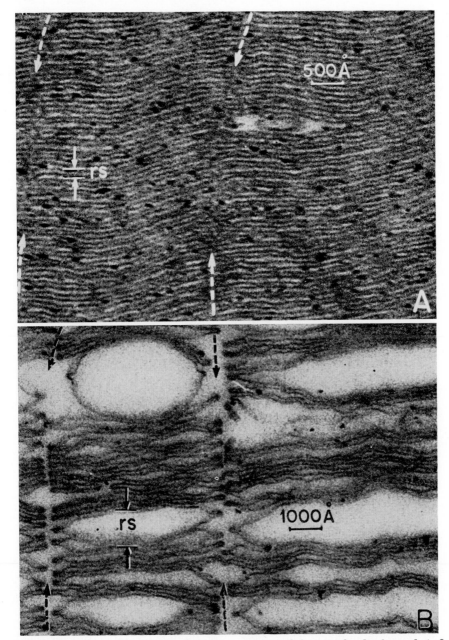

FIGURE 8–7.   Electron micrographs of the outer segment of the retinal rods of a toad. **A,** fixation with isotonic osmium tetroxide maintains the regular organization of the retinal sacs, ×190,000; **B,** fixation with hypotonic osmium tetroxide (Palade's method) produces great swelling of the sacs and separation of the membranes. (From De Robertis and Lasansky.[12])

interpreted. Electron microscope studies, begun in 1950, have since revealed its true structure. As shown in Figure 8–9B, the striated border consists of microvilli 0.6 to 0.8 μ long and only 1000 Å in diameter. These microvilli are dense cytoplasmic processes covered by the plasma membrane, which has the complex fine structure described at the beginning of this chapter. They increase the effective surface of absorption. A single cell may have as many as 3000 microvilli, and in a square millimeter of intestine there may be 200,000,000. The narrow spaces between the microvilli form a kind of sieve through which submicroscopic fat globules have been observed to pass during absorption (Fig. 20–10).

Numerous other cells have microvilli,

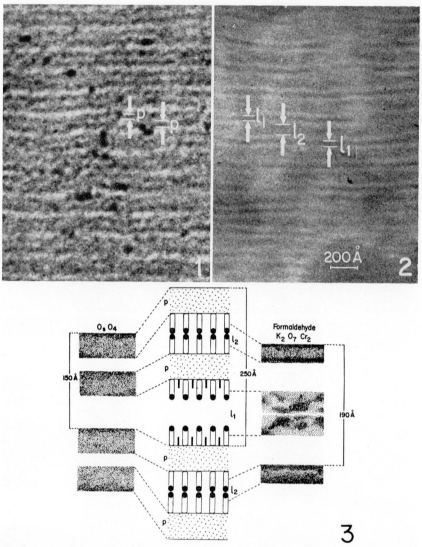

FIGURE 8–8.   1, electron micrograph of retinal sacs of the rod similar to those shown in Figure 8–7A but at higher magnification, ×370,000. Fixation in osmium tetroxide shows the localization of protein in the membranous sacs. 2, fixation with formol dichromate shows lipid layers l_1 and l_2. 3, molecular diagram representing one of the possible interpretations. (From De Robertis and Lasansky.[12])

although fewer in number. They have been found in mesothelial cells, in the epithelial cells of the gallbladder, uterus and yolk sac, in hepatic cells, and so forth.

The *brush border* of the kidney tubule is similar to the striated border, although of larger dimensions. An amorphous substance between the microvilli gives a periodic acid–Schiff reaction for polysaccharides. Between the microvilli, at the base, the cell membrane invaginates into the apical cytoplasm (Fig. 8–9A). These invaginations are apparently pathways by which large quantities

of fluid enter by a process similar to pinocytosis. (Other specializations of the cell surface, such as cilia and flagella, are studied in Chapter 21.)

Cells in contact with each other give rise to several different types of specialization. The so-called *desmosomes* found in a number of epithelial cells are depicted in Figure 8–9C, D. Under the light microscope they appear as darkly stained bodies at the midpoint of what was once interpreted as an intercellular bridge. Fine *tonofibrils* converge upon the desmosome and were thought to pass through the bridge. The electron mi-

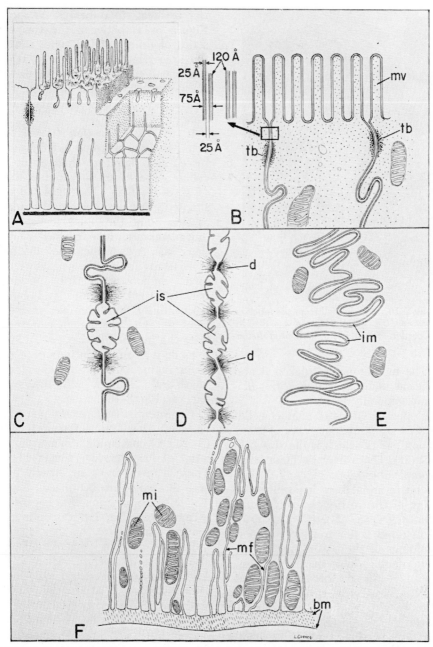

FIGURE 8–9. General diagram of some of the differentiations of the plasma membrane and the intercellular relationships (see the description in the text). *bm*, basement membrane; *d*, desmosome; *im*, interdigitating membranes; *is*, intercellular space; *mi*, mitochondria; *mf*, membrane folds; *mv*, microvilli; *tb*, terminal bar.

croscope shows that there is no real continuity between the cells (Fig. 8–11). The desmosomes are local thickenings of the opposing membranes from which fine filaments radiate into the cytoplasm. Frequently there are regions of looser contact between the desmosomes and even real intercellular spaces for free circulation of fluids (Fig. 8–9C, D).

Desmosomes have been observed in numerous epithelial cells, and in each case have shown particular characteristics.

The so-called *terminal bars* are generally found at the interface between columnar cells just below the free surface (Figs. 8–9B and 8–11). Under the electron microscope the terminal bar appears somewhat similar to the desmo-

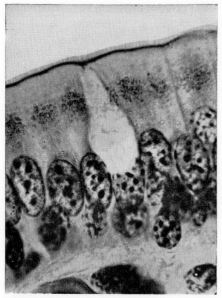

FIGURE 8–10. Goblet cell from the intestine of *Ambystoma*. The other cells show a definite striated border. Staining method: iron hematoxylin.

some. The membrane is thickened and the adjacent material is dense, but filaments are generally lacking.

Other specializations of contact cellular surfaces are numerous types of interdigitations, one of which is illustrated in Figure 8–9E. These may be made even more complex by the presence of desmosomes and terminal bars in addition to the fitting of the corrugated surfaces.

At the *cell base* of certain cells involved in rapid water transport numerous infoldings of the plasma membrane penetrate deeply into the cell (Figs. 8–9F, 8–12). In a three-dimensional view, these folds form septa that subdivide the basal cytoplasm into narrow compartments containing large mitochondria. It is presumed that these membranes contain enzymes involved in transport mechanisms and that they are in close proximity to the energy-yielding enzyme systems present in mitochondria (Fig. 8–9F).

Junctional Complex

With improved techniques it has been observed that cell contact in different epithelial tissues of animals is specially differentiated, apparently to create a bar-

rier or "seal" to diffusion. As shown in Figure 8–11, between the two cells a series of differentiated zones start from the apical region and form a tripartite junctional complex with the following components: the tight junction, the intermediary junction and the desmosome.[20]

In the *tight junction* (zonula occludens) the adjacent cell membranes have fused, and therefore there is no intercellular space for a variable distance (Fig. 8–11, *1–2*). The tight junction is situated just below the apical border and at this point the outer leaflets of the unit membranes fuse in a single intermediary line. A continuous belt-like attachment forms around the cell. Experiments have demonstrated the relationship between tight junctions and epithelial permeability. For example, macromolecules put into the lumen cannot penetrate the intercellular space. Tight junctions may also play an important role in brain permeability at the level of the blood-brain barrier and the synaptic barrier (Fig. 8–13).

The *intermediary junction* (zonula adhaerens) has an intercellular space (~ 200 Å) containing an amorphous material of low density (Fig. 8–11, *2–3*). The cell membranes are strictly parallel and the adjacent cytoplasm is dense. This intermediary junction is continuous in most epithelia, but discontinuous in some.

The *desmosome* (macula adhaerens) also has an intercellular space (~ 240 Å) containing a central disc or line (Fig. 8–11, *4–5*). At this point there is a plaque of dense material in the cytoplasm of both cells into which fine cytoplasmic fibrils converge. Desmosomes are discontinuous attachments as are the other zones of the complex.

CHEMICAL COMPOSITION OF THE PLASMA MEMBRANE. GANGLIOSIDES

Most information on the chemical composition of the plasma membrane comes from the study of red cell envelopes[21] and bacteria membranes.[22] After hemolysis of the erythrocyte in

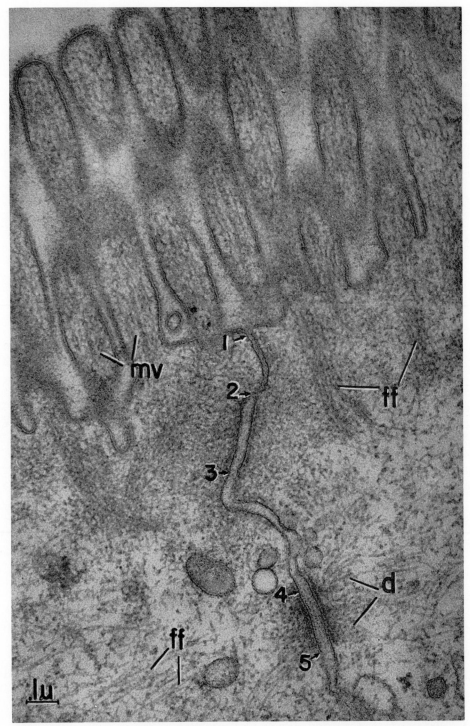

Figure 8–11. Electron micrograph showing the apical region of contact between two intestinal cells. *1–2*, tight junction; *2–3*, intermediary junction; *4–5*, desmosome. (See the description in the text.) *d*, desmosome: *ff*, fine filaments in the matrix; *mv*, microvilli. ×96,000. (Courtesy of M. Farquhar and G. E. Palade.[20])

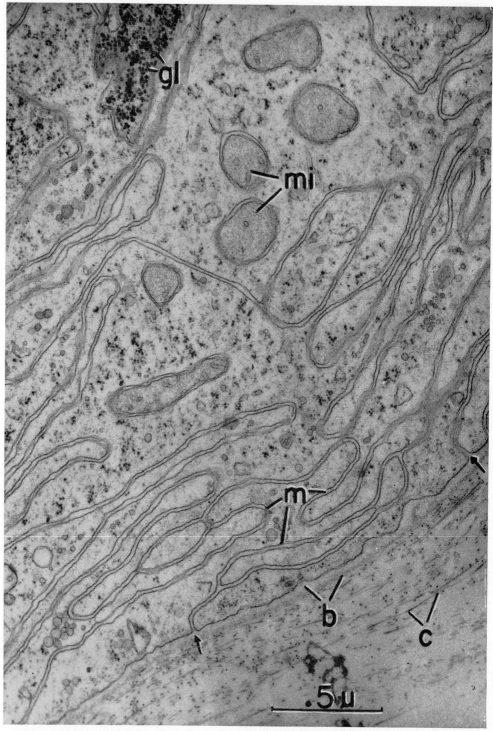

FIGURE 8–12. Electron micrograph of the basal region of a Müller cell of the toad showing numerous infoldings of the basal cell membrane (*m*). Arrows indicate openings of the intermembranal space at the base. *b*, basement membrane; *c*, collagen fibrils; *gl*, glycogen; *mi*, mitochondria. ×60,000. (Courtesy of A. Lasansky.)

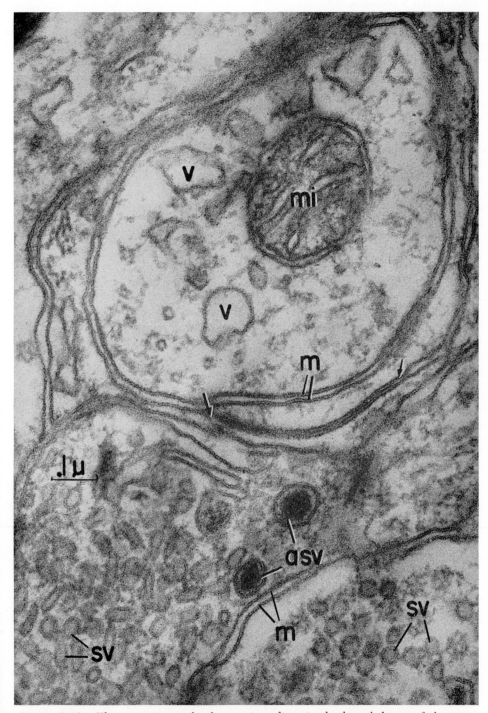

FIGURE 8–13.   Electron micrograph of synaptic endings in the hypothalamus of the rat. *asv*, adrenergic synaptic vesicle; *m*, cell membrane; *mi*, mitochondrion; *sv*, synaptic vesicle; *v*, vacuoles. Note that the membranes of all these components show the unit structure with a triple layered organization. Notice between the arrows the tight junction that surrounds a synaptic ending. ×135,000. (From E. De Robertis.)

a hypotonic solution a thin envelope or "ghost" is left which is composed almost exclusively of the plasma membrane (Fig. 8–14). Biochemical analysis of masses of ghosts gives a lipid-protein ratio of 1.0 to 1.7. The protein component, called stromatin, is acidic and fibrous and has a high molecular weight. The main lipid components are phospholipids (55 to 75 per cent), of which lecithin and cephalin predominate. Cholesterol is present in 15 to 32 per cent. There are about 75 to 90 lipid molecules per protein molecule.

Recently considerable importance has been given to the presence of *gangliosides* in cell membranes. These have a hydrophobic chain, as in the phospholipids, but the polar portion is long and terminates in *neuraminic acid* (sialic acid), which has a free carboxyl group (Fig. 3–11). The polar end also contains N-acetylgalactosamine, galactose and glucose.[23, 24] The negative charge of the cell surface has been related to the concentration of terminal ends of neuraminic acid. After mild hydrolysis with

a specific neuraminidase, neuraminic acid is removed from the living cells and the negative surface charge is decreased. Such experiments indicate that gangliosides are important structural components of some cell membranes. Apart from providing ionogenic carboxyl groups at the cell surface, neuraminic acid is a component of certain surface antigens for viruses and toxins. Gangliosides are important constituents of the neuronal surface membrane, and are probably involved in ionic transfers.[25, 26]

EXTRANEOUS COATS OF THE CELL MEMBRANE. GLYCOPROTEINS

At the beginning of this chapter the *extraneous coats* surrounding certain cell membranes were mentioned. These are very conspicuous in eggs of marine animals and in amphibia. A *mucin* of glycoprotein nature is the main constituent. Mucins also cover and protect the cell surface lining the gastrointestinal tract.

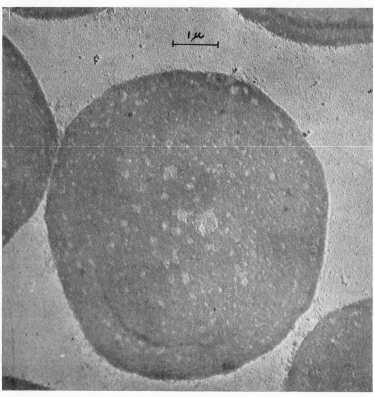

FIGURE 8–14.   Electron micrograph of a cell membrane from a human erythrocyte after hemolysis. Shadow-cast with palladium. ×11,800.

Polysaccharides constitute the *pectin* and *cellulose* of plant cell walls and the *chitin* of crustacea.

At the base of most epithelial cells, in capillaries and also in many intercellular spaces glycoproteins and polysaccharides in the form of hyaluronic acid are found. Recently the name *glycocalyx*[27] has been coined to designate the glycoprotein and polysaccharide covering that surrounds many cells.

These coats are considered as sloughed off by-products of the cell surface. They are not absolutely necessary for cell integrity, but, as is shown later, they are involved in the association between tissue cells. The following functions can be attributed to these coats:

Immunologic Properties. At the surface of mammalian cells are specific genetically determined substances corresponding to the A, B, and O blood groups. These substances are firmly bound to the surface of erythrocytes and contain different carbohydrates in addition to amino acids.[28] (The possible role of hexose-containing gangliosides as antigens for viruses and toxins was mentioned in the preceding section.)

Filtration Properties. The extracellular coats that surround many vertebrate capillaries, especially the kidney glomerulus, act as a filter and regulate the passage of molecules according to size. Hyaluronate in connective tissue may control diffusion.

Maintenance of the Microenvironment of the Cell. These extraneous coats can affect the concentration of different substances at the surface of the cell, not only functioning as diffusion barriers but also affecting the cationic environment of the cell because of their charge. In this respect they are similar to exchange resins used in chemistry. For example, a muscle cell with its excitable plasma membrane is surrounded by a glycocalyx that can trap sodium ions. Certain components, such as hyaluronate, can change drastically the electrical charge and pH at the cell surface. Because of this, enzymes present at the plasma membrane may change their activity while they are kept in the microenvironment of the cell.[24]

CELL DISSOCIATION AND REASSOCIATION

The cell surface with the described differentiations of the plasma membrane and the extraneous coats is intimately related to the specific association of cells to form tissues. It is also involved in the morphogenetic movements and inductions of embryonic development.[29]

In 1908, Wilson described how living sponges forced through a fine silk mesh disaggregate into isolated motile cells, and then, upon standing, reaggregate to form fresh sponges. In this way sponges with cells of different colors could be mixed into new associations. Much later it was found that embryonic tissues treated with trypsin dissociate into individual cells and then reaggregate to form the specific patterns of the original tissue.[30] Since trypsin acts on certain peptide linkages, it is supposed that the association of cells depends on some surface coating containing such linkages. It has been suggested that cells produce some sort of colloidal exudate that may act as a guiding factor.[31] A mucoidal material appears around cells treated with trypsin.

The process of reaggregation depends on the motility of cells. If all the cells of a chick embryo are dissociated with trypsin and allowed to stand they will reaggregate, but this process can be enhanced by a controlled motion of the cells to increase the random collisions. When similar cells collide, they attach to each other, forming aggregates that are characteristic for a given cell population, e.g., retinal cells, kidney or bone.[32]

The process of reaggregation is not species-specific. If cells of chick and mouse embryos are mixed, they reaggregate mainly according to the cell population rather than the species. (Reaggregation does not take place in the absence of calcium ions or if the treatment used to disaggregate the tissue selectively blocks certain carbohydrates and glycoproteins.)

The mechanism by which a cell can "recognize" and aggregate with another of similar kind takes place at the cell surface, but its intimate nature is un-

126   PART THREE — STRUCTURAL BASES OF THE CELL

known. It has been suggested that the surface of the cell is highly ordered in the tangential direction and that this is reflected in the spatial organization of ionized acid groups that bind Ca^{++} and Mg^{++}.[33] The surface material of the adjacent cells may have a molecular fit of reactive groupings. Names such as "mutual recognition" in cell populations, "surface coding" and "preferential affinities" have been used to explain the mechanism, and immunochemical interactions have been postulated.[34] The properties and biochemical constitution of the cell surface and the specific enzymes at the surface are of increasing interest in cell biology, and this rapidly expanding field is now called *ectobiology.*

GENERAL REFERENCES

Davson, H., and Danielli, J. F. (1943) *The permeability of natural membranes.* Cambridge University Press, London.

Fawcett, D. W. (1958) Structural specialization of the cell surface. In: *Frontiers in cytology.* (Palay, S. L., ed.) Yale University Press, New Haven, Conn.

Harris, E. J. (1957) Transport through biological membranes. *Amer. Rev. Physiol., 19:*13.

Heilbrunn, L. V. (1952) *An outline of general physiology.* 3rd Ed. W. B. Saunders Co., Philadelphia.

Robertson, J. D. (1959) The ultrastructure of cell membranes and their derivatives. *Biochem. Soc. Symp., 16:*3.

Ussing, H. H. (1949) Transport of ions across cellular membranes. *Physiol. Rev., 29:*127.

Ussing, H. H. (1957) General principles and theories of membrane transport. In: *Metabolic aspects of transport across cell membranes.* (Murphy, R. R., ed.) University of Wisconsin Press, Madison, Wis.

CITED REFERENCES

1. Mercer, E. H., and Wolpert, L. (1958) *Exp. Cell Res., 14:*629.
2. Cole, K. S., and Curtis, H. J. (1938) *J. Gen. Physiol., 22:*37.
3. Ponder, E. (1953) *J. Gen. Physiol., 36:*723.
4. Mitchison, J. M., and Swann, M. M. (1954) *J. Exp. Biol., 31:*443.
5. Danielli, J. F. (1952) *Symp. Soc. Exp. Biol., 6:*1.
6. Danielli, J. F., and Harvey, E. N. (1934) *J. Cell. Comp. Physiol., 5:*483.

7. Robertson, J. D. (1959) *Biochem. Soc. Symp., 16:*3.
8. Zetterquist, H. (1956) *The ultrastructure organization of the columnar epithelic cells of mouse intestine.* Thesis, Karolinska Institute, Stockholm.
9. Sjöstrand, F. S. (1963) *Nature, 199:*1262.
10. Schmitt, F. O., Bear, R. S., and Palmer, K. J. (1941) *J. Cell. Comp. Physiol., 18:*31.
11. Finean, J. B. (1957) *Acta Neurol. Psychiat. Belg., 5:*462.
12. De Robertis, E., and Lasansky, A. (1961) Ultrastructure and chemical organization of photoreceptors. In: *The structure of the eye.* (Smelser, G. K., ed.) Academic Press, New York.
13. Engström, A., and Finean, J. B. (1958) *Biological ultrastructure.* Academic Press, New York.
14. Sjöstrand, F. S. (1949) *J. Cell. Comp. Physiol., 33:*383.
15. Sjöstrand, F. S. (1953) *Experientia, 9:*68.
16. De Robertis, E. (1956) *J. Biophys. Biochem. Cytol., 2:*319.
17. De Robertis, E., and Lasansky, A. (1958) *J. Biophys. Biochem. Cytol., 4:*743.
18. Sjöstrand, F. S. (1956) *Internat. Rev. Cytol. 5:*455.
19. Fawcett, D. (1958) Structural specializations of the cell surface. In: *Frontiers in cytology.* (Palay, S. L., ed.) Yale University Press, New Haven, Conn.
20. Farquhar, M., and Palade, G. E. (1963) *J. Cell Biol., 17:*375.
21. Parpart, A. K., and Ballentine, R. (1952) Molecular anatomy of the red plasma membrane. In: *Modern trends in physiology and biochemistry.* (Barrón, E. S. G., ed.) Academic Press, New York.
22. Miles, A. A., and Pirie, N. W. (1950) *The nature of the bacterial surface.* Charles C Thomas, Springfield, Ill.
23. Hoelzi-Wallach, D. F., and Eylar, E. H. (1961) *Biochim. Biophys. Acta, 52:*594.
24. Weiss, L. (1963) *Biochem. Soc. Symp., 22:* 32.
25. Bogoch, S. (1957) *Nature, 180:*197.
26. Balakrishnan, S., and McIlwain, H. (1961) *Biochem. J., 81:*72.
27. Bennett, H. S. (1963) *J. Histochem. Cytochem., 11:*14.
28. Kabat, E. A., and Mayer, M. A. (1958) *Experimental immunochemistry.* Charles C Thomas, Springfield, Ill.
29. Experimental Cell Research, suppl. 8. (1961) Academic Press, New York.
30. Moscona, A. (1957) *Proc. Nat. Acad. Sci. (Wash.), 43:*184.
31. Weiss, P. (1961) *Exp. Cell Res., 8:*260.
32. Moscona, A. (1962) *J. Cell. Comp. Physiol., 60:*65.
33. Steinberg, M. S. (1962) *Exp. Cell Res., 28:* 1.
34. Burnet, F. M. (1961) *Science, 133:*307.

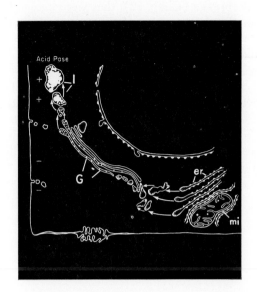

PART FOUR

THE
CYTOPLASM
AND
CYTOPLASMIC
ORGANOIDS

In the following four chapters the structural, biochemical and physiological characteristics of the cytoplasm and its main organoids are studied. The discussion is based on the latest studies of electron microscopy, cytochemistry and structural evolution of biologic systems.

Chapter 9 is a discussion of the structure and function of the basic cytoplasm, which comprises the matrix, which is the true internal milieu of the cell capable of carrying on biosynthesis, and the ribosomes, which are the fundamental ribonucleoprotein structures capable of carrying on protein synthesis. Related to the latter are the polyribosomes, the active form of ribosomes. Some concepts that are of historical interest, such as the Golgi apparatus and the ergastoplasm, are discussed in relation to the new concepts brought forth by electron microscopy.

Chapter 10 is a discussion of the cytoplasmic vacuolar system, which comprises the nuclear envelope, the endoplasmic reticulum and the Golgi complex. Combining electron microscopy, cell fractionation methods and biochemical analysis has proved to be a most valuable approach to the investigation of the structure and function of intracellular membranes. The vacuolar system subdivides the cytoplasm into several compartments that function independently. It is postulated that this system interchanges, circulates and segregates the products that are absorbed by the cell or that are synthesized on the ribosomes. Some of these products may be prepared for export (i.e., secretion) out of the cell. Investigation of the functions of the vacuolar system is one of the fields of cell

127

biology that has been greatly influenced by cytochemistry and electron micros
copy and in which the change of thought has been considerable.

Equally important have been the studies of the cytoplasmic organoids, such
as mitochondria (Chap. 11) and chloroplasts (Chap. 12), that were known from
light microscopy. The structural-functional integration of these organoids within
their intimate chemical and molecular organization is admirable. Reference is
made also to the plant cell wall and to some special characteristics of the cyto
plasmic components of the plant cell (Chap. 12).

In general terms, most of the metabolic and biosynthetic functions of the
cell occur in the cytoplasm. The cytoplasm is differentiated through the activity
of the genes contained in the nucleus and becomes adapted to the division of
cellular work. It may show cell differentiations, such as myofibrils, neurotubules
and tonofibrils. Therefore, in different cells the cytoplasm may be highly differ
ent while the nucleus appears to be comparatively uniform.

CHAPTER 9

THE CYTOPLASMIC MATRIX AND RIBOSOMES

At present our concepts of the structure of the cytoplasm are changing considerably. For example, the previously popular terms "ground substance," "hyaloplasm," "ergastoplasm" and "Golgi apparatus," refer to cytoplasmic areas that have been identified by observation with the light microscope or by some special local staining properties of the cytoplasm. They are not well-defined components of the cell, such as the organoids, which have been demonstrated with improved instruments and techniques. To comprehend the emerging concepts, keep in mind the preceding discussions on the evolution of cellular structures while studying the historical notes that are presented in this chapter.

In discussing the minimal mass of living matter in Chapter 1, it was stated that between the lower organisms, the prokaryotic cells, which lack a true nucleus, and the eukaryotic cells, which have a true nucleus, there are several intermediary forms. The evolution of cellular structure between the two extremes is depicted in the diagrams of Figures 1–2 and 2–5, in which the smallest living microbe and a cell from a higher organism are represented. At first glance the differences are extraordinary, but if one considers both structures at the same level of organization, the similarities are also notable. For example, most of the cytoplasm of the cell has the same components as the microbe. The basic molecular fabric of the primitive cell—the *ribosomes* (ribonucleoprotein particles), ribonucleic acid (RNA) molecules, globular and fibrous proteins (which include many enzymes), small molecules and water—is found in the so-called *cytoplasmic matrix* of the higher cell. What have evolved are the many intracellular membranes, with the result that deoxyribonucleic acid (DNA) and other molecules are contained in the nucleus, and the many cell organoids (e.g., mitochondria, chloroplasts and centrioles) constitute a large part of the cytoplasm. In certain embryonic plant and animal cells most of the cytoplasm is composed of the matrix and the ribosomes, and there is little development of the intracellular membranes (Fig. 9–1).

The cytoplasmic matrix is thus the fundamental and *most important part of the cell* and the true *internal milieu*. Its components carry out the biosynthetic functions of the cell and it contains the enzymes necessary for energy-production, mainly by anaerobic glycolysis (Chap. 4).

The colloidal properties of the cell, such as those basic to sol-gel transformations, viscosity changes, intracellular motion (cyclosis), ameboid movement, spindle formation and cell cleavage, depend mostly on the cytoplasmic matrix. Furthermore, the cytoplasmic matrix is the site of many fibrillar differentiations found in specialized cells, such as keratin fibers, myofibrils and neurotubules, which are studied in later chapters.

Historical Notes on the Cytoplasm

Hyaloplasm. Because of the limitations in resolving power of the optical microscope, early observations of the

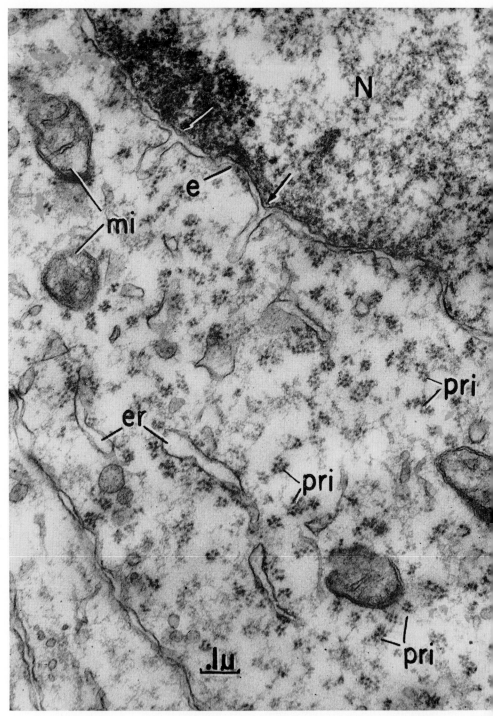

FIGURE 9–1. Electron micrograph of a neuroblast of the cerebral cortex of a rat embryo, showing the cytoplasm rich in matrix with numerous ribosomes and little development of the vacuolar system. *e*, nuclear envelope sending projections into the cytoplasm (arrows); *er*, endoplasmic reticulum; *mi*, mitochondria; *N*, nucleus; *pri*, polyribosomes (groups of ribosomes). ×45,000. (From E. De Robertis.)

cytoplasm revealed a homogeneous, amorphous region in which some discrete particles, such as mitochondria, vacuoles and inclusions, were embedded (see Figs. 2–2 and 10–1A). This was called the *ground*, or *fundamental, cyto plasm*, or the *hyaloplasm*.

Ergastoplasm. At the end of last cen

ury it was discovered that portions of he ground cytoplasm in certain cells have a differential staining property. Because these areas stained with basic dyes, as the nucleus did, they were called the *basophilic*, or *chromidial, cytoplasm* Hertwig). The still common name *ergastoplasm* (Gr. *ergazomai* to elaborate .nd transform), was coined by Garnier n 1887 to imply that biosynthesis is the undamental role of this substance.

The ergastoplasm includes basophilic egions of the ground cytoplasm, such .s the Nissl bodies of the nerve cells, he basal cytoplasm of serous cells (e.g., ecretory cells of the pancreas and the oarotid gland and chief cells of the tomach) and the basophilic clumps of iver cells. Caspersson, Brachet and oth-rs demonstrated that the intense baso-ohilic property of the ergastoplasm is lue to the presence of ribonucleic acid Figs. 6–4 and 9–2).

In fact, the ergastoplasm loses its taining properties if the cell is treated vith ribonuclease, an enzyme that hy-lrolyzes RNA (Figs. 6–4 and 9–2). RNA s mainly contained in the ribosomes.

Golgi Apparatus. In 1898, by means of a silver staining method, Golgi dis-overed a reticular structure in the ;round cytoplasm. The name "appa-atus" generally given to this structure

is confusing, because it suggests a definite relationship with the physiologic processes of the cell. It seems more appropriate to use the name "Golgi substance," or "Golgi complex," referring to a material that has special properties (Fig. 9–3).

The Golgi substance can be considered as a differentiation of the hyaloplasm, as is the ergastoplasm. Because its refractive index is similar to that of the hyaloplasm, the Golgi substance is difficult to observe in living cells. As a result, throughout the years an enormous and confusing literature has accumulated, most of which should be disregarded now (see references 1 to 4). The use of the electron microscope has provided a clearer image of this substance, and some facts regarding its submicroscopic structure have been discovered. However, little is known about its biochemical properties and function. The Golgi complex is mainly a system of intracellular membranes and is now thought to be a differentiated part of the cytoplasmic vacuolar system (see Chap. 10).

Early Submicroscopic Studies of the Cytoplasm

Before the introduction of the electron microscope there were some indications

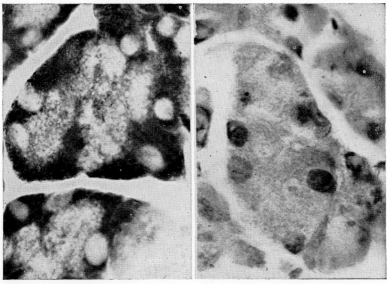

FIGURE 9–2. **Left,** pancreatic acini frozen and dried and stained with toluidine blue. The baso-hilic substance appears intensely stained. **Right,** same, but after digestion with ribonuclease; the asophilic substance has disappeared.

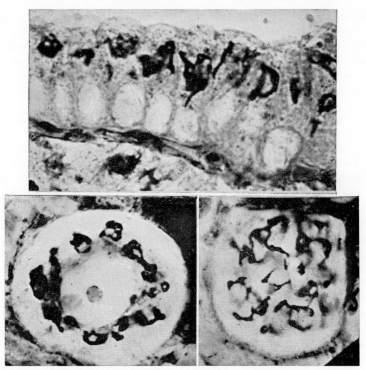

FIGURE 9–3.   **Above,** Golgi apparatus in cells of the thyroid gland of the guinea pig, apical pos tion. Osmic impregnation. **Below left,** ganglion cell, perinuclear Golgi apparatus. **Below right,** sam optical section tangential with respect to the nucleus. Silver impregnation.

of a finer organization of the hyaloplasm. In 1910, Gaidukow observed with the ultramicroscope that parts of the cytoplasm contained refractile bodies that appeared empty in transmitted light. In 1920, Bayliss used a similar method to observe the hyaloplasm of amebae, and found small particles undergoing Brownian movement.

Polarization microscopy provided additional information. It was found that in most cells the hyaloplasm is isotropic and appears dark between the crossed Nicol prisms. However, a weak birefringence was observed in some regions of the cytoplasm, particularly when the cell was subjected to mechanical forces. Birefringence was observed in a variety of epithelial cells.[5] The cortex of some eggs showed a distinct birefringence that was positive in the radial direction.[6, 7] Birefringence due to a fibrillar structure was observed when the cytoplasm of a plasmodium was drawn with a microneedle or during the formation of pseudopodia or during the fertilization of certain eggs.

When cultured cells that had phago-

cytized small magnetic particles wer placed in a magnetic field, an elastic re coil was observed, which also indicate the presence of asymmetric particles i the cytoplasmic matrix.[8]

Some Physicochemical Properties of the Cytoplasmic Matrix

Since some basic colloidal activities of the cell take place in the cytoplasmi matrix, the matrix together with the in tracellular membranes of the vacuola system can be considered as a high heterogeneous, or *polyphasic, colloi system.* This complex organization has framework of long macromolecula chains or molecular aggregates that in teract by reversible cross linkages. Som physicochemical properties that an based on this polyphasic colloid syster are:

Polarity of Eggs.   After certain egg have been centrifuged, the cell compo nents become stratified (Fig. 2–3), bu the original polarity during cell cleavag is maintained.[9] This indicates that po rity is determined by the cell matrix and that it cannot be altered by cen- rifugation.

Action of Hydrostatic Pressure. Mod- rate hydrostatic pressure (5000 pounds er square inch) applied to cells inhibits group of physiologic activities that are elated to solation-gelation changes in ne ectoplasm (plasmagel), e.g., cyclo- is, ameboid movement, cell division and nigration of pigment in chromato- hores.[10] This inhibition is due to the egree of solation that the pressure in- uces in the plasmagel system and to the esulting changes in viscosity.[11] After ressure has been applied, especially vhen the cytoplasm is packed with par- cles, cytoplasmic activity changes and ne viscosity is increased. This is some- mes called *dilatancy*.

Changes in Viscosity. Environmental r internal factors can change the vis- osity of different cells. As shown in 'igure 9–4, the relative viscosity of moeba and other cells is *temperature- ependent* and is reversible within cer- ain limits. Beyond 30° C., as in Cum- ningia, the viscosity increases abruptly ecause the cell is permanently injured y heat.[12]

In *anaerobiosis* the viscosity of proto- lasm is generally decreased. Hypertonic olutions increase viscosity; hypotonic so- tions decrease it. During the mitotic ycle and in ameboid movement there re continuous changes in viscosity. mong other possible factors causing

these changes are the absorption and elimination of water by the cell.

Table 9–1 shows some viscosity values of different cells.

TABLE 9–1.   VISCOSITY OF VARIOUS CELLS*

SUBSTANCE	TEMPERATURE (°C.)	VISCOSITY (IN CENTIPOISES)
Water	25	0.8937
Sucrose solution		
(20%)	20	1.960
(60%)	20	56.5
Nerve fiber	20	5.5
Amoeba dubia	18	2
Slime molds	20	9 to 18
Chara	20	10
Arbacia egg	20	7
Paramecium	20	50

* From Heilbrunn, 1952, *An outline of general physiology*, 3rd Ed.

Mechanical Properties. Some me- chanical properties of the cell, such as elasticity, contractility, cohesion and ri- gidity and intracellular movements, are related to the cytoplasmic matrix. Other components, such as the vacuolar sys- tem, may also be involved. The matrix is the least compact part of the cytoplasm whereas the membrane systems are dense.

pH and Oxidation-Reduction of the Cytoplasm. By injecting pH indicators, which change color according to the hydrogen ion concentration of the me-

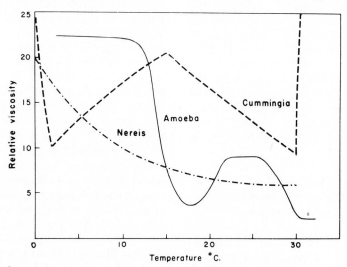

IGURE 9–4.   Changes in viscosity of various cells with changes in temperature. (From Heilbrunn.)

dium, the pH of the cytoplasm and of other parts of the cell can be determined. The most widely used indicators are water-soluble sulfonated acid salts, which, after microinjection, stain the aqueous phase of the protoplasm diffusely. In general, the cytoplasmic matrix is slightly acid (pH about 6.8).

Differences of pH have been recorded in at least three regions of the cell. For example, in the ameba the pH can be better determined after the granular material has been displaced by centrifugation. A number of vacuoles surrounded by a membrane that has properties similar to the plasma membrane can be observed in animal cells and, particularly, in protozoa and plant cells. The content of these vacuoles may be either basic (high pH) or acid (pH may be as low as 5.0). The third region that has a differential pH is the nucleoplasmic aqueous matrix, which in a variety of plant and animal cells has a pH of 7.6 to 7.8.[13, 14]

Characteristic of the protoplasm is its buffering power. The pH of the cell can be altered by adding acids or alkalis to the medium or by injecting the same into the cell, but the original pH value is rapidly reestablished as long as the vitality of the cell has not been altered.[15]

The *oxidation-reduction potential* (the reducing ability) of the cytoplasm can be determined by introducing into the cell dyes that change color or are decolorized when reduced. This color reaction is of great importance because it depends on and therefore indicates the partial pressure of oxygen of the medium and the concentration of enzyme systems and metabolites found in the cell. Furthermore, it indicates the process by which chemical energy is used by the cell. For example, in the ameba the oxidation-reduction potential of the cytoplasm is approximately -0.275 volt in anaerobiosis and $+0.070$ volt in aerobiosis.

Chemical Organization of the Cytoplasmic Matrix. Structural Proteins and Soluble Enzymes

Most of the protein content of the matrix is in the form of globular proteins, but in certain physiologic activities fibrillar structures may arise. Proteins that can undergo a fibrillar-globular transformation are often called *structural proteins*. One of the best known examples of this process is the development of the asters and spindle that form the mitotic apparatus of the cell, which is considered from a structural and chemical viewpoint in Chapter 14.

Following the cell fractionation procedure that was discussed in Chapter 6 after the nuclear, mitochondrial and microsomal fractions have been separated, the remaining supernatant fraction, or *soluble fraction* (Fig. 6–5), contains the soluble proteins and enzymes that are found in the cytoplasmic matrix. These constitute 20 to 25 per cent of the total protein content of the cell. Among the important *soluble enzymes* present in the matrix are those involved in glycolysis (Chap. 4) and in the activation of amino acids for protein synthesis. The enzymes of many reactions that require ATP are found in the soluble fraction. Soluble (transfer) RNA is also found in this part of the cell (see Chap. 17).

Ultrastructure of the Cytoplasmic Matrix

Under the electron microscope the cytoplasmic matrix appears homogeneous or finely granular and has a low electron density. In some cells fine filaments of less than 100 Å can be observed. These filaments are especially obvious when they are organized in a parallel array. It is assumed that such filaments would polymerize out of the matrix in response to environmental stresses or cell motion or as a part of the organization essential to cell division. They would presumably give the cell its gelled consistency. Organizations of filaments of similar size and relation to other cytoplasmic components constitute the framework of keratin fibrils (Fig. 19–1) and myofibrils (Fig. 22–18).

With improved techniques it has been found that the macromolecular organization of the cell matrix varies in different cells and also in different regions of the cell matrix. For example, in the intestinal cells shown in Figure 8–11, notice the fine filaments that form the so-called *terminal web*, just below the apical membrane. Filaments are also concenrated on both sides of the desmosomal attachment.

All these facts suggest elongated components by which the structural relationships of protoplasm are maintained. It is postulated that in the network formed by these structural proteins polypeptide chains may be held together by cross linkages of hydrogen bonds or van der Waals forces or even by stronger valences. Changes in the strength of these cross linkages and in the degree of folding or in the length or aggregation of the chains may transform a sol into a gel, and vice versa, in a particular region of the protoplasm. These filamentous components would not need to be constantly united, for there may be long-range forces holding them together, thus maintaining protoplasmic cohesion.

THE RIBOSOME

The concept of the *ribosome* as a definite submicroscopic particle composed of ribonucleic acid and protein was introduced in Chapters 1 and 2. From a physiological viewpoint, ribosomes are "engines" used by the cell for protein synthesis, the process by which amino acids are assembled in a definite sequence to produce the polypeptide chain. The concensus is that in addition to activated amino acids, protein synthesis requires the ordered interaction of three types of RNA molecules of nuclear origin: ribosomal, transfer and messenger RNA. (A more complete discussion of protein synthesis is therefore presented after the study of the cell nucleus [see Chap. 18].)

First observed under the electron microscope as *dense particles* or *granules*,[16, 17] ribosomes were then isolated and their RNA content was demonstrated.[18] The rapid advances made by observation with the electron microscope; ultra-centrifugation techniques, by which ribosomes were isolated and their particle size determined; and the use of radioisotopes to study the synthetic properties of these particles, have led in the last few years to the concept that ribosomes are universal components of biologic organisms.

In cytology textbooks the ribosome is generally studied in relation to the vacuolar system because in higher cells ribosomes are frequently attached to some intracellular membranes of the vacuolar system (see Chap. 10). Furthermore, in cell fractionation experiments most ribosomes are in the microsomal fraction, which also includes parts of the vacuolar system. Breaking with this tradition, we consider the ribosomes as a constant part of the cellular matrix. (The lipoprotein membranes of the vacuolar system are discussed in the following chapter.)

Occurrence and Distribution

In his recent and complete review, Ts'o[19] states, "The ubiquitous occurrence of ribosomes suggests to us that the ribosome is an obligatory component of all living organisms, just as DNA and RNA."

In relation to cytologic evolution, ribosomes are an essential part of the protoplasm of many bacteria in which the vacuolar system has not yet been developed and of mycobacteria in which only few cytoplasmic membranes appear. Most ribosomes are also free in the matrix of yeast cells, reticulocytes, meristematic plant tissues (Fig. 12–4) and embryonic nerve cells (Fig. 9–1). In plant cells it can be observed that ribosomes precede the development of membranes.[20]

In cells that are engaged in protein synthesis, such as enzyme-secreting cells and plasma cells, most ribosomes are attached to the membranes of certain parts of the vacuolar system. This relationship is still not well understood, but some evidence suggests that the lipoprotein membrane assists in removing the newly synthesized protein from the ribosomes and helps in transporting and excreting it.[21] The two-dimensional array of ribosomes upon the membrane may also facilitate synthesis.

Number and Concentration

The number and concentration of ribosomes are directly related to the RNA content of the cell and to the baso-

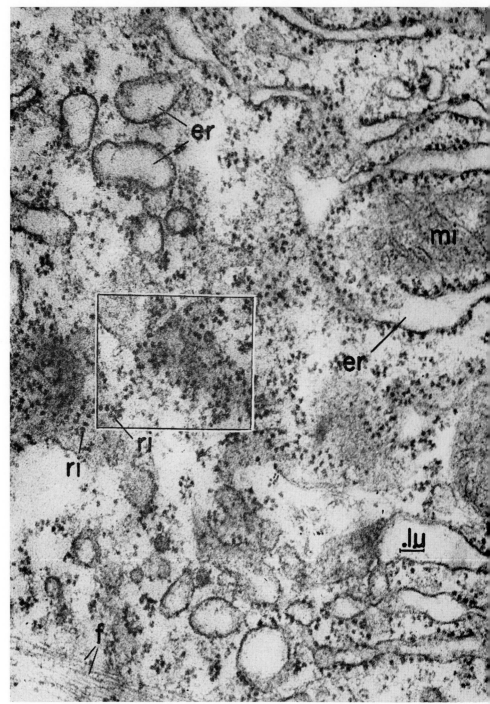

Figure 9–5.   Electron micrograph of an apical region of an intestinal cell of the rat showing the granular endoplasmic reticulum (*er*) and numerous ribosomes (*ri*); *f*, filaments of the matrix; *mi* mitochondria. The inset is further magnified in Figure 9–6. ×82,000. (From E. De Robertis and A. Pellegrino de Iraldi.)

philic properties of the cytoplasm. In all cells that contain *ergastoplasm* (*basophilic substance*), masses of ribosomes can be observed (see Figs. 9–1, 9–5, and 9–6). For example, at the base of gland cells (Fig. 10–3), in plasma and liver cells, in the Nissl bodies of nerve cells in all rapidly growing plant and anima

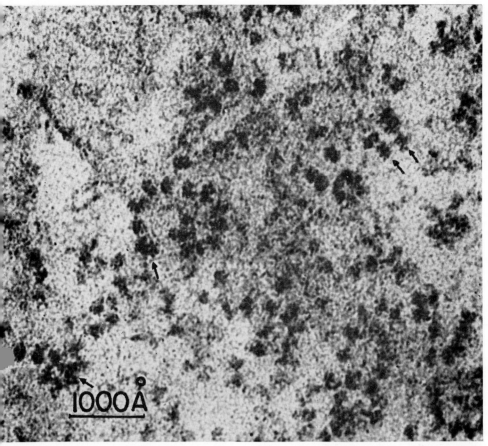

FIGURE 9–6. Inset of Figure 9–5 at higher magnification, showing the fine structure of the ribosomes. ×270,000. (From E. De Robertis and A. Pellegrino de Iraldi.)

cells and in bacteria the staining properties and RNA content can be correlated with the concentration of ribosomes. In rabbit reticulocytes there are about 100 ribosomes per μ^3, which corresponds to $\times 10^5$ particles per cell and about 0.5 per cent of the total cell volume. A *coli* bacillus contains 6000 ribosomes; a simi-lar concentration has been found in yeast cells (see reference 19).

Chemical Composition

Ribosomes are remarkably uniform in size, structure and composition in the different biologic systems in which they

TABLE 9–2. CHARACTERISTICS OF RIBOSOMES ISOLATED FROM VARIOUS ORGANISMS*

SOURCE OF RIBOSOME	SEDIMENTATION CONSTANT	ESTIMATED MOLECULAR WEIGHT	DIAMETER (Å)	PROTEIN CONTENT (%)	RNA CONTENT (%)
Pea seedlings	80 S	4,000,000	280	55	45
White clover	80 S	—	—	46	54
Yeast	80 S	4,100,000	240	58	42
Rat liver	78 S	—	170	60	40
Rabbit reticulocytes	78 S	4,100,000	340	50	50
Escherichia coli	70 S	2,800,000	200	41	59
Azotobacter vinelandii	86 S	—	250	—	—

* From Webster and Whitman.[28]

have been studied (Table 9–2).[22] The major constituents of ribosomes are protein and RNA in approximately equal proportions with little or no lipid material. The protein is somewhat similar to histone (see Chap. 17) in that it has a higher content of basic than acid amino acids. RNA is strongly acidic, and since it has about 6000 nucleotides per ribosome, there are as many negatively changed groups. The positive charges of protein are not sufficient to compensate for those of RNA. The net charge of the ribosome is thus strongly negative. For this reason ribosomes bind cations and basic dyes.

RNA is contained in the two subunits of the ribosome (see below), forming a particle of 26 S and another of 18 S with molecular weights of 1,300,000 and 600,000 respectively. The 6000 nucleotides are probably in six chains of about 1000 each, four of which are in the 28 S particle and two in the 16 S particle. The structural proteins of ribosomes from different cells show a striking similarity in the proportion of various amino acids. This protein is different from that being synthesized by the ribosome. In contrast to the protein, the nucleotide composition of ribosomes of different origin varies (Table 9–3).

The base composition of ribosomal RNA does not follow the complementary base rule proposed by Watson and Crick for DNA (see Chap. 3). The ribosome contains in its small subunit the enzyme ribonuclease, which is in latent (not active) form.

Origin

The origin of ribosomes is intimately related to RNA synthesis in a cell and the nuclear-cytoplasmic relationship (se Chap. 13). The possibility that ribosoma RNA forms and accumulates in the n cleolus under DNA control is much con sidered at present.

Ribosomes are generally considered a cytoplasmic components of the cel However, early electron microscopy re vealed dense particles of similar size an electron opacity within the nucleus, pa ticularly near the nuclear membrane an in the nuclear sap.[23–25] It was then theo rized that cytoplasmic ribosomes orig inated in the nucleus. Recent evidenc indicates that nuclei isolated from thy mocytes contain ribosomes that synthe size protein.[26, 27] These nuclear ribo somes are more heterogeneous in siz and also in RNA/protein content tha cytoplasmic ribosomes.

Macromolecular Organization

Knowledge of the macromolecular o ganization of ribosomes comes mainl from ultracentrifuge studies of isolate ribosomes. Isolation is simple in bacteri and in reticulocytes, in which the ribo somes are not attached to membrane In higher cells the membranes must fir be made soluble by a surface-activ agent (e.g., deoxycholate) to free th ribosomes (Fig. 10–15).

By ultracentrifugation the sedimenta tion coefficient can be measured. Th varies between 70 and 80 S. From th a molecular weight of 3 to 4.5 $\times$ 10^6 ca be calculated (Table 9–2).[28] The ribo somal unit is generally an oblate sphe roid (about 250 Å by 150 Å). Ribosome are usually associated to form polyribo somes, which are apparently the one actively engaged in protein synthesi

---

TABLE 9–3. NUCLEOTIDE COMPOSITION OF RNA OF RIBOSOMES
OF DIFFERENT ORIGIN*

MATERIAL	PROTEIN SYNTHESIZED	MOLES/100 MOLES			
		ADENINE	URACIL	GUANINE	CYTOSIN
Pea ribosomes	pea stem enzymes	24.0	21.5	32.9	21.5
Rabbit reticulocyte ribosomes	rabbit hemoglobin	18.5	18.5	34.4	28.6
Sheep reticulocyte ribosomes	sheep hemoglobin	18.0	17.2	34.4	30.3

* From Bonner, 1961.[22]

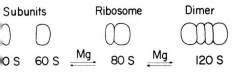

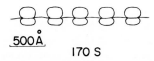

Polyribosome

170 S

FIGURE 9–7. Diagram of the subunit structure of the ribosome and the influence of Mg. A polyribosome formed by five ribosomes is indicated. The filament uniting the ribosomes is considered to be messenger RNA. The sedimentation constants (S) of the different particles are indicated.

Ribosomes require low concentrations of Mg (0.001 M) for structural cohesion. If the Mg concentration is increased 10-fold, two ribosomes combine to form a "dimer" with twice the molecular weight. If the Mg concentration is lowered, the single ribosome can be dissociated reversibly into *subunits* (Fig. 9–7). For a ribosome of 80 S the two subunits produced are of 60 S and 40 S, and in the presence of this bivalent cation can reform the 80 S unit (Fig. 9–7). Likewise the dimer can be converted back into two ribosomes by lowering the Mg concentration. The binding with Mg seems to be through the RNA phosphate and

not through the protein. Since the ribosome is highly porous and hydrated, the double-stranded RNA and the protein are probably intertwined within the two subunits.

When isolated ribosomes are subjected to negative staining, only a cleft between the two subunits can be observed in electron microscopy.[29] In sections treated with uranyl ions, which stain RNA selectively, each ribosome appears as a star-shaped body of 150 Å with four to six arms or as an elongated particle of 250 × 150 Å with a dense axis in which short arms are implanted (Fig. 9–6). Frequently a line of several ribosomes can be seen attached to a thin filament.

Polyribosomes and Protein Synthesis. The initial electron microscope observations of cell sections revealed that ribosomes associate in recurrent patterns.[16] Ribosomes isolated from bacteria were frequently dimers made of two units with a sedimentation of 100 S. However, it is only recently that the *polyribosomes*, or *polysomes*,[30] also called *ergosomes*,[31] the ribosomal aggregates engaged in protein synthesis, have been discovered.

After treating cells with C[14]-labeled amino acids and using gentle methods of isolation, e.g., lysis of reticulocytes in hypotonic buffer solutions, it was found that in addition to the sedimentation band typical of isolated ribosomes (Fig.

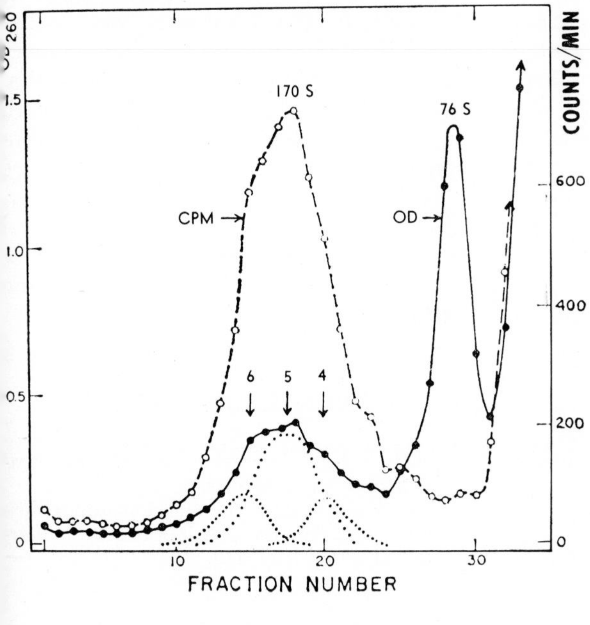

FIGURE 9–8. Experiment done to demonstrate that the synthesis of hemoglobin occurs in polyribosomes. Reticulocytes were incubated for 45 seconds in the presence of a pool of amino acids labeled with C[14]. The cells were lysed osmotically and the soluble part (hemoglobin) was centrifuged for two hours on a continuous density gradient of sucrose. After this the tube was punctured and thirty fractions were collected and observed under the electron microscope. Similar fractions were analyzed for optical density at 2600 Å, for RNA and for the number of counts. While the optical density (OD) shows a peak at 76 S (sedimentation constant corresponding to single ribosomes, the peak of radioactivity corresponds to the ribosomal tetramers, pentamers and hexamers indicated with arrows. (From J. R. Warner, A. Rich and C. E. Hall.[30])

9–8), larger units were present. These ranged from 108 S (a dimer) to 170 S (a pentamer). At the same time it was observed that the maximal radioactivity indicating the synthesis of hemoglobin molecules was in the fraction of 170 S. The suggestion that there were a series of polyribosomes was confirmed by electron microscopy. At the 170 S peak, the largest percentages of ribosomes were found in the pentamer (75 per cent), tetramer and hexamer groups (Fig. 9–8).

Considerable importance has been given to the nature of the attachment between ribosomes. Electron microscopy has revealed that ribosomes are held in line by a thin filament, which has been interpreted as a single strand of messenger RNA (mRNA), which carries the genetic information from the nucleus (see Chaps. 17 and 18). In the polyribosome the distance between the centers of individual ribosomes is about 340 Å. (The total length of mRNA is 1500 Å [Fig. 9–7].) In ribosomes of *E. coli* the incorporation of leucine, an amino acid, increases with the number of ribosomes until the octamer polysome is reached. In cultured cells infected with polioviruses, clusters of 40 to 50 ribosomes have been observed.[32]

Polyribosomes and Length of mRNA and the Protein Chain. The number of ribosomes active in the synthesis of a protein molecule varies. This has been attributed to the length of mRNA, which carries the message from the nuclear DNA to be translated into the amino acid sequence of the protein (see Chap. 18). For example, the hemoglobin molecule has four polypeptide subunits of 16,000 molecular weight, each of which contains 150 amino acids. If, as is probable, each amino acid is determined by three nucleotides in mRNA and the distance between nucleotides is 3.4 Å, a 1500 Å mRNA molecule will contain the necessary information to make a polypeptide chain of hemoglobin of 16,000 molecular weight. By the same reasoning, eight to twelve ribosomes will be used by a chain of 900 nucleotides (mRNA of 300,000 molecular weight) to make a 35,000 molecular weight protein, and twenty ribosomes (mRNA of 600,000 molecular weight) for a 70,000 molecular weight protein molecule.

Although further analysis of the process of protein synthesis require knowledge of the role played by the nucleus, transfer RNA, enzymes and co factors, which are considered in late chapters, remember that the polyribosome is the active synthesizing unit of the cell.

The ribosomes are thought to travel along mRNA in a dynamic process during which the message contained as a code in mRNA is translated into the protein molecule (see Fig. 18–10). In this process the ribosome attaches first to one end of mRNA and then makes its way along it, while the polypeptide chain grows and finally is detached at the opposite end. It is known that the hemoglobin chain is synthesized sequentially starting from the $-NH_2$ terminal and proceeding all the way to the free carboxyl end.

According to some views, the ribosome provides a stabilizing surface for mRNA and other reacting molecules during synthesis.[33, 34]

From this viewpoint, another interesting problem refers to the relationship between the ribosome and the membrane of the vacuolar system. In protein-secreting cells most ribosomes are attached to such a membrane. In a recent study starting with ribosomes attached to the membrane (microsomes, Chap. 10) the subunits of the ribosomes were separated by a chelating agent that removes Mg. It was found by ultracentrifugation that the first to be removed is the small subunit. This demonstrates that the ribosomal attachment is through the large subunit. Also by electron microscopy after negative staining, it was observed that the groove between the two sub units is parallel to the membrane surface.[35]

GENERAL REFERENCES

Brachet, J. (1957) *Biochemical cytology.* Academic Press, New York.
Haguenau, F. (1958) The ergastoplasm; its history, ultrastructure and biochemistry. *Internat. Rev. Cytol.,* 7:425.

chneider, W. C., and Hogeboom, G. H. (1951) The isolation of cell components by differential centrifugation: a review. *Cancer Res.*, 11:1.

's'o, P. O. P. (1962) The ribosomes. Ribonucleoprotein particles. *Ann. Rev. Plant Physiol.*, 13:45.

CITED REFERENCES

1. Hirsch, C. G. (1939) *Protoplasma. Monogr.*, 18:1, 394.
2. Hibbard, H. (1945) *Quart. Rev. Biol.*, 20:1.
3. Bourne, G. (1951) Mitochondria and Golgi apparatus. In: *Cytology and cell physiology.* (Bourne, G., ed.) Oxford University Press, London.
4. Palay, S. L. (1958) The morphology of secretion. In: *Frontiers in cytology.* (Palay, S. L., ed.) Yale University Press, New Haven, Conn.
5. Hillarp, N. A., and Olivecrona, H. (1946) *Acta Anat.*, 2:119.
6. Monné, L. (1948) *Advanc. Enzymol.*, 8:1.
7. Swann, M. M., and Michison, J. M. (1953) *J. Exp. Biol.*, 30:506.
8. Crick, F. H. C., and Hughes, A. F. W. (1950) *Exp. Cell Res.*, 1:37.
9. Child, C. M. (1941) *Patterns and problems of development.* University of Chicago Press, Chicago, p. 584.
0. Heilbrunn, L. V. (1956) *The dynamics of living protoplasm.* Academic Press, New York.
1. Marsland, D. A. (1942) Protoplasmic streaming in relation to gel structure in the cytoplasm. In: *Structure of protoplasm.* (Seifriz, W., ed.) Iowa State College Press, Ames, Iowa.
2. Heilbrunn, L. V. (1958) The viscosity of protoplasm. In: *Protoplasmatologia*, II, C,1. (Heilbrunn, L. V., and Weber, F., eds.) Springer-Verlag, Vienna.
3. Chambers, R. (1940) *J. Roy. Micr. Soc.*, 60:113.
4. Chambers, R. (1949) *Biol. Rev.*, 24:2346.

15. Ries, E. (1938) *Grundriss der Histophysiologie.* Akademische Verlagsgesellschaft, Leipzig.
16. Palade, G. E. (1953) *J. Appl. Physiol.*, 24:1419.
17. Palade, G. E. (1955) *J. Biophys. Biochem. Cytol.*, 1:59.
18. Palade, G. E., and Siekevitz, F. (1956) *J. Biophys. Biochem. Cytol.*, 2:171.
19. Ts'o, P. O. P. (1962) *Ann. Rev. Plant Physiol.*, 13:45.
20. Porter, K. R., and Machado, R. D. (1960) *J. Biophys. Biochem. Cytol.*, 7:167.
21. Siekevitz, P., and Palade, G. E. (1960) *J. Biophys. Biochem. Cytol.*, 7:619.
22. Bonner, J. (1961) Structure and origin of the ribosomes. *Protein biosynthesis.* (Harris, R. J. C., ed.) Academic Press, New York.
23. De Robertis, E. (1954) *J. Histochem. Cytochem.*, 2:341.
24. De Robertis, E. (1956) *J. Biophys. Biochem. Cytol.*, 2:785.
25. Watson, M. L. (1955) *J. Biophys. Biochem. Cytol.*, 1:257.
26. Allfrey, V. G., and Mirsky, A. E. (1961) In: *Protein biosynthesis.* (Harris, R. J. C., ed.) Academic Press, London, p. 49.
27. Wang, T. Y. (1961) *Biochim. Biophys. Acta*, 51:180.
28. Webster, G., and Whitman, S. L. (1961) Structure and function of ribosomes. In: *Functional biochemistry of cell structures.* Proceedings of the Fifth International Congress of Biochemistry. (Lindberg, O., ed.) Moscow, Vol. II, p. 30.
29. Huxley, A. F., and Zubay, G. (1960) *J. Molec. Biol.*, 2:10.
30. Warner, J. R., Rich, A., and Hall, C. E. (1962) *Science*, 138:1399.
31. Wettstein, F. O., Staehelin, T., and Noll, H. (1963) *Nature*, 197:430.
32. Rich, A., Warner, J. R., and Goodman, H. M. (1963) *Symp. Quant. Biol.*, 28:269.
33. Zubay, G. (1963) *Science*, 140:1092, 3571.
34. Watson, J. D. (1963) *Science*, 140:17.

CHAPTER 10

THE CYTOPLASMIC

VACUOLAR SYSTEM

AND

MICROSOMES

The *vacuolar system* was introduced in Chapters 2 and 9. It was then said that through cytologic evolution the cytoplasm became pervaded by numerous intracellular membranes that subdivided it into numerous compartments and sub-compartments.

As shown in the diagrams of Figures 2–5 and 12–3, which represent typical cells from higher animals and plants, the cytoplasm is traversed by a complex system of membrane-bound tubules, vesicles and flattened sacs, the latter also called *cisternae,* that have many inter-communications. This membrane system should be interpreted in its three-dimensional array as a vast network of virtual or open cavities that subdivide the cytoplasm into two main compartments: one enclosed within the membrane; the other situated outside (the cytoplasmic matrix [Chap. 9]).

The name *cytoplasmic vacuolar system* seems the most appropriate and descriptive for this intracellular membranous organization. The main components are: the *endoplasmic reticulum* (*granular* and *agranular*), the *nuclear envelope* and the

Golgi complex. The diagram of Figure 2–5 emphasizes that these different parts of the vacuolar system are continuous at certain points by permanent or temporary channels.

This vacuolar system was not discovered until the techniques for electron microscopy of intact cultured cells and thin sections became available. Other advances were made by cell fractionation methods followed by biochemical analysis and the use of cytochemical techniques for the study of specific components—particularly enzymes—at both the light and electron microscope levels. As in many other areas of cell biology, rapid progress has resulted from the convergence of various technical and scientific approaches.

Recent knowledge of the structural organization of the cell has had considerable impact on biochemistry and cell physiology, since it has clearly shown the relationship between structural factors and cellular functions. A cell can no longer be considered as a bag containing enzymes, ribonucleic acid (RNA), deoxyribonucleic acid (DNA) and solutes surrounded by an outer membrane, as in the most primitive bacterium (Fig. 1–2). As will be shown in this chapter, numerous membrane-bound compartments are responsible for vital cellular functions, among which are: the segregation and association of enzyme systems; the creation of diffusion barriers; the regulation of membrane potentials, ionic gradients, and different intracellular pH values; and other manifestations of cellular heterogeneity. Furthermore there is evidence that enzymes are spatially organized, forming multienzyme systems within the insoluble membranous framework of the cell. For this reason, in studying the cell we are dealing not with individual enzymatic reactions but with integrated enzyme systems.[1]

Together with the vacuolar system, the so-called *microsomal fraction* of the cell will be studied. *Microsomes* are not specific components of the cell. They constitute a heterogeneous group of cellular structures that can be isolated by centrifugation. However, the vacuolar system and the ribosomes are the main constituents of the microsomal fraction.

142

GENERAL MORPHOLOGY OF THE VACUOLAR SYSTEM

In 1945, the first observations of cultured fibroblasts revealed a lacelike reticular component of the cytoplasm[2] (Fig. 10–1). Under the phase contrast microscope the cytoplasm of a living cell, excluding the mitochondria and some inclusions, appears structureless, while in a similar but fixed specimen, the electron microscope reveals a definite structure. Besides the mitochondria and some lipid droplets, a special reticular component can be observed. This is a network of membrane-bound cavities that may vary considerably in size and shape. Since this network is more concentrated in the endoplasm of the cell than in the so-called ectoplasm (peripheral region), the name *endoplasmic reticulum* was proposed. In addition to vesicles and tubules, this system may show large flattened sacs (cisternae). An electron micrograph of a culture cell examined *in toto* shows a three-dimensional view of the endoplasmic reticulum. In it the shape, distribution and interconnections of the tubules, vesicles and cisternae throughout the cytoplasm are clearly visible.

A more detailed analysis of the vacuolar system was possible after thin sectioning was introduced, by which a great variety of animal and plant cells could be observed.[4-8] It was soon discovered that the vacuolar system varied considerably in different cells and within a single cell in the different cytoplasmic regions. In embryonic cells the vacuolar system appears simple (Fig. 9–1). In other cells its complexity increases greatly with differentiation. In cells that have involuted, e.g., reticulocytes, the membranes disappear.

A further complication was introduced with the discovery of ribosomes, which may be free in the cell matrix or more frequently attached to some parts of the vacuolar system (Chap. 9).

Based on localization within the cell, association with ribosomes and general morphology, we have simplified the subdivision of the membranes of the vacuolar system into the following classes (Fig. 2–5): (a) *membranes of the endo-plasmic reticulum* with their *granular* and *agranular* portions, the *nuclear envelope* and some special differentiations, and (b) *membranes of the Golgi complex* with the vesicular components of the *centrosphere*.

Endoplasmic Reticulum

At the time of the early studies with the electron microscope, many observers postulated that the vacuolar system was a fixation artifact. This has been disproved because the components of the endoplasmic reticulum have been observed in studies using fixatives other than osmium tetroxide, including fixation by freezing-drying (Chap. 6). Furthermore, in some living cells the large cisternae may be observed with the phase contrast microscope. For example, in Figure 10–2 similar spermatid cells are shown as they appear under the phase and the electron microscopes. It is evident that there is an exact correspondence between the endoplasmic reticulum and the parallel lines observed in the intact living cell.[9] A birefringence has been observed at the base of the living pancreatic cell where the endoplasmic reticulum is represented by closely packed parallel cisternae.[10] Also, in cinematographic pictures of cultured cells, structures that have the characteristic form of endoplasmic reticulum elements have been observed.[11, 12]

As said, the development of the endoplasmic reticulum varies considerably in the different cell types. In spermatocytes only a few vacuoles can be observed. A simple endoplasmic reticulum is found in cells engaged in lipid metabolism, such as adipose, brown fat adrenocortical cells. However, in the interstitial cells of the testis of the opossum a considerable amount of agranular endoplasmic reticulum has been observed.[13] On the contrary, in cells actively engaged in protein synthesis, such as those of the pancreatic acinus (Fig. 10–3) and the base of the muciparous (*goblet*) cells (Fig. 10–4), the system is highly developed and consists of large cisternae covered with ribosomes (granular endoplasmic reticulum). In liver cells it can be ob-

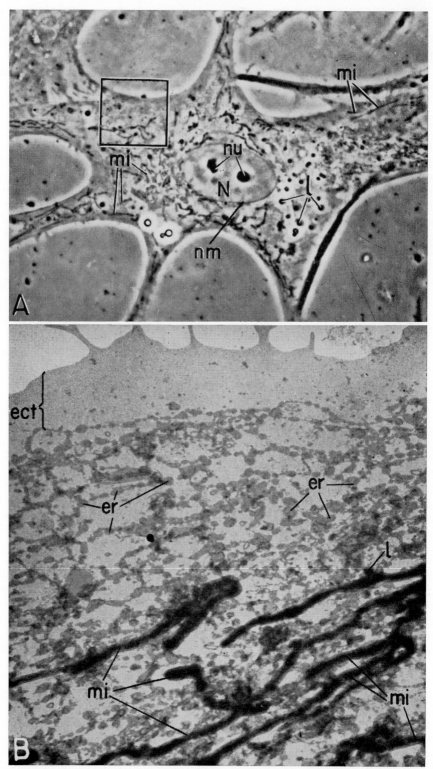

FIGURE 10–1. A, living cell of a tissue culture observed under the phase microscope: *l*, lipid; *mi*, mitochondria; *nm*, nuclear membrane; *nu*, nucleoli. The region indicated in the inset is similar to B. (Courtesy of D. W. Fawcett.) B, electron micrograph of the marginal region of a mouse fibrocyte in tissue culture: *er*, endoplasmic reticulum; *mi*, filamentous mitochondria; *l*, lipid. The peripheral region (*ect*), is homogeneous. ×7000. (Courtesy of K. R. Porter.)

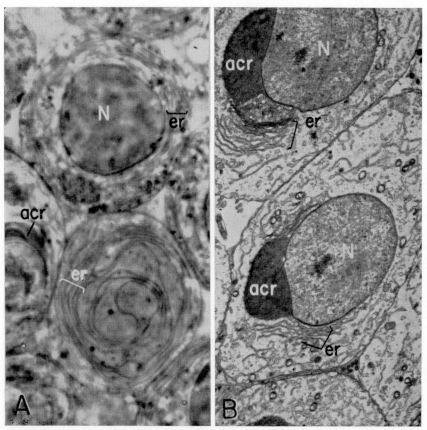

FIGURE 10–2. A, spermatid of a guinea pig observed in vitro with phase contrast: *acr*, acrosome; *er*, membranes of the endoplasmic reticulum; *N*, nucleus. ×2500. B, similar cell observed under the electron microscope. The disposition of the endoplasmic reticulum (*er*) corresponds to that observed under phase contrast in A. (Courtesy of D. W. Fawcett and S. Ito.)

served that the regions rich in glycogen deposits contain a tubular agranular endoplasmic reticulum, while the basophilic regions have a granular endoplasmic reticulum composed of cisternae. However, the continuities between both types of endoplasmic reticulum are evident at many points (Fig. 10–5).

The cavity of the endoplasmic reticulum is sometimes virtual with the two membranes closely apposed, but more frequently there is a true space between the membranes that may be filled with a material of varying opacity (Fig. 10–6). This space is much distended in certain cells actively engaged in protein synthesis, such as the plasma cells (Fig. 10–9) and goblet cells (Fig. 10–4). In these cases a dense macromolecular material can be observed inside the cisternae. In the pancreas, intercisternal secretion granules, smaller than the zymo-

gen granules, have been observed occasionally.[14]

The Nuclear Envelope and Nuclear Permeability

This membrane divides the cell into its two main regions, the nucleus and the cytoplasm, which have different physical and chemical structures. Metabolites and other substances, some of which are associated with gene activity and protein synthesis, flow through this membrane.

One of the most interesting discoveries in electron microscopy is that the *nuclear membrane*, or *envelope*, is a dependence of the cytoplasmic vacuolar system. This has been demonstrated not only by observing the continuities at many points but also by studying these structures in different stages of cellular

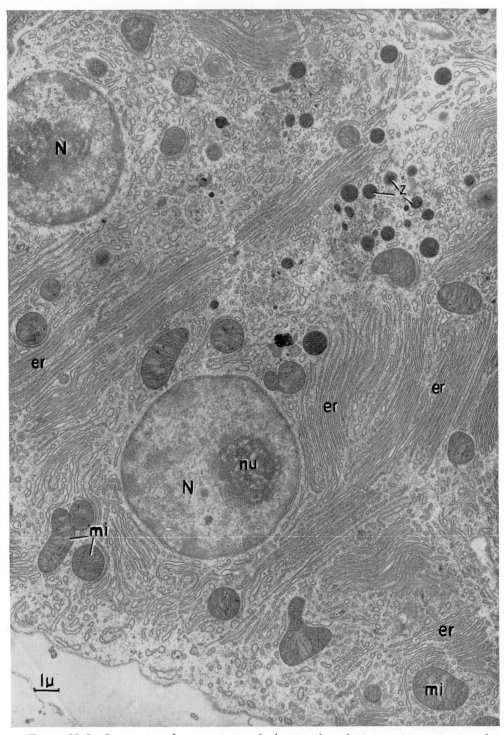

Figure 10–3. Low power electron micrograph showing the submicroscopic organization of a cell of the pancreatic acinus. At the base and lateral portions, the cell is rich in granular endoplasmic reticulum (*er*). In the apex the zymogen granules (*z*) are apparent. *mi*, mitochondria; *N*, nucleus; *nu*, nucleolus. ×8000. (Courtesy of K. R. Porter.)

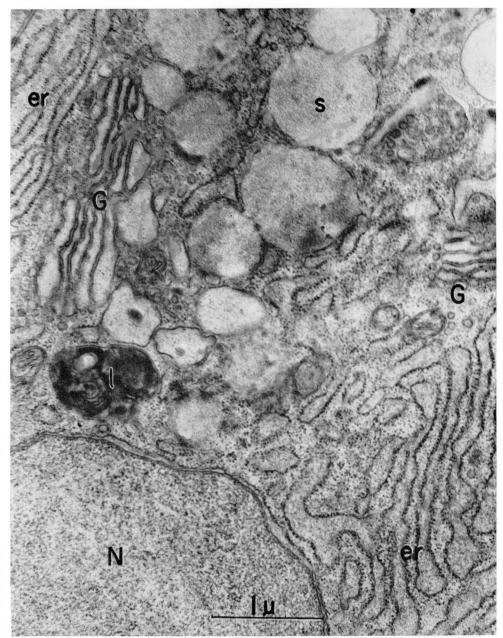

FIGURE 10–4.   Electron micrograph of the supranuclear region of a muciparous (goblet) cell of the intestine. Notice the development of the granular endoplasmic reticulum (*er*) at the base. Notice also the Golgi complex (*G*) with the flat cisternae that become filled with the muciparous secretion (*s*). *l*, lysosome; *N*, nucleus. ×36,000. (From E. De Robertis and A. Pellegrino de Iraldi.)

activity and by following them phylogenetically. For example, most bacteria lack internal membranes and the nucleoid has no envelope; mycobacteria have a few cytoplasmic membranes, but none around the nucleus.[15] Only in fungi and in cells of higher organisms does a definite nuclear envelope appear.[16]

The early electron microscope studies of the nuclear envelope were carried out on isolated nuclear membranes of amphibian oocytes in which an outer porous layer and an inner continuous one were recognized.[17] The pores are about 400 Å in diameter with a regular disposition and an interpore distance of 1000 Å. Similar observations were made in oöcytes, amebae and giant nuclei of insects.[18] A

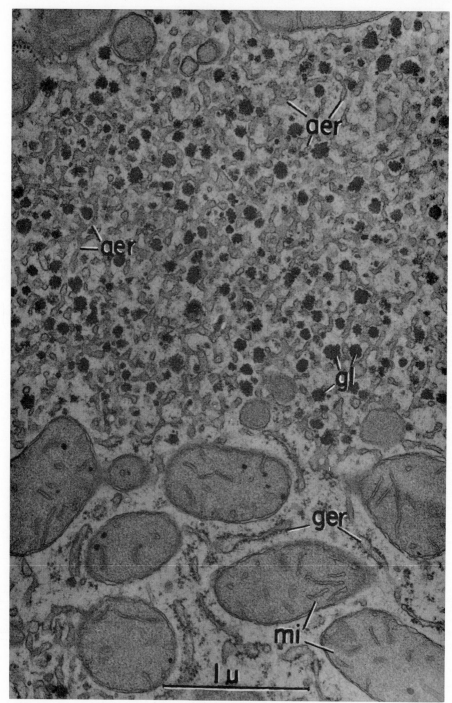

FIGURE 10–5.   Electron micrograph of the cytoplasm of a liver cell, which shows: at the bottom, the granular endoplasmic reticulum (*ger*) and mitochondria (*mi*); at the top, the agranular endoplasmic reticulum (*aer*) is mixed with glycogen particles (*gl*). ×45,000. (Courtesy of G. E. Palade.)

sea urchin oöcyte has 40 to 80 pores per μ^2, which are covered by a single membrane and encircled by a cylindrical wall, which has been called the *annulus*[19–21] and also the *pore complex*.[22] In

the ameba a system of closely packed hexagonal prisms related to the pores has been observed.[23] In a variety of mammalian cells numerous pore complexes have been found at the nuclear

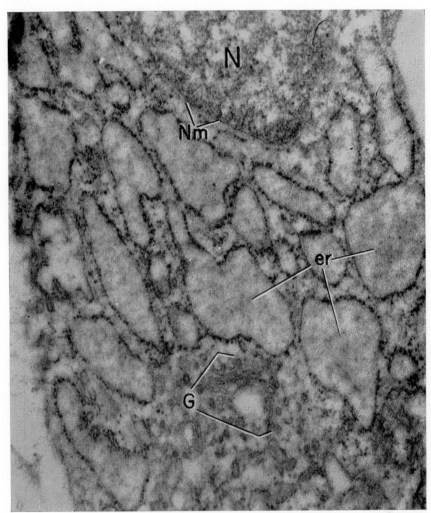

FIGURE 10–6.   Electron micrograph of a Schwann cell in the active process of myelination: *er*, endoplasmic reticulum formed by large vacuoles with amorphous content; *G*, Golgi complex; *N*, nucleus; *Nm*, nuclear membrane, or envelope. ×57,000. (From De Robertis, Gerschenfeld and Wald.)

envelope. It has been calculated that approximately 10 per cent of the surface corresponds to the pores and the rest to the membranes of the endoplasmic reticulum.[18–22]

The two membranes of the envelope are interpreted as large flattened cisternae apposed to the surface of the nucleus. In numerous cells the continuity of this envelope with other parts of the endoplasmic reticulum has been observed (Fig. 2–5). During differentiation of the nerve cell the endoplasmic reticulum apparently develops from the nuclear envelope and then penetrates into the cytoplasm (Fig. 9–1).

More recent investigations have shown that the nuclear pores are plugged and not freely communicating orifices (Fig. 10–7). In liver cells the annuli of 800 Å have central orifices of only 100 Å (Fig. 10–7). On the outer surface of the envelope numerous ribosomes are disposed in rows or spirals (Fig. 10–7).[24]

These structures should be correlated with some of the electrochemical properties of the nuclear membrane that can be investigated with fine microelectrodes (Fig. 10–8).[25] With this technique two types of nuclear membranes have been recognized. When a giant cell of the salivary gland of *Drosophila* is penetrated with a microelectrode, there is an abrupt change in potential at the plasma membrane (−12 mv); then, when the microelectrode enters the nucleus, there

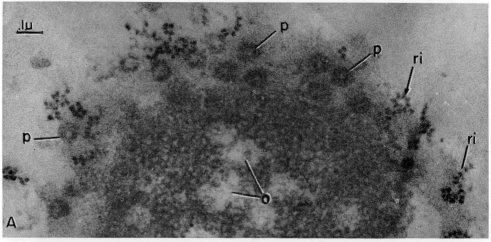

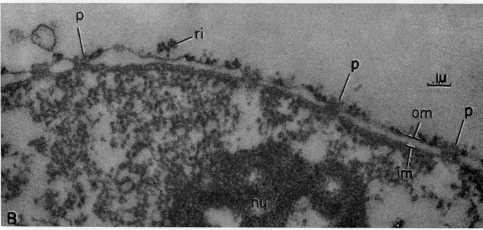

Figure 10-7. Electron micrographs of isolated liver nuclei. **A,** tangential section through the surface of the nucleus showing the pores (*p*) or annuli. *o,* orifices or spaces below the pore in the nucleoplasm; *ri,* ribosomes. ×77,000. **B,** perpendicular section which shows the plugged pores and the outer membrane (*om*) and the inner membrane (*im*) of the nuclear envelope. *nu,* nucleolus. ×64,000. (Courtesy of G. E. Palade.)

is another drop in negative potential at the nuclear membrane (−13 mv). At this surface there is also an electrical resistance. Although this is much smaller than that of the cell membrane, it is large enough to indicate that the nuclear membrane must be a formidable diffusion barrier even for ions as small as K^+, Na^+ or Cl^-. These results suggest that either the pores do not communicate freely or the plugging material has a high impedance. However, in the other type of nuclear membrane present in oöcytes there is no detectable potential, which indicates a free interchange of ions between the nucleus and the cytoplasm.

Another interesting possibility suggested by the continuities of the nuclear envelope with the endoplasmic reticulum is that of a direct interchange of the nucleus with the medium surrounding the cell. There is some evidence that certain areas of the endoplasmic reticulum are dynamically related to the plasma membrane. Probably by this mechanism fat droplets absorbed at the surface of the intestinal cell travel inside the endoplasmic reticulum and the Golgi membranes and sometimes are found in the cavity of the nuclear envelope.[26] The penetration of acridine dyes into the nucleus without staining the cytoplasm has also been interpreted in this way.[16, 27] Probably one of the most clear demonstrations that the nuclear envelope is an endoplasmic reticulum derivative is observed during mitosis. At telophase, cis-

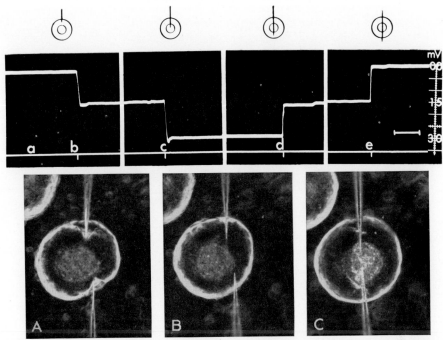

FIGURE 10–8. Experiment of microsurgery to study the potential of the nuclear membrane in giant nuclei of the salivary gland of *Drosophila*. **Above,** a diagram of the penetration of the micro-electrode into the cell is shown together with the membrane or steady potentials registered at each position. **Below,** photomicrographs of cells penetrated by two microelectrodes. **A,** beginning; **B,** into the cytoplasm; **C,** into the nucleus. (Courtesy of W. R. Loewenstein and Y. Kanno.)

ternae of the endoplasmic reticulum collect around the chromosomes to reform the nuclear envelope.[28]

The Golgi Complex and Dictyosomes

In Chapter 9 the Golgi complex was considered historically as a differentiated part of the cytoplasm that has special staining properties (Fig. 9–3). Electron microscopy has revealed that this complex consists mainly of membranes that belong to the vacuolar system of the cell. One of the main characteristics of the Golgi complex is lack of ribosomes, which suggests that it is part of the agranular endoplasmic reticulum, but this is not the case. Several important characteristics based on the localization and organization of Golgi membranes and certain cytochemical properties clearly differentiate the Golgi complex from the endoplasmic reticulum.

The Golgi complex comprises the following morphologic components: flattened sacs (cisternae) that appear in the

section as dense parallel membranes (Figs. 10–4 and 10–9); clusters of dense vesicles of about 600 Å that are intimately associated with the cisternae; and large, clear vacuoles generally present at the edge of the Golgi complex. In some cells these dilated vacuoles may contain dense masses or granules (e.g., in duodenal epithelium, liver and pancreas). The packed cisternae are often arrayed concentrically, enclosing regions of the cytoplasm filled with numerous large vesicles (Fig. 10–9). Of these three components of the Golgi complex the flattened sacs are the most constant; the small vesicles and large vacuoles may be interpreted as arising from modifications of the sacs.

In plant cells and in invertebrate tissues the Golgi complex is scattered throughout the cytoplasm into bodies called *dictyosomes*, which are almost exclusively formed by the flattened sacs with clusters of small vesicles at the edge (Fig. 12–5).

The thickness of the membranes is about 60 to 70 Å; the width of the inter-

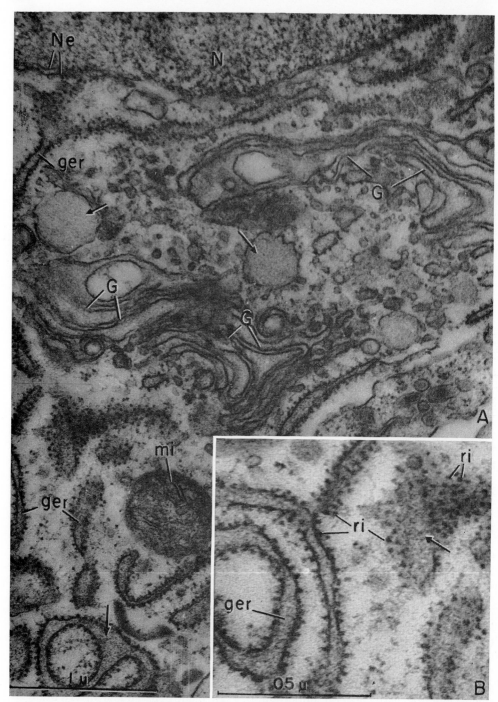

FIGURE 10–9. Electron micrograph of a plasma cell showing near the nucleus (*N*) a large Golgi complex (*G*) formed of flat cisternae and small and large vesicles. Some of the large vesicles (arrows) are filled with material. Surrounding the Golgi complex is abundant granular endoplasmic reticulum (*ger*) and the cisternae filled with amorphous material (arrows). *mi*, mitochondrion; *Ne*, nuclear envelope; *ri*, ribosomes. ×48,000; inset ×100,000. (From E. De Robertis and A. Pellegrino de Iraldi.)

space between membrane pairs is 60 to 90 Å; and the interspace between sacs may vary between 50 and 200 Å.[6, 29, 30]

The *localization, size* and *development*

of the Golgi complex varies from one cell type to another and also with the physiological stage of the cell. The position is relatively fixed. In secretory cells the Golgi complex is polarized and frequently disposed between the nucleus and the apical pole.

Electron microscopy has brought new evidence of the morphologic relationship between the *Golgi complex* and *secretion*, which was postulated by Cajal in 1914 in his study on goblet cells. In Figure 10–4, which corresponds to this type of cell, the sacs of the Golgi complex are related to the cisternae of the endoplasmic reticulum and to the secretion droplets. Notice that the Golgi sacs in the apical region of the cell have become progressively filled with the se-

cretion product. In the plasma cell shown in Figure 10–9 the Golgi complex occupies a large region near the nucleus while the granular endoplasmic reticulum surrounds it; the smaller vesicles are in the center corresponding to the centrosphere region. In this and other cells the Golgi complex is topographically related to the centrioles.

A particularly interesting example of the Golgi complex is that present in developing mammalian spermatids.[31] In early stages the Golgi complex appears as a spherical body consisting of parallel flattened sacs and numerous small vacu-

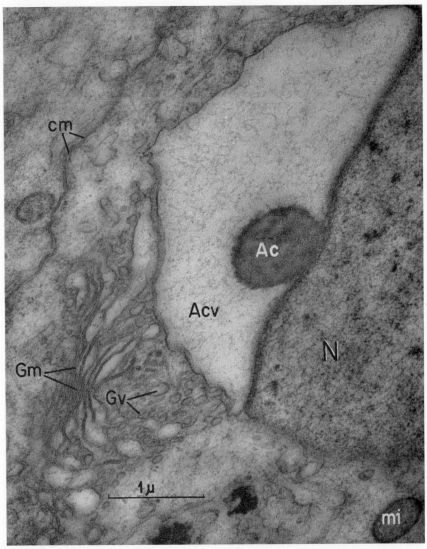

FIGURE 10–10.   Electron micrograph of a cat spermatid showing the Golgi complex and its relationship to the formation of the acrosome. *Ac*, acrosome; *Acv*, acrosomal vacuoles; *Gm*, Golgi membranes; *Gv*, Golgi vacuoles; *mi*, mitochondrion; *N*, nucleus. (Courtesy of M. H. Burgos and D. W. Fawcett.)

oles (Figs. 10–10 and 10–11). As development proceeds, the Golgi complex becomes irregular in shape, and large vacuoles are formed by dilatation of the flattened sacs (Fig. 10–11A–C). In the center of the complex large vacuoles are present, and in one or more of them a dense granule, the *proacrosomal granule,* appears (Fig. 10–11C–D). This approaches the anterior pole of the nucleus (Fig. 10–11E) and adheres to the nuclear membrane, constituting the *acrosomal granule* (Fig. 10–11F). With elongation of the spermatid, the acrosomal vesicle collapses over the pole of the nucleus and forms the head cap (Fig. 10–11F), while the granule becomes the *acrosome.*

Although the present trend is to consider that the Golgi membranes are dynamically related to other parts of the agranular and granular endoplasmic reticulum and even to the nuclear envelope, they constitute a definite morphologic entity. In fact, the Golgi complex of certain cells can be isolated and studied under the electron microscope (Fig. 10–12). Furthermore it has some differential staining and cytochemical properties. The ability of the Golgi complex to reduce osmium after long treatment, one of the methods used to detect the Golgi complex with the light microscope (Fig. 9–3), has also been demonstrated at the electron microscope level.[32]

SOME CYTOCHEMICAL PROPERTIES OF THE VACUOLAR SYSTEM

While most of our knowledge of the chemical organization of the vacuolar system comes from the isolation of microsomes and the Golgi complex (see the following section), some information can be obtained by methods of enzyme cytochemistry at the light and electron microscope levels (see Chap. 6). These studies point toward a chemical specialization of the different intracellular membranes and a dynamic relationship between them. This is particularly evident for different phosphatases. For example, in liver cells glucose-6-phosphatase is found in the endoplasmic reticulum while ino-

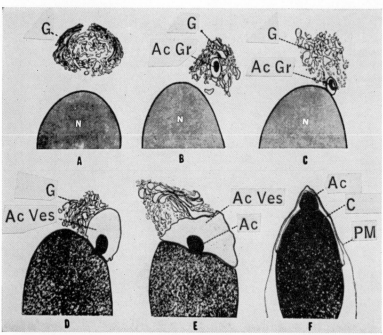

Figure 10–11. Diagram indicating the sequence in the formation of the acrosome (*Ac*) and the head cap (*C*), beginning within the Golgi complex (see the description in the text). *Ac Gr,* acrosomal granule; *Ac Ves,* acrosomal vesicles; *G,* Golgi complex; *PM,* plasma membrane. (From Burgos and Fawcett, 1955.)

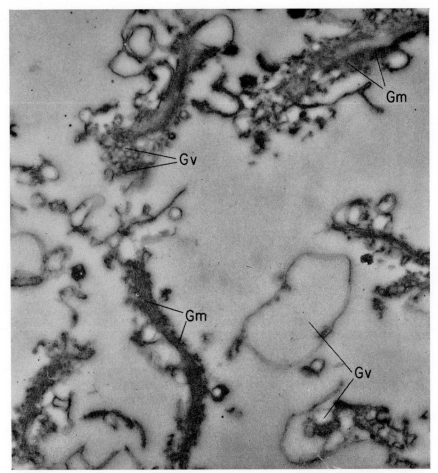

FIGURE 10–12.   Electron micrograph of the Golgi complex isolated from the epididymis. *Gm*, Golgi membranes; *Gv*, Golgi vacuoles. (Courtesy of A. J. Dalton.)

sine diphosphatase is present in the Golgi complex (Fig. 10–13).[33] In some hepatoma cells the endoplasmic reticulum is active on diphosphates of uridine, guanosine and inosine, while the Golgi complex has high levels of thiamine pyrophosphatase.[34]

In these studies the Golgi membranes give a negative acid phosphatase reaction while some secretory vacuoles formed in this region give a positive reaction. The diagram of Figure 10–14 indicates the possible interrelationship suggested by these studies. According to this view, the granular endoplasmic reticulum can give rise to agranular endoplasmic reticulum and to Golgi membranes, which in turn produce the membranes of the secretory vacuoles. These transformations would imply not only morphologic but cytochemical differentiation.

BIOCHEMICAL STUDIES. MICROSOMES

At the beginning of the chapter it was said that the so-called *microsomes* constitute a heterogeneous subcellular fraction which includes most of the vacuolar system and the ribosomes. As shown in Figure 6–5, after homogenation of the cell the different nuclear, mitochondrial, microsomal and soluble fractions can be isolated by differential centrifugation. The nuclear envelope and the nucleus are isolated in the same fraction (Fig. 10–7), but the other components of the vacuolar system, including the granular and agranular endoplasmic reticulum and the Golgi membranes, are isolated with the microsomes. The Golgi complex can be isolated in a separate fraction only in certain cells.

Electron microscope observations of

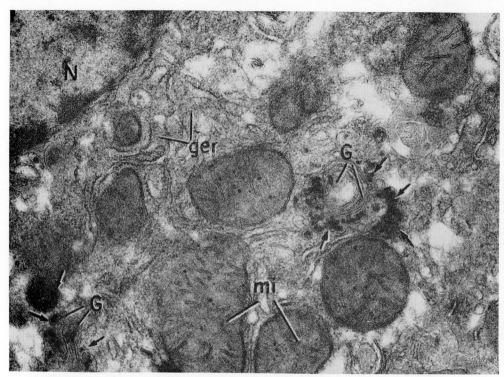

Figure 10–13.   Electron micrograph of a liver cell showing the nucleoside diphosphatase activity localized in the Golgi zone (arrows). Fixation in glutaraldehyde and incubation in inosine diphosphate. *G*, Golgi complex; *ger*, granular endoplasmic reticulum; *mi*, mitochondria; *N*, nucleus. ×25,000. (Courtesy of D. D. Sabatini, K. G. Bensch and R. J. Barrnett.)

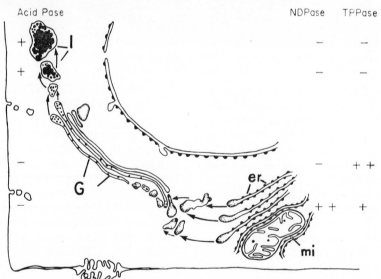

Figure 10–14.   Diagram to suggest the relationship between granular endoplasmic reticulum, agranular endoplasmic reticulum, Golgi complex (*G*), secretory granules and lysosomes. Based on the reaction of the following enzymes: *acid Pase* (acid phosphatase), *NDPase* (nucleoside diphosphatase), and *TPPase* (thiamine pyrophosphatase). *er*, endoplasmic reticulum; *mi*, mitochondrion. (From E. Essner and A. B. Novikoff.)

liver microsomes have revealed fragments of the vacuolar system in the form of isolated vesicles, tubules and some cisternae with ribosomes attached (Fig. 10–15). In pancreas microsomes, the vacuolar system becomes more fragmented and appears in general as round vesicles surrounded by dense particles. It has been suggested that in the pancreas this process of fragmentation does not result from mechanical tearing but from a generalized pinching-off process of the vacuolar system that takes place upon cell injury.[35] On the whole, the microsomal fraction of the pancreas is more homogeneous than that of the liver, and this is a reflection of the different organization of the vacuolar system in both types of cells (Figs. 10–3 and 10–5). However, there is no doubt that in addition to the

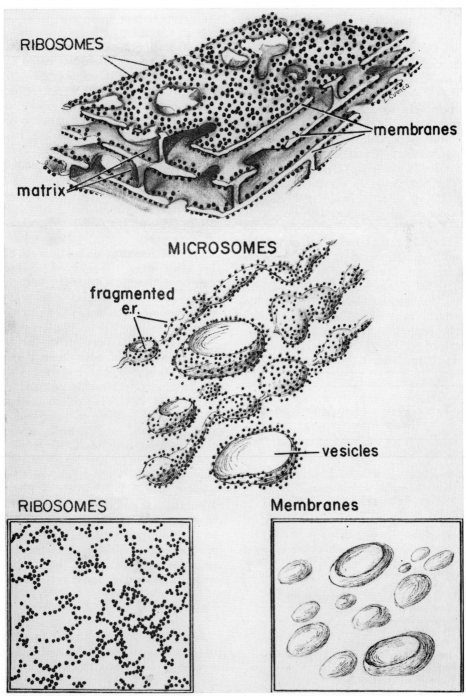

FIGURE 10–15. Diagram showing: **Above,** the three-dimensional disposition of the granular endoplasmic reticulum with the membranes and ribosomes. **Middle,** the fragmentation of the endoplasmic reticulum to form the microsomes. **Below,** isolated ribosomes and membranes.

endoplasmic reticulum, the microsomal fraction contains Golgi membranes, ruptured plasma membranes and other cell fragments. In liver microsomes, depending on the physiological state, glycogen and ferritin and some lipid droplets may also be found.[36]

The microsomes constitute about 15 to 20 per cent of the total mass of the cell. Since the early studies it has been shown that this fraction contains as much as 50 to 60 per cent of the RNA of the cell;[37, 38] now it is known that this RNA corresponds to the ribosomes. Microsomes have a high lipid content, which includes phospholipids, inositol, acetylphosphatides (plasmalogens) and gangliosides (see Chap. 3).

The complexity in chemical composition is also reflected in the great number of microsomal enzymes. The first to be identified were a group of stearases and NAD-cytochrome c reductase, which has been frequently used as a marker of the microsomal membranes.[35]

The list presented in Table 10–1 indicates that microsomes have different biochemical functions: through nucleotide diphosphate they function in the biosynthesis of phosphatides, ascorbic acid and glucuronide and in hexose metabolism;

they are active in steroid biosynthesis; they are involved in a series of reaction requiring $NADPH_2$ and O_2; and they also act at certain points in the synthesis o glyceride, phospholipid, glycolipid and plasmalogen.[39]

Subfractionation of Microsomes

Further analysis of the microsomal fraction involved the dissociation of the membranes from the ribosomes.[35] Treatment with a surface-active agent, such a desoxycholate, allowed the solubilization of the membranes and separation of the ribosomes (see Chap. 9 and Fig. 10–15). The protein, phospholipid, hemochromogen and NAD-cytochrome c reductase part of the membrane disappeared with increased concentrations of desoxycholate, while RNA remained constant (Fig. 10–16). By means of refined technique of differential centrifugation, which involve the use of a discontinuous gradient of densities, the microsomal fraction can be subfractioned further into agranular vesicles and granular vesicles having the ribosomes attached.[39] With this technique some metabolic differences between these two portions of the endoplasmic reticulum have been detected. Several enzymes that metabolize drug, such as aminopyrine, chlorpromazine, codeine and NADPH-oxidase are more concentrated in the agranular endoplasmic reticulum. In liver cells, following the incorporation of C^{14}-leucine into serum albumin, it can be observed that the granular endoplasmic reticulum (rough surface) is involved first and then the agranular endoplasmic reticulum (smooth surface) (Fig. 10–17).[40] This can be interpreted as indicating that serum albumin is first synthesized in the granular reticulum and then is transferred into the agranular reticulum.

Isolation of Golgi Membranes

Important progress in our knowledge of the chemical composition of the Golgi substance has been made by isolating the Golgi substance from cells of the epididymis.[29, 41, 42] After mechanical disintegration of the cells, the Golgi substance can be recognized under the phase o

---

**TABLE 10–1.   SOME MICROSOMAL
ENZYME ACTIVITIES***

Synthesis of glycerides:
    Triglycerides
    Phosphatides
    Glycolipids and plasmalogens
Metabolism of plasmalogens
Fatty acid synthesis
Steroid biosynthesis:
    Cholesterol biosynthesis
    Steroid hydrogenation of unsaturated bonds
$NADPH_2 + O_2$-requiring steroid transformations:
    Aromatization
    Hydroxylation
$NADPH_2 + O_2$-requiring drug detoxification:
    Aromatic hydroxylations
    Side-chain oxidation
    Deamination
    Thio-ether oxidation
    Desulfuration
L-Ascorbic acid synthesis
UDP-uronic acid metabolism
UDP-glucose dephosphorylation
Aryl- and steroid-sulfatase

---

* Modified from Rothschild.[39]

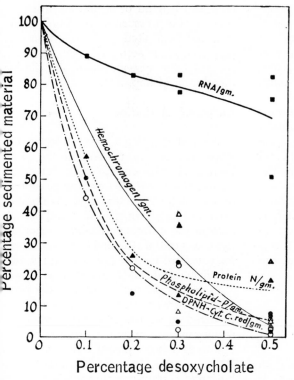

FIGURE 10–16. Curve representing the effect of deoxycholate on liver microsomes. Results indicate that by increasing the concentration of desoxycholate the different components (hemochromogen, protein, phospholipid, DPNH-cytochrome c reductase) associated with the membranes diminish. On the other hand, the ribonucleic acid (RNA) of the granules remains constant. (From Palade and Siekevitz, 1956.)

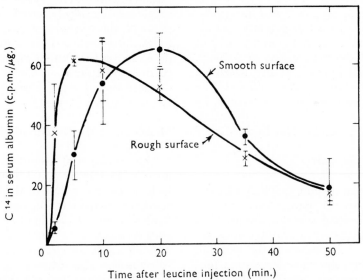

FIGURE 10–17. Incorporation of serum albumin labeled with C14-leucine in the granular endoplasmic reticulum (rough surface) and agranular endoplasmic reticulum (smooth surface). The incorporation after the injection of C14-leucine is more rapid in the granular endoplasmic reticulum. c.p.m., counts per minute. (From T. Peters.[40])

darkfield microscope and some of its histochemical properties can be studied. This substance has a cuplike shape and a brilliant refringence that diminishes considerably after treatment with 70 per cent alcohol. The other component contributing to the refringence is insoluble and stains with black Sudan. The isolated Golgi substance gives a positive PAS reaction, but not if treated with alcohol. This would indicate that this reaction takes place in the lipid fraction.

The Golgi complex was isolated by centrifugation, using an appropriate density gradient (see Chap. 6).[36, 42] An isolated fraction, G, contained mainly Golgi body fragments and some submicroscopic material (Fig. 10–12). In fraction G the concentration of phospholipids and alkaline phosphatase was 3.5 to 5 times the concentration of the total cell homogenate. Acid phosphatase was associated with the larger Golgi structures. Ascorbic acid, ribonucleic acid, cytochrome oxidase, β-glucuronidase and deoxyribonuclease are lacking in the Golgi complex.

The fact that there is little enzymatic activity might be significant in itself. It has been suggested that Golgi membranes carry out their roles in secretion and absorption chiefly without enzymes.[36]

FUNCTIONS OF THE VACUOLAR SYSTEM

The role of the endoplasmic reticulum and Golgi complex in cell physiology is little known. Many functional interpretations are based on the polymorphic aspects of these components in a variety of cells and at different stages of activity. More reliable hypotheses are based on the isolation studies just mentioned. The following list of possible functions is by no means complete and includes well-known facts together with hypotheses.[43]

Mechanical Support

The vacuolar system, together with the cytoplasmic matrix, participates in many of the mechanical functions of the cell that were discussed in Chapter 9. By dividing the fluid content of the cell into compartments, the vacuolar system provides supplementary mechanical support for the colloidal structure of the cytoplasm.

Exchange

The membranes of the vacuolar system may regulate the exchange between the inner compartment and the outer compartment, or cytoplasmic matrix. It is known that in the cell the system has *osmotic properties*. After isolation, mi-crosomes expand or shrink according to the osmotic pressure of the fluid. Diffusion and facilitated and active transport may take place across the membranes of the vacuolar system, as in the plasma membrane (Chap. 20).

Enzymatic Activities

We just mentioned the numerous enzymes that are associated with the membranes of the endoplasmic reticulum (Table 10–1) and the low enzyme content of the Golgi complex. The membranes provide a larger inner surface and participate in the different metabolic reactions by means of the attached enzymes. These enzymes are mainly involved in the metabolism of steroids and phospholipids.

As in the plasma membrane the presence of *carriers* and *permeases* that are involved in active transport across the membrane and in pinocytosis and phagocytosis has been postulated (see Chap. 20). According to some views the distribution of certain enzymes indicates a dynamic relationship between the different parts of the vacuolar system, with the following directional flow: granular endoplasmic reticulum → agranular endoplasmic reticulum → Golgi membrane → secretion (and lysosomes).[34] (See Chap. 20 and Fig. 10–14.)

Membrane Flux and Circulation

The existence of a similar directional flow of membranes and material with locks at certain points of the system has also been postulated. The endoplasmic reticulum may act as a kind of *circulatory system* involved in the import, export and intracellular circulation of various substances.[5] This concept is reinforced by observations on cells that actively take in fluid from the surrounding medium. This phenomenon, described as *pinocytosis* (Chap. 20), is apparently well developed at a submicroscopic level. In numerous cells it is possible to see, with the electron microscope, invaginations of the plasma membranes forming pockets that are associated with intracytoplasmic vacuoles.

The interesting hypothesis has been advanced that this membrane flow is an

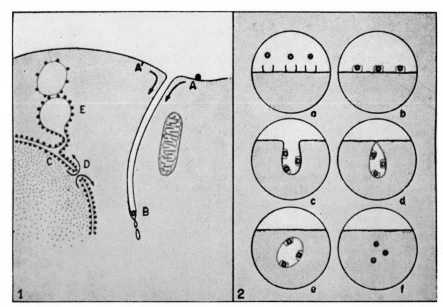

FIGURE 10–18.   1, diagram representing the hypothesis of membrane flux. 2, diagram representing the concept of transportation by vesiculation of the membranes (see the description in the text). (From Bennett, 1956.)

important mechanism for carrying particles, molecules and ions into and out of the cells by way of the vacuolar system.[44] As shown in the diagram of Figure 10–18(1), if there is a region, AA′, in which the plasma membrane is being actively synthesized and another, B, in which it is broken down, membrane flow in the direction of the arrow will occur. By this mechanism, particles attached to the surface of the cell and the fluid medium can be incorporated into the cytoplasm as shown in Figure 10–18(2). A similar mechanism, but working in a reverse direction (f to a), can effect the transport of a particle from the interior of the cytoplasm to the outer medium (i.e., secretion, Chap. 23). The continuities observed in some cases between the endoplasmic reticulum and the two layers of the nuclear envelope suggest that the membrane flow may also be active at this point. This flow would provide one of the several mechanisms for export of RNA and nucleoproteins from the nucleus to the cytoplasm (see Chap. 17).

More will be said later about this possible mechanism of membrane flow, particularly in the chapters concerned with pinocytosis, phagocytosis, secretion and fat absorption. It is important to understand, however, how the vacuolar system is involved in such important physiologic activities of the cell as permeability, circulation of substances, synthesis and storage within membranes, secretion and so forth. Another important concept is that at this level of structure certain cell components, such as the plasma membrane and the membranes of the vacuolar system, are highly dynamic. They can be formed and destroyed, probably in a continuous manner, within the realm of the cytoplasm.

Protein Synthesis and Segregation of Products

As indicated in the preceding chapter, protein synthesis is intimately related to the ribosomes. The existence of the granular endoplasmic reticulum poses the question of the role played by the membranes in this process. It is evident that when proteins are synthesized to be incorporated or used by the cell, e.g., hemoglobin and fibrous proteins, the membranes of the vacuolar system are not involved and the products are stored in the cell matrix. The vacuolar system seems to be active in those activities in which the protein is made for export, e.g., synthesis of tropocollagen, serum proteins and secretion granules. The two-dimensional array of polyribosomes on the surface of the endoplasmic reticulum probably accelerates the activity of messenger RNA and protein synthesis (see Chap. 18). By some unknown mechanism the protein molecules that are discharged from the ribosomes penetrate into the cavity of the endoplasmic reticulum and are stored and segregated for export outside the cell. In the case of some serum proteins (particularly γ-globulin) synthesized within the plasma cells, it has been possible to follow the storage by means of an antibody conjugated to ferritin.[45] As shown in Figure 10–19, the ferritin molecules, which act as markers for the γ-globulin antibodies, are localized exclusively within the cisternae of the endoplasmic reticulum where the γ-globulin is being stored for export.

Cell Secretion and the Golgi Complex

We will not consider here the enormous literature regarding the possible relationships between secretion and the Golgi complex.[46–48] Numerous studies with the light microscope showed that in this region different absorbed substances, e.g., trypan blue, iron or copper compounds, could be accumulated. These early results suggested that the Golgi complex acts as a condensation membrane for the "concentration into droplets or granules of products elaborated in other locations that diffuse through the cytoplasm." These products could be lipids, yolk, bile components, enzymes, hormones and so forth.[49] According to this theory, the Golgi complex acts by surface action without intervening in the synthesis or transformation of the products. Nevertheless this action may not be purely passive and may have a dynamic character.

In the cells of the intestinal epithelium, alkaline phosphatase is concentrated in the Golgi complex.[50] This has been confirmed in the Golgi substance isolated by centrifugation.[41] Acid and alkaline phosphatase are also present in the Golgi region of several kinds of epithelial cells.[51] These facts may suggest a limited participation of the Golgi complex in metabolic processes.

Better evidence that the Golgi substance is related to cell secretion and other physiologic processes has been obtained by electron microscopy of several types of cells (see Chap. 23).[52]

Another function that should not be disregarded is the probable concentrating role of the Golgi membranes by withdrawing water from the maturing secretory granules. By this process the secretion product could be packed in a more compact granule used for storage and final delivery. A similar intervention of the Golgi complex in the segregation of lipids absorbed by the duodenal epithelium has been postulated.[53] Also related to this function is the homology that has been suggested between the Golgi complex and the contractile vacuole found in lower animals and protozoa, around which typical dictiosome-like bodies are found. Under the electron microscope it can be observed that the structure of these bodies closely resembles the Golgi substance of metazoa.[54]

The role of the Golgi complex in concentrating the products of secretion synthesized in the endoplasmic reticulum has also been demonstrated by radioautography at the optical and electron microscope levels.[55] The Golgi complex has been considered as a stock of intracellular membranes that are prepared to package the secretory products of the cell for export.

Agranular Endoplasmic Reticulum and Glycogen Metabolism

It was mentioned that in the liver, glycogen particles accumulate in regions in which the agranular endoplasmic reticulum is well developed (Fig. 10–5). This topographical relationship led to studies of the possible function of this system in glycogen metabolism.[56]

In fasted animals it was found that the residual glycogen remained associated with the tubules and vesicles of the endoplasmic reticulum. Upon refeeding there was an increase in agranular endoplasmic reticulum which maintained its association with the accumulating glycogen. Also, in plant cells the agranular endoplasmic reticulum develops along

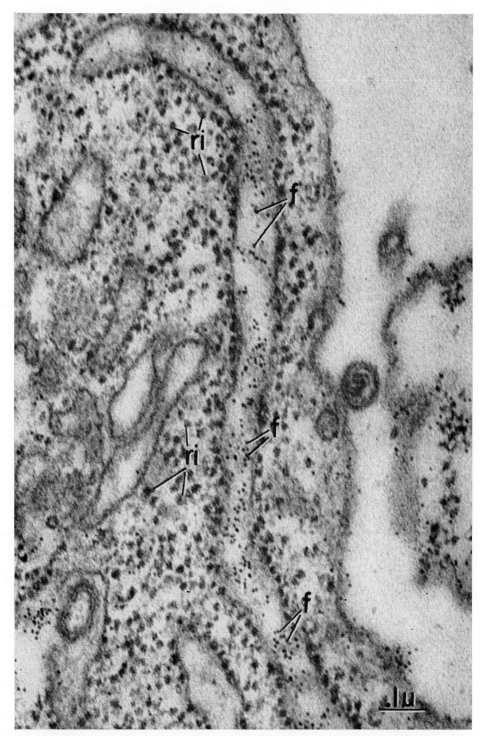

Figure 10–19.   Electron micrograph of the peripheral portion of a plasma cell (myeloma). The cisternae of the endoplasmic reticulum contain numerous ferritin molecules, indicating the localization of γ-globulin. In this technique the tissue is exposed to an antibody labeled with ferritin. *f*, ferritin; *ri*, ribosomes. ×140,000. (Courtesy of R. A. Rifkind.)

the surface where the cellulose walls are being formed.[57] Although these observations suggest a relationship between the endoplasmic reticulum and the metabolism of polysaccharides, the true chemical mechanism is still not well defined. Furthermore, in other cell types such an association between the agranular endoplasmic reticulum and glycogen has not been found.[58] Recently it has been suggested that the agranular reticulum is related to glycogenolysis, but not to glycogenesis, because glucose-6-phosphatase is found in the membranes of the reticulum.[59]

An attempt to localize the enzyme UDPG-glycogen transferase,[60] which is directly involved in the synthesis of glycogen by addition of uridine diphosphate glucose (UDPG) to primer glycogen, has shown that this enzyme is bound to the glycogen particle rather than to the membranous component.[61]

According to some views, the exit of glucose from the glycogen deposits outside the cell could be mediated by the agranular endoplasmic reticulum in which glucose-6-phosphatase is present. This phosphatase would be thus active in the transport of glucose across the membrane. By this mechanism the endoplasmic reticulum could be involved in the secretion of glucose to the exterior and also in its protection from the action of glycolytic enzymes in the cytoplasmic matrix, thus regulating the pathway of glucose metabolism in the cell.[1, 61]

Intracellular Impulse Conduction

The existence of a vacuolar system separating the cytoplasm into two compartments makes possible the existence of ionic gradients and electrical potentials across these intracellular membranes. This concept has been applied especially to the *sarcoplasmic reticulum*, a specialized form of endoplasmic reticulum found in striated muscle fibers, which is now being considered as an intracellular conducting system.[62] On the bases of some experimental evidence and of morphologic observations, it has been postulated that the sarcoplasmic reticulum transmits impulses from the surface

membrane into the deep regions of the muscle fiber. (A more detailed study of the sarcoplasmic reticulum and its postulated function is presented in Chapter 21.)

GENERAL REFERENCES

Bensley, R. R. (1951) Facts versus artifacts in cytology; the Golgi apparatus. *Exp. Cell Res.,* 2:1.

Bourne, G. (1951) Mitochondria and Golgi apparatus. In: *Cytology and cell physiology.* (Bourne, G., ed.) Oxford University Press, London.

Claude, A. (1954) Cell morphology and the organization of enzymatic systems in cytoplasm. *Proc. Roy. Soc. London, ser. B, 142:* 177.

Dalton, A. J., and Felix, M. D. (1954) Cytology and cytochemical characteristics of the Golgi substance of epithelial cells of the epididymis in situ, in homogenates and after isolation. *Amer. J. Anat.,* 94:171.

Haguenau, F. (1958) The ergastoplasm; its history, ultrastructure and biochemistry. *Internat. Rev. Cytol.,* 7:425.

Hibbard, H. (1945) Current status of our knowledge of the Golgi apparatus in the animal cell. *Quart. Rev. Biol.,* 20:1.

Palay, S. L. (1958) The morphology of secretion. In: *Frontiers in cytology.* (Palay, S. L., ed.) Yale University Press, New Haven, Conn.

Porter, K. R. (1961) The ground substance; observations from electron microscopy. In: *The cell,* Vol. 2, p. 621. (Brachet, J., and Mirsky, A. E., eds.) Academic Press, New York.

CITED REFERENCES

1. Siekevitz, P. (1959) *Ciba Foundation symposium on the regulation of cell metabolism.* (Wolstenholme, G. E. W., and O'Connor, C. M., eds.) J. & A. Churchill, London, p. 17.

2. Porter, K. R., Claude, A., and Fullman, E. F. (1945) *J. Exp. Med.,* 81:233.

3. Porter, K. R. (1953) *J. Exp. Med.,* 97:727.

4. Palade, G. E. (1956) *Henry Ford Hospital Int. Symposium,* pp. 185–215.

5. Palade, G. E. (1956) *J. Biophys. Biochem. Cytol.,* 2:85.

6. Sjöstrand, F. S. (1956) *Internat. Rev. Cytol.,* 5:456.

7. Haguenau, F. (1958) *Internat. Rev. Cytol.,* 7:425.

8. Porter, K. R. (1961) The ground substance; observations from electron microscopy. In: *The cell,* Vol. 2, p. 621. (Brachet, J., and Mirsky, A. E., eds.) Academic Press, New York.

9. Fawcett, D. W., and Ito, S. (1958) *J. Biophys. Biochem. Cytol., 4*:135.

10. Munger, B. L. (1958) *J. Biophys. Biochem. Cytol., 4*:177.

11. Thiéry, J. P. (1958) *Rev. Hémat., 13*:61.

12. Rose, G. G., and Pomerat, C. M. (1960) *J. Biophys. Biochem. Cytol., 8*:423.

13. Christensen, A. K., and Fawcett, D. W. (1960) *Anat. Rec., 136*:333.

14. Palade, G. E. (1956) *J. Biophys. Biochem. Cytol., 2*:417.

15. Fauré-Fremiet, E., and Roullier, C. (1958) *Exp. Cell Res., 14*:29.

16. Mirsky, A. E., and Osawa, S. (1961) The interphase nucleus. In: *The cell*, Vol. 2, p. 677. (Brachet, J., and Mirsky, A. E., eds.) Academic Press, New York.

17. Callan, H. G., and Tomlin, S. G. (1950) *Proc. Roy. Soc. London, ser. B, 137*:367.

18. Watson, M. (1955) *J. Biophys. Biochem. Cytol., 1*:257.

19. Afzelius, B. A. (1955) *Exp. Cell Res., 8*:147.

20. Gall, J. G. (1956) *Brookhaven Symp. Biol., 8*:17.

21. Wischnitzer, S. (1958) *J. Ultrastruct. Res., 1*:201.

22. Watson, M. L. (1959) *J. Biophys. Biochem. Cytol., 6*:147.

23. Pappas, G. D. (1956) *J. Biophys. Biochem. Cytol., 2*:221.

24. Maggio, R., Siekevitz, P., and Palade, G. E. (1963) *J. Cell Biol., 18*:267.

25. Loewenstein, W. R., and Kanno, Y. (1962) *Nature, 195*:462.

26. Palay, S. L. (1960) *J. Biophys. Biochem. Cytol., 7*:391.

27. Brachet, J. (1961) Nucleocytoplasmic interactions in unicellular organisms. In: *The cell*, Vol. 2, p. 771. (Brachet, J., and Mirsky, A. E., eds.) Academic Press, New York.

28. Barer, R., Joseph, S., and Merck, G. A. (1959) *Exp. Cell Res., 18*:179.

29. Dalton, A. J., and Felix, M. D. (1954) *Amer. J. Anat., 94*:171.

30. Dalton, A. J. (1961) Golgi apparatus and secretion granules. In: *The cell*, Vol. 2, p. 603. (Brachet, J., and Mirsky, A. E., eds.) Academic Press, New York.

31. Burgos, M. H., and Fawcett, D. W. (1955) *J. Biophys. Biochem. Cytol., 1*:4.

32. Dalton, A. J., and Felix, M. D. (1956) *J. Biophys. Biochem. Cytol., 2*:79.

33. Sabatini, D. D., Bensch, K. G., and Barrnett, R. J. (1963) *J. Cell Biol., 17*:19.

34. Essner, E., and Novikoff, A. B. (1962) *J. Cell Biol., 15*:289.

35. Palade, G. E., and Siekevitz, F. (1956) *J. Biophys. Biochem. Cytol., 2*:171.

36. Kuff, L., and Dalton, A. J. (1959) Biochemical studies of isolated Golgi membranes. In: *Subcellular particles.* (Hayashi, T., ed.) The Ronald Press Co., New York, p. 114.

37. Claude, A. (1946) *J. Exp. Med., 84*:51.

38. Claude, A. (1949) *Advanc. Protein Chem., 5*:423.

39. Rothschild, J. (1963) The isolation of microsomal membranes. In: The structure and function of the membranes and surfaces of cells. *Biochem. Soc. Symp., 22*:4. Cambridge University Press.

40. Peters, T. (1962) *J. Biol. Chem., 237*:1181.

41. Schneider, W. C., Dalton, A. J., Kuff, E. L., and Felix, M. D. (1953) *Nature, 172*:161.

42. Schneider, W. C., and Kuff, E. L. (1954) *Amer. J. Anat., 94*:209.

43. de Duve, C. (1962) Enzymes and drug action. *Ciba Foundation Symposium.* Little, Brown and Co., Boston.

44. Bennett, S. (1956) *J. Biophys. Biochem. Cytol., 2*:99.

45. Rifkind, R. A., Morgan, C., and Harvet, M. R. (1962) The ferritin-conjugated antibody technique. *Fifth Internat. Congress for Electron Microscopy.* Academic Press, New York.

46. Bourne, G. (1951) Mitochondria and Golgi apparatus. In: *Cytology and cell physiology.* (Bourne, G., ed.) Oxford University Press, London.

47. Palay, S. L. (1958) The morphology of secretion. In: *Frontiers in cytology.* (Palay, S. L., ed.) Yale University Press, New Haven.

48. Zeigel, R. F., and Dalton, A. J. (1962) *J. Cell Biol., 15*:45.

49. Kirkman, H., and Severinghaus, A. E. (1938) *Anat. Rec., 70*:413; *71*:557.

50. Emmel, V. M. (1945) *Anat. Rec., 91*:39.

51. Deane, H. W., and Dempsey, E. W. (1945) *Anat. Rec., 93*:401.

52. De Robertis, E., and Sabatini, D. D. (1960) *Fed. Proc., 19*:70.

53. Weiss, J. M. (1955) *J. Exp. Med., 102*:775.

54. Gatenby, J. B., Dalton, A. J., and Felix, M. D. (1955) *Nature, 176*:301.

55. Caro, L. G. (1961) *J. Biophys. Biochem. Cytol., 10*:37.

56. Porter, K. R., and Bruni, C. (1960) *Cancer Res., 19*:997.

57. Porter, K. R., and Machado, R. D. (1960) *J. Biophys. Biochem. Cytol., 7*:167.

58. Revel, J. P., Napolitano, L., and Fawcett, D. W. (1960) *J. Biophys. Biochem. Cytol., 8*:575.

59. Peters, V. B., Dembitzer, H. M., Kelly, G. W., and Baruch, E. (1962) Ergastoplasmic changes asosciated with glycogenolysis. *Fifth Internat. Congress for Electron Microscopy*, Vol. 2. Academic Press, New York.

60. Leloir, L. F., and Cardini, C. E. (1957) *J. Amer. Chem. Soc., 79*:6340.

61. Luck, D. J. L. (1961) *J. Biophys. Biochem. Cytol., 10*:195.

62. Porter, K. R. (1961) *J. Biophys. Biochem. Cytol., 10*:219.

CHAPTER 11

MITOCHONDRIA

Mitochondria (Gr. *mito-* thread + *chondrion* granule), granular or filamentous organoids present in the cytoplasm of protozoa and animal and plant cells, are characterized by a series of morphologic, biochemical and functional properties. Among these are their size and shape, visibility in vivo and special staining properties, the specific structural organization, the lipoprotein composition and the content of a large "battery" of enzymes and coenzymes that work in an integrated fashion to produce cellular energy transformations. From the physiological viewpoint, mitochondria are biochemical "machines" that recover the energy contained in foodstuffs (through the Krebs cycle and the respiratory chain), and convert it by phosphorylation into the phosphate bond of adenosine triphosphate (ATP) (see Chap. 4). Thus mitochondria are the "power plants" of the cell, which produce the energy necessary for many cellular functions (Fig. 11–1).

First observed at the end of last century and described as "bioblasts" by Altmann (1894), these structures were called mitochondria by Benda (1897). In 1900, Michaelis first stained them supravitally with Janus green.

Considerable advances in the study of mitochondria have been made in the last decade, particularly by electron mi-

croscopy, which revealed a specific ultrastructural organization, and by biochemical analysis after isolation. The study of mitochondria is particularly thrilling because the mitochondrion is one of the best known examples of structural-functional integration within the cell.[1,2]

VITAL EXAMINATION

Although the examination of mitochondria in living cells is somewhat difficult due to their low refractive index, they can be observed easily in cells cultured in vitro, particularly under darkfield illumination and phase contrast.

Vital and supravital examination has been greatly facilitated by coloration with a dilute solution of *Janus green*, which stains mitochondria greenish blue. This staining is due to the action of the cytochrome oxidase system present in mitochondria, which maintains the dye in its oxidized (colored) form. In the surrounding cytoplasm the dye is reduced to a colorless leukobase (see Chap. 6).

By micromanipulation it has been demonstrated that mitochondria are relatively stable and can be displaced by the microneedle without alterations. The *specific gravity* is greater than that of the cytoplasm. By ultracentrifugation of living cells at 200,000 to 400,000 g, mitochondria are deposited at the centrifugal pole and are intact.

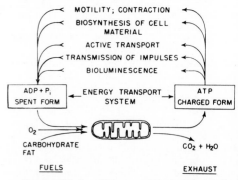

FIGURE 11–1. Diagram showing that mitochondria constitute the central "power plant" of the cell. The adenosine triphosphate (ATP) produced is used in the different functions that are indicated. (From A. L. Lehninger.)

Volume-Shape Changes in Vivo

Vital observation is of particular interest when supplemented with lapse cinematography. In cultured fibroblasts continuous, and sometimes rhythmic, changes in volume, shape and distribution of mitochondria can be observed. The two main types of *motion* are agitation and displacement from one part of the cell to another. Movements are more active during interphase than during mitosis. Sometimes mitochondria become attached to the nuclear envelope at a site near the nucleolus.[4, 5] Furthermore, filamentous mitochondria can fragment into granules, and these may unite again. Some movements may be passive and due to cytoplasmic streaming.

Active changes in volume and shape of mitochondria may be due to chemical, osmotic and mechanochemical changes. In living cells, low amplitude contraction cycles associated with oxidative phosphorylation have been observed. It is known that cyanide, dinitrophenol and other oxidative inhibitors produce swelling and that ATP in excess produces contraction of mitochondria.[6, 7] Swelling and contraction of mitochondria also occur by changing the osmotic pressure of the medium. Inorganic phosphate, reduced glutathione, Ca^{++} and fatty acids cause swelling, while ATP prevents it. Contraction depends on a contractile protein present in mitochondria and which has properties similar to actomyosin of muscle. Higher *amplitude changes* in the volume of mitochondria can be induced by a multiplicity of factors, among which the swelling effect of Ca^{++} and thyroxine are outstanding. The physiological effect of thyroid hormone in hyperthyroidism may be due to swelling of mitochondria, which uncouples oxidation and phosphorylation. Other hormones including the growth factor, oxytocin, vasopressin and insulin and certain corticosteroids may cause mitochondrial swelling.[2] This is also produced in pathological conditions, such as those caused by carcinogens and toxins. This property of swelling and contraction is best studied in isolated mitochondria and will be considered again in the discussion of the physiology of mitochondria.

FIXATION AND STAINING

It has long been recognized that mitochondria are labile structures that are readily disintegrated by the action of fixatives. For this reason, mitochondria are fixed by methods that stabilize the lipoprotein structure by the prolonged action of oxidizing agents, such as osmium tetroxide, chromic acid and potassium dichromate. As a stain, one usually uses iron hematoxylin (Regaud) or acid fuchsin (Altmann). In Chapter 6 some of the cytochemical staining methods for mitochondria were mentioned, such as the Nadi reaction for cytochrome oxidase and the use of different tetrazolium compounds, which form insoluble chromogens of formazan with mitochondrial dehydrogenases (Fig. 6–11). These cytochemical studies have been carried out also at the electron microscope level using potassium tellurite to localize succinic dehydrogenase and nitro-blue tetrazolium[8] and tetranitro-blue tetrazolium for succinic and $NADH_2$ dehydrogenases.[9] The products of the reaction were found in close association with the mitochondrial crests.

MORPHOLOGY

Shape

The shape of mitochondria is variable, but in general is *filamentous* or *granular* (Fig. 11–2). During certain functional stages other derived forms may be seen. For example, a long mitochondrion may swell at one end to assume the form of a *club* or hollow out to take the form of a *tennis racket*. At other times mitochondria may become *vesicular* by the appearance of a central clear zone. In the liver cells, morphologic cycles related to nutrition have been described. In liver cells of fishes, a few hours after the ingestion of food, the filamentous mitochondria change into club and racket shapes as well as into vesicular mito-

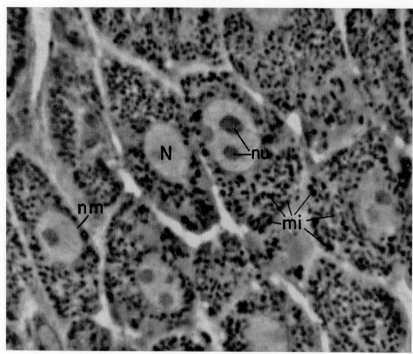

FIGURE 11–2.   Liver cells of the rat fixed at −180°C. and dehydrated in acetone at −40°C. Observation with phase contrast in a medium of n = 1460. *mi*, mitochondria; *N*, nucleus; *nm*, nuclear membrane; *nu*, nucleoli. (Courtesy of S. Koulish.)

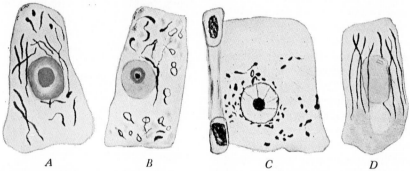

FIGURE 11–3.   Mitochondria of the hepatic cells of *Cnesterodon decemmaculatus* in different stages of nutrition. **A**, at the time of ingestion of the food, long mitochondria; **B**, at nine hours, shorter mitochondria with club and tennis racket shapes; **C**, at 24 hours, increase and clearing of the cytoplasm with short mitochondria around the nucleus; **D**, at 48 hours, similar to A, long mitochondria. (Fixation: Regaud; stain: iron hematoxylin.) (From Rojas, De Robertis and Castellengo.)

chondria. After 48 hours these changes cease and the mitochondria take on their original form (Fig. 11–3).

Size

The size of mitochondria is also variable. In most cells the width is relatively constant (about 0.5 μ) and the length is variable, reaching a maximum of 7 μ. However, depending on the functional stage of the cell, it is possible to find very thin (0.2 μ) or thick rods (2 μ). The size and shape of the fixed mitochondria depend also on the osmotic pressure and the pH of the fixative. In acid pH they tend to fragment and to become vesicular. The importance of using buffered fixatives at physiologic pH has been demonstrated.

Distribution

The distribution of mitochondria is in

general uniform throughout the cytoplasm, but there are many exceptions to this rule. For example, in kidney cells they are concentrated in the basal region next to the blood capillaries; the same is true of different glands of fixed polarity. In some cases, they accumulate preferentially around the nucleus or in the peripheral cytoplasm. Such distributions are more frequent in pathologic conditions. Some of these changes depend also on overloading with inclusions, such as glycogen and fat, which displace these organoids. During mitosis, mitochondria concentrate near the spindle, and upon division of the cell they are distributed in approximately equal quantity among the daughter cells (Fig. 14–4).

The distribution of mitochondria within the cytoplasm should be considered in relation to their function as energy suppliers. In some cells they can move freely, carrying ATP where needed, but in others they are located permanently near the region of the cell where presumably more energy is needed. For example, in certain muscle cells (e.g., diaphragm), mitochondria are shaped as rings or braces around the I-band of the myofibril. In the rod and cone cells of the retina all mitochondria are located in a portion of the inner segment. The basal mitochondria of the kidney tubule are intimately related to the infoldings of the plasma membrane in this region of the cell (Fig. 10–7B). It is assumed that this close relationship with the membrane is related to the supply of energy for the active transport of water and solutes. (The possible active role of mitochondria in water shifts is considered later in this chapter.)

Orientation

Mitochondria may have a more or less definite *orientation*. For example, in cylindrical cells they are generally oriented in the basal-apical direction, parallel to the main axis. In leukocytes, mitochondria are more or less radially arranged with respect to the centrioles. It has been suggested that these orientations depend upon the direction of the diffusion currents within cells and are related to the submicroscopic organization of the cytoplasmic matrix and vacuolar system.

Number

The mitochondrial content of a cell is difficult to determine, but in general it varies with the cell type and functional stage. It is estimated that in liver, mitochondria constitute 30 to 35 per cent of the total protein content of the cell, and in kidney, 20 per cent. In lymphoid tissue the value is much lower.[10, 11] In mouse liver homogenates there are about 8.7×10^{10} mitochondria per gram of fresh tissue.[12] A normal liver cell contains about 2500 mitochondria (Table 11–1), but this number diminishes during regeneration and also in cancerous tissue.[13, 14] This last observation may be related to the decrease in oxidation with increase of anaerobic glycolysis in cancer. There is a direct correlation between the number of mitochondria and secretory activity in salivary gland cells.[15]

In summary, the morphology of mitochondria varies from one cell to another, but it is more or less constant in cells of a similar type or having the same function.

TABLE 11–1. QUANTITATIVE DATA ON MITOCHONDRIAL DENSITY IN NORMAL, NEOPLASTIC AND REGENERATING MOUSE LIVER*

MATERIAL	NUMBER OF MITOCHONDRIA PER GRAM WET WEIGHT	NUMBER OF MITOCHONDRIA PER CELL	MG N PER MITOCHONDRION
Normal rat liver	3.30×10^{11}	2554	2.23×10^{-11}
Liver tumor	1.23×10^{11}	1391	3.08×10^{-11}
Regenerating liver { 1 day	2.42×10^{11}	1800	2.80×10^{-11}
{ 20 days	2.58×10^{11}	2150	2.52×10^{-11}

* Data from Allard, Lamirande and Cantero.[13–14]

GENERAL STRUCTURE

The first electron microscope observations of mitochondria in thin sections revealed that below the apparent homogeneous structure shown by the optical microscope (Fig. 11–2) was a membranous organization of high complexity.[16]

As indicated in the diagram of Figure 11–4, a mitochondrion consists of two membranes and two compartments, the larger of which represents the *mitochondrial matrix*. The mitochondrion is surrounded by an outer limiting membrane of about 60 Å that is probably concerned with the permeability of the organoid. Within this membrane, and separated by a space of about 60 to 80 Å, is an inner membrane that sends into the mitochondrial cavity complex infoldings called the *mitochondrial crests*. This inner membrane, also about 60 Å thick, divides the mitochondrion into two chambers or spaces: (1) the outer chamber contained between the two membranes and in the core of the crests and (2) the inner chamber, bounded by the inner membrane. This inner chamber is filled with a relatively dense material that is usually called the *mitochondrial matrix*. This is generally homogeneous,

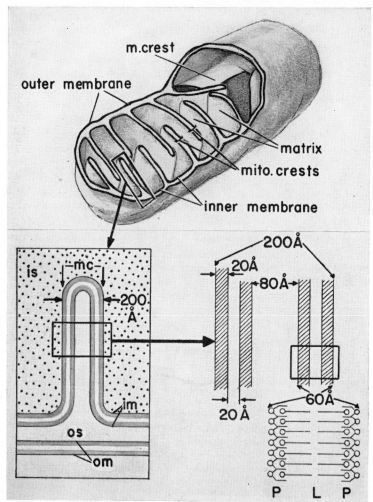

Figure 11–4. Diagram of the ultrastructure of a mitochondrion. **Above,** three-dimensional diagram showing outer and inner membranes with the crests (*m. crest*) and the mitochondrial matrix. **Below left,** at higher magnification; the inset of the previous figure corresponding to a mitochondrial crest. **Below right,** higher magnification of a molecular diagram interpreting the structure. *im,* inner membrane; *is,* inner space; *L,* lipid; *mc,* mitochondrial crest; *om,* outer membrane; *os,* outer space; *P,* protein.

but in some cases it may show a finely filamentous material[17] or small granules of high density (see Fig. 11–13). These granules are now considered as sites for binding bivalent cations, particularly Mg and Ca.[18] The mitochondrial crests that project from the inner membrane are in general incomplete septa or ridges that do not interrupt the continuity of the inner chamber; thus the matrix is continuous within the mitochondrion.

Further studies have shown that the mitochondrial membranes may be more complex, with two outer layers of high electron opacity and a lighter middle layer. This corresponds to the unit membrane structure mentioned in Chapter 8. In the diagram of Figure 11–4 the membrane is assumed to be formed by two layers of lipid molecules (L) with the nonpolar groups in the center, and the two electron-dense outer regions by protein molecules (P) (see Chap. 8). The diagram also emphasizes the differences in molecular packing between the membranes and the matrix. The outer and inner membranes and the crests can be considered as solid molecular films with a compact molecular structure; the matrix is a liquid phase containing soluble proteins and smaller molecules. This double (solid-liquid) structure is important in explaining some of the mechanical properties of mitochondria, e g., deformation and swelling in physiologic or experimental conditions.

More recently the use of negative staining has permitted the recognition of other details of structure. If a mitochondrion is allowed to swell and break in a hypotonic solution and is then immersed in phosphotungstate, the inner membrane and the crests appear to be covered by particles of 80 to 100 Å that have a stem that links them with the membrane (Fig. 11–5). These so-called "elementary particles"[19] are regularly spaced at 100 Å intervals on the inner surface of these membranes. According to some estimates, there would be 10^4 to 10^5 elementary particles per mitochondrion.[20] While their interpretation is still under discussion,[19, 21–23] there is some evidence that they contain some of the fixed components of the electron transfer system of the mitochondrion.[24]

Structural Variations

The preceding general description is valid for identifying mitochondria in most cells—not only in all types of mammalian cells but also in invertebrate cells, protozoa, algae and cells of higher plants. (Later on we will consider also the so-called *mesosomes* of bacteria.) "It appears, therefore, that we are dealing with a common pattern of mitochondrial structure which was presumably developed at an early stage in evolution and subsequently transmitted without considerable modifications from protozoa to mammals and from algae to flowering plants."[25] However, when one studies the detailed structure of mitochondria in different cell types, considerable variations can be observed. For example, the laminated infoldings of the inner membrane, or crests (Fig. 11–6), may be disposed longitudinally (e.g., in nerve and striated muscle). The crests may be simple or branched, forming complex networks. In protozoa, insects and adrenal cells of the glomerular zone, the infoldings may be tubular instead of lamellar, and the packing of the tubules may give rise to structures that have a regular organization (Fig. 11–7A).

Another variation that seems important is that of the number of crests per unit volume of the mitochondrion. This is complementary to the variation in amount of matrix. Whereas mitochondria in liver and germinal cells have few crests and an abundant matrix, mitochondria in certain muscle cells have numerous crests and little matrix (Fig. 11–13). The greatest concentration of crests is found in the flight muscle of insects. In general, there seems to be a correlation between the number of crests and the oxidative activity of the mitochondrion (see below).

A particularly interesting variation in fine structure is observed in cells of the different regions of the adrenal cortex (Fig. 11–7). One characteristic of these mitochondria is the enlargement of the space within the crests or tubules, which, according to the diagram of Figure 11–4, corresponds to the outer compartment of the mitochondrion. This is very conspicuous and appears as tubular or

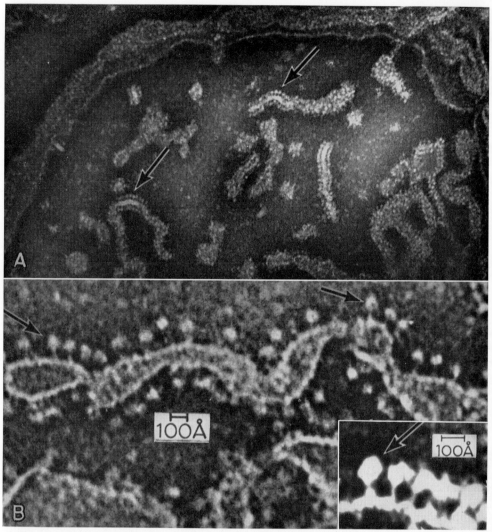

FIGURE 11–5. Electron micrograph of a mitochondrion swollen in a hypotonic solution and negatively stained with phosphotungstate. **A,** at low power; isolated crests can be observed in the middle of the swollen matrix. Arrows point to some of these crests. **B,** at higher magnification ($\times 500,000$), a mitochondrial crest showing the so-called "elementary particles" on the surface adjacent to the matrix. Inset at $650,000\times$, showing the elementary particles with a polygonal shape and the fine attachment to the crest. (Courtesy of H. Fernández-Morán.)

vesicular openings, which are much less opaque than the inner matrix (Fig. 11–7). These structures seem to be related to the specific secretory activity of the gland. In this case, mitochondria, in addition to functioning in cell oxidations, are actively engaged in the synthesis of steroid hormones.[26]

One interesting example of the physiological changes that mitochondria may undergo during the life cycle of a cell is given by the *mitochondrial body* found in the spermatids of some insects.[17] In the early spermatid all mitochondria ag- gregate in a region of the cytoplasm near the nucleus, at which time there may be an early fusion of some mitochondria, giving rise to some bizarre forms. Later, all mitochondria agglutinate and form a single *mitochondrial body*, which undergoes an intense process of fusion and remodeling (Fig. 11–8).

Structural Variations and Functional States

Some variations in mitochondrial structure are related to the special func-

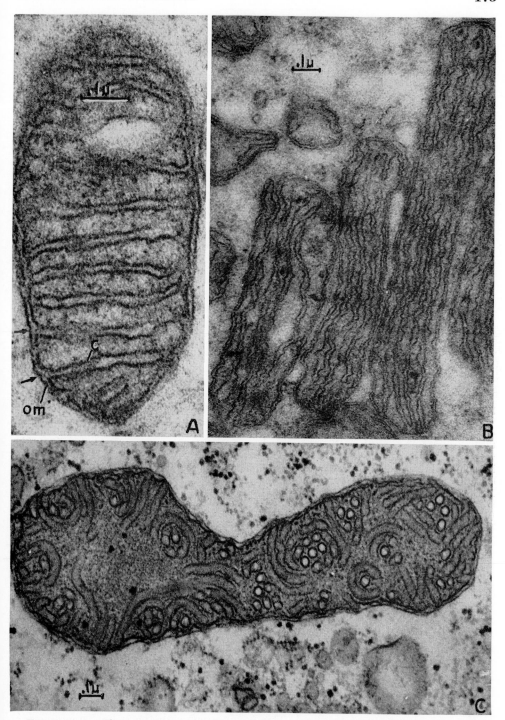

Figure 11–6.   Electron micrographs showing variations in mitochondrial ultrastructure. **A**, from rat testicle: *c*, transverse crests; *om*, outer membrane; arrows show origin of crests at the inner membrane. **B**, from ovotestis of *Helix*. Longitudinal crests in mitochondria of spermatocytes. **C**, from *Paramecium*, tubular crests. **A**, ×130,000; **B**, ×68,000; **C**, ×60,000. (Courtesy of J. Andrè.)

tional state of the cell. For example, after an animal has starved for several days, liver mitochondria are swollen, with clarification of the matrix and diminution in the number of crests. After refeeding, these changes revert to normal.[27]

Relationship with Lipids.   Various authors since the time of Altmann have

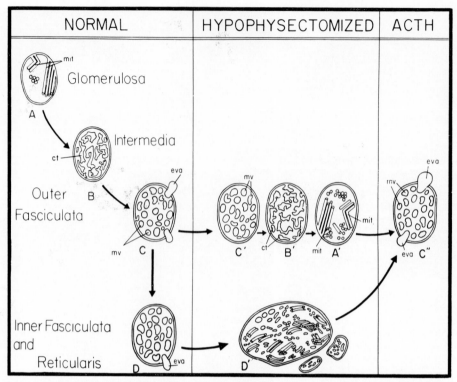

FIGURE 11–7.   General diagram of the mitochondrial changes found in adrenal cortex after hypophysectomy and restorational therapy. A, B, C and D, normal mitochondria at the glomerulosa, intermedia, outer fasciculata, inner fasciculata and reticularis. C′, B′ and A′, progressive changes of mitochondria of the outer fasciculata, leading to a pattern similar to that of glomerular cells (A). (Notice the lack of extruding vacuoles). D′, a chondriosphere of the inner fasciculata and reticularis formed by fusion of altered mitochondria. C″, mitochondria of the fasciculata after the injection of ACTH in a hypophysectomized animal. Notice the restoration of the vesicular pattern and the extruding vacuoles. eva, extruding vacuoles; mit, mitochondrial tubules; mv, mitochondrial vesicle. (From D. D. Sabatini, E. De Robertis and H. B. Bleichmar.)

observed that the *deposit of lipids* may be related to mitochondria. In liver cells of amphibia, the process is seen especially in the small mitochondria situated near the vascular pole, where the fat forms a type of crescent or peripheral cap, which stains with osmium tetroxide or Sudan III. An interesting example of the close topographic relationship between lipid droplets and mitochondria is shown in Figure 11–9. In pancreas and liver cells, after a short period of starvation, mitochondria come into contact with lipid droplets by becoming attached to the curved surface of the lipid. The relationship may be so tight that only the inner mitochondrial membrane can be seen adjacent to the lipid at some regions. Frequently at the surface of the lipid droplets are less dense zones that suggest a process of lipid utilization by the mitochondria. All electron microscope images suggest that an active proc-

ess of fat metabolism takes place under the action of the fatty acid oxidases present in mitochondria.[28] It is known that after a short period of starvation the metabolism of the cell changes and instead of carbohydrates, fatty acids are actively oxidized and degraded to be utilized in the common pathway of the Krebs cycle (see below).

Accumulation of Protein and Other Substances. In mitochondria of liver cells of amphibia the accumulation of pigment derived from hemoglobin with a positive reaction for ionic iron was observed with the optical microscope.[29] Electron microscopy has revealed ferritin molecules within mitochondria in subjects suffering of Cooley's hereditary anemia.[30] Another example is the formation of yolk bodies in eggs of the mollusk *Planorbis*.[31] One of the ways in which these protein-containing bodies are formed is by transformation of mito-

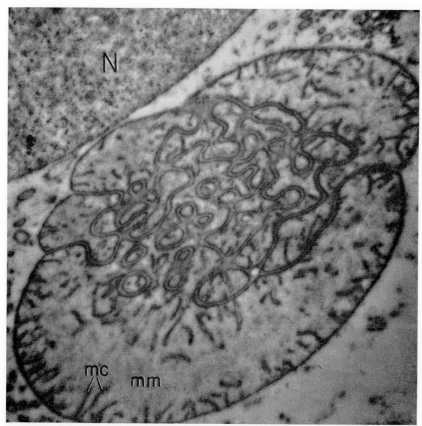

FIGURE 11–8. Electron micrograph of the mitochondrial body of a spermatid of the locust. The mitochondrial body results from the fusion of all mitochondria. *mc,* mitochondrial crests; *mm,* mitochondrial matrix; *N,* nucleus. (From De Robertis and Franco Raffo, 1956.)

chondria. For example, early oöcytes contain typical mitochondria, in which numerous dense protein molecules appear. These protein molecules are then grouped into masses that may displace the crests toward the periphery (Fig. 11–10). In more advanced stages, mitochondria may become transformed into larger yolk bodies. In these the masses of protein molecules may assume a regular crystalline disposition. In amphibian oöcytes, hexagonal, crystalline yolk bodies also form within mitochondria.[32] The discovery of protein crystals within mitochondria does not indicate that the entire synthesis takes place within this organoid. It is more probable that the first stages of synthesis occur in other parts of the cell and that only the final deposit takes place within the mitochondrion.

Degeneration of Mitochondria. Mitochondria are labile structures that can be altered readily by the action of vari-

ous agents. They are one of the most sensitive indicators of injury to the cell. Some of the changes may be reversible at the beginning. Mitochondria may fragment into smaller ones that may swell or may accumulate dense material in their interior. All these changes within certain limits may revert to normal. However, if the alteration reaches a certain critical point it is irreversible, which is generally considered as degeneration of the mitochondria. Essentially there are three types of change: fragmentation into granules followed by lysis and dispersion; intense swelling with transformation into large vacuoles; and a large accumulation of materials with transformation of mitochondria into hyalin granules. This last change is characteristic of the so-called cloudy swelling and hyalin degeneration that frequently results in cellular death.[27]

A now relatively frequent observation in an otherwise normal cell is the pres-

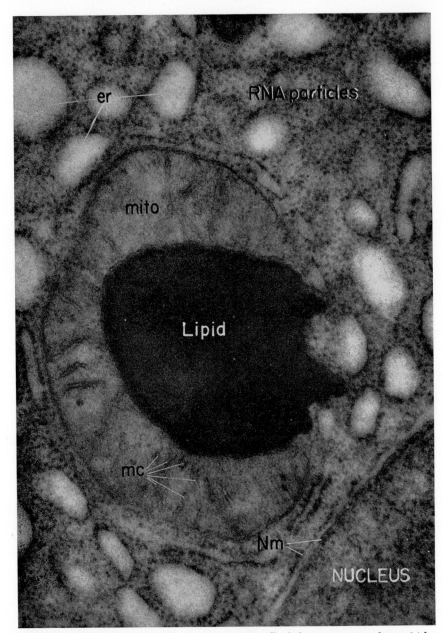

FIGURE 11–9.   Electron micrograph of a pancreatic cell of the guinea pig after a 24-hour fast. Note the intimate relation between a mitochondrion (*mito*) and a lipid droplet (*Lipid*). *er*, ergasto-plasm with RNA particles; *mc*, mitochondrial crests; *Nm*, nuclear membrane. ×70,000. (Courtesy of G. E. Palade.)

ence of degenerating mitochondria in foci of autolysis, constituting a type of lysosome (cytolysosome) (see Chap. 20). These occur rather frequently in the kidney after injection of different proteins.

Another type of degeneration is that of fusion of mitochondria to form large bodies called *chondriospheres*.[33] This degeneration has been found in patients with scurvy and seems to be normal in the adrenal gland of the hamster.[34] In this case, in the deepest region of the cortex there are mitochondria that undergo a process of flattening into thin, multilamellar sheaths. At the same time there is a concentric apposition of several of these mitochondria, a process that results in the formation of large lamellar chondriospheres.

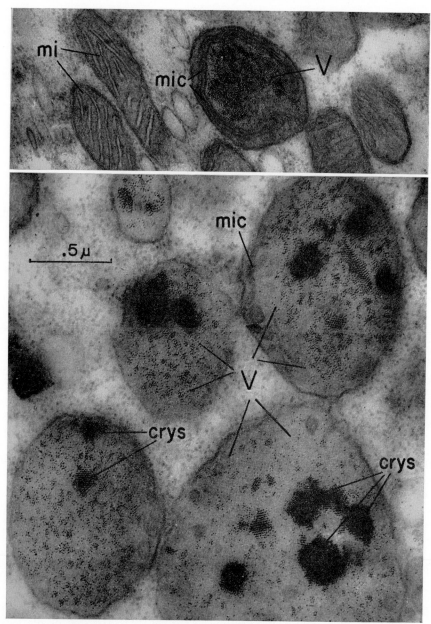

FIGURE 11–10. Electron micrographs of mitochondria of the egg of *Planorbis*. **Above,** normal mitochondria (*mi*) with crests, one showing an accumulation of protein molecules. *mic,* mitochondrial crests; *V*, yolk. **Below,** same, but with more development of the yolk. Mitochondria are being transformed into yolk platelets. The protein molecules have a crystalline disposition (*crys*). ×50,000. (Courtesy of P. Favard and N. Carasso.)

FUNCTIONS OF MITOCHONDRIA

The different functions of mitochondria are so intimately related to mitochondrial structure that one cannot be studied without the other. Therefore, a great deal of what must be said about mitochondrial functions has already been mentioned.

Early cytologists, such as Altmann, predicted that mitochondria are related to cellular oxidation. Batelli and Stern (1912) and Warburg (1913) observed that the respiratory enzymes were contained in the insoluble part of the cell. These findings were forgotten until 1929, when Keilin isolated from muscle cells particles that contained the succinic and cytochrome oxidase system. This was the first multienzyme system to be isolated, but it was not identified by the proper cytologic methods. The fundamental work of Bensley and Hoerr,[35] who isolated a granular material from liver cells and identified it as mitochondria, opened the way to our present knowledge of the enzymatic functions of mitochondria. The isolated mitochondria were found to oxidize actively glutamic and succinic acids and to give a positive reaction for cytochrome oxidase with the Nadi reagent. It was also observed that disintegration of mitochondria by freezing and thawing the cell lowered the cellular oxygen consumption and succinic oxidase and cytochrome oxidase activity.[36] Finally, the work of Hogeboom, Claude and Hotchkiss in 1946 proved that both cytochrome oxidase and succinic oxidase were associated with the mitochondrial fraction. Thereafter isolation of mitochondria became a routine procedure in many laboratories and rapid progress was made in investigating the function of mitochondria.[11, 37, 38]

Since the early investigations it has been demonstrated that the mitochondrion has a lipoprotein composition: 65 to 70 per cent is protein and 25 to 30 per cent is lipid. Most of the lipid content consists of phosphatides (e.g., lecithin and cephalin); cholesterol and other lipids are present in small amounts. Ribonucleic acid was constantly found in about 0.5 per cent of dry weight.

After isolation of mitochondria, two main technical approaches are employed: the mitochondrion is studied as an intact or unit particle, or this particle is divided into smaller and smaller units, each containing some of its active enzymatic groups. Both procedures have provided important information about the macromolecular and functional organization of mitochondria.

The Mitochondrial Enzyme System

To understand this section requires some knowledge from biochemistry textbooks of the many enzymatic mechanisms in which mitochondria are involved (see Chap. 4). For example, to express the complexity in numerical terms, in a mitochondrion more than 70 enzymes and coenzymes work in an orderly fashion, in addition to numerous cofactors, vitamins and metals essential to mitochondrial functions.

The only fuel that a mitochondrion needs is phosphate and adenosine diphosphate (ADP); the final product is ATP plus CO_2 and H_2O. Figure 11–11 indicates the final common pathway of biologic oxidation, which takes place within the mitochondrion. The three major foodstuffs of the cell (carbohydrate, fat and protein) are ultimately degraded in the cytoplasm to a two-carbon unit that is bound to coenzyme A: acetyl coenzyme A. When this penetrates the mitochondrion the acetate group enters the *Krebs tricarboxylic (citric) acid cycle* in which, after a complex series of steps involving several enzymes, it is decarboxylated, losing CO_2. At several points in the cycle, pairs of electrons (or their equivalent H atoms) are removed by dehydrogenases and enter into the *respiratory chain (electron transport system)*, at the end of which they combine with molecular oxygen to form water (Fig. 11–11).

The respiratory chain (also called the electron transport pathway) is the main energy transforming system of mitochondria. Its components are related not only functionally but spatially, and are intimately related to mitochondrial structure. The main components of the respiratory chain are two flavoprotein enzymes (succinic and DPN dehydrogenases), four cytochromes and also non-heme iron, copper and coenzyme Q (Fig. 11–12). At three points along this chain transforming mechanisms use the energy lost by a pair of electrons to form ATP from ADP and phosphate (Fig 11–12). Because of this, the *respiratory chain* is said to be normally *coupled to phosphorylation*. Little is known about the nature of this energy coupling mechanism. One possible interpretation is given in the diagram of Figure 11–12.

Localization of the Mitochondrial Enzyme System. As mentioned in the preceding section, an approach to the study of the intramitochondrial localization of enzymes has been the breaking

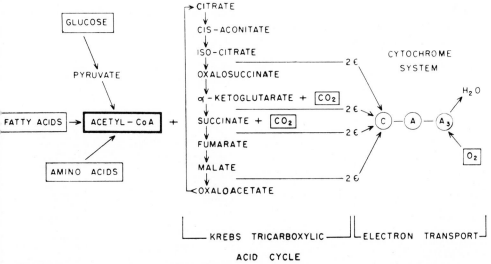

FIGURE 11–11. Schematic representation of the Krebs tricarboxylic acid cycle and the electron transport system occurring in mitochondria. (From A. L. Lehninger.)

up of the mitochondrion into fragments of different sizes and properties. If a suspension of mitochondria is submitted to sonic vibrations, the soluble proteins contained in the matrix are released, leaving the membranous parts in the sedimentable fraction. As shown in Figure 11–13, the amount of soluble protein released is related to the structure. For example, liver mitochondria contain more soluble proteins than heart mitochondria, which have a more compact structure and a greater number of crests than liver mitochondria.

These soluble proteins comprise most of the enzymes involved in the Krebs and fatty acid cycles (see Table 11–2). The matrix also contains different nucleotides as well as nucleotide coenzymes and inorganic electrolytes, such as K^+, HPO_4^-, Mg^{++}, Cl^- and $SO_4^=$. The insoluble fraction contains all the enzymes comprised in the respiratory chain together with the energy-coupling enzymes of oxidative phosphorylation[2, 39–41] (Table 11–2).

Because there is a direct correlation between the number of crests and of respiratory chains it has been suggested that the crests and the inner membranes of the mitochondrion contain most if not all the enzymes involved in this chain.

An important concept that has emerged from spectrophotometric observations is that the components of the respiratory chain are in equimolecular quantities, i.e., there is a molecule of succinic dehydrogenase or DPN dehydrogenase for each cytochrome and cytochrome oxidase in the chain[42, 43]

TABLE 11–2. LOCALIZATION OF ENZYMES IN MITOCHONDRIA

MATRIX	MEMBRANES
Krebs cycle:	Respiratory chain enzymes:
Aconitase	DPN dehydrogenase
Malic dehydrogenase	Succinic dehydrogenase
Fumarase	Cytochrome b
Isocitric dehydrogenase	" c_1
Condensing enzyme	" c
Pyruvic and ketoglutaric	" a
dehydrogenase, etc.	" a_3 oxidase
Fatty acid cycle:	Phosphorylating enzymes
Crotonase	
Acyl dehydrogenase, etc.	

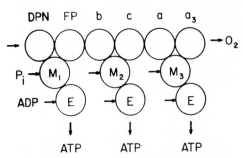

FIGURE 11–12.   Reaction pattern of respiration and the "coupled" oxidative phosphorylation. **Top row,** a "respiratory assembly" is shown schematically. This is composed of a DPN-flavoprotein enzyme (DPN-FP) and the cytochromes b, c, a and cytochrome oxidase (a_3). It is possible that coenzyme Q and cytochrome c_1 are also members of this carrier system. At three points of the respiratory chain electrons are transferred to enzymes (M_1, M_2, M_3 and E) required to produce ATP from ADP and phosphate (P_i). Presumably a similar reaction occurs at all three phosphorylation sites. (From A. L. Lehninger.[2])

(Table 11–2). These and other results suggest that the enzymes are organized in compact "assemblies" that are regularly spaced on the mitochondrial crest. In a liver mitochondrion there would be 15,000 assemblies. A mitochondrion in the flight muscle of an insect may have as many as 100,000.

Some mitochondrial fragments produced by sonic vibration or other methods are still capable of carrying on oxidative phosphorylation (e.g., ETPH in Table 11–3), but further fragmentation produces particles that contain the respiratory chain but can no longer couple oxidation to ATP synthesis (e.g., ETP in Table 11–3).

Some calculations indicate that 25 to 40 per cent of the membrane protein may be respiratory chains disposed in a

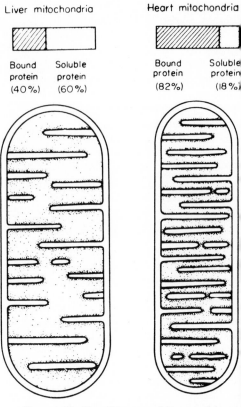

FIGURE 11–13.   Diagram of liver and heart mitochondria showing the different amounts of bound and soluble protein and the number of crests per mitochondrion. (From D. E. Green.)

"solid state" arrangement. Also, 60 to 70 per cent of structural proteins do not contain oxidation-reduction groups.

Recently it has been suggested[24] that the ultimate particle containing all the fixed components of the electron transfer system has a molecular weight of only 1.4×10^6. This supports the postulate that the elementary particles shown by electron microscopy[19, 20] are the highly compact multienzyme units in which the electron transfer system resides. However, this has been disproved by a study of cytochrome composition in membranes stripped of these particles.[59]

Mesosomes and Respiratory Chains in Bacteria.   From the evolutionary viewpoint, in bacteria the enzymes of the electron transport system (respiratory chain) are localized in the plasma membrane, which thus has the same role as mitochondria in higher cells. At one time it was thought that mitochondria were bacterial parasites of cells. (Remember

TABLE 11–3.   STRUCTURAL-FUNCTIONAL RELATION AND MITOCHONDRIAL FRAGMENTATION*

	MITOCHONDRION	ETPH	ETP
Citric acid cycle oxidations	+	0	0
Oxidative phosphorylation	+	+	0
Electron transport	+	+	+

*From Green, 1962.

that the size of a bacterium is approximately that of a mitochondrion.)

By electron microscopy a membranous organoid of about 2500 Å was observed in certain bacteria. This was called the *mesosome*, and its similarity to mitochondria was postulated.[44] It sometimes appears to be continuous with the plasma membrane. Mesosomes have now been isolated and their electron transport system has been demonstrated, thus confirming that they are true mitochondria for the bacterial cell.[45]

MITOCHONDRIAL SWELLING AND CONTRACTION

At the beginning of this chapter we mentioned the swelling-contraction changes that can be observed in mitochondria of living cells. Similar but more precise and quantitative observations can be made with isolated mitochondria (Fig. 11–14).[46] Altogether these studies demonstrate that mitochondria have an important function in the uptake and extrusion of intracellular fluid. An iso-

lated mitochondrion reacts as an osmometer, but, as stated previously, other important factors produce similar changes. Swelling agents are phosphate, Ca^{++}, reduced glutathione and particularly the thyroid hormone thyroxine. Thyroxine is by far the most effective and is capable of producing swelling in physiologic concentrations.

Isolated liver and kidney mitochondria may swell as much as three- to four-fold in volume. Since mitochondria have two membranes and two compartments from the structural viewpoint, they may swell in two general ways (Fig. 11–15). Water, K^+ and Na^+ penetrate both membranes very rapidly and may produce the structural changes shown in Figure 11–15C and E with dilution of the matrix. On the other hand, sucrose penetrates the outer membrane more readily than the inner membrane and may produce an "inflation" of the outer chamber or the space within the crest without dilution of the matrix (Fig. 11–15B and D).

Figure 11–16 shows the swelling effect of thyroxine as measured by light ab-

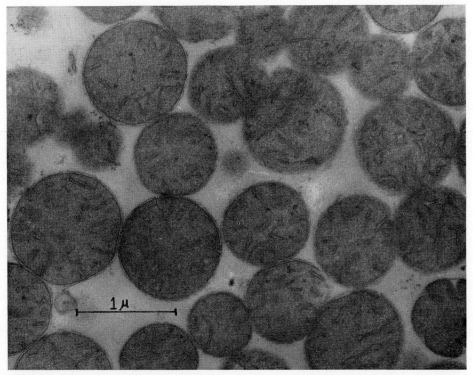

Figure 11–14.   Electron micrograph of mitochondria isolated from liver cells. In this case there is no swelling and the mitochondria show exactly the same morphologic characteristics as the normal cell. ×27,000. (Courtesy of S. Malamed.)

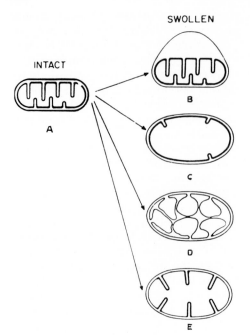

FIGURE 11–15. Structure of a normal intact mitochondrion (**A**) and of different types of swelling. Entrance of solutes in the outer chamber produces dilation of the intermembranal space (**B**), or of the intracristal spaces (**D**). Penetration in the inner chamber produces dilution of the matrix with (**C**) or without (**E**) unfolding of the crests. (From A. L. Lehninger.[2])

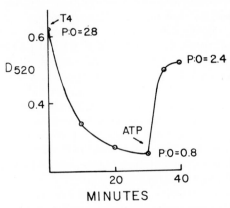

FIGURE 11–16. Swelling of rat-liver mitochondria in the presence of thyroxine and their contraction by ATP. The decrease in optical density corresponds to an increase in water content, and vice versa. It is also seen that the P:O ratio declines during swelling, but is restored again during the contraction stage. (From A. L. Lehninger, 1960, *Pediatrics*, 26:466.)

sorption and the reversible contraction produced in the same system by the addition of ATP. This experiment also demonstrates that the P:O ratio (i.e., the relationship between the phosphorus fixed and the O_2 consumed) is lowered by thyroxine and returned to normal range by ATP. These facts show that the water uptake is associated with the uncoupling of oxidative phosphorylation, which is restored to normal levels after the water extrusion.[2] Measurements of the ATP used during contraction indicate that mitochondria can actively squeeze out water and small molecules in the proportion of several hundred per each ATP molecule split.

These findings suggest that mitochondria contain a contractile protein, which contracts in the presence of ATP, as does actomyosin from muscle. It has been suggested that this contraction involves the same enzymes that couple phosphate to ADP in oxidative phosphorylation (M_1, M_2, M_3 and E in Figure 11–12), and that these enzymes belong to a type of "mechanoenzymes"

that change in shape depending on whether or not they are phosphorylated.[2]

These findings as well as the low amplitude changes observed in the living cell[47] suggest that in addition to being fundamentally centers of oxidative phosphorylation, mitochondria can actively transport water and ions (see Chap. 20). These two types of functions are tightly integrated at the physiological and structural levels. The volume and shape of mitochondria in the living cell appear to be the result of an equilibrium between factors that tend to promote swelling or contraction.

This balance can be altered easily in physiological conditions by local intracellular changes in O_2, CO_2 tension, pH or gradient concentration of phosphate, ATP and substrates. The soluble part of the cytoplasm contains a so-called *C factor*, which promotes contraction of mitochondria. In addition, some fatty acids and phospholipids may regulate the mechanism of swelling and contraction. Upon aging of mitochondria, a *U factor* appears, which produces swelling and a decline in oxidative phosphorylation. This factor has essentially a fatty acid composition.[2] Since free fatty acids are found in the microsomes of the cell and the endoplasmic reticulum shows direct contact with mitochondria, it has been suggested that at these points local welling of mitochondria may be produced.[48] (These important concepts are considered again in the discussion of active transport of water and ions across the plasma and intracellular membranes (see Chap. 20).

ORIGIN OF MITOCHONDRIA

Three possible mechanisms of mitochondrial formation based on light miroscopy have been suggested: division of preexisting mitochondria; *de novo* synthesis; and formation from a nonmitochondrial structure.

Early workers considered that mitochondria, like chromosomes, were carriers of hereditary information and could propagate by division. This implies the formation of new mitochondria from the preexisting ones by division and growth of the resulting units.[38, 49]

The viewpoint that mitochondria arise *de novo* resulted mainly from centrifugation experiments on sea urchin eggs.[50] It was found that certain fractions that did not contain mitochondria, as judged by staining methods, developed a full set of these organoids in later stages of development. These findings were interpreted as an indication that mitochondria originated without preexistent elements. However, it is possible that mitochondria were present in the portions but were not visualized by the methods employed.[38]

The third assumption is based on electron microscopy. Continuities of the mitochondrial membrane with the plasma membrane or the endoplasmic reticulum and nuclear envelope have been observed.[51-53] This has led to the suggestion that mitochondria are formed by these membranes. A mechanism of mitochondriogenesis based on the growth and flux of membranes from the plasma membrane as well as from the membranes of the vacuolar system has thus been postulated.[54]

Similar observations have been made on nerve fibers in the infrared receptor organ of certain vipers whose endings are a solid mass of mitochondria. At a short distance from the ending, infold-

ings from the axon membrane have been observed, which suggest a mechanism of mitochondriogenesis in which the participation of both the axon membrane and the matrix of the axoplasm is emphasized.[55] It is interesting to recall that mesosomes in bacteria are derived from the plasma membrane.

The problem of mitochondriogenesis is by no means solved. In studying with radioactive choline the mitochondria from a mutant of *Neurospora crassa* that is deficient in choline, it has been concluded that the mitochondrial mass increases by the continuous addition of new lecithin units to the existing mitochondrial framework, thus excluding the possibility of *de novo* formation of mitochondria.

Evidence favors the view that new lipoprotein material is inserted at a finer level of structure.[56] Some recent biochemical evidence indicates that the half-life of liver mitochondria is about 5 to 10 days,[57] which indicates that cellular synthesis of mitochondria may be a continuous process. In this case it will be important to establish by which mechanism all the enzymatic systems present in the membranes and the matrix are assembled to organize the fully active mitochondrion. An interesting example in this direction concerns yeast cells, which—unlike cells of higher organisms—can grow in the presence or absence of oxygen. In the latter case (anaerobiosis), cytochromes b and a are not present and there is not a true respiratory chain. Also, it has been observed that during anaerobiosis the yeast cells do not contain true mitochondria, but have a special membrane system that contains the two primary dehydrogenases of the respiratory chain. Under the action of oxygen, these membranes fuse, infold and form true mitochondria containing the cytochromes.[58]

GENERAL REFERENCES

Bourne, G. (1951) Mitochondria and Golgi apparatus. In: *Cytology and cell physiology*. (Bourne, G., ed.) Oxford University Press, London.

Chance, B. (1956) Interaction of adenosinedi-phosphate with the respiratory chain. *Henry Ford Hosp. Internat. Symp.,* 447.

Dalton, A. J., and Felix, M. D. (1957) Electron microscopy of mitochondria and the Golgi complex. *Symp. Soc. Exp. Biol., 10*:148.

Green, D. E. (1956) Structural and enzymatic pattern of the electron transfer system. *Henry Ford Hosp. Internat. Symp.,* 465.

Lehninger, A. L. (1962) Water uptake and extrusion by mitochondria in relation to oxidative phosphorylation. *Physiol. Rev., 42*:467.

Lindberg, O., and Ernster, L. (1954) Chemistry and physiology of mitochondria and microsomes. *Protoplasmatologie, 3*:1.

Novikoff, A. B. (1961) Mitochondria (chondriosomes). In: *The cell,* Vol. 2, p. 299. (Brachet, J., and Mirsky, A. E., eds.) Academic Press, New York.

Palade, G. E. (1956) Electron microscopy of mitochondria and other cytoplasmic structures. *Henry Ford Hosp. Internat. Symp.,* 185.

Slater, E. C. (1957) Sarcosomes (muscle mitochondria). *Symp. Soc. Exp. Biol., 10*:110.

Zollinger, H. U. (1950) Les mitochondries. *Rev. Hemat., 5*:694.

CITED REFERENCES

1. Goodwin, T. W., and Lindberg, O. (1961) Biological structure and function. *Proc. First IUB/IUBS Internat. Symp.,* Vol. 2. Academic Press, New York.

2. Lehninger, A. L. (1962) *Physiol. Rev., 42*: 3, 467.

3. Lazarow, A., and Copperstein, S. J. (1953) *J. Histochem. Cytochem., 1*:234.

4. Frédéric, J., and Chèvremont, M. (1953) *Arch. Biol.* (Liège), *63*:109.

5. Frédéric, J. (1954) *Ann. N.Y. Acad. Sci., 58*:1245.

6. Tobioka, M., and Biesele, J. J. (1956) *J. Biophys. Biochem. Cytol., 2*:4, suppl., 319.

7. Frédéric, J. (1958) *Arch. Biol.* (Liège), *69*: 167.

8. Barrnett, R. J., and Palade, G. E. (1957) *J. Biophys. Biochem. Cytol., 3*:577.

9. Sedar, A. W., Rosa, C. G., and Tsou, K. C. (1962) In: *Fifth Internat. Congress for Electron Microscopy,* Vol. 2, p. L-7. (Breese, S. S., Jr., ed.) Academic Press, New York.

10. Schneider, W. C., and Hogeboom, G. H. (1951) *Cancer Res., 11*:1.

11. Lindberg, O., and Ernster, L. (1954) *Protoplasmatologia, 3*:135.

12. Shelton, E., Schneider, W. C., and Striebich, N. J. (1953) *Exp. Cell Res., 4*:32.

13. Allard, G., de Lamirande, G., and Cantero, A. (1952) *Cancer Res., 12*:580.

14. Allard, G., de Lamirande, G., and Cantero, A. (1953) *Canad. J. Med. Sci., 30*:543.

15. Junqueira, L. C. U. (1951) *Exp. Cell Res., 2*:327.

16. Palade, G. E. (1952) *Anat. Rec., 114*:427.

17. De Robertis, E., and Franco Raffo, F. (1957) *Exp. Cell Res., 12*:66.

18. Peachey, L. D. (1962) In: *Fifth Interna Congress for Electron Microscopy,* Vo 2, p. OO-3. (Breese, S. S., Jr., ed.) Ac: demic Press, New York.

19. Fernández-Morán, H. (1962) *Circulatio 26*:1039.

20. Fernández-Morán, H. (1963) *Science, 14C* 381.

21. Parsons, D. F. (1963) *Science, 140*:985.

22. Stoeckenius, W. (1963) *J. Cell Biol., 17*:44£

23. Sjöstrand, F. S. (1963) *Nature, 199*:1262.

24. Blair, P. V., Green, D. E., and Oda, 7 (1963) *Science, 140*:382.

25. Palade, G. E. (1956) Electron microscopy c mitochondria and other cytoplasm structures. *Henry Ford Hosp. Interna Symp.,* 185.

26. Sabatini, D., De Robertis, E., and Bleichma H. (1962) *Endocrinology, 70*:390.

27. Gansler, H., and Rouiller, C. (1956 *Schweiz. Ztschr. allg. Path., 19*:2, 217.

28. Palade, G. E. (1958) *Anat. Rec., 130*:352.

29. De Robertis, E. (1939) *Rev. Soc. Arg. Biol 15*:94.

30. Bessis, M., and Breton-Gorius, J. (1957 *C. R. Acad. Sci., 244*:2846.

31. Carasso, N., and Favard, P. (1958) *C. F Acad. Sci., 246*:1594.

32. Ward, R. T. (1962) *J. Cell Biol., 14*:309.

33. Bourne, G. (1951) Mitochondria and Golg apparatus. In: *Cytology and cell physio ogy.* (Bourne, G., ed.) Oxford Universit Press, London.

34. De Robertis, E., and Sabatini, D. (1958 *J. Biophys. Biochem. Cytol., 4*:667.

35. Bensley, R. R., and Hoerr, N. L. (1934 *Anat. Rec., 60*:251, 449.

36. De Robertis, E., and Nowinski, W. W (1942) *Rev. Soc. Arg. Biol., 18*:333.

37. Hogeboom, G. H. (1951) *Fed. Proc., 1C* 640.

38. Novikoff, A. B. (1961) Mitochondria (chor driosomes). In: *The cell,* Vol. 2, p. 299 (Brachet, J., and Mirsky, A. E., eds. Academic Press, New York.

39. Siekevitz, P., and Watson, M. L. (1956) *J Biophys. Biochem. Cytol., 2*:653.

40. Ball, E. G., and Barrnett, R. J. (1957) *J Biophys. Biochem. Cytol., 3*:1023.

41. Green, D. E. (1958) *Harvey Lect.* ser. 5 (1956–1957), p. 177.

42. Chance, B., and Williams, G. R. (1955 *J. Biol. Chem., 217*:383, 395, 409, 42£ 439.

43. Chance, B., and Williams, G. R. (1956 *Advanc. Enzymol., 17*:65.

44. Fitz-James, P. C. (1960) *J. Biophys. Bi(chem. Cytol., 8*:507.

45. Salton, M. R. J., and Chapman, J. A. (1962 *J. Ultrastruct. Res., 6*:489.

46. Tedeschi, H., and Harris, D. L. (1958) *Bio chim. Biophys. Acta, 28*:392.

47. Packer, L. (1961) *J. Biol. Chem., 236*:214.

48. Avi-dor, Y. A. (1960) *Biochim. Biophy Acta, 39*:53.

9. Rouiller, Ch. (1960) *Internat. Rev. Cytol.,* *9*:227.

0. Harvey, E. B. (1946) *J. Exp. Zool., 102*:253.

1. Hoffman, H., and Grigg, G. W. (1958) *Exp. Cell Res., 15*:118.

2. Policard, A., and Collet, A. (1958) *Bull. Micr. Appl., 3*:71.

3. Brandt, P. W., and Pappas, G. D. (1959) *J. Biophys. Biochem. Cytol., 6*:91.

4. Robertson, J. D. (1961) Cell membranes and the origin of mitochondria. In: *Regional neurochemistry.* (Kety, S. S., and Elkes, J., eds.). Pergamon Press, New York, p. 497.

55. De Robertis, E., and Bleichmar, H. B. (1962) *Ztschr. Zellforsch., 57*:572.

56. Luck, D. J. L. (1963) *J. Cell Biol., 16*:483.

57. Fletcher, M., and Sanadi, D. R. (1961) *Biochim. Biophys. Acta, 51*:356.

58. Linnane, A. W., Vitols, E., and Nowland, P. G. (1962) *J. Cell Biol., 13*:345.

59. Chance, B., Parsons, D. F., and Williams, G. R. (1964) *Science, 143*:136.

CHAPTER 12

THE PLANT CELL AND THE CHLOROPLAST

The general plan of cellular organization presented so far is similar in animal and plant cells. Other similarities referring to the cell nucleus, chromosomes and the mitotic and meiotic processes will be studied and illustrated in the corresponding chapters.

The emphasis in this chapter is on some special characteristics of plant cells, particularly the thick *cell wall* outside the plasma membrane and certain organoids—the *plastids*—that are related to the synthesis and accumulation of different substances. Of these the most important are the *chloroplasts,* which together with the mitochondria are biochemical machines that produce energy transformations. In this case the electromagnetic energy contained in light is trapped and converted into chemical energy by the process of *photosynthesis.* The chloroplast is an even more interesting example than the mitochondrion of structural-functional integration within the cell, because this is achieved at the molecular level.

Cell Walls

Characteristic of the structure of the plant cell are rigid walls that surround

186

and protect the plasma membrane (Fig 2–4). These walls constitute a framework that provides for the mechanical support of plant tissues. The regular pattern observed in the thick cell walls wa the first structure recognized microscopically by Robert Hooke, and this suggested to him the name *cell* (Chap. 1) The cell walls are mainly composed o *cellulose* produced by the cell. Adjacent cell walls are cemented with *pectin.*

Cell walls are complex and highly differentiated in some tissues. In addition they develop in special sequence. Thu in certain cells, primary, secondary and tertiary walls have been described. These are deposited in layers one after the other during cell growth and differentiation. These three types of cell walls can be differentiated by the special disposition of the *microfibrils,* which are the building blocks of most cell walls, and also by chemical composition (Fig. 12–1)

Both the *primary* and *secondary wall* are mainly composed of the polysaccharide cellulose, but other substances may be incorporated, especially in secondary walls. Lignin or suberin may be added to the primary wall, and, in epidermal cells, cutin and cutin waxes may produce an impermeable surface coating that reduces water loss. In many fungi and in yeasts the cell wall is composed o *chitin,* a polymer of glucosamine. Other substances that may be found in the cell wall, in addition to cellulose, are indicated in Table 12–1, which also present some data on the chemical composition and staining reactions of these substances.

In some tissues the *tertiary wall* is deposited at the interior of the secondary wall and has a special structure as well as different chemical and staining properties. This wall is composed mainly o *xylan* instead of cellulose.

The deposition of the various wall should be considered in time sequence along with cellular growth and differentiation. During growth the outermost older parts of the cell wall are severely stretched, which may reorient and even tear the microfibrils. Various processes of tearing, called multinet, tip and mosaic growth, may thus be produced.[1] Th cell wall determines to a great extent th

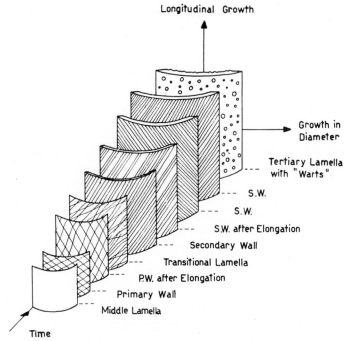

Longitudinal Growth

Growth in Diameter

Tertiary Lamella with "Warts"

S.W.

S.W.

S.W. after Elongation

Secondary Wall

Transitional Lamella

P.W. after Elongation

Primary Wall

Middle Lamella

Time

FIGURE 12–1. Diagram showing the time sequence of the formation of the various types of cell wall layers in a tracheid. *P.W.*, primary wall; *S.W.*, secondary wall. Notice the arrangement of fibrils and other structures in the different membranes. (From K. Mühlethaler.[1])

TABLE 12–1.   PLANT WALL SUBSTANCES

SUBSTANCE	CHEMICAL UNIT	STAINING REACTION
Cellulose	Glucose	Chlorzinciodide (stains violet)
Hemicellulose	Arabinose, xylose, mannose, galactose	None specific
Pectic substances	Glucuronic and galacturonic acids	Ruthenium red
Lignin	Coniferyl alcohol	Phloroglucinol hydrochloride (stains rose); chlorzinciodide (stains yellow)
Cuticular substances	Fatty acids	Sudan III (stains orange)
Mineral deposits	Calcium and magnesium in the form of carbonates or silicates	

shape of the cell, and serves as a criterion for the classification of plant tissue, e.g., parenchyme, collenchyme and fibers.[2] (Consideration of these classifications is beyond the scope of this book.)

The cell wall is a product of the cytoplasm, and its development begins with the formation of the *phragmoplast*, or *cell plate*, immediately after nuclear division. The primary cell wall is essentially composed of microfibrils of cellulose that may run in all directions within the plane of the wall. These constitute a loose framework that contains large amounts of water and noncellulose substances. It is generally admitted that the growth of both the primary and secondary walls is by apposition. The difference in the secondary wall is that the microfibrils are parallel and more densely packed[1] (Fig. 12–1).

Figure 12–2 indicates schematically the structural elements of cellulose down to the molecular level. Macrofibrils visible with the light microscope are composed of *microfibrils* about 250 Å in diameter, which are in turn composed of about 2000 cellulose chains. About 100 cellulose chains are held together in an elementary fibril (or micelle), which has

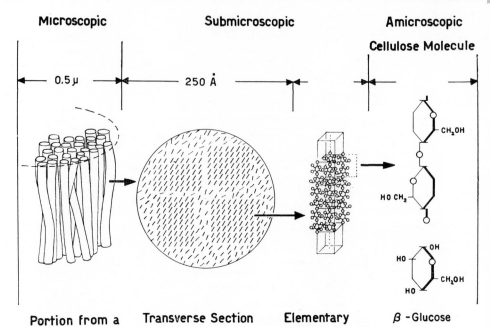

FIGURE 12–2.   Structural elements of cellulose at different levels of organization. (From K. Mühle thaler.[1])

a crystalline molecular organization. By x-ray diffraction, cellulose gives a crystalline pattern with a repeating period of 10.3 Å along the fiber axis. This corresponds to a *cellobiose* unit composed of two β-glucose molecules.

Plasmodesmata: Continuity of Cell Cytoplasm[1, 3]

Figure 2–4 illustrates a promeristematic cell of the root tip observed at low magnification under the electron microscope. The primary cell wall is clearly visible and separates the cell from the six adjacent cells. This separation is not complete, and at several points in the cell wall, bridges of cellular material are seen across the gap. These bridges are the so-called *plasmodesmata*. According to classic concepts in cytology, these canaliculi bored within the thickness of the pectocellulose membrane contain cell expansions that penetrate and come in contact but do not fuse. According to this interpretation the cytoplasm of the different plant cells would be autonomous.

On the contrary, electron microscope studies of several meristematic cells indicate that within plasmodesmata the thin plasma membrane of a cell is continuous with that of an adjacent cell, and the cytoplasm of both cells may communicate. Within the plasmodesmata tubules in continuity with vacuoles or cisternae of the cytoplasmic vacuolar system (endoplasmic reticulum), have been observed (Fig. 12–3). This probably involves intercellular circulation of solutions containing nutritional products dissolved gases, ions or other substances. The presence of plasmodesmata permits the free circulation of fluid, which is essential to maintenance of plant cell tonicity, and probably also allows passage of solutes and even of macromolecules. According to these concepts, cell walls do not represent complete partitions between cells, but constitute a vast syncytium supported by a skeleton that is formed by the pectocellulose membranes.

The plasmodesmata are apparently formed early together with the formation of the phragmoplasts, which appear during telophase at the equator of dividing cells (see Chap. 14).

Cytoplasmic Matrix and the Vacuolar System

In Chapter 2 the basic similarities between the cytoplasm of animal and plant cells were mentioned.[4, 5] In meristematic

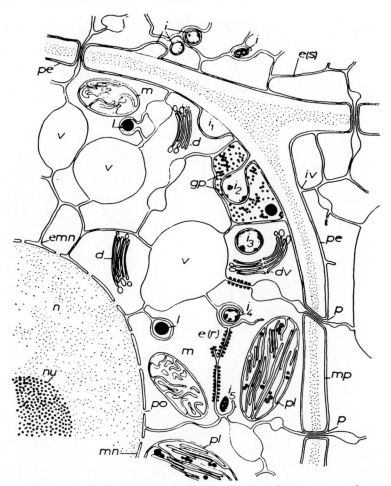

FIGURE 12–3. Diagram showing the interpretation of plant ultrastructure and its intercellular elationships. *d*, dictyosome; *er*, endoplasmic reticulum; *m*, mitochondrion; *mn*, nuclear membrane; , nucleus; *nu*, nucleolus; *p*, plasmodesmata; *pl*, plastid; *po*, pores. (Courtesy of R. Buvat.)

ells the membranes of the cytoplasmic acuolar system are relatively scanty and re best observed after fixation in permanganate (Fig. 2–4). With this treatment most of the ribosomes are removed r invisible. When the cell is fixed in smium tetroxide the vacuolar system is masked by the numerous ribosomes that ill the cytoplasmic matrix. Indeed, most f these particles are not attached to the membranes but are free in the matrix Fig. 12–4).

At the periphery of meristematic cells a tubular vacuolar system develops and pparently is involved in some way with he formation of the cell wall. At certain oints the plasma membrane is not coninuous and numerous tubules and vesies of the vacuolar system seem to form a new plasma membrane. In the forma-tion of the phragmoplast a tubular lattice develops in between the two daughter cytoplasms and then the so-called *pectin vesicles* appear, which fuse and thus separate the two cells.[6, 7] More recently this process of cell plate formation has been attributed to the Golgi or dictyosome portion of the vacuolar system (see the following section).[8]

The vacuolar system becomes more and more developed with the differentiation of the cell. In leaf primordia, granular and agranular endoplasmic reticulum has been observed, but the more differentiated cells show fewer ribosomes and the vacuolar system has large vacuoles filled with fluid.

The diagram of Figure 12–3 indicates the possible connections of the vacuolar system with the nuclear envelope and

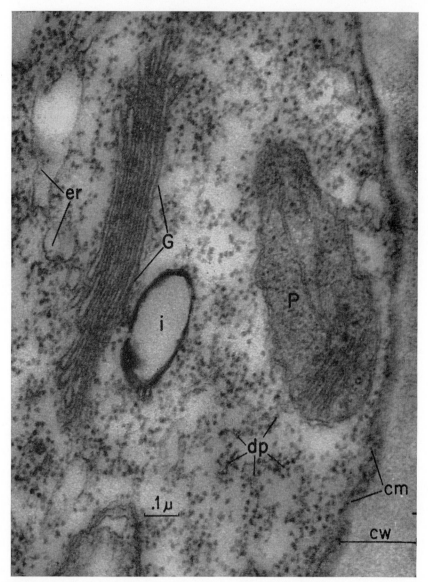

Figure 12–4. Electron micrograph of the foliar primordium of *Elodea canadensis*. *cm*, cell membrane; *cw*, cell wall; *er*, endoplasmic reticulum, which is scarce and has numerous RNP particles many of which are free in the hyaloplasm (*dp*); *G*, golgiosome or dictyosome; *i*, inclusion; *P*, plastid (Courtesy of R. Buvat.)

the plasma membrane. It has been postulated that the plasma membrane of the plant cell invaginates and actively takes in fluid (pinocytosis), as occurs in numerous animal cells.[9]

The great development of the vacuolar system during cell differentiation is related to the intense hydration of the cytoplasm. This process may give rise to huge vacuoles that are filled with liquid and that may be confluent. As a result, the cytoplasm may become compressed in a thin layer against the cellulose

membrane and may show cytoplasmic movements, also called *cyclosis* (Chap. 21).

The Golgi Complex and Dictyosomes

The existence of a Golgi complex in plant cells was discussed by early cytologists,[10, 11] but it was practically unknown until the advent of electron microscopy. In fact, with the usual staining techniques the results were inconclusive.

The demonstration of the structure of the Golgi complex in animal cells with the electron microscope provided the background for the detection of this component in plant cells. As in inverte-brate material, the Golgi complex in plants appears as discrete bodies dispersed throughout the cytoplasm—the so-called *dictyosomes* or *golgiosomes* (Fig. 12–5). A dictyosome has a platelike

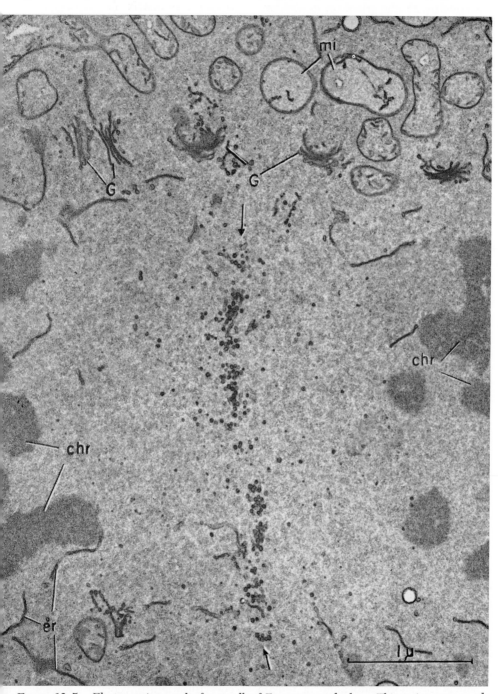

FIGURE 12–5.   Electron micrograph of root cells of *Zea mays* at telophase. This region corresponds to the cell plate. Note at the top the marginal mitochondria (*mi*) and the golgiosomes (*G*) (dictyosomes). Between the arrows the vesicles are aligned to form the first evidence of a cell plate. *chr*, telophase chromosomes in the two daughter cells; *er*, endoplasmic reticulum. ×45,000. (Courtesy of W. Gordon Whaley and H. H. Mollenhauer.)

arched shape and is the size of a mito-chondrion or smaller. The fine structure is typical. It consists of a stack of flat-tened vesicles (cisternae) that are slightly dilated at the edges. They are isodiametric in the plane of flattening. Surrounding the cisternae are vesicles formed by localized dilatations; these vesicles are probably a product of dic-tyosome activity.

Dictyosomes are dispersed throughout the cytoplasm without a definite polar-ization. At telophase the dictyosomes are grouped at the periphery of the cell plate and form small vesicles, which fuse to form the plate (Figs. 12–5 and 12–6). At certain stages there is distinct secretion within these vesicles. After mechanical injury a great number of small vesicles are produced.[8] As in animal cells the Golgi complex of some plant cells (e.g., root cap cells of maize) show a direct relationship with secretion. The Golgi cisternae become filled with secretion products, which are then concentrated and discharged.[12]

Mitochondria

Mitochondria of plant cells have a structure essentially similar to that of animal cells. In meristems, mitochondria have relatively few crests and an abun-dant matrix. During differentiation this internal structure may vary. In cells en-gaged in photosynthesis (leaf cells), mitochondria show an increase in crests; in cells containing starch granules (amyloplasts), mitochondria remain un-differentiated, as in meristems.

One of the important points still under discussion is the relationship between mitochondria and chloroplasts. Guiller-mond[13] studied this problem in leaf meristems and postulated that in early stages there are two types of organoids. One is typically made of short mitochon-dria and the other of long filamentous bodies. These elongated organoids in-crease in thickness and may give rise to vesicles, starch granules or chloroplasts, whereas the short mitochondria remain unchanged. According to this view, al-though both types of organoids are re-lated, they are generally independent. The study of these organoids with the

electron microscope tends to confirm this hypothesis. Early plastids—the so-called *proplastids*—resemble mitochondria that have few developed cristae, but are larger and contain small dense granules within the matrix (Fig. 12–4). (This problem is considered later in this chap-ter.)

PLASTIDS: CHLOROPLASTS

Plastids are cytoplasmic organoids in-timately related to the metabolic proc-esses of plant cells. They are found throughout the plant kingdom, except possibly in bacteria, certain algae, myxo-mycetes and fungi. They are character-ized by the presence of pigments, such as *chlorophyll* and *carotenoids*, and the capacity to synthesize and accumulate reserve substances, such as starch, fats and proteins.

In embryonic and sexual cells, color-less rodlike or spheroid plastids are found (*leukoplasts*), which are some-times difficult to distinguish from mito-chondria (Fig. 12–4). During embryonic development leukoplasts in certain dif-ferentiated zones of the root produce starch granules, *amyloplasts* (Fig. 12–7). These are evident under the polarization microscope, owing to their characteristic birefringence, or can be distinguished by means of histochemical reactions for starch. Leukoplasts are also found in meristematic cells and in those regions of the plant not receiving light.

Plastids located in the cotyledon and the primordium of the stem are colorless at first, but become filled with chloro-phyll and acquire the characteristic green color of chloroplasts.

In addition to chloroplasts, other col-ored plastids can be observed. These are grouped under the name *chromoplasts*. For instance, the red color of ripe to-matoes is due to chromoplasts that have the red pigment lycopene, which belongs to the carotenoid family. Chromoplasts containing various pigments (e.g., phy-coerythrin and phycocyan) are found in algae. Figure 12–7 is a diagram of the re-lationship between types of plastids.

Here we shall consider mainly the chloroplasts. These are the most common

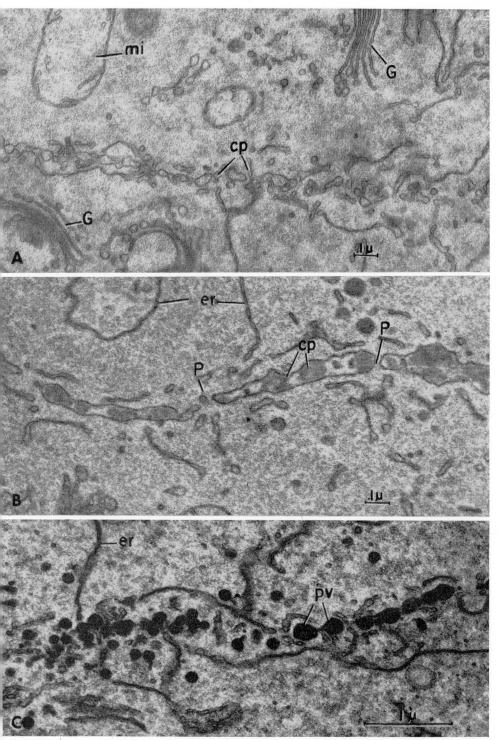

FIGURE 12–6.   Electron micrographs of root cells of *Zea mays*, which show three stages in the development of the cell plate at telophase. *cp*, vesicles of the cell plate; *er*, endoplasmic reticulum; *G*, golgiosomes; *mi*, mitochondrion; *p*, future plasmodesmata; *pv*, pectin vesicles. A and B, ×80,000; C, ×30,000. (Courtesy of W. Gordon Whaley and H. H. Mollenhauer.)

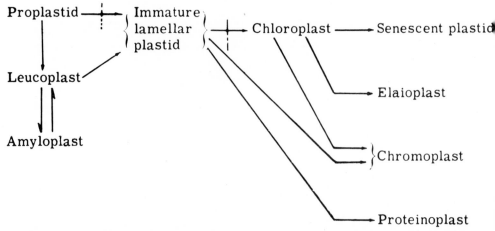

FIGURE 12–7.   Diagram showing the relationship between plastid types. Senescent plastids are found in autumn leaves. (From S. Granick.[23])

plastids and of greatest biologic importance, since by *photosynthesis* they produce most of the chemical energy used by living organisms. Without chloroplasts there would be no plants and animals, because animals feed on the foodstuffs produced by plants.

Morphology

The *shape, size* and *distribution* of chloroplasts vary in the different cells and within species, but are relatively constant in the same tissue.

In leaves of the higher plants, each cell contains a large *number* of spheroid, ovoid or discoid chloroplasts. Some are club-shaped, with a thin middle zone and bulging ends filled with chlorophyll. Others, such as those of *Lilium candidum,* appear to be surrounded by a colorless cortex. Chloroplasts are frequently vesicular with a colorless center. The presence of starch granules is detected by the characteristic blue iodine reaction. Algae often possess a single huge chloroplast, which appears as a network, a spiral band or a stellate plate. The number of chloroplasts is kept relatively constant in the different plants. When the number of chloroplasts is insufficient, they are increased by division; when excessive, they are reduced by degeneration.

The *size* of chloroplasts varies considerably. The average diameter in higher plants is 4 to 6 μ. This is constant for a given cell type, but sexual and genetic differences are found. For instance, chloroplasts in polyploid cells are larger than those in the corresponding diploid cells. In general, chloroplasts of plants grown in the shade are larger and contain more chlorophyll than those of plants grown in sunlight.

Chloroplasts are sometimes distributed homogeneously within the cytoplasm, but are frequently packed near the nucleus or close to the cell wall. Their *distribution* often depends on external conditions, such as light intensity. It has been calculated that the leaf of *Ricinus communis* has about 400,000 chloroplasts per square millimeter of surface area.

In growing leaves chloroplasts apparently multiply by division. This takes place by elongation of the plastid and constriction in the central portion. The total time required for division of a chloroplast has been calculated to be about eight days.

Observation of living epidermal cells from leaves of Iris and other species has shown that chloroplasts are displaced and deformed by the action of cytoplasmic streaming (cyclosis). In addition to this passive *motility,* active movements of an ameboid or contractile type, which are sometimes related to the degree of illumination, have been observed.

Chloroplasts are distinguished from mitochondria and other plastids by their greater resistance to osmotic changes and fixatives.

Chloroplasts are strong reducing agents. For example, they can instantly reduce silver nitrate in the dark. This property is related to photosynthesis.

Chloroplasts have a higher density than the cytoplasm and go to the centrifugal pole of the cell when submitted to the action of centrifugal force. When placed in distilled water they generally swell and appear granular. In an isotonic sucrose solution their size and morphologic characteristics remain unchanged. These osmotic properties are related to the membrane surrounding the chloroplast.

Chemical Composition

Chloroplasts are isolated by differential centrifugation after the cell has been homogenized by special procedures. Table 12–2 shows the approximate chemical composition of isolated chloroplasts in higher plants. About 80 per cent of the protein is insoluble and intimately bound to lipids to form lipoproteins. Most of these are structural proteins, but an important part is represented by chloroplast enzymes, which may be soluble or built into the structure. The lipid fraction comprises neutral fats, steroids, waxes and phospholipids.

One of the main components is *chlorophyll*. This is an asymmetric molecule that has a hydrophilic head made up of four pyrrolic nuclei located around a magnesium atom and a long tail formed by a hydrophobic chain (phytol chain). (Chlorophyll is a porphyrin similar to that found in several animal pigments, such as hemoglobin and the cytochromes. In this case Mg is replaced by Fe.)

The other pigments that belong to the group of *carotenoids* are hidden by the green color of chlorophyll. In autumn, chlorophyll decreases, and the other pigments become apparent. These belong to the carotenes and xanthophylls, which are related to vitamin A. Carotenes are characterized chemically by the presence of a short chain of unsaturated hydrocarbon, which makes them completely hydrophobic. Xanthophylls, on the contrary, have several hydroxyl groups.

Different data suggest the presence of ribonucleic acid (RNA) in chloroplasts and also of deoxyribonucleic acid (DNA) in some of these plastids. RNA has been found in an average of 3 to 4 per cent of dry weight. The presence of DNA may be due to nuclear contamination. However, in *Chlamydomonas,* bodies giving a Feulgen reaction typical of DNA have been observed within the chloroplast.[14] These bodies disappear after treatment with DNA. In these and other chloroplasts, DNA has been related to the presence of a special nonchromosomal genetic system (cytoplasmic heredity).[15]

TABLE 12–2.   APPROXIMATE CHEMICAL ANALYSIS OF CHLOROPLASTS
OF HIGHER PLANTS*

CONSTITUENT	PER CENT OF DRY WEIGHT	COMPONENTS			
Proteins	35–55	About 80% is insoluble			
Lipids	20–30	Fats	50%		
		Sterols	20	Choline	46%
		Waxes	16	Inositol	22
		Phosphatides	2–7	Glycerol	22
				Ethanolamine	8
				Serine	0.7
Carbohydrates	Variable	Starch, sugar phosphates (3–7 C)			
Chlorophyll	9	Chlorophyll a	75%		
		Chlorophyll b	25		
Carotenoids	4.5	Xanthophyll	75		
		Carotene	25		
Nucleic acids					
RNA	2–3				
DNA	0.5 (?)				

* From S. Granick, 1961.

Chloroplasts also contain some cyto-chromes, vitamins K and E, and metallic atoms, such as Fe, Cu, Mn and Zn.

Some enzymes of chloroplasts will be considered later in this chapter in relation to the function of chloroplasts.

Ultrastructure and Grana

Many chloroplasts have a heterogeneous structure made up of small granules called "grana," which are embedded within the stroma. These grana have been identified in numerous cryptogams and phanerogams. They were first photomicrographed in vivo in transparent water plants using red light, but later were also demonstrated in many other species in vivo as well as after fixation. The size of the grana varies between 0.3 and 1.7 μ, depending on the species. The smallest ones, within the limit of microscopic visibility, are more numerous. They are described as flat bodies shaped like platelets or disks, which in a lateral view appear as dense bands perpendicular to the chloroplast surface (Fig. 12–8A).

Besides electron microscopy several indirect methods have been employed in the study of the molecular organization of chloroplasts. Both the chloroplasts and the chlorophyll dissolved in an alcohol or acetone solution show a red *fluorescence*. However, chlorophyll in colloidal suspension in water is not fluorescent. On the other hand, fluorescence persists if chlorophyll is absorbed and forms a monomolecular film. These facts led to the interpretation that chlorophyll within the plastids is disposed in monomolecular layers.

The lamelliform chloroplasts of certain algae, such as *Spirogyra* and *Mougeotia*, are birefringent in cross section and when viewed from above. This birefringence is negative with reference to an axis perpendicular to the chloroplast surface. By imbibition methods in media of a different refractive index a negative form birefringence and a positive intrinsic birefringence have been demonstrated (see Chap. 5). Form birefringence depends on the submicroscopic platelet or lamellar structure, whereas intrinsic birefringence is related to the presence of

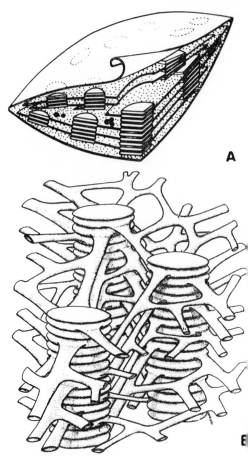

A

B

FIGURE 12–8. **A,** diagram of a chloroplast showing the inner structure with the grana disposed in stacks perpendicular to the surface. (From G. A. Erickson, E. Kahn, B. Wallis and D. von Wettstein.) **B,** diagram of the ultrastructure of three grana showing the anastomosing tubules that join some of the membranous compartments of the grana. (From T. E. Weier, C. R. Stocking, W. W. Thomson and H. Drever.[20])

lipids oriented with their axes perpendicular to the chloroplast surface. This last interpretation agrees with the fact that chloroplasts produce tubular myelin forms when placed in a slightly alkaline medium, having a positive birefringence with reference to the radius of the tubule.

Observation of thin sections under the electron microscope has revealed that the chloroplast has a double limiting outer membrane. The inner structure varies considerably whether chloroplasts of algae or of higher plants are considered. In both cases the basic structure is made of thin membranes. These are more or less continuous, forming flattened sacs or discs without grana in green algae and forming grana structures linked by membranes or tubules in the higher plants. In addition the membranes are embedded in a matrix of low density, and in some cases starch granules are present. In green algae the *pyrenoid*, which is a nonlamellated region associated with starch synthesis, and the *eye spot*, which contains carotenoid granules between discs, have been described.[16]

In certain algae the single chloroplast with the double outer membrane is surrounded by another double membrane that is dependent upon the nuclear envelope. This relationship suggests a direct interaction between the nucleus and the chloroplast.[17]

Electron microscopy has permitted a more detailed study of grana. In spinach cells it has been found that each chloroplast contains from 40 to 60 grana, each about 0.6 μ in diameter.

Grana are cylindrical structures made by the superimposition of double membranous sacs (Fig. 12–8). In some chloroplasts these sacs seem to be linked by a system of intergrana lamellae. If so, the membrane duplicates at the grana, which explains its more compact structure.

More recently a slightly different concept has emerged from different studies.[18-20] As shown in Figure 12–8B, the grana are distinct subplastid organelles formed by superimposed closed compartments. The number of grana may vary from a few to 50 or more. For some cases the grana extend as a cylinder across the entire width of the plastid. Adjacent grana may be interconnected by a network of flexuous, anastomosing tubules, which join certain compartments but not others. The contiguous compartments share common partitions. Under conditions that produce swelling of grana in vivo (e.g., in plants returned to light after continued existence in darkness or in Zn deficiency), or in vitro (e.g., by osmotic action in isolated plastids), the swelling is confined to the cavity contained within the compartment, a finding that is similar to the retinal rods (Fig. 8–7). After destruction of the intergrana network, grana may separate and become individual entities.

Origin of the Lamellar Structure of the Chloroplast

Figure 12–9 shows the development of a chloroplast during the ontogenesis of the plant. Proplastids are limited by a double membrane. In the presence of light the inner membrane grows and gives off vesicles that arrange themselves to form larger discs. At the grana regions stalks of closely packed lamellar sacs are built. In the mature chloroplasts some compartments of the grana remain connected by intergrana membranes or tubules; this developmental process is strongly affected by the lack of light. When plants are grown under low light intensity (i.e., etiolation), the vesicles formed in the proplastid aggregate, forming one or several prolamellar bodies. Sometimes the vesicles form a crystalline pattern consisting of regularly connected tubules[21, 22] (Fig. 12–9B). When these plants are exposed to light again, the vesicles may fuse into layers and develop again into grana. The entire development of the chloroplast is controlled by a number of genes that regulate the formation of the lamellar structure and its molecular organization.[23]

Function of Chloroplasts. Photosynthesis

Photosynthesis is one of the most fundamental biological functions. By means of the chlorophyll contained in the chloroplasts green plants trap the energy of sunlight emitted as photons (*quanta*) and transform it into chemical energy. This energy is stored in the chemical bonds that are produced in the synthesis of the many foodstuffs.

We have seen in the previous chapter how mitochondria can utilize and transform the energy contained in the foodstuffs by oxidative phosphorylation. Photosynthesis is somewhat the reverse process (Table 12–3). Chloroplasts and mitochondria have many structural and functional similarities, but also differences.

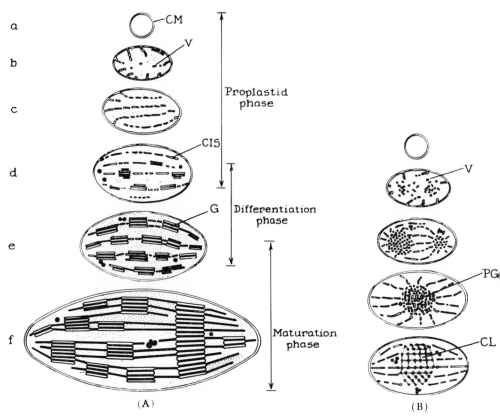

FIGURE 12–9. **A,** phases in the development of a proplastid into a chloroplast in the presence of light. **B,** same, but in the dark, showing the formation of the primary granum (*PG*), or prolamellar body. *CIS*, flattened cisternae; *CL*, crystal lattice; *CM*, double chloroplast membrane; *G*, granum; *V*, vesicles. (Modified from D. von Wettstein.)

The overall reaction of photosynthesis is:

$$CO_2 + H_2D \xrightarrow[\text{chlorophyll}]{\text{light}}$$
$$(CH_2O)n + O_2 \quad (1)$$

This indicates that essentially photosynthesis is the combination of carbon dioxide and water to form different carbohydrates with loss of O_2.

It has been calculated that each CO_2 molecule from the atmosphere is incorporated into a plant every 200 years and that all the oxygen in the atmosphere is renewed by plants every 2000 years. Without plants there would be no oxygen in the atmosphere and life would be almost impossible.

The carbohydrates first formed by photosynthesis are soluble sugars, which can be stored as granules of starch or other polysaccharides inside the chloroplasts or, more usually, inside the leukoplasts (amyloplasts). After several steps

that involve different types of plastids and enzymatic systems, the photosynthesized material is either stored as a reserve product or used as a structural part of the plant (i.e., cellulose).

In early studies it was suggested that in reaction (1) H_2O was the hydrogen donor much in the same way as H_2S is the donor in sulfur bacteria. Thus reaction (1) can be written as follows:

$$2H_2O + CO_2 \longrightarrow$$
$$H_2O + O_2 + (CH_2O)n \quad (2),$$

This shows that water is the H_2 donor and all the O_2 liberated comes from water.

Light (Photochemical) Reaction in Photosynthesis. Biochemical studies soon made apparent that reaction (2) involves a complex series of steps, of which some take place only in the presence of light and the others take place also in darkness. Thus the names *light* and *dark reactions.* In the first, light is absorbed and used by chlorophyll; this is the *pho-*

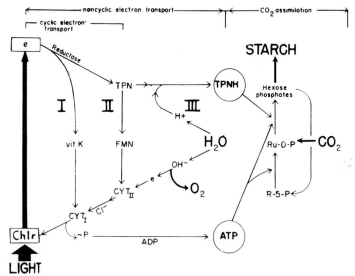

FIGURE 12–10.   Diagram of photochemical reactions in photosynthesis according to D. I. Arnon. Chlorophyll (*Chlr*), on absorbing a light quantum, becomes excited and electrons (*e*) are raised to high energy levels. This energy is used to reduce different coenzymes and to produce high energy bonds of ATP. In the cyclic pathway (I and II), reduction is by way of vitamin K and riboflavin phosphate (FMN). In the noncyclic pathway (III), the transport of electrons is to triphosphopyridine nucleotide (TPN$^+$). The TPNH and ATP formed are used in the dark reaction to assimilate CO_2 in the formation of carbohydrates (see Fig. 12–11).

tochemical (Hill) reaction. (In 1939, Robert Hill found that leaves ground in water, to which hydrogen acceptors were added [e.g., quinone], give off O_2 when exposed to light, without synthesizing carbohydrates.) In the second reaction CO_2 is fixed and reduced by thermochemical mechanisms.

At present the photochemical reaction is explained on lines somewhat similar to the oxidative phosphorylation occurring in mitochondria (see Chap. 11).[24, 25] Electrons in chlorophyll are excited to high energy states by light absorption. The energy of these electrons can then be used to form ATP from ADP or to reduce coenzymes (Fig. 12–10). This photosynthetic phosphorylation can occur in isolated chloroplasts if appropriate factors and cofactors are added.

The photochemical reaction takes place in the following steps: (1) *photophosphorylation*, in which ATP is formed from ADP through a chain of carriers, and (2) *hydrolysis and ionization of water*, in which TPN$^+$ is reduced to TPNH.

In contrast to the oxidative phosphorylation of mitochondria, in photophosphorylation O_2 is not used (Table 12–3). Green plants can produce 30 times as much ATP by photophosphorylation than by oxidative phosphorylation of their own mitochondria. In addition, these plants contain many more chloroplasts than mitochondria. The electron

TABLE 12–3.   DIFFERENCES BETWEEN PHOTOSYNTHESIS AND OXIDATIVE PHOSPHORYLATION

PHOTOSYNTHESIS	OXIDATIVE PHOSPHORYLATION
Only in presence of light	Independent of light
Thus periodical	Thus continuous
Uses H_2O and CO_2	Uses molecular O_2
Liberates O_2	Liberates CO_2
Hydrolyzes water	Forms water
Endergonic reaction	Exergonic reaction
$CO_2 + H_2O$ + energy → food stuff	Food stuff + O_2 → $CO_2 + H_2O$ + energy
In chloroplasts	In mitochondria

carriers used in photophosphorylation are not yet fully identified. They involve molecules containing vitamin K, TPN+ and FMN (flavin mononucleotide), in addition to special cytochromes that are not found in animal cells or microorganisms.

Figure 12–10 is a diagram of the three main pathways of the photochemical reaction and how it is coupled to the dark reactions (CO_2 fixation and reduction) to form carbohydrates (starch).

Dark (Thermochemical) Reaction in Photosynthesis. The diagram of Figure 12–10 shows that together with the energy provided by ATP the reduced TPNH can bring about the reduction of atmospheric CO_2 and combine it with the hydrogen to form the different carbohydrates. This process involves many steps and enzymes, which have been mainly elucidated by the use of radioactive CO_2 in a series of brilliant experiments.[26] The reactions involved (Fig. 12–11) are so rapid that they appear one second or less after the addition of $C^{14}O_2$. These reactions occur in complete darkness if the plant was previously il-

luminated. For details of the photosynthetic carbon cycle, see Figure 12–11 and refer to biochemistry textbooks.

In cells exposed to $C^{14}O_2$ for five seconds, the dominating compound is 3-phosphoglyceric acid, and from this all the compounds shown in the cycle of Figure 12–11 originate. Two triose phosphate molecules unite to form hexose (fructose) diphosphate, from which glucose phosphate is then formed. Then from glucose phosphate various disaccharides and polysaccharides are formed. As shown in Figure 12–11, the initial enzyme, *carboxydismutase*, is responsible for the formation of phosphoglyceric acid molecules from ribulose diphosphate and CO_2. Then under the action of many enzymes different hexoses, heptoses and pentoses are formed.

Correlation between Structure and Function in Chloroplasts

As in the case of mitochondria, it is now possible to correlate structure and function at a molecular level.

Isolated chloroplasts have the bio-

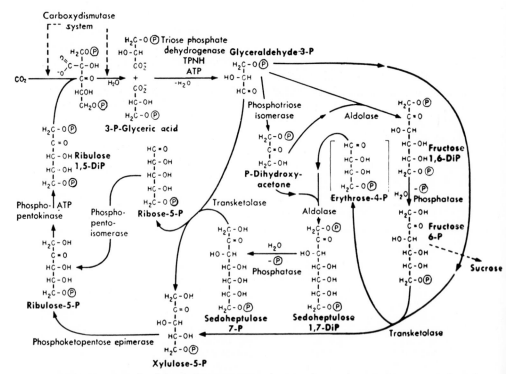

FIGURE 12–11. Details of the dark reactions in photosynthesis. The initial enzyme *carboxydismutase* is responsible for the formation of glyceraldehyde-3-phosphate into which the CO_2 is added. The different steps in the pentose cycle are indicated. (From J. A. Bassham and M. Calvin.)

chemical machinery necessary to perform both the light and dark reactions.[27] However, the enzymes involved in the dark reactions can be easily washed off with water. By fractionation of chloroplasts both series of reactions can be separated.[28] After sonic disruption a green sediment is obtained that carries out the light reactions (production of O_2, reducing power and ATP) while the supernatant contains the enzymes involved in the dark reactions (fixation of CO_2, etc.). Observation of these different fractions under the electron microscope has revealed that the green sediment is composed of the lamellar system of the chloroplast specially forming the grana. These lamellae consist of two layers, which are osmophilic in the outer surface. Chlorophyll is uniformly distributed within the lamellar structure.[29] Small fragments of these lamellae give the Hill

reaction, but fix CO_2 only in the presence of the supernatant containing the stroma proteins. The enzyme carboxydismutase (Fig. 12–11) is contained almost exclusively in the supernatant together with the other enzymes of the carbon cycle.

The Quantasome Concept

In the studies just mentioned it has been demonstrated that the inner surface of the two layers, or subunits, forming the lamellae has a granular organization (Fig. 12–12). This is made of fairly uniform oblate spheroids of 200×100 Å, which have been called *quantasomes*.

Three to six quantasomes aggregate and form particles or discs of 500×100 Å, which still retain the Hill reaction and fix CO_2 by the addition of CO_2. The quantasome would thus be the smallest

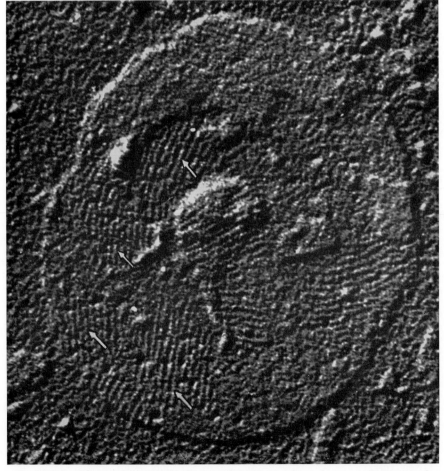

FIGURE 12–12.   Electron micrograph showing the inner surface of one compartment of grana. By shadow-casting, a uniform linear arrangement of spheroids of 100×200 Å, called *quantasomes*, can be demonstrated (arrows). (Courtesy of M. Calvin.)

particle that can carry on the photochemical reaction. It has been estimated that the quantasome contains 200 chlorophyll molecules, of which only about 10 would be highly oriented, serving to trap or concentrate the quantal energy. Associated with quantasomes would be one molecule of cytochrome and one or more acceptor molecules. This site of the quantasome that is directly involved in the transfer of electrons is now called the *quantatrope*.[26, 30]

These and other studies have shown that the chloroplast is one of the most elaborate biochemical "machines" producing energy transformation at a molecular level.

GENERAL REFERENCES

Arnon, D. I. (1956) Localization of photosynthesis in chloroplasts. *Henry Ford Hosp. Internat. Symp.*, 279.

Buvat, R. (1959) Recherches sur les infrastructures du cytoplasme dans le cellules du méristème apical des ébauches foliaires et des feuilles dévélopées de l'Elodea canadiensis. *Ann. Sc. Nat. Bot.*, 11ᵉ série, 121.

Erickson, R. O. (1959) Patterns of cell growth and differentiation in plants. In: *The cell*, Vol. 1, p. 497. (Brachet, J., and Mirsky, A. E., eds.) Academic Press, New York.

Frey-Wyssling, A. (1953) *Submicroscopic morphology of protoplasm and its derivatives.* Elsevier Co., New York.

Granick, S. (1961) The chloroplasts: Inheritance, structure and function. In: *The cell*, Vol. 2, p. 489. (Brachet, J., and Mirsky, A. E., eds.) Academic Press, New York.

Guillermond, A., Mangenot, G., and Plantefol, L. (1933) *Traité de cytologie végétale.* Le François, Paris.

Hodge, A. J., McLean, J. D., and Mercer, F. V. (1955) Ultrastructure of the lamellae and grana in the chloroplasts of *Zea mays. J. Biophys. Biochem. Cytol.*, 1:254.

Mühlethaler, K. (1961) Plant cell walls. In: *The cell.* Vol 2, p. 85. (Brachet, J., and Mirsky, A. E., eds.) Academic Press, New York.

Rabinowitch, E. (1945) *Photosynthesis.* Interscience Publishers, New York.

CITED REFERENCES

1. Mühlethaler, K. (1961) Plant cell walls. In: *The cell*, Vol. 2, p. 85. (Brachet, J., and Mirsky, A. E., eds.) Academic Press, New York.

2. Erickson, R. O. (1959) Patterns of cell growth and differentiation in plants. In: *The cell*, Vol. 1, p. 497. (Brachet, J., and Mirsky, A. E., eds.) Academic Press, New York.

3. Frey-Wyssling, A. (1953) *Submicroscopic morphology of protoplasm and its derivatives.* Elsevier Co., Amsterdam.

4. Porter, K. R. (1957) *Harvey Lect.*, ser. 51 (1955–1956), p. 175.

5. Buvat, R., and Carasso, N. (1957) *C. R. Acad. Sci.*, 244:1532.

6. Porter, K. R., and Machado, R. D. (1960) *J. Biophys. Biochem. Cytol.*, 7:167.

7. Porter, K. R. (1961) The ground substance, observations from electron microscopy. In: *The cell*, Vol. 2, p. 621. (Brachet, J., and Mirsky, A. E., eds.) Academic Press, New York.

8. Whaley, W. G., and Mollenhauer, H. H. (1963) *J. Cell Biol.*, 17:216.

9. Buvat, R. (1959) *Ann. Sc. Nat. Bot.*, 11ᵉ série, 121.

10. Guillermond, A., Mangenot, G., and Plantefol, L. (1933) *Traité de cytologie végétale.* Le François, Paris.

11. Guillermond, A. (1934) *Rév. Cytl. et Cytophysiol. végét.*, 1:197.

12. Mollenhauer, H. H., and Whaley, W. G. (1963) *J. Cell Biol.*, 17:222.

13. Guillermond, A. (1922) *C. R. Acad. Sci.*, 175:283.

14. Ris, H., and Plaut, W. (1962) *J. Cell Biol.*, 13:383.

15. Rhoades, M. M. (1955) *Encyclopedia Plant Phys.*, 1:19.

16. Sager, R., and Palade, G. E. (1957) *J. Biophys. Biochem. Cytol.*, 3:463.

17. Gibbs, S. P. (1962) *J. Cell Biol.*, 14:433.

18. Gibbs, S. P. (1960) *J. Ultrastruct Res.*, 4:127.

19. Weier, T. E., and Thomson, W. W. (1962) *J. Cell Biol.*, 13:89.

20. Weier, T. E., Stocking, C. R., Thomson, W. W., and Drever, H. (1963) *J. Ultrastruct. Res.*, 8:122.

21. Wilsenach, R. (1963) *J. Cell Biol.*, 18:419.

22. von Wettstein, D. (1959) *J. Ultrastruct. Res.*, 3:235.

23. Granick, S. (1961) The chloroplasts: Inheritance, structure and function. In: *The cell*, Vol. 2, p. 489. (Brachet, J., and Mirsky, A. E., eds.) Academic Press, New York.

24. Arnon, D. I. (1959) *Nature*, 184:10.

25. Arnon, D. I. (1960) *Sci. Amer.*, 203:104.

26. Calvin, M. (1962) *Science*, 135:879.

27. Arnon, D. I., Allen, M. B., Whatley, F. R., Capindale, J. B., and Rosenberg, L. L. (1956) *Proc. Intern. Congr. Biochem. 3rd Congr. Brussels*, 1955, p. 277.

28. Trebst, A. V., Tsujimoto, H. Y., and Arnon, D. I. (1958) *Nature*, 182:351.

29. Park, R. B., and Pon, N. G. (1961) *J. Molec. Biol.*, 3:10.

30. Sauer, K., and Calvin, M. (1962) *J. Molec. Biol.*, 4:451.

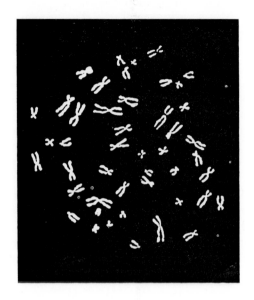

PART FIVE

CELLULAR

BASES

OF

CYTOGENETICS

In the following four chapters the nucleus and the chromosomes are studied as entities involved in genetic activity at the cellular level. This is also called the chromosomal bases of genetics. This study, which began at the end of the last century, developed so rapidly that for many years it was the best known field of cytology. The development of cariology (Gr. *carion* nucleus) was somewhat detrimental to the study of the cell as a whole and in its molecular and biochemical aspects which are now comprised within the realm of cell biology.

This part begins with the study of the life cycle of different cells, from those that divide continuously to others that remain in interphase throughout the life of the individual (e.g., nerve cells). The life cycle is directly related to the processes of mitotic and meiotic division and to the concept of continuity of chromosomes as entities capable of autoduplication and of maintaining their morphologic characteristics and function throughout successive cell divisions. In cytogenetics it is of great importance to recognize the morphologic constants of the chromosomes, such as the number, shape, size and primary and secondary constrictions, which as a whole are known as the karyotype.

A prerequisite to the study of mitotic and meiotic division is knowledge of the cycles of the chromonema, or chromosomal filament, and of the centriole. The centriole is a cytoplasmic component that, in the majority of animal cells, is directly related to the formation of the mitotic apparatus. The importance of isolating the mitotic apparatus, as a method of learning more about its composition and functioning, is emphasized. Some more rare but important chromosomal cycles, such as polyploidy and endomitosis, which result in polyteny, are mentioned.

Cytogenetics proper can be understood only with a clear comprehension of

203

meiosis as the division that brings about the reduction in the number of chromosomes and the recombination and interchange of blocks of genes by way of crossing over. Crossing over is cytologically expressed by the chiasma.

Chapter 15 on cytogenetics presents in a very general way the chromosomal bases of Mendel's principles of heredity and of the linkages between different genes, depending on their position in the chromosome and the presence or absence of crossing over. In relation to these concepts, the bases on which genetic maps of the chromosomes are built are mentioned. An important part of this chapter is dedicated to mutation, as a genetic concept, and to the different chromosomal aberrations that can be produced spontaneously or by radiation and chemical agents. The chromosomal aspects of evolution are considered briefly.

In the last five years the study of the human normal and abnormal karyotype has developed considerably and acquired great importance in cytogenetics. This material has been incorporated in Chapter 16 together with the discussion of chromosomal sex determination. These studies have considerable theoretical and applied value, because they include investigations of congenital and hereditary diseases and the varied sexual alterations that can be produced in the human. This material is of great importance to students of medicine, because they will be able to interpret better the pathogenic mechanism of numerous hereditary diseases and congenital malformations.

CHAPTER 13

GENERAL INTRODUCTION TO THE STUDY OF THE NUCLEUS AND CHROMOSOMES

life cycle the nucleus undergoes a series of complex but remarkably regular and constant changes in which the nuclear envelope and the nucleolus disappear and the chromatin substance becomes condensed into dark-staining bodies—the *chromosomes* (Gr. *chroma* color + *soma* body). The number of chromosomes is constant for a species and each pair of chromosomes is in general morphologically and physiologically different. Chromosomes are constantly present in the nucleus. During interphase they are not visible generally because they are dispersed or hydrated and their macromolecular components are loosely distributed within the nuclear sphere.

The study of the nucleus and chromosomes is certainly the most interesting in cytology because of their fundamental role in heredity and in the control and regulation of most cellular activities. In the deoxyribonucleic acid (DNA) molecule contained in chromosomes is the major amount of genetic information, which is transmitted from one cell or individual to another. The following chapters will show that this information is also responsible for the regulation and control of protein synthesis and for many nucleocytoplasmic relationships.

THE NUCLEUS

Morphology

A nucleus possessing the general characteristics described in Chapter 2 is found in all cells of higher animals and plants. On the other hand, in certain lower organisms such a nucleus is not apparent. In some Flagellata and Infusoria the nucleus is represented by granules of nuclear substance (chromatin) scattered throughout the cytoplasm. In bacteria, the nucleus is represented by granules or a diffuse, uniform material having the microchemical characteristics of nuclear substance. With the electron microscope, *nucleoid* bodies have been observed. They appear as regions less opaque to electrons than the cytoplasm. Within the nucleoplasm are filaments of nucleoprotein material. Between the cytoplasm and the karyoplasm of bacteria

Since the discovery of the nucleus as a constant part of the cell (Brown, 1831), cytologists have been interested in the extraordinary changes that the nucleus undergoes during the life cycle of the cell.

In general, every cell has essentially two periods of cellular life: *interphase* (nondivision) and *division* (which produces two daughter cells). This cycle is repeated at each cell generation, but the length of the cycle varies considerably in different types of cells. As will be studied in Chapter 19, some types of cells have a short life cycle and cell division takes place frequently, whereas others have a long interphase which may be as long as the life of the organism (e.g., nerve cells). During this

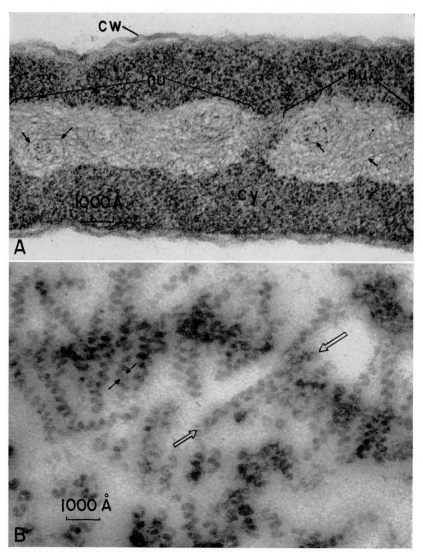

FIGURE 13–1. A, electron micrograph of thin sections of the bacterium *Escherichia coli.* The nucleoid (*nu*) shows the presence of microfibrils of DNA (arrows). Note that the nucleoid lacks a membrane. The cytoplasm (*cy*) is very dense; *cw,* cell wall. ×100,000. (Courtesy of E. Kellenberger.) **B,** electron micrograph of a Feulgen-positive region of the nucleus of *Amoeba proteus.* Double coiled filaments with a period of 300 to 375 Å. The two filaments form a *paranemic* coil (see Fig. 13–9). ×100,000. (G. D. Pappas.)

there is no definite nuclear envelope or membrane (Fig. 13–1).

The *shape* of the nucleus is sometimes related to that of the cell, but it may be completely irregular. In isodiametric cells (spheroid, cuboid, or polyhedral), the nucleus is generally a spheroid. In cylindrical, prismatic or fusiform cells it tends to be an ellipsoid. In squamous cells it is discoid. Examples of irregular nuclei are found in some leukocytes (horseshoe-shaped or multilobate nuclei), certain *Infusoria* (moniliform nuclei), glandular cells of many insects

(branched nuclei), spermatozoa (ellipsoid, pyriform and lanceolate nuclei and so forth, according to the species).

The *size* of the nucleus is variable, but in general it is directly proportional to that of the cytoplasm. This may be expressed numerically by the so-called *nucleoplasmic index* (NP) (R. Hertwig).

$$NP = \frac{Vn}{Vc - Vn}$$

(*Vn,* nuclear volume; *Vc,* volume of the cell.)

When the volume of the cytoplasm increases, the volume of the nucleus should increase also. The NP ratio seems to be a stimulus to cell division.

Almost all cells are *mononucleate*, but *binucleate* cells (some liver and cartilage cells) and *polynucleate* cells also exist. The nuclei of polynucleate cells may be numerous (up to 100 in the polykaryocytes of bone marrow [osteoclasts], Fig. 19–3). In the syncytia, which are large protoplasmic masses not subdivided into cellular territories, the nuclei may be extremely numerous. Such is the case with striated muscle fiber and certain siphonal algae, which may contain several hundred nuclei.

The *position* of the nucleus is variable, but is in general characteristic for each type of the cell. The nucleus of embryonic cells almost always occupies the geometric center, but commonly becomes displaced as differentiation advances and as specific parts or reserve substances are formed in the cytoplasm. In glandular cells the nucleus is located in the basal cytoplasm; the granules are in the apical cytoplasm. Whatever the position the nucleus in differentiated cells, it is almost always surrounded by a zone of cytoplasm, maintaining its undifferentiated embryonic aspect.

General Structure of the Interphase Nucleus

In describing the microscopic structure of the nucleus in the living cell (Chap. 2), we stated that, with some exceptions, vital or supravital observation reveals the presence of only a nuclear membrane (karyotheca) and one or more nucleoli (Fig. 2–2). On the other hand, in fixed and stained material the structure of the nucleus is distinguished by its complexity and varies according to the type of cell and the fixative used (see Fig. 6–7). In general, we can distinguish the following: (1) A *nuclear membrane* (karyotheca) appears in optical section as a clear outline on both the cytoplasmic and nuclear sides. The nuclear membrane cannot be seen with the optical microscope, but is detected by the apposition of the chromatin on the inner surface and the cyto-

plasm on the outer surface. (The structure of the nuclear membrane as revealed by electron microscopy was studied in Chapter 10.) (2) An unstained or slightly acidophilic mass, the *nuclear sap*, completely fills the nuclear space between the other nuclear components. From the physicochemical viewpoint the nucleus is a colloid system in which water is the dispersing phase. This give to the nucleus the turgescence and transparency that is observed under phase contrast (Figs. 2–2 and 10–1). Under the action of certain fixatives, the protein part of the nucleoplasm precipitates to form artificial fibrillar structures called *linin*. (3) Flakes of twisted filaments containing *chromatin*, a substance that has characteristic staining properties, are distributed throughout the nuclear sap. At present the chromatin is considered as the interphase form of the chromosomes before they organize and contract for the next cell division. Chromosomes are autonomic entities present during interphase, although apparently losing their morphologic individuality. (4) Flakes of chromatin are situated among the smaller ones, the *chromocenters* or *karyosomes*, also called nucleinic nucleoli or false nucleoli. These are more condensed regions also called *heterochromatin* (see below), in which parts of the chromosomes remain condensed (spiralized). Some of these chromocenters may adhere to the nucleolus, forming the so-called chromatin associated with the nucleolus. (5) Spheroidal bodies or *nucleoli* often of considerable size (in nerve cells, oöcytes and so forth), either single or multiple, resemble the karyosomes but differ by their staining affinity which is, in general, acidophilic.

Mitosis and Meiosis

It is important to introduce at this point the essentials of mitosis and meiosis, which are studied in more detail in the following chapters.

All organisms that reproduce sexually develop from a single cell, the *zygote*, produced by the union of two cells, the *germ cells* or *gametes* (a *spermatozoon* from the male and an *ovum* from the female). The union of an egg and a spermatozoon is called *fertilization*. The zygote produced by fertilization develops into a new individual of the same species as the parents.

Every cell of the individual with the exception of *gametes* contains the same number of chromosomes. In the somatic cells of a plant or an animal, chromosomes are paired, one member of each pair originally derived from one parent, the other member from the other parent. The member of a pair of chromosomes is called a *homologue,* and commonly we speak of pairs of chromosomes (or of homologues) when we refer to the chromosome number of a species. Man has 46 chromosomes or 23 pairs, onion has 8 pairs, toad 11 pairs, mosquitoes 3 pairs and so on (see Table 13–1). Homologues of each pair are alike, but the pairs are generally different. The original chromosome number of each cell (diploid number) is preserved during successive nuclear divisions involved in the growth and development of a multicellular organism.

Mitosis - Cell Division

The continuity of the chromosomal set is maintained by *cell division,* which is called *mitosis*. At the time of cell division the nucleus becomes completely reorganized, as illustrated in Figure 13–2. Mitosis takes place in a series of consecutive stages known as prophase, prometaphase, metaphase, anaphase and telophase. In a somatic cell the nucleus divides by mitosis in such a fashion that each of the two daughter cells receives exactly the same number and kind of chromosomes that the parent cell had.

Figure 13–2 represents two pairs of homologous chromosomes in a diploid nucleus. Each chromosome duplicates some time during *interphase* before the visible mitotic process begins. At this stage and at early *prophase* chromosomes appear as extended and slender threads. At late prophase chromosomes become short, compact rods by a process of spiral packing. A spindle arises between the two centrioles and the chromosomes line up across the equatorial plane of the spindle at the *metaphase* plate. At *ana-*

phase each chromosome separates, forming two daughter chromosomes, which go to opposite poles of the cell. Finally, at *telophase* the daughter chromosomes at each pole resolve themselves into a reticulum and two daughter nuclei are formed.

In mitosis the original chromosome number is preserved during the successive nuclear divisions. Since the somatic cells are derived from the zygote by mitosis, they all contain the normal double set, or diploid number ($2n$), of chromosomes.

Meiosis

If the gametes (ovum and spermatozoon) were diploid, the resulting zygote would have twice the diploid chromosome number. In order to avoid this, each gamete undergoes a special type of cell division called *meiosis,* which reduces the normal diploid set of chromosomes to a single (*haploid*) set (n). Thus when the ovum and spermatozoon unite in fertilization, the resulting zygote is diploid. The meiotic process is characteristic of all plants and animals that reproduce sexually and it takes place in the course of gametogenesis (Figs. 13–2 and 14–12).

Meiosis is the reduction of the chromosome number by means of two nuclear divisions, the *first* and *second meiotic divisions,* which involve only a single division of the chromosomes.

The essentials of the process are simple. The homologous chromosomes which can be distinguished by their identical morphologic characteristics, pair longitudinally; they come to lie in close contact, forming a bivalent. Each chromosome is composed of two spiral filaments, which are called the *chromatids*. The bivalent thus contains four chromatids and is also called a *tetrad*. In the tetrad only one chromatid of the homologue has a single pairing partner. Portions of these paired chromatids may be exchanged from one homologue to the other, giving rise to cross-shaped figures, which are called *chiasmata*. The chiasma is a cytologic manifestation of an underlying genetic phenomenon called *crossing over* (see Chap. 15).

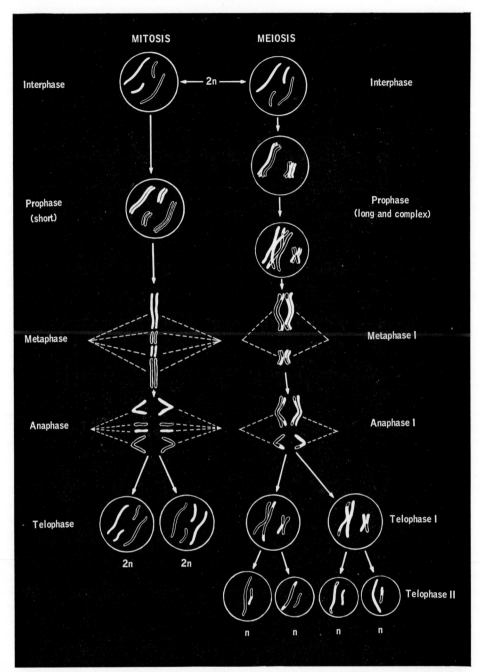

FIGURE 13–2. Comparative diagram of mitosis and meiosis in ideal cells having four chromosomes (2n). The chromosomes belonging to each progenitor are represented in white and black. In mitosis the division is equational while in meiosis it is reductional, the two divisions giving rise to four cells having only two chromosomes (n). In meiosis there is in addition an interchange of black and white segments of the chromosomes.

At metaphase I the bivalents arrange themselves on the spindle, and at anaphase I the homologous chromosomes with their two associated chromatids go to opposite poles. Thus in the first meiotic division the homologous pairs of chromosomes are segregated. After a short interphase the two chromatids of each homologue are separated in the second meiotic division, so that the original four chromatids are distributed in each of the four gametes. The result is four nuclei with only a single set (haploid number) of chromosomes (Fig. 13–2).

In the male, all four cells develop into spermatozoa. In the female, one cell develops into an ovum and the other three are the small *polar bodies*. The formation of germ cells in plants is complicated because before fertilization the haploid products of meiosis undergo two or more mitotic divisions. However, the essential features of the meiotic process are similar in all sexually reproducing plants and animals. Fertilization, also called *syngamy*, restores the diploid number of chromosomes.

Summary

In mitosis the chromosomes duplicate once for every cell division, whereas in meiosis chromosome duplication is followed by two cell divisions. In mitosis homologous chromosomes duplicate individually and do not pair. In meiosis homologous chromosomes form pairs and are then segregated into the two daughter cells of the first division. In the second division every homologue splits and enters into each of the four resulting cells.

CHROMOSOMES

Of all cell components observed during mitosis and meiosis, chromosomes have been the most thoroughly investigated. Their presence was demonstrated long before they were named "chromosomes" by Waldeyer in 1888. Forty years earlier the botanist Hofmeister, while studying the pollen mother cells of *Tradescantia*, portrayed chromosomes in drawings taken directly from living cells. This was the first concrete representation of chromosomes in biologic literature.

A chromosome may be considered as a nuclear component endowed with a special organization, individuality and function. It is capable of self reproduction and of maintaining its morphologic and physiologic properties through successive cell divisions.

Morphology

The morphologic characteristics of chromosomes are best studied during metaphase and anaphase of cell division. Then they appear as cylindroids and stain intensely with basic dyes and the Feulgen method (Chap. 6). They are easily observed in vivo by phase microscopy (Fig. 2–2), and they absorb ultraviolet light intensely at 2600 Å.

Chromosomes may be studied in tissue sections, but whole preparations obtained by crushing or smearing a small piece of tissue are better suited. Sex glands, plant meristem, pollen mother cells or other tissues can be crushed between a slide and a coverglass and simultaneously fixed and stained by the acetic hematoxylin or acetocarmine methods. The use of hypotonic solutions prior to squashing produces swelling of the nucleus and better separation of the individual chromosomes. Human chromosomes are easily studied in smears of bone marrow, cultures of leukocytes or other tissues. Such investigations have been of great value to cytogenetics and pathology (see Chap. 16).

Chromosomes are classified into three types by their shape in metaphase or in anaphase (Fig. 13–3): *acrocentric* chromosomes are rodlike and have a small or even imperceptible arm; *submetacentric* chromosomes have unequal arms and are thus L-shaped; and *metacentric* chromosomes have equal or almost equal arms and thus are V-shaped. The different chromosomal types are constant for each homologous chromosome. Therefore, a submetacentric chromosome invariably shows this configuration in all cells of an individual. The chromosomal type may also be constant throughout a species or even a genus; thus individual chromosomes can be identified by their shape.

Centromere (Gr. *meros* part). The shape of chromosomes is determined by the *primary constriction* located at the point where the arms of a chromosome meet (Fig. 13–4). Within the constriction is a clear zone containing a small granule, or spherule. This clear region is the so-called *centromere* (also called the *kinetochore* or *kinomere*). It is func-

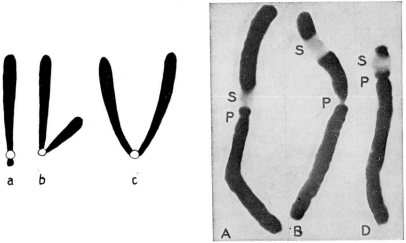

FIGURE 13–3. **Left,** the three morphologic types of chromosomes according to the position of the centromere: *a,* acrocentric; *b,* submetacentric; *c,* metacentric. **Right,** nucleolar chromosomes of the lily (**A, B, D**): *P,* primary or centromeric constriction; *S,* nucleolar or secondary constriction. (According to Stewart and Bamford, 1943.)

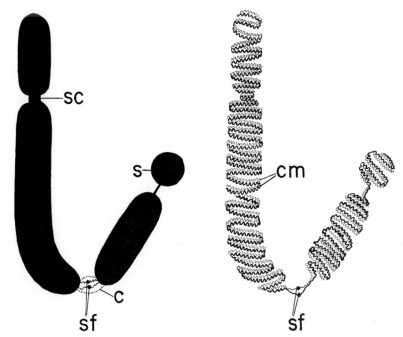

FIGURE 13–4. Diagram of a metacentric chromosome. **Left,** external view with the centromere (*c*), the satellite (*s*), secondary constrictions (*sc*) and the spindle fiber (*sf*). **Right,** same chromosome showing the inner structure with the two chromonemata (*cm*) and major and minor spirals.

tionally related to the chromosomal movements that occur during mitosis. For some time the centromere was described as the point of insertion of the spindle fiber. In the chromosomes of *Trillium* the centromere has a diameter of 3 μ and the spherule of about 0.2 μ. Usually each chromosome has only one centromere (monocentric); however,

there may be two (dicentric) or more (polycentric or with a diffuse centromere, e.g., *Ascaris megalocephala* and Hemiptera).

The structure of the centromere appears to be more complex than was thought previously. As shown in Figure 13–5, it is composed of three zones present in duplicate. The middle zone main-

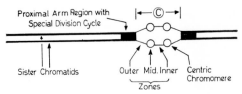

Proximal Arm Region with
Special Division Cycle

|←—ⓒ—→|

Sister Chromatids   Outer Mid. Inner Centric
                                            Chromomere
                               ⌣___⌣
                                Zones

FIGURE 13–5.   Diagram showing the organization of the centromere (C). (According to A. Lima-de-Faria.)

tains the relation of the chromosome to the spindle. In the diagram the two sister chromatids forming each metaphase chromosome are held by a region having a special division cycle.[1]

Secondary Constrictions. Other morphologic characteristics peculiar to the chromosomes are the *secondary constrictions.* Constant in their position and extent, these constrictions are useful in identifying particular chromosomes in a set. They may be either short or long; they are distributed along the chromosome and are distinguished from the primary constriction by the absence of marked angular deviation of the chromosomal segments (Fig. 13–4).

Telomere (Gr. *telo* far).   This term is applied to each of the extremities of a chromosome. If chromosomes are fractured by x-rays, the resulting segments may fuse again; however, the resulting pieces do not fuse to the telomere. It seems that the telomere has a polarity that prevents other segments from joining with it.

Satellite.   Another morphologic element present in certain chromosomes is the *satellite.* This is a round, elongate body separated from the rest of the chromosome by a delicate chromatic filament. The diameter may be the same as that of the chromosome or much smaller. Likewise, the filament of union may be long or short (Fig. 13–4). It is customary to designate as SAT-chromosomes those having a satellite. The satellite and the filament are also constant in shape and size for each particular chromosome.

Nucleolar Zone.   Certain secondary constrictions are intimately associated with the formation of the nucleoli, yet are usually not distinguishable from the other secondary constrictions. These specialized regions are the *nucleolar zone* or *nucleolar organizer.* Generally there

are two chromosomes in each nucleus, called nucleolar chromosomes, that have this special characteristic (Fig. 13–3).

Morphologic Constants in Chromosomes. Karyotype.   The most important characteristics identifying individual chromosomes in mitosis are their number, relative size, structure, behavior and internal organization. Other characteristics, such as linear contraction and degree of coiling, may be subject to physiologic variations.

The *number* of chromosomes is one of the best known constants (Table 13–1), and serves as an aid in determining the phylogeny and taxonomic position of plant and animal species. The organism with the lowest chromosome number is the nematode, *Ascaris megalocephala univalens.* It has only two chromosomes in each somatic cell, and therefore n = 1. The highest chromosome number among animals is found in the protozoa of the group *Agregata,* which have more than 300 chromosomes per cell.

The *shape* of chromosomes is also helpful in identifying a particular complex. The chromosomes of some species can be identified with ease (Fig. 13–6); in some it is practically impossible to distinguish the different chromosomes of a cell (Fig. 13–6).

The shape of the chromosomes may be altered by chemical agents or radiation. Furthermore, spontaneous alterations occur in nature, but it is difficult to determine their origin and to differentiate them from accidental alterations (see Chap. 15). As mentioned, some of the criteria employed for morphologic identification are based upon the position of the centromere, the secondary constrictions and the existence and localization of satellites.

Some zoologic groups have typical morphologic characteristics, such as the family Acrididae (locusts), the chromosomes of which are generally acrocentric (Fig. 13–6,6), or amphibia (Fig. 13–6,1), which have metacentric chromosomes. Among plants, the form of the chromosomes is more varied, with characteristic satellites and constrictions (Fig. 13–6,3 and 7). The size of the chromosome is relatively constant and individualizes a member of a set. The length of a chromosome may vary from 0.2 to 50 μ; the diameter from 0.2 to 2 μ. In humans the approximate length of chromosomes is 4 to 6 μ.

In a mitotic nucleus each homologue is not always found near its mate, since the location of each chromosome during this cycle is entirely independent. A given chromosome may occupy any part of the nucleus.

The name *karyotype* is given to the group of characteristics that identify a particular chromosomal set. The karyo-

type is characteristic of an individual, species, genus or larger grouping, and may be represented by a diagram that is called an *idiogram,* in which the pairs of homologues are ordered in a series of decreasing size (see Chap. 16 for human chromosomes).

Chromonema and Chromonema Cycle

Most chromosomes in the compact stages of metaphase and anaphase do not

TABLE 13–1. DIPLOID (2n) NUMBER OF CHROMOSOMES IN SOME PLANTS AND ANIMALS

PLANTS COMMON AND SCIENTIFIC NAMES	CHROMOSOMES	ANIMALS COMMON AND SCIENTIFIC NAMES	CHROMOSOMES
Yellow pine, *Pinus ponderosa*	24	Roman snail, *Helix pomatia*	54
Cabbage, *Brassica oleracea*	18	Silkworm, *Bombyx mori*	56
Radish, *Raphanus sativus*	18	Housefly, *Musca domestica*	12
Flax, *Linum usitatissimum*	30, 32	Vinegar fly, *Drosophila melanogaster*	8
Ombu, *Phytolacca dioica*	36	Spanish butterfly, *Lysandra nivescens*	380
Watermelon, *Citrullus vulgaris*	22	Grasshoppers, many Acrididae	24
Cucumber, *Cucumis sativus*	14	Grouse locusts, Tetrigidae	14
Papaya, *Cärica papaya*	18	*Dichroplus silveiraguidoi*	
Upland cotton, *Gossypium hirsutum*	52	(S. American Acrididae)	8
Cherry, *Pronus cerasus*	32	Honeybee, *Apis mellifica*	32, 16
Plum, *Prunus domestica*	48	Mosquito, *Culex pipiens*	6
Pear, *Pyrus communis*	34, 51, 68	Frogs, *Rana* spp.	26
Peanut, *Arachis hypogaea*	40	Tree frogs, *Hyla* spp.	24
Ceibo, *Erythrina cristagalli*	42	Toads, *Bufo* spp.	22
Coffee, *Coffea arabica*	44	Chicken, *Gallus domesticus*	ca. 78
Sunflower, *Helianthus annuus*	34	Turkey, *Meleagris gallipavo*	82
Luzula purpurea	6	Pigeon, *Columba livia*	80
Potato, *Solanum tuberosum*	48	Duck, *Anas platyrhyncha*	80
Tomato, *Lycopersicum solanum*	24	Opossum, *Didelphys virginiana,*	
Tobacco, *Nicotiana tabacum*	48	*D. paraguayensis*	22
Tradescantia virginiana	24	Mouse, *Mus musculus*	40
Banana, *Musa paradisiaca*	22, 44, 55, 77, 88	Rabbit, *Oryctolagus cuniculus*	44
Garden pea, *Pisum sativum*	14	Albino rat, *Rattus norvegicus*	42
Bean, *Phaseolus vulgaris*	22	Common rat, *Rattus rattus*	42
Orange, *Citrus sinensis*	18, 27, 36	Golden hamster, *Mesocricetus auratus*	44
Apple, *Malus silvestris*	34, 51	Chinese hamster, *Cricetus griseus*	22
Oats, *Avena sativa*	42	Guinea pig, *Cavia cobaya*	64
Indian corn, *Zea mays*	20	Mulita, *Dasypus hybridus* S. America	64
Barley, *Hordeum vulgare*	14	Armadillo, *Dasypus novemcinctus*	
Summer wheat, *Triticum dicoccum*	28	N. America	64
Bread wheat, *Triticum vulgare*	42	Dog, *Canis familiaris*	78
Rye, *Secale cereale*	14	Cat, *Felis domestica*	38
Rice, *Oryza sativa*	24	Horse, *Equus caballus*	66
Sorghum spp.	10, 20, 40	Donkey, *Equus asinus*	66
Black sorghum, *Sorghum almum*	40	Pig, *Sus scrofa*	40
Sugar cane, *Saccharum officinarum*	80	Sheep, *Ovis aries*	54
Field bean, *Vicia faba*	12	Goat, *Capra hircus*	60
Onion, *Allium cepa*	16	Cattle, *Bos taurus*	60
Eucalyptus, *Eucalyptus* spp.	22	Rhesus monkey, *Macaca mulatta*	42
Passion flower, *Passiflora coerulea*	18	Gorilla, *Gorilla gorilla*	48
		Orangutan, *Pongo pygmaeus*	48
		Chimpanzee, *Pan troglodytes*	48
		Man, *Homo sapiens*	46

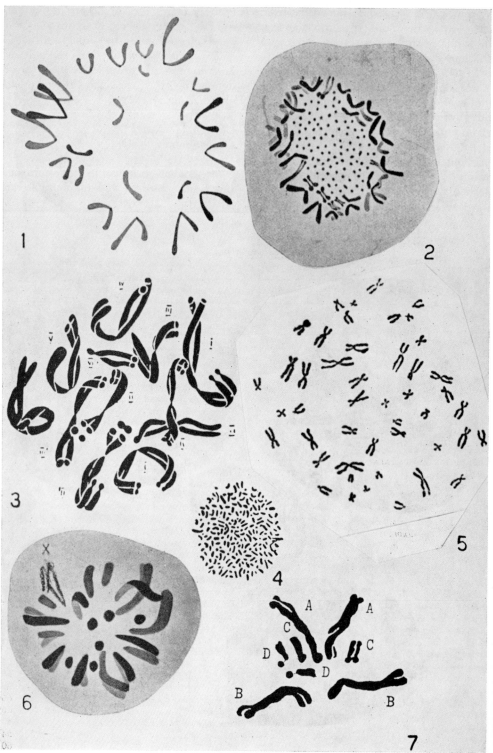

FIGURE 13–6. The characteristics of the somatic chromosomes of some plants and animals. All the figures correspond to metaphase in polar view.

1, the 22 chromosomes of the toad *Bufo arenarum,* showing their morphologic characteristics. In some chromosomes a black point corresponding to the centromere can be seen.

2, the chromosomes of the lizard *Tupinambis teguixin,* showing their 140 elements distributed as microchromosomes in the center and macrochromosomes at the periphery.

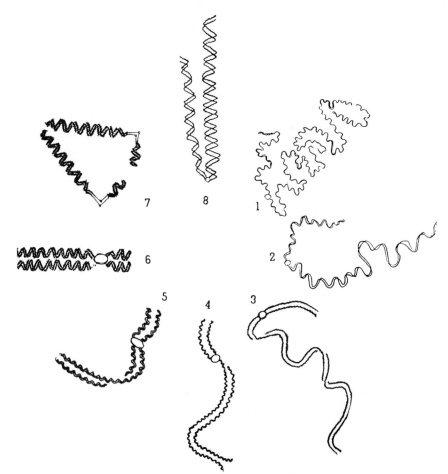

FIGURE 13–7.   Diagram of the spirilization cycle of the chromonema during mitosis. **1,** interphase with the remnant spiral and the superspirals. **2, 3** and **4,** prophase with the remnant spiral. **5,** prometaphase; each chromatid has two chromonemata. **6,** metaphase; the chromonemata show the major and minor spiral. **7,** anaphase. **8,** telophase; the circle represents the centromere.

show any special internal structure under the optical microscope (Fig. 13–4). However, in the less compact stages a coiled filament is visible within the chromosome. This structure was first observed by Baranetzky in 1880 in the pollen mother cells of *Tradescantia* and named *chromonema* by Vejdovsky in 1912. This coiled chromonema can be observed best after special treatments involving the action of agents that tend to separate the coils, such as hot water, acid vapors, alkaline solutions and potassium cyanide. By this treatment the coiling cycle of the chromonema has been studied in mitosis and meiosis (Figs. 13–7 and 13–8). To the right in Figure 13–4 the inner structure of a metaphase chromo-

3, the complex of chromosomes composed of 12 elements of a member of the Ranunculaceae, *Nigella orientalis,* in which some chromatids can be seen wound about each other, thus forming the relational spiral. The Roman numerals indicate the pairs of homologous chromosomes.

4, the 208 chromosomes of the decapod crustacean *Paralithodes camtschatica,* showing that they are rod-shaped and punctiform.

5, the 46 chromosomes of the human species.

6, the 23 telocentric chromosomes of the locust *Chromacris miles.* The sex chromosome, indicated by X, is found in negative heteropyknosis.

7, the eight chromosomes of the composite plant *Hypochoeris tweedie,* showing a pair of satellites. The letters indicate the pairs of homologous chromosomes. (1, from Saez, Rojas and De Robertis, 1936; 2, from Matthey, 1933; 3, from Lewitsky, 1931; 4, from Niyama, 1935; 5, from La Cour, 1944; 6, from Saez, 1930; 7, from Saez, 1945.)

some is diagrammatically represented. The number of threads within the chromonema may be two, four or more, depending on the material studied. The chromonema may be single during one stage of development and double- or four-stranded during another.

Two types of coils are formed between two or more chromonemal threads: the *paranemic* coil has freely separable subunits (Fig. 13–9a); the *plectonemic* coil has intertwined subunits, which, if stretched, form a so-called *relational* coil (Fig. 13–9b). By microscopic observations it is sometimes difficult to distinguish between paranemic and plectonemic coils. The degree of coiling in meiotic or mitotic chromosomes is variable and depends on the length of the chromosomes. Meiotic chromosomes have two distinct coils: a *major* coil, which has 10 to 30 gyres, and a *minor* coil, which lies perpendicular to the major coil and has many more gyres than the major coil (Fig. 13–6). In mitotic chromosomes a helical structure similar to the major coil of meiotic chromosomes has been described. This is the *standard* or *somatic* coil.

The coiling cycle of the chromonema is characteristic of mitosis as well as meiosis (Tables 13–2 and 13–3).

During interphase chromosomes reach their maximum length. They assume a zig-zag shape with broad turns called *supercoils* (Fig. 13–7,1). During prophase each chromosome is composed of two chromatids, which wind and are intertwined. At the end of prophase the somatic coil appears (Fig. 13–7,2–4). The number of gyres is reduced and the chromosome shortens and increases in width until metaphase, when the chromosomes are at the maximum state of contraction (Fig. 13–7,6). Following anaphase the somatic coil is relaxed

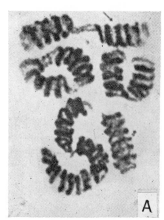 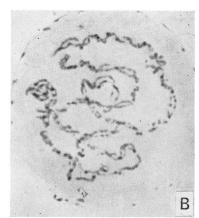

FIGURE 13–8. A, spiral structure in the chromosomes of *Tradescantia congesta* during the first meiotic division. The arrow indicates the minor spiral. B, prophase of a pollen grain (microspore) of *Trillium grandiflorum*, showing the large turns of the spiral, which remain from the time of their origin in the cycle of the previous division; simultaneously, a new cycle of spiralization has begun, which is shown in the small turn of each chromatid. (A, after Coleman and Hylary, 1941; B after Sparrow, 1942.)

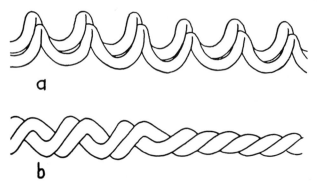

FIGURE 13–9. Diagram of the two types of coils formed between two or more chromonemal threads: a, paranemic; b, plectonemic. When plectonemic coils are stretched, a relational spiral is formed between the two chromonemata. (From Ris, 1957.)

Fig. 13–7,7), and during the next cell division it constitutes the relic coil.

TABLE 13–2. LENGTH IN MICRONS AND NUMBER OF COILS OF THE CHROMATIDS OF *Trillium grandiflorum* DURING MITOSIS OF POLLEN GRAINS (MICROSPORES)*

CONDITION	LENGTH OF THE CHROMATID	NUMBER OF TURNS
Relic coils of 60 turns	450–600	480–600
Prophase	346	554
Middle prophase	202	242
Middle prophase	205	276
Final prophase	173	151
Final prophase	154	170
Final prophase	142	187
Metaphase	77	130
Anaphase (15 cells, average)	95.0 ± 2.9	130 ± 3.3

* Data from Sparrow, 1942.

TABLE 13–3. CHROMOSOME AND CHROMONEMA LENGTHS IN MEIOSIS OF *Trillium erectum**

STAGE	LENGTH (IN MICRONS)	
	CHROMOSOME	CHROMONEMA
Leptotene	—	920
Zygotene	—	1040
Pachytene	—	640
Diakinesis (early)	86	109
Diakinesis (mid)	125	187
Metaphase I	99	320
Anaphase I	93	327
Anaphase II	76	310

* Data from Sparrow, A. H., Huskins, C. L., and Wilson, G. B., 1941. "Studies on the Chromosome Spiralization Cycle in Trillium," Can. J. Research, C, 19, Table I, p. 325.

Euchromatin, Heterochromatin and Chromomeres

In 1928, Heitz defined as "heterochromatin" the chromosomal regions that remain condensed during interphase, forming the so-called *chromocenters* or false nucleoli. This is in contrast with the rest of the chromosome substance that uncoils and swells during the same period and is called "euchromatin." Heterochromatin may be in close contact with the nucleolus, forming a Feulgen-positive coat or ring around it (Fig. 6–7).

During mitosis the heterochromatic regions may stain more strongly or more weakly than the euchromatic regions. These phenomena are called, respectively, *positive* and *negative heteropyknosis* (Figs. 13–10 and 13–11). Heteropyknosis (Gr. differential staining) is characteristic of the sex chromosomes of many species, but may also be observed in other chromosomes (see reference 2). Heteropyknosis may be localized at the extremities or intercalated along the chromosome. In some cases it may affect almost the entire chromosome. The toad *Bufo arenarum Hensel* has a chromosome with a negative heteropyknosis during the metaphase of the first meiotic division (Fig. 13–10,2).

Several experimental procedures give rise to the appearance of heteropyknotic segments. Figure 13–11 shows the effect of cold on dividing cells.[3] With this method it is possible to investigate heterochromatic zones in the chromosomes of an organism. The clear segments show low concentrations of nucleic acids during cell division. The constancy of distribution of such clear segments characterize each chromosome of the set. In prophase, heterochromatic segments produced by low temperature may appear condensed, resembling true chromocenters (Fig. 13–11a).

It has been suggested that DNA may be more labile in heterochromatin than in euchromatin.[4–6] Morphologically these heterochromatic regions are interpreted as segments in which the chromonema has a different degree of coiling or packing.

Even in the dense, uniform regions found in prophase and interphase chromosomes, the coiled chromonema can be made visible by the use of uncoiling agents, such as KCN (see reference 7). Thus the chromonema seems to be continuous from the euchromatic to the heterochromatic regions. Also, the electron microscope shows that the heterochromatic regions correspond to parts in which the packing of the microfibrils is differential.

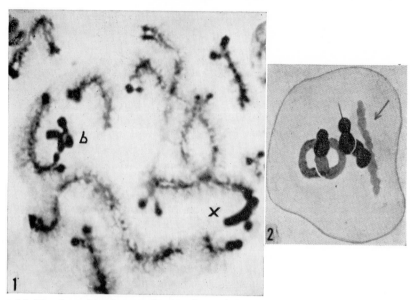

FIGURE 13–10.   1, positive heteropyknosis of two chromosomes, the sex chromosome indicated by *x* and a bivalent indicated by *b*, during early diplotene in the grasshopper *Laplatacris* spp. 2, negative heteropyknosis of a chromosome, indicated by the arrow, during meiotic metaphase I in the toad *Bufo arenarum*. (1, after Saez, 1951, unpublished data; 2, after Saez, Rojas and De Robertis, 1936.)

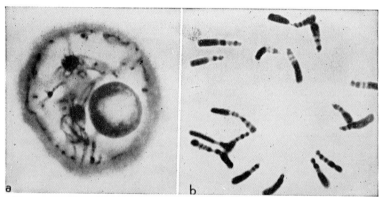

FIGURE 13–11.   Effects of cold on the chromosomes. a, nucleus of the embryo sac of *Fritillaria pudica* at prophase, showing the three heterochromatic bodies stained black (in positive heteropyknosis) with abundant nucleic acid. The nucleolus, which appears as a large sphere, has not been colored by the Feulgen stain and its color is due to the osmic acid with which the cell has been fixed. b, metaphase chromosomes of *Fritillaria pudica*, showing the clear zones produced by a temperature of 0° C. These zones correspond to the heterochromatin (in this case a negative heteropyknosis). The dark parts of the chromosomes correspond to the euchromatin. (After Darlington and La Cour, 1941.)

Another structure related to the chromonema is the so-called *chromomere*. In the thin chromosomes of meiotic prophase and early mitotic prophase, the chromonema may show alternating thick and thin regions. The general aspect is that of a string of beads scattered along the length of the chromosome. The bead-like structures are called *chromomeres,* and the regions in between *interchromomeres*. The position of each chromo-mere is relatively constant for a given chromosome.

The morphologic interpretation of the chromomeres has varied widely. While some investigators believe that they represent condensations of nucleoprotein material, others favor the view that they are regions of superposed coils. Some support for this last concept comes from electron microscope observations of leptotene chromosomes, which show that the strands of the chromosomes are folded back and forth in the chromomeres. Two other morphologic concepts —that of an amorphous matrix between coils of the chromonema and that of a pellicle surrounding each chromosome— have been disproved by electron microscopic observations.[7, 8]

Special or Giant Chromosomes

In certain cells, particularly at certain stages of their life cycle, special types of giant chromosomes may be observed. These are characterized by their enormous size and the corresponding increase in volume of the nucleus and the cell. To these special chromosomes belong the so-called *polytenes* found in larvae of *Diptera*, particularly in the salivary glands, and the *lampbrush chromosomes* observed in oöcytes of different vertebrates and invertebrates. Interest in these chromosomes has increased in recent years because several cytologic and cytochemical investigations indicate that synthesis takes place in them (see Chap. 17).

Polytene Chromosomes

In tissues of dipteran larvae, such as the salivary glands, gut, trachea, fat body cells and malpighian tubules, some chromosomes are strikingly different from the somatic chromosomes of the same organisms. First observed by Balbiani in 1881, polytene chromosomes received little attention until after 1930 when their cytogenetic importance was demonstrated by Kostoff, Painter, Heitz and Bauer. Since then interest in these chromosomes has greatly increased.

In *Drosophila melanogaster* the volume of polytene chromosomes is about 1000 times larger than that of the somatic chromosomes. The total length of the four-paired set is 2000 μ, compared to 7.5 μ in somatic cells. Figure 13–12,7 indicates at the same magnification the entire somatic set as compared with the smallest pair (IV) of giant chromosomes. This enormous size is reached by a series of 9 to 10 consecutive duplication cycles of the chromosomes, which increase the DNA content about 1000 times.[9] Another characteristic of polytene chromosomes is that the homologous pairs are closely associated as in meiotic prophase (see Chap. 14). This phenomenon is called *somatic pairing* and the chromosomes are considered to be in a permanent prophase (see Fig. 13–12,1).

The structure of polytene chromosomes is of great cytogenetic interest. Along the length of the chromosome a series of dark *bands* alternates with clear zones called *interbands* (Fig. 13–13). The dark bands stain intensely, are Feulgen-positive and absorb ultraviolet light at 2600 Å. These bands may be considered as disks of varying sizes that occupy the whole diameter of the chromosome. The larger bands have a more complicated structure. They often form *doublets*. The interbands are fibrillar, do not stain with basic stains, are Feulgen-negative and absorb little ultraviolet light. The constancy in number, localization and distribution of the disks or bands in the two homologous (paired) chromosomes is notable. It is easy to construct, from a giant chromosome, topographic maps of the bands and interbands parallel to the genetic map (Chap. 15) and to verify any disarrangement or alteration in the order of their linear structure. In the four chromosomes of *Drosophila* over 5000 bands are found. Detailed maps of each one of the chromosomes of this and other species have been drawn in which the genetic characteristics of each band and of the intermediate regions are meticulously recorded.

The interpretation of the fine structure of the giant salivary chromosomes is still under discussion. The evidence that the chromosomes are polytenic (i.e., multistranded) seems conclusive. The peculiar constitution and diameter of these chromosomes is due to their formation from a number of fibers (four at the origin for each chromosome) which multiply many times, remaining together like the thread of a rope (Fig. 13–12). Each fiber is delicate and difficult to perceive, and may be considered as a chromonema.

This process of reduplication of the strands is called *endomitosis* (see Chap.

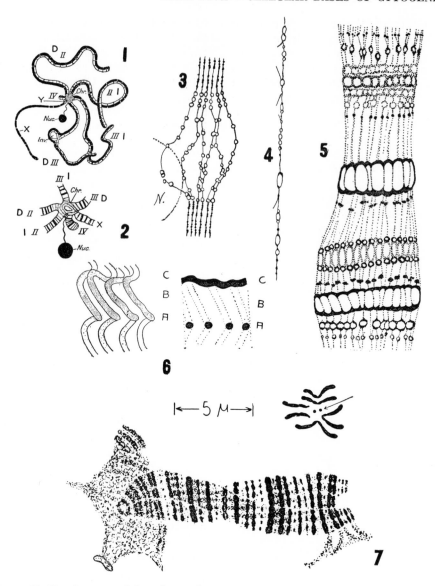

FIGURE 13–12. Structure of the polytene chromosomes.

1, general schematic aspect of the chromosomes of the salivary gland of a male of *Drosophila melanogaster* after they have been spread out by crushing the nucleus. The paternal chromosome (in white) and the maternal one (in black) are paired. *Chr.*, chromocenter; *D II* and *II I*, right and left arms of chromosome II; *D III* and *III I*, right and left arms of the third chromosome; *IV*, the fourth chromosome; *Inv.*, an inversion in the right arm of the third chromosome; *Nuc.*, nucleus; *X* and *Y* indicate respectively the sex chromosomes.

2, the chromocenter (*Chr.*) formed by the union of the heterochromatic parts of all the chromosomes in a female of *D. melanogaster*. (The other symbols are the same as for 1.)

3, a heterochromatic region of the X chromosome of *D. pseudoobscura*, showing its relations with the nucleolus (*N.*) and the filamentous (chromonemic) constitution of the chromosome.

4, detail of a component chromonema of the polytene chromosome in which the different chromomeres are seen.

5, schematic structure of the chromosome of *Simulium virgatum*, showing the organization of the chromonemata, chromomeres and vesicles, which together give the appearance of the bands. The segment drawn corresponds to a euchromatic zone.

6, diagram to illustrate the interpretation of the helicoidal chromonema and the false chromomeres produced by the turns of the spiral. A zone (*B*) with four chromonemata is shown between two consecutive bands (at the left). To the right is the aspect of the same region when observed in a different focusing plane. *A* has a granular aspect, which simulates chromomeres. *C* appears as a continuous solid line.

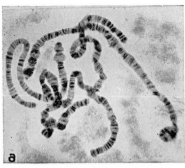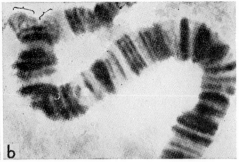

FIGURE 13–13.   Polytene chromosomes of *Drosophila melanogaster*. **a**, view of the chromosomes of one nucleus, showing the dark bands and the clear interbands. Preparation by crushing in aceto-carmine. **b**, part of the sex chromosome X, as observed with ultraviolet light. Photograph taken at 2570 Å, which is the spectral band of maximum absorption for nucleic acid. (b, After Schultz, 1941.)

5). About nine reduplications are probably produced, which result in about 1000 fibers (Fig. 13–12). The length of a polytene chromosome is more or less that of a mitotic chromosome during prophase. Some investigators have postulated that the chromonemata are drawn out without spiralization. In addition to these observations on the development of the giant chromosome, the polytene constitution can be demonstrated morphologically by the fact that certain regions may split into numerous subunits.[10, 11] According to this view the bands consist of the association of the replicated chromosomes side by side.

Puffs and Balbiani Rings.   Of interest are observations at specific times during larval growth of local variations in the size and degree of condensation of certain bands. These appear as local swellings or "puffs." In addition there are the so-called *Balbiani rings*, which are larger than the swellings, but of similar nature to the puffs.

The formation of puffs (also called "puffing") may occur at single bands or include adjacent ones (Fig. 13–14).[12] At the Balbiani rings the chromonemata running through a specific band could be spun laterally, forming a series of loops and giving to them a similarity with the lampbrush chromosomes.[13, 14] As will be studied in Chapter 17, puffing is accompanied generally by production of RNA and proteins. There is some evidence of a local increase in DNA also (Fig. 13–14).

The changes involved in puffing are completely reversible and there is a cycle during which the puffs and Balbiani rings appear, grow and disappear. As will be discussed in Chapter 17, the polytene chromosome is a model of what normally occurs at the interphase nucleus, that is, when the chromosomes are most elongated and have the greatest synthetic activity.[15]

Lampbrush Chromosomes

The lampbrush chromosomes were discovered by Ruckert in 1892, but only recently have been interpreted appropriately. These are even longer than the polytene chromosomes and are found in oöcytes during the extended diplotene phase of the first meiotic division. In general, this phase corresponds to a period of maximum synthesis in which the yolk is produced.

Maximum size is reached in some urodele oöcytes, in which the total length of the chromosomal set may be 5900 μ, which is three times longer than that of the polytene chromosomes.[16, 17]

The growth of lampbrush chromosomes results from an increase in the

7, the fourth polytene chromosome of *D. melanogaster*, adhering to the chromocenter, which is at the left. Above, at the right, the somatic chromosomes of the same fly as they appear in mitosis. The difference in size between the giant chromosome IV and the somatic chromosome IV is indicated by the arrow and drawn to the same scale. (1 and 2, after White, 1942; 3, after Bauer, 1936; 4, after Painter and Griffen, 1937; 5, after Painter, 1946; 6, after Ris and Crouse, 1945; 7, after Bridges, 1935.)

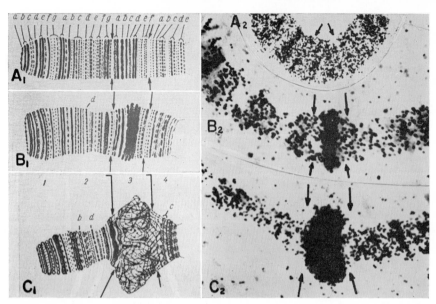

FIGURE 13–14.   "Puffs" of the chromosome of *Rynchosciara angelae* in different stages of development (A_1, B_1, C_1) stained with Feulgen dye. (From Pavan and Breuer, 1952.) A_2, B_2, C_2, the same
region of the chromosome but from larvae injected with H³-thymidine. Note the great increase of
DNA within the "puff." (Courtesy of A. Ficq and C. Pavan.)

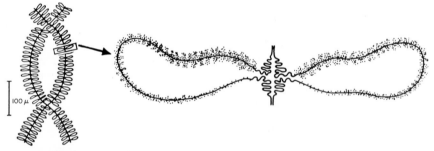

FIGURE 13–15.   Diagram of the lampbrush chromosomes of the oöcyte of *Triturus*. Left, low
magnification. Right, higher magnification, showing the lateral expansions in the form of a handle
and the spiralization of the chromonemata. (From Gall, 1956.)

size of the chromonemata. The chromosomes have many fine lateral projections,
which give them the appearance of a
test-tube brush or lampbrush. The central axis of these chromosomes is probably composed of at least four chromatids, to which the fine lateral projections
are attached. Each bivalent chromosome
consists of two homologues held together
at "contact points" or chiasmata (see
Chap. 15). The axis consists of a row
of granules (chromomeres) and the lateral projections are looplike (Fig. 13–
15) and occur in pairs.

It is now generally agreed that the
loops represent lateral extended portions
of the chromatids (half chromosome).
The loop is coated with protein and RNA
material.[17] The chromomeres in the axis
are regions in which there is a tight
coiling of the chromonemata (see Fig.
13–15).[7] The axis with its chromomeres
is Feulgen-positive, whereas the loops
apparently contain mainly RNA and protein.

These and other findings showing the
active formation of material from the
loops (which is then released into the
nucleoplasm) lead to the comparison of
these structures with the polytene chromosomes. The comparison is still more
interesting when made with the puffs
and Balbiani rings (see the preceding
section). In both these regions and at
the loops of the lampbrush chromosomes
material is synthesized and then released

into the nucleus and cytoplasm. They correspond to a special physiologic activity of the nucleus at a moment of development of the oöcytes. The reduction in size of the lampbrush chromosomes in later stages of prophase probably results from elimination of material at a submicroscopic level.

Some interesting calculations regarding the probable length of the chromonema in the chromosomes (about 5 cm) and of DNA (about 90 cm) have led to the postulation of the existence of a certain number of DNA strands in each lampbrush chromosome.

The physiological significance of both the lampbrush and polytene chromosomes[18] is considered again in Chapter 17.

GENERAL REFERENCES

Churney, L. (1941) *The physico-chemical properties of the nucleus.* University of Pennsylvania Bicentennial Conference, University of Pennsylvania Press, Philadelphia.

De Robertis, E. (1956) Electron microscope observations on the submicroscopic morphology of the meiotic nucleus and chromosomes. *J. Biophys. Biochem. Cytol., 2:*785.

Denues, A. R. T. (1958) Chromosomes: their constitution and function. In: *Frontiers in cytology.* Yale University Press, New Haven.

Gall, J. G. (1952) On the submicroscopic structure of chromosomes. Mutation. *Brookhaven Symp. Biol., 8:*17.

Hamerton, J. L., ed. (1963) *Chromosomes in medicine.* Medical advisory committee of the National Spastics Society in association with Wm. Heinemann. Little Club Clinics in Developmental Medicine, No. 5.

Hughes, H. (1952) *The mitotic cycle.* Academic Press, New York.

Lewis, K. R., and John, B. (1963) *Chromosome marker.* J. & A. Churchill, London.

Mathey, R. (1949) *Les chromosomes des vertébrés.* L. Rouge, Lausanne.

White, M. J. D. (1942) *The chromosomes.* 2nd ed. Methuen & Co., London.

CITED REFERENCES

1. Lima-de-Faria, A. (1956) *Hereditas, 42:*85.
2. Oestergren, G. (1950) *Hereditas, 36:*511.
3. Darlington, C. D., and La Cour, L. (1938) *Ann. Bot., 2:*615.
4. Sparrow, A. H., Moses, M. J., and Dubow, R. J. (1952) *Exp. Cell Res.,* Suppl. 2: 245.
5. Bendich, A. (1952) *Exp. Cell Res.,* Suppl. 2:182.
6. La Cour, L. F., Deeley, E. M., and Chayen, J. (1956) *Nature, 177:*272.
7. Ris, H. (1957) Chromosome structure. In: *The chemical basis of heredity.* (McElroy, W. D., and Glass, B., eds.) Johns Hopkins Press, Baltimore.
8. De Robertis, E. (1956) *J. Biophys. Biochem. Cytol., 2:*785.
9. Kurnick, N. B., and Herskovitz, I. (1952) *J. Cell. Comp. Physiol., 39:*281.
10. Bauer, H., and Beermann, W. (1952) *Chromosoma, 4:*630.
11. Mechelke, M. (1952) *Chromosoma, 5:*246.
12. Pavan, C. (1958) Morphological and physiological aspects of chromosomal activities. *Proc. X Internat. Congress Genetics., 1:*321. McGill University, Montreal.
13. Beermann, W. (1961) *Chromosoma, 12:*1.
14. Beermann, W. (1962) *Protoplasmologia,* VI, D. Wien, Springer.
15. Lewis, K. R., and John, B. (1963) *Chromosome marker.* J. & A. Churchill, London.
16. Duryee, W. R. (1950) *Ann. N.Y. Acad. Sci., 50:*920.
17. Gall, J. G. (1956) *Brookhaven Symp. Biol., 8:*17.
18. Gall, J. G., and Callan, H. G. (1962) *Proc. Nat. Acad. Sci.* (Wash.), *48:*562.

CHAPTER 14

CELL DIVISION:

MITOSIS

AND

MEIOSIS

The *growth* and development of every living organism depends on the growth and multiplication of its cells. In unicellular organisms, cell division is the means of reproduction, and by this process two or more new individuals arise from the original. On the other hand, multicellular organisms come from a single primordial cell, the zygote, and it is the multiplication of this cell and its descendants that determines the development and growth of the individual.

The size of most organisms is determined by the number of component cells, not the volume of individual cells. Each class of cells shows a general uniform volume, which may differ markedly in cells of a different type. In many instances cells appear to grow to a limit before division occurs. This process is repeated in the two daughter cells so that the total volume eventually becomes four times that of the original cell. In other words, the growth of living material is produced rhythmically and according to a geometric progression by cell division, and often is accompanied

224

by a corresponding increase in total volume. This has been expressed as follows

$$\frac{Mn}{Mc}, \quad \frac{2Mn}{2Mc}, \quad \frac{4Mn}{4Mc}, \quad \frac{8Mn}{8Mc}, \quad \text{etc.}$$

Mn is the nuclear mass and *Mc* is the cytoplasmic mass of the cells. The two masses are in a state of optimum equilibrium, the so-called *nucleoplasmic ratio* or *index*. This ratio may vary within certain limits, but these limits cannot be exceeded without important changes in cell physiology.

This equilibrium not only refers to a relationship of volumes but implies a chemical relationship as well. We have seen that in polytene chromosomes by the process of endomitosis DNA may increase as much as 1000 times (Chap 13); consequently, the volume of the cytoplasm also increases considerably. This phenomenon is shown diagrammatically in Figure 14–1, in which a typical somatic cell is compared to a similar giant cell of the same animal. For an even more dramatic comparison, notice the

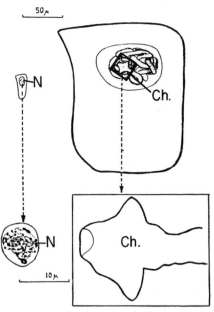

FIGURE 14–1. Diagram indicating the relationship of cellular and nuclear volume in polyteny. **Left,** diploid somatic cell of normal size **Right,** similar cell but from the salivary gland of a larva. **Below,** notice that the volume of the nucleus of a diploid cell is similar to that of a small segment of one giant polytene chromosome. *N*, nucleus; *Ch.*, chromosome. (Courtesy of C. Pavan.)

size of the nuclei. The entire nucleus of a somatic cell corresponds in volume to a small portion of a polytene chromosome.

Cell division is the complex phenomenon by which cellular material is divided equally between daughter cells. This process is only the final and microscopically visible phase of an underlying change that has occurred at a macromolecular and biochemical level. Before the cell divides by mitosis, all its fundamental components have duplicated and divided, particularly those involved in hereditary transmission. In this respect, cell division or mitosis can be considered as the final separation of the already duplicated macromolecular units (see Chap. 17).

This chapter is a detailed cytologic analysis of mitosis and meiosis, the essentials of which were considered in the preceding chapter. The biochemical aspects of cell division are discussed in Chapter 17.

MITOSIS

In the process of division, every cell is characterized by two fundamental components that constitute the mitotic figure: the chromatic and the achromatic apparati. The chromatic apparatus is formed by the chromosomes; the nucleoli may also be considered as components of this apparatus, since they take part in the mitotic cycle. The achromatic apparatus is formed by: (1) the centers or poles and (2) the spindle.

Analysis of Mitosis

Figure 14–2 is a general diagram of the different stages of mitosis. These are considered as phases of a cycle that starts at the end of the intermitotic period, or *interphase,* and ends at the beginning of a new interphase. The main divisions of this cycle are: *prophase, prometaphase, metaphase, anaphase* and *telophase.*

Prophase is characterized by physicochemical changes in the cytoplasm. The cell becomes spheroid and more refractive and viscous. The prophase chromosomes appear as delicate, longitudinally coiled filaments extended or twisted within the nuclear sphere (Fig. 14–2, *1–3*).

Each prophase chromosome is composed of two coiled filaments, called *chromatids,* which are closely associated along their entire length. As prophase progresses, the chromatids shorten and become thicker. The appearance of the chromosomes in prophase depends in part on the duration of the preceding interphase. When this has been short and the number of chromosomes of the species is small, the position occupied by each prophase chromosome is the same as in telophase of the preceding division.

With careful observation one can see the centromere as a small, clear, circular zone in a constant position in each chromosome (Fig. 14–2,*1–3*). This region appears to play a fundamental role in the movement of the chromosomes and maintains a close dynamic relation to the cell centers or poles. As the chromosome becomes thicker, the centromeric region becomes more accentuated and appears in metaphase as a constriction, the *centric* or *primary constriction.*

During early prophase, the chromosomes are evenly distributed in the nuclear cavity. As prophase progresses, the chromosomes approach the nuclear membrane, and thus the central space of the nucleus becomes empty. The centrifugal movement of the chromosomes indicates that the disintegration of the nuclear membrane is approaching and with it the end of prophase. At this time each chromosome appears to be composed of two cylindrical, longitudinal elements called the *longitudinal halves.* These are parallel and in close proximity. The maximum shortening of the chromosomes is nearly reached, and some may have shrunk to $\frac{1}{25}$ their early prophase length.

The formation of the spindle shows a number of variations. In one type of spindle formation known as the *central spindle,* this begins in the vicinity of the centrioles, which lie at one side of the nuclear membrane. Each centriole, which is really double, shows an *aster* with astral rays, and, arising between the two asters, is a bundle of delicate filaments,

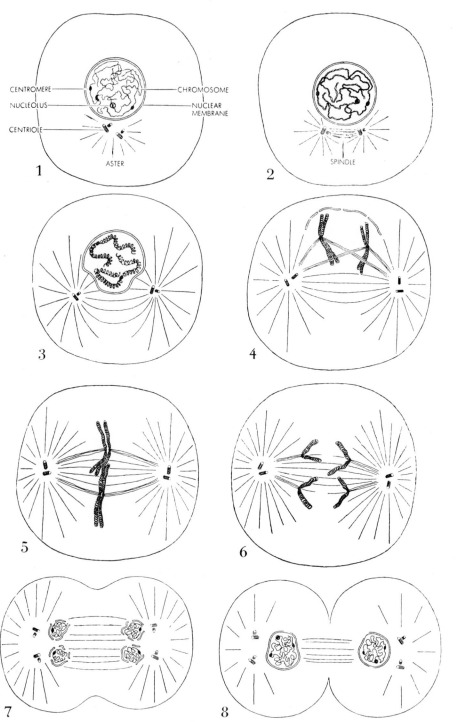

FIGURE 14-2.   Schematic view of the mitotic process in an ideal cell containing two chromosomes. The cycles of the chromosomes and centrioles are emphasized. 1–3, prophase, 4, prometaphase, 5, metaphase, **6**, anaphase, 7–8, telophase. (From Mazia, 1961, *Scient. Amer., 205*(3):100.)

the *spindle*. The centrioles continue their migration along with the asters, describing a semicircular path toward the poles, until they become situated in antip-

odal positions. (For the replication cycle of the centriole, see below.)

There is another type of spindle formation, the *metaphase spindle*, in which the

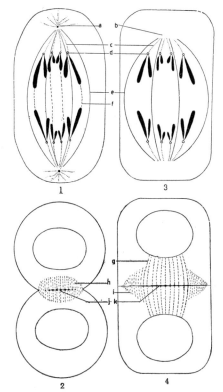

FIGURE 14-3. Diagram of the constitution of the spindle during anaphase and telophase in an animal cell (1 and 2) and in a plant cell (3 and 4). *a*, centriole; *b*, polar center; *c*, tractor or chromosomal fiber; *d*, centromere (kinetochore); *e*, continuous fiber of the spindle; *f*, fiber or interzonal connection; *g*, spindle of cytokinesis; *h*, remains of the spindle; *i*, phragmoplast; *j*, intermediate bodies; *k*, cell plate. **1**, anaphase; **2**, telophase with cytokinesis by constriction; **3**, anaphase; **4**, telophase with cytokinesis by formation of the cell plate.

centrioles are polarized before division begins, the spindle being formed at metaphase. Mitoses in which the achromatic figure and spindle are formed by centers (centrioles and asters) are called *astral* or *amphiastral* mitoses and are common in animal cells and in some lower plants. Mitoses that lack these centers are called *anastral* and are characteristic of higher plants (Fig. 14-3) and certain invertebrates (e.g., hemiptera).

Prometaphase generally begins with the disintegration of the nuclear membrane. When this has occurred, a more fluid zone is noted in the center of the cell in which the chromosomes move freely and in apparent disorder, making their way toward the equator (Fig. 14-2,4).

Metaphase begins when the chromosomes reach the plane of the equator, where they arrange themselves radially at the periphery of the spindle as if they were repelling each other (Fig. 14-2,5). In plant cells, chromosomes are irregularly arranged and occupy the entire surface of the equatorial plane of the spindle. The distinction between these two arrangements is not always clear. If small chromosomes are in the group, they are commonly situated toward the interior; the larger ones are customarily found in the periphery.

The array of chromosomes of the spindle is called the *equatorial plate*. In metaphase, the chromosomes are connected to the fibers of the spindle by means of the centromeres. Those fibers of the spindle that connect to the chromosomes are called the *chromosomal fibers* (Fig. 14-3c); those that extend without interruption from one pole to the other are called *continuous fibers* (Fig. 14-3e). When the chromosomes are observed in polar view, one can determine easily their number, shape and dimensions.

The equilibrium of forces that characterizes metaphase is broken by the division of the centromere that has united the chromatid up to this time. This division is carried out simultaneously in all the chromosomes. The daughter centromeres move apart and the chromatids separate, beginning their migration toward the poles (Fig. 14-2,6). This process characterizes the beginning of *anaphase*. From this time the chromatids, now called *daughter chromosomes*, become shorter and separate.

During the latter half of anaphase the aspect of the spindle changes. In the zone between the two groups of chromosomes the spindle fibers appear stretched and constitute the *interzonal fibers* (Fig. 14-3f).

The end of the polar migration of the two daughter groups marks the beginning of *telophase*. In this stage, favorable preparations may show the spiralized structure of the chromosomes with their chromonemata. A little later the process of nuclear reconstruction occurs. This appears to be a prophase process in reverse. The chromosomes become less compact, the coils of the chromonemata unwind and imbibition from the surrounding karyoplasm occurs, while the membrane of the daughter nuclei is reconstructed (Fig. 14–2,7-8). During the final stages the nucleoli reappear at the nucleolar organizers, or *SAT-zones.*

Simultaneously *cytokinesis* occurs. This is the process of segmentation and separation of the cytoplasm. In animal cells the cytoplasm constricts in the equatorial region, and this constriction is accentuated and deepened until the cell divides (Fig. 14–2,8). This process can be followed in living cells with the phase microscope (Fig. 14–4).

In cells of higher animals the period of cytokinesis is marked by active move-

ment at the cell surface that is best described as "bubbling." This bubbling is generally concentrated at late anaphase and telophase. This typical movement can be induced in nondividing cultured cells by adding substances that bind bivalent cations (e.g., Ca^{++}). Some investigators suggest that bubbling may reflect the activity of a rapidly expanding membrane.[1] In ameboid cells at telophase both daughter cells have active movements, which appear to pull them apart. This is best observed in films of dividing cells.

Other cytoplasmic changes occur in telophase. The high viscosity characteristic of metaphase and anaphase de-

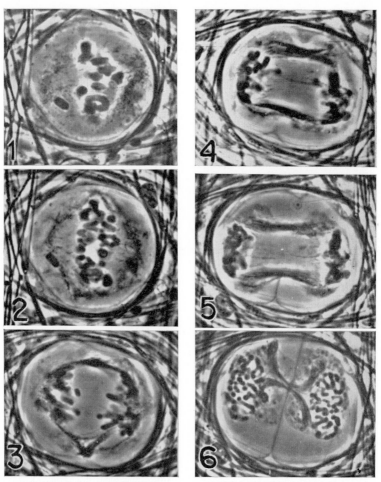

FIGURE 14–4. Division of the spermatocyte of the locust observed under phase contrast in a medium of bovine plasma of 12.3 per cent that allowed the observation of the cell without crushing it. **1,** final prometaphase; the sex chromosome is to the left. Mitochondria appear as short filaments and granules. **2,** final metaphase; the orientation of mitochondria begins. **3,** anaphase; mitochondria concentrate at the equator. **4** and **5,** telophase; all mitochondria are on the sides of the spindle. In **5,** beginning of the constriction. **6,** telophase, showing that mitochondria constitute a bundle that expands into both daughter cells. (Courtesy of R. Barer and S. Joseph, 1957.)

creases during telophase; the centrioles cease their activity, and the asters become less conspicuous. During cytokinesis the cytoplasmic components are distributed, including the mitochondria and the Golgi complex. Table 14–1 indicates the duration of the different phases of mitosis in various cell types.

The Cell Center and Mitotic Apparatus

The study of mitosis is not complete without a discussion of the cell center and the mitotic apparatus. The cell center is a cytoplasmic organoid that has been found so far in animal cells and in some lower plants. Since the classic work of van Beneden, Boveri, Heidenhain, Wilson and others, it has been shown that this cell component is represented by a small single or double (diplosome) granule called the *centriole*. Whereas this is generally observed in interphase, in mitosis the cell center reaches a higher degree of complexity, in which it is a part of a large and elaborate structure called the *mitotic apparatus*.

The centriole is not observed in vivo in most cells. This is not surprising, since its dimensions approximate the resolving power of the light microscope. However, it has been observed in living cells and followed during the mitosis of fibroblasts in its division and migration toward the poles.[2]

Since the development of electron microscopy there is no doubt about the existence and constancy of the centriole in most cells excluding those of higher plants; however, the interpretation of the surrounding zones has been more difficult. In fixed and stained preparations of cells in mitosis, the centriole is frequently surrounded by a clear zone—the so-called *microcentrum* or *centrosome*—and then by a denser zone, the *centrosphere,* from which the *aster* or *astrosphere* radiates (Fig. 14–5). During mitotic prophase, as the centrioles separate toward the poles, the microcentrum forms an elongated body or bridge, the so-called *centrodesmus,* from which the spindle seems to arise.

Another concept of general interest is that the centrioles and the so-called *"basal granules"* of cilia are identical bodies. This hypothesis was advanced by Henneguy in 1897 and supported by other early cytologists (Henneguy-Lenhossék hypothesis). It has been confirmed with electron microscopy.

Centriole and Pericentriolar Structures

Under the electron microscope the centriole appears as a cylinder 150 mμ in diameter. The interior is of low density, but the wall of the cylinder is electron-dense and contains small rods or tubules 150 to 200 Å in diameter that are oriented parallel to the axis (Fig. 14–6). Nine tubules appear; as in the basal granules of cilia, this number seems to be constant. There are nine groups of tubules, each of which may contain one to three units (Fig. 14–7). The structure of the centriole may be even more complex.[3, 4] *Pericentriolar structures* or *"satellites"* have been observed as dense masses of about 700 Å sometimes attached to the wall of the centriole (Fig. 14–6). Of even more in-

TABLE 14–1. DURATION OF MITOTIC PHASES OF LIVING DIVIDING CELLS*

CELL	MINUTES			
	PROPHASE	METAPHASE	ANAPHASE	TELOPHASE
Yoshida sarcoma (35°C.)	14	31	4	21
Mouse spleen in culture	20–35	6–15	8–14	9–26
Triton liver fibroblast (26°C.)	18 or more	17–38	14–26	28
Chortophaga (grasshopper) neuroblast (38°C.)	102	13	9	57
Pea endosperm	40	20	12	110
Iris endosperm	40–65	10–30	12–22	40–75

* From Mazia.[24]

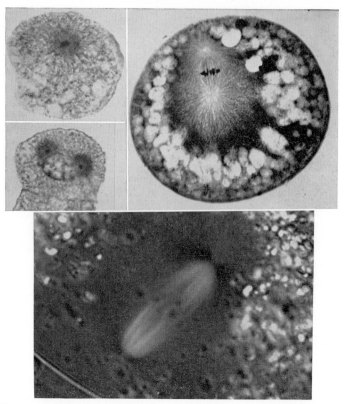

FIGURE 14–5. **Upper left,** photomicrograph of the cell center in the egg of *Ascaris megalocephala.* **Upper right,** section of an egg of *Nereis limbata,* showing the spindle and the asters. ×610. (Courtesy of D. P. Costello.) **Below,** mitotic apparatus (asters and spindle) of the first division of the oöcyte of *Chaetopterus pergamentaceus* observed with the polarizing microscope. The spindle fibers show a positive birefringence. The aster rays appear dark because they are oriented perpendicular to the spindle. ×1500. (Courtesy of S. Inoué.)

terest is the observation of structures that can be interpreted as small *daughter centrioles* or *procentrioles,* which seem to arise by sprouting at an angle from the mother centriole (Fig. 14–6). This disposition is related to the mechanism of centriolar reduplication and to the fact that the two centrioles in the diplosome are generally disposed at right angles (Fig. 14–2). It has been suggested that the organization of centrioles is polarized.[4, 5] The distal end is concerned with the formation of cilia, flagella (see below) or other products and the proximal end is concerned with replication.[5]

The relationship of the centriole to the other cell components has been clarified. The *position* of the centriole is, in general, fixed for each type of cell. In some cells, the centriole has a tendency to occupy the geometric center. This happens, in ideal conditions, in leukocytes that have a horseshoe-shaped nucleus,

or when the nuclear mass is small and displaced. In general, however, the centriole is pushed back by the nucleus and by the products elaborated by the cytoplasm. Nevertheless, even in these cases, the position may be relatively fixed and axial; if one draws a line between the center of the nucleus and the centriole, it will coincide with the axis of the cell. Such is the case in some cylindroid epithelial cells in which the centriole or centrioles are in the central part of the apical end beneath the membrane.

The relationship of the centriole to the Golgi complex and the mitochondria has been observed with the light microscope. These organoids may form a crown around the centriole. Golgi membranes may be observed in contact with the cell center, as shown in Figure 14–6, and may contribute to the formation of the so-called *centrosphere* of light microscopy.

Electron microscopy has not confirmed

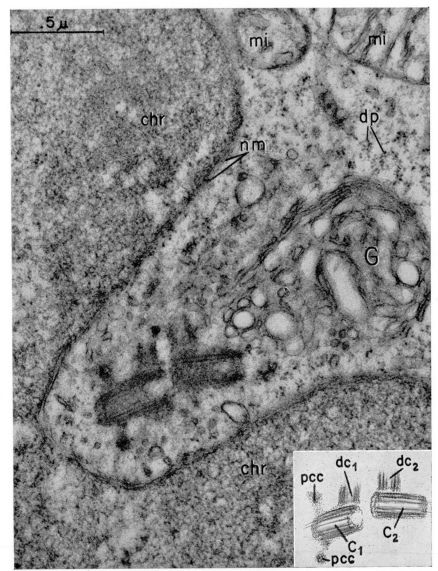

FIGURE 14–6. The two centrioles C_1 and C_2 are in the invaginated portion of the nuclear membrane near the Golgi complex (G). *chr*, chromatin with filamentous structure; dc_2, daughter centriole of C_2; *dp*, dense particles; *mi*, mitochondria; *nm*, nuclear membrane; *pcc*, pericentriolar bodies. ×60,000. (Courtesy of E. De Harven and W. Bernhard.)

the existence of the so-called centrosome (microcentrum) and the centrodesmus of light microscopy. It is possible that the pericentriolar structures (satellites and daughter centrioles) are related to the centrosome.

Centriole Cycle during Mitosis

The centrioles situated at the poles of the mitotic spindle have a structure that is identical to that found during interphase.[4] Both the astral and the spindle fibers appear under the electron microscope as fine fibrils 150 to 200 Å thick and several microns long; their relationship to the centrioles seems to be indirect, as in the case of cilia. The spindle fibers apparently end a certain distance from the centrioles, and the axis of the organoid generally does not coincide with the spindle axis (Fig. 14–2). Centrioles are normally double and always appear in pairs during interphase. Before they act as division centers, each member of the pair must divide. This

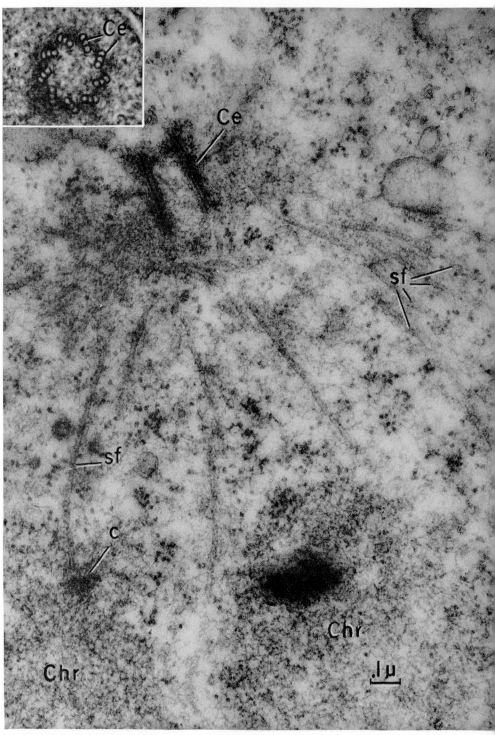

FIGURE 14–7.   Electron micrograph of the polar region of a cell in mitosis, showing one of the centrioles (*Ce*). Notice the tubular aspect of the spindle fibers (*sf*), which converge upon the centriole. At the bottom of the figure are two chromosomes (*Chr*) and one centromere (*c*). ×80,000. Inset: a centriole cut transversely, showing nine groups of three tubules each. (Courtesy of J. André.)

duplication is effected by the formation and growth of the small daughter centrioles, which were mentioned in the preceding section (see Fig. 14–6). For example, in Figure 14–8A, which corresponds to the fertilization of a sea urchin egg, notice that duplication of the centrioles begins during fusion of the pronuclei and is completed at metaphase. Then the two daughter centrioles start to duplicate again at telophase and the next interphase. This cycle of the centrioles can be altered by the drug *mercaptoethanol,* which inhibits the duplication of the centrioles at telophase (Fig. 14–8B). The consequence is that the four centrioles separate without duplication and upon removal of the drug initiate a four-polar mitosis after which they renew the centriole duplication.[6] This drug is interesting because it affects only the duplication of the centrioles and not their separation or movement in cell division.

Centrioles and Cilia

The fine structure of the so-called *basal*

granules of cilia and of the proximal centriole of spermatids is similar to that recognized in other centrioles.[7-9] The formation of cilia has been followed in some developing cells. It has been observed that the pairs of filaments (or tubules) that constitute the typical structure of a cilium and sperm tail are formed in direct continuity with the tubule of one centriole, while the other centriole remains inactive (see Fig. 21–17).

Stages in formation of the cilium and of the relationship of the centriole to the cell membrane have been recognized in a number of different cell types (see Fig. 21–17). An interesting example is that of the morphogenesis of the outer segment of the retinal rods and cones, which develops from a primitive cilium and is also related to the activity of one centriole (see Figs. 21–15 and 21–16).[10]

Mitotic Apparatus

Intimately related to the function of the cell is the development of the so-

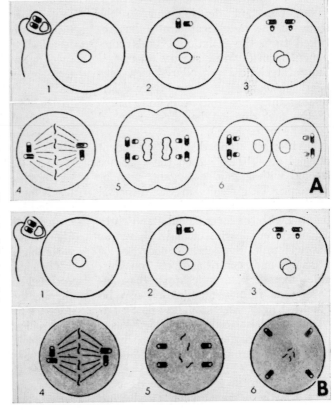

FIGURE 14–8.   A, normal centriole reproduction in a fertilized sea urchin egg. *1* to *2,* fertilization and penetration of the two centrioles. *3,* fusion of pronuclei and the beginning of the formation of daughter centrioles. *4,* metaphase; the centrioles are fully duplicated. *5,* telophase; new reproduction of centrioles begins. *6,* interphase. **B,** centriole reproduction after treatment with mercaptoethanol. *1, 2, 3,* same as in A. *4,* beginning of treatment at metaphase. *5, 6,* inhibition of centriole reproduction. (From D. Mazia, 1961, *Scient. Amer., 205*(3): 100.)

called "mitotic apparatus" during cell division. This term has been applied to the ensemble of structures that constitutes the achromatic figure in the classic description of mitosis.[11] This structure includes the *aster* (also called the *astrosphere*), which surrounds the centriole, and also the *mitotic spindle.*

The aster appears in fixed preparations as a group of radiating refringent fibrils that converge toward the microcentrum and continue in the centrosphere (Fig. 14–5). The aster is also evident in vivo because of its greater refringence, but in this case the fibrillar structure of the aster is not seen, and its constitution seems homogeneous. However, studies with polarized light[12, 13] have demonstrated in vivo a submicroscopic organization characterized by a macromolecular orientation. Fixation accentuates the fibrillar character of the aster (Fig. 14–5). The electron microscope has shown the fine structure of this fibrillar component (Fig. 14–7).

Isolation and Biochemical Studies of the Mitotic Apparatus

An important development in the study of the mitotic apparatus has resulted from the isolation of this component from dividing sea urchin eggs.[11] Several technical procedures were applied, but essentially these involved fertilizing the eggs until a definite stage of the first division has been reached (usually metaphase).

Division is stopped in 30 per cent ethanol at $-10°$ C.; then the eggs are treated with a mild detergent, such as digitonin. This results in the dispersal of the cytoplasm while the mitotic apparatus with the aster, spindle and chromosomes remains intact and behaves as a single unit. By gentle procedures of washing and centrifugation, considerable amounts of mitotic apparatus relatively free from contamination can be obtained (Fig. 14–9).[14] The mitotic apparatus thus isolated and purified has a positive birefringence as in the living cell and the chromosomes are evident in phase contrast (Fig. 14–9). The isolated mitotic apparatus is difficult to dissolve except with an agent such as alkaline

thioglycolate that splits disulfide bonds $(-S-S-)$.

The main component of the mitotic apparatus is a protein that is low in aromatic amino acids and contains 3 to 5 per cent nucleic acid, most of which is RNA. The contribution of chromosomal DNA is quantitatively negligible. The protein is relatively homogeneous by electrophoresis, and a single component seems to be responsible for the formation of the astral and spindle fibers. The mitotic apparatus in metaphase accounts for about 12 per cent of the total protein in the sea urchin egg, and this component probably arises from the cytoplasm, since the nucleus cannot account for a considerable contribution.[14] This and other findings have suggested that $-S-S-$ linkages may be acting in this protein.

The action of a strong solution of urea on the isolated apparatus indicates that hydrogen bonds may be important also. The reduction of $-SH$ groups to form $-S-S-$ bridges could be carried out physiologically by glutathione (see Fig. 14–10). In 1931, Rapkin demonstrated a cycle in the glutathione content of sea urchin eggs with a minimum just before spindle formation. This data has led to the postulation of a dual mechanism in the formation of the mitotic apparatus. The first, by a simple polymerization of the protein units, leads to the formation of an amorphous gel; the second, by the development of secondary bonds, gives rise to definite fibers.[14] Support for this hypothesis is the fact that colchicine, a mitotic inhibitor, produces an amorphous gel without birefringence and evidences of microscopic fibers. Also, with the electron microscope the lack of the astral or spindle fibers has been observed in cells treated with colchicine.[15]

The importance of $-SH$ groups in mitosis has been demonstrated cytochemically: the asters and spindle stain deeply during mitosis, whereas the reaction is almost negative during interphase (Fig. 14–11).[16]

Related to these concepts is the hypothesis that centrioles are involved in the formation of astral and spindle fibers by acting on the secondary bonding. For

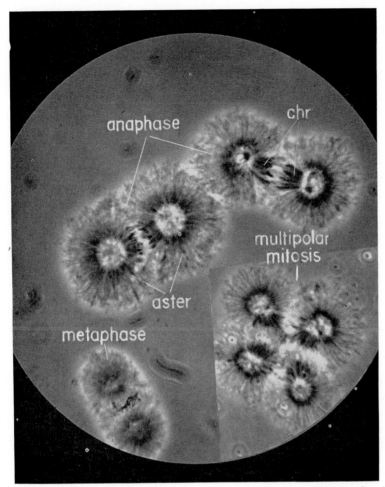

FIGURE 14–9. Mitotic apparatus isolated from the sea urchin egg in division. *chr*, chromosomes. (Courtesy of D. Mazia.)

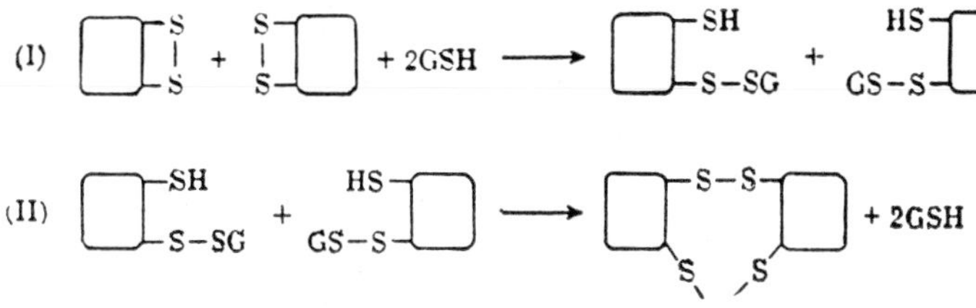

FIGURE 14–10. Possible mechanism of the action of —SH groups in the formation of the spindle. In phase **I** the reduction of the –S–S– groups by glutathione is shown. In phase **II** the –S–S– groups would be restored, forming intermolecular bonds. (From D. Mazia.)

a long time the process of formation of the aster and spindle has been compared with other fibrillogenetic processes occurring extracellularly, such as blood clotting. In this case molecular units of fibrinogen polymerize to form the fibrin fibrils. It can be observed that, from the very start of blood clotting, fibrin radiates from the blood platelets, which serve as orientation centers of fibril formation.[10]

RNA may possibly be involved in the function of the mitotic apparatus. The presence of RNA in the spindle can be demonstrated histochemically,[17, 18] and biochemically in the isolated mitotic apparatus. It has been suggested that the incorporation of RNA in the spindle is a

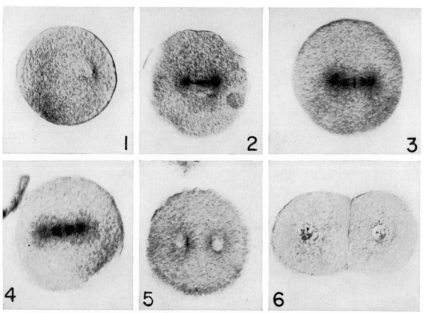

FIGURE 14–11. Sulfhydryl groups stained with Bennett's reagent in the first division of the sea urchin egg: **1**, three minutes after fertilization; **2**, prophase; **3**, metaphase; **4**, anaphase; **5** and **6**, telophase. (Courtesy of N. Kawamura and K. Dan.)

mechanism for insuring an even distribution of this genetically important cytoplasmic material.[19] Another hypothesis is that RNA plays a direct role in the building up of the spindle and asters.[20, 21]

Mitotic Apparatus and Anaphase Movements

The role of the spindle in the movements of the chromosomes during anaphase is still under discussion. The contraction and shortening of the spindle fibers appear to take place at early mitosis. This contraction appears to depend on the presence of adenosine triphosphate (ATP). In fact, in cells extracted with glycerin in a tissue about to divide, contraction of the spindle can be induced by ATP. Other evidences suggest that at anaphase the two sets of daughter chromosomes are pushed apart by an elongation of the spindle fibers in between the poles (theory of the pushing body).

There are thus two types of anaphase movements, each probably having a different molecular mechanism. One concerns the chromosomal fibers and the other the spindle proper. These two types of movements may participate in more or less proportion according to the cell type.[22–24]

The problem of the actual attachment of the spindle fibers to the centromeres is an important point in this discussion. This has been confirmed by electron microscopy (see Fig. 14–7) and it has been postulated that the chromosomal spindle fibers are developed from the centromere of each chromosome and grow toward the poles of the cell.[25] The fact that chromosomal fragments that have no centromere do not undergo anaphase movements, confirms the importance of these spindle fibers in chromosomal movement.

Cytokinesis (Cell Cleavage)

Cytokinesis, or cell cleavage, of the dividing cell is to some extent independent of mitotic nuclear changes. In some cells (e.g., striated muscle cells) telophase is not followed by division of the cytoplasm, and thus a multinucleate plasmodium is formed.

The mechanism of cell cleavage is different in animal cells than in plant cells. In plant cells the formation of the phragmoplast and the cell plate leads to a division of the cytoplasmic territories without furrow formation (see Chap. 12). Animal cells generally divide by furrowing. Cleavage of animal cells has been studied mainly in tissue culture, in eggs and, more recently, in some cell models. These studies have led to the postulation of several mechanisms involving either the mitotic apparatus (aster and spindle) or the cell cortex.[1]

The first hypothesis has been ruled out by experiments that demonstrate that the removal of the whole mitotic apparatus of the sea urchin egg does not inhibit cell cleavage.[26] At present the mitotic apparatus is left with the vague role of producing a signal for cleavage.[27] Those hypotheses involving the cell cortex postulate the contraction of the cortical gel, the expansion or the growth of the membrane, or an active ameboid movement.[24, 28–30]

If the cortex contracts actively, one must postulate that a contractile protein is involved, which may be similar to that of muscle. Some experiments with cell models bear out this possibility. Usually fibroblasts or spermatocytes were treated with glycerol to extract soluble components. Then, by the addition of ATP, remarkable changes were observed, such as the elongation of the spindle in anaphase or the completion of cell cleavage in telophase.[31, 32] Furthermore, a contractile protein having ATPase activity was isolated from dividing cells. These experiments should be correlated with other results showing that ATP may produce cytoplasmic contraction in different cell types.[19] However, the importance of these and other factors involved in cell cleavage remains to be proved.

In summary: For animal cells, the theories of cell cleavage stress a number of possible mechanisms: ameboid movement; a contractile equatorial ring; the expansion of the cell membrane; and the interaction of the spindle and asters with the cell surface (see reference 24). For plant cells, the movements of the endoplasmic reticulum and dictyosomes and the fusion of vesicular material at the equator are essential events of normal cytokinesis (see Chap. 12).

MEIOSIS

A general introduction to meiosis was presented in Chapter 13. This process takes place only in germ cells of sexually reproducing animals and plants. In both cases these cells are localized in the gonads.

Germ Cells of Animals
(Fig. 14–12)

Germ cells originate from initial cells that divide to give rise to somatic and germ cells. The latter, by repeated divisions, give rise to several generations of *gonocytes*, which after a variable period become primary *gonial* cells which are transformed into spermatogonia in the male and *oögonia* in the female.

Later, by division of the primary gonial cell, secondary gonial cells develop. Each secondary spermatogonium gives rise in a final division to two daughter cells, which begin to increase in volume and are called primary spermatocytes or *spermatocytes I*. At division the *primary spermatocyte* (primary meiotic division) gives rise to two daughter cells or *secondary spermatocytes*, which divide again (secondary meiotic division), resulting in four cells called the *spermatids*. These cells, by differentiation (spermiogenesis) are transformed into spermatozoa. In the female the successive stages are oögonia, primary oöcytes, secondary oöcytes, oötids and ova. In place of four functional gametes there is only one, the mature *ovum*, since the other three become infertile *polocytes*, or *polar bodies*. (For a more complete study of the germ cells, consult embryology textbooks.)

Germ Cells of Flowering Plants
(Fig. 14–13)

In higher plants the early cells of the germ line are derived from the zygote and multiply by mitosis. The reproductive organs—anthers in male and ovary or pistil in female—produce microspores and megaspores, respectively. The cells that undergo meiosis to produce megaspores are called megasporocytes. Microspores are produced by microsporocytes

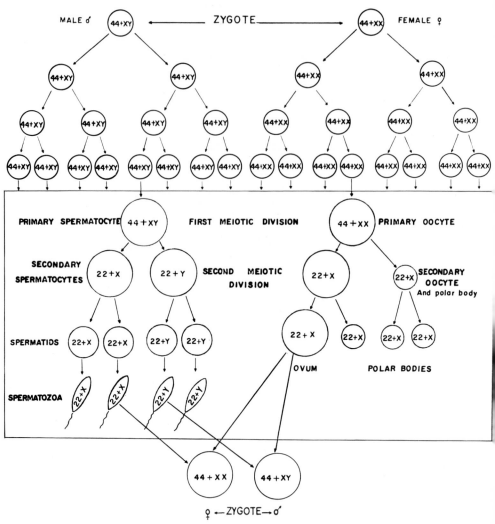

FIGURE 14–12. Diagram of spermatogenesis and ovogenesis in the human. **Above,** mitosis of gonial cells. **Middle** (within the box), the meiotic divisions. **Below,** fertilization and zygote. Notice the 44 autosomes and the XY sex chromosomes.

(pollen mother cells). Each microsporocyte gives rise by meiosis to four functional microspores. Each megasporocyte produces four megaspores by meiosis, of which three degenerate. The remaining megaspore develops into the female gametophyte, which gives rise to the egg cell.

In plants, as in animals, there are many variations in the location and differentiation of the germ line, but in general the meiotic process is similar in both kingdoms.

In plants microspores and megaspores are not the final gametes. Before fertilization, they undergo two mitotic divisions in the anther or three in the ovary to produce the male and female gameto-phytes, respectively (Fig. 14–13). The time at which meiosis occurs during the life cycle varies in different organisms but is constant for each particular species. (In Chapter 15 gametogenesis in the mold *Neurospora* is analyzed.)

Analysis of Meiosis

As mentioned in Chapter 13, meiosis is essentially two cell divisions involving one division of the chromosomes. Four nuclei result from this process, each of which has a single set (haploid number) of chromosomes. These two divisions are the first and second meiotic divisions, or simply divisions I and II (Fig. 13–1).

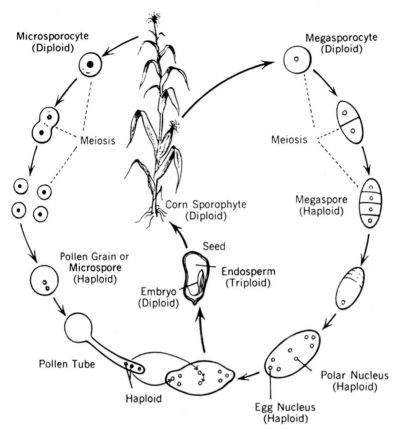

FIGURE 14–13. Vital cycle of a plant. (After Sinnott, Dunn and Dobzhansky (1958) *Principles of genetics.* 5th Ed.)

The first meiotic division is characterized by a long prophase during which homologous chromosomes pair closely and interchange hereditary material.

The classic stages of mitosis do not suffice to describe the complex movements of the chromosomes in meiosis. These successive stages are as follows:

Meiotic Division I
(Figs. 14–14 to 14–18)

Preleptonema corresponds to early prophase of mitosis. Chromosomes are extremely thin and difficult to observe. Only the sex chromosomes may stand out as compact heteropyknotic bodies.

MEIOSIS			
	DIVISION I	Prophase I	Preleptonema Leptonema Zygonema Pachynema Diplonema Diakinesis
		Prometaphase I Metaphase I Anaphase I Telophase I	
	DIVISION II	Interphase	
		Prophase II Metaphase II Anaphase II Telophase II	

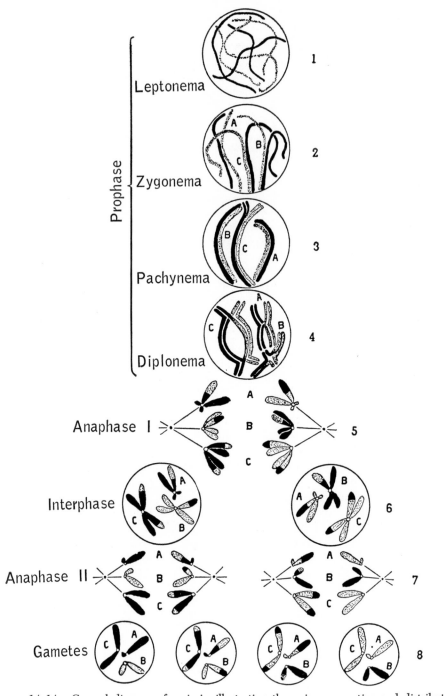

Figure 14–14. General diagram of meiosis, illustrating the union, separation and distribution of the chromosomes.

In *leptonema* chromosomes become more apparent as long threads showing chromomeres (Fig. 14–14, *1*). In cells that have few chromosomes the number of filaments can be counted. Frequently the leptotenic chromosomes have a definite orientation and polarization to-

ward the centrioles. This peculiar arrangement is called a "bouquet."

At the beginning of *zygonema* the homologous chromosomes begin to pair (Fig. 14–14,2). Sometimes the chromosomes unite at their polarized ends and continue pairing to the antipodal extremity; in other cases fusion occurs simultaneously at various places along the length of a filament (localized pairing). The presence of a "bouquet" and polarization in general seem to favor regularity in pairing. The pairing is remarkably exact and specific. It takes place point for point and chromomere for chromomere in each homologue.

The nucleus is at *pachynema* when the pairing of the chromosomes is completed (Fig. 14–14,3). The chromosomes contract longitudinally, which results in shorter and thicker threads. At this moment, with the aid of refined techniques, the double constitution of the filament can be observed (Fig. 14–15). By middle pachynema, the nucleus contains half the number of chromosomes, but this reduction is only apparent, since each unit is a *bivalent* or *tetrad* composed of two homologous chromosomes in close longitudinal union.

Each homologous chromosome has its independent centromere, thus each bivalent has two centromeres. At about middle pachynema a longitudinal cleavage becomes apparent in each homologue in a plane perpendicular to that of the pairing. This means that at this stage each pachytene element consists of four chromatids (Fig. 14–18). The chromatids of each homologue are called sister chromatids.

While each chromosome is cleaving longitudinally, transverse breaks may occur at the same level on two of the homologous chromatids. This is followed by an interchange of chromatid segments between homologous chromatids, which consists of a break, then a transposition, and finally a fusion of the segments.

At *diplonema* the intimately paired chromosomes begin to separate, repelling each other (Fig. 14–18,4). However, this separation is not complete, since the homologous chromosomes remain united by their points of interchange, or *chiasmata*. Chiasmata are generally regarded as the expression of the phenomenon called *crossing over*, by which chromosomal segments with blocks of genes are exchanged between homologous members of the pairs. With few exceptions, chiasmata are found in all

plants and animals. At least one chiasma is formed for each bivalent (Fig. 14–16). Their number is variable, since some chromosomes have one chiasma and others have many.

At *diakinesis* the contraction of the chromosomes is accentuated. Meanwhile, *terminalization*—which is the movement of chiasmata from the centromere toward the ends of the chromosome—continues while the number of interstitial chiasmata diminishes. The chromatids remain connected by terminal chiasmata until metaphase (Fig. 14–18).

At *prometaphase I* spiralization reaches its virtual maximum. With the formation of the major coil, the nuclear membrane disappears. The chromosomes become arranged on the equator of the cell to begin *metaphase I*. At this stage the two members of each homologous pair are found with their centromeres directed toward opposite poles (Fig. 14–16). The repulsion of the centromeres is accentuated, and the chromosomes are ready to separate. If the bivalent is long, it presents a series of annular apertures between the chiasmata in perpendicularly alternating planes. If the chromosomes are short, they have a single annular aperture.

In certain cases there is a third splitting by which the bivalents show a double chromonema in each of their chromatids. In such instances each bivalent is composed of eight filaments instead of four.

At *anaphase I* the daughter chromatids of each homologue, united by their centromeres, move toward their respective poles (Fig. 14–16). The short chromosomes, generally connected by a terminal chiasma, separate rapidly. Separation of the long chromosomes, which have interstitial and unterminalized chiasmata, is delayed. In side view, anaphase chromosomes show different shapes, depending on the position of the centromere.

It should be recalled that, by way of the chiasmata, segments were transposed between two of the chromatids of each homologue. Thus, when the homologous paternal and maternal chromosomes separate in anaphase, their composition is different from that of the originals. Two of their chromatids are

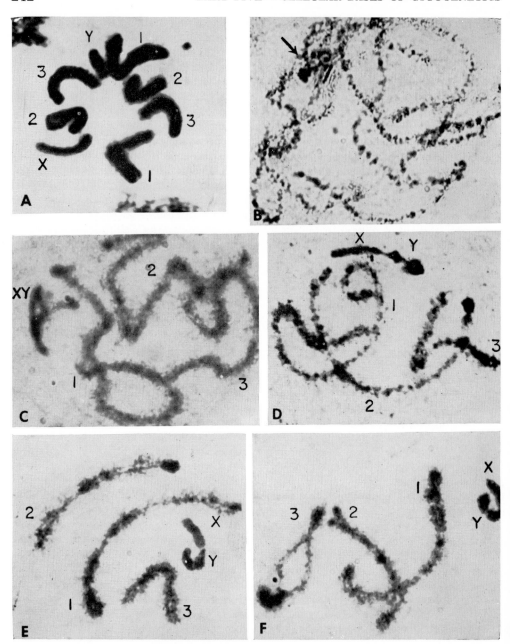

FIGURE 14–15. Stages of meiosis as shown in the South American locust *Dichroplus silveira guidoi* (2n = 8). **A,** spermatogonial metaphase in polar view, showing the three pairs of autosomes (*1, 2, 3*) and the sex chromosomes (*XY*). **B,** early pachynema. The homologous chromosomes have paired. The XY pair is indicated by an arrow. **C,** pachynema, showing the three bivalents (*1, 2, 3*) and the XY sex bivalent. **D,** pachynema. The bivalents begin to shorten and the two components of the XY pair are resolved and show marked positive heteropyknosis. **E,** the end of pachynema, showing the linear differentiation of the bivalents. The sex chromosomes have contracted, maintaining their positive heteropyknosis. **F,** early diplonema. The homologous chromosomes start to separate by their ends and the condensation of the sex chromosomes continues. (From F. A. Saez.)

mixed; the other two maintain their initial nature with reference to a single locus (Figs. 14–14 and 14–17).

Telophase I begins when the anaphase groups arrive at their respective poles.

Chromosomes may persist for some time in a condensed state, showing all their morphologic characteristics. Following telophase is a short *interphase* which has characteristics similar to mitotic inter-

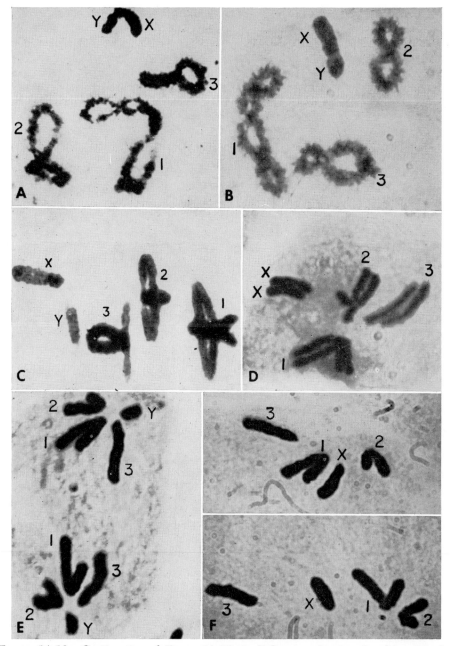

FIGURE 14–16. Continuation of Figure 14–15. A, diplonema, showing the chiasmata of each bivalent. The sex chromosomes are greatly condensed (positive heteropyknosis). B, end of diplonema. Chiasmata of the autosomal bivalents are shown clearly. The sex chromosomes are still in positive heteropyknosis. C, metaphase I in side view. Each autosomal bivalent shows the typical configuration corresponding to metacentric (1 and 2) and to acrocentric chromosomes (3). X and Y now show negative heteropyknosis and are at early anaphase. D, metaphase II in polar view. Each chromosome is composed of two chromatids (including the X). E, F, anaphase II in side view. Chromosomes are constituted by a single chromatid. As a result of this division, two spermatids are formed, two with Y chromosomes (E) and two with X (F). (From F. A. Saez.)

phase. Sometimes interphase is of long duration.

The result of the first meiotic division is the formation of the daughter nuclei, which in animals are called spermatocytes II (in the male) and oöcyte II plus the first polar body (in the female).

Meiotic Division II

A short *prophase II* is followed by the formation of the spindle, which marks the beginning of metaphase II.

At *metaphase II* the number of chromosomes is half the somatic number. Chromosomes become arranged on the equatorial plane, the centromeres divide and the two sister chromatids go toward the opposite poles during *anaphase II* (Fig. 14–16). Since in this division the longitudinal halves of each parental chromosome (chromatids) separate, each of the four nuclei of *telophase II* has one chromatid, which is now called a chro-

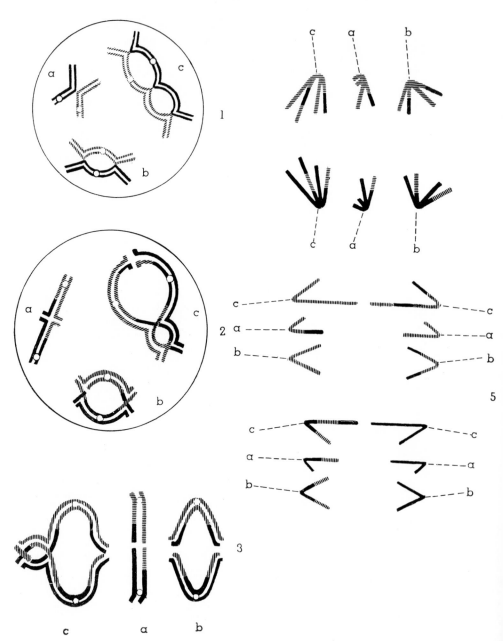

FIGURE 14–17. Diagram showing the genetic consequences of the meiosis of three pairs of chromosomes with (*a*) one chiasma, (*b*) two chiasmata and (*c*) three chiasmata. 1, diplonema; 2, advanced diplonema showing the process of terminalization; 3, metaphase I; 4, anaphase I; 5, anaphase II; showing the distribution of the chromosomes in the four nuclei formed. In black, the paternal chromosomes; in dashed line pattern, the maternal. The centromere is represented by a circle.

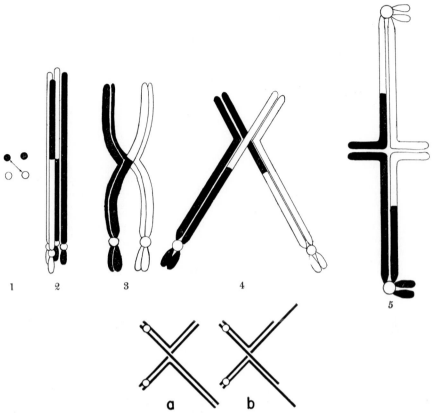

FIGURE 14–18. **Above.** 1 and 2, diagrams showing the process of crossing over. 3, formation of a chiasma; 4, terminalization; 5, rotation of the chromatids of one bivalent. **Below,** some proofs of the chiasmatypy theory. If only one chiasma is formed between the two chromatids in a pair of heteromorphic chromosomes, the separation at anaphase will be as indicated in *a*, not as indicated in *b*.

mosome. Each nucleus has an haploid number of chromosomes, in which each chromosome is represented once (Figs. 14–14 and 14–16).

The essence of the meiotic process is seen in the formation of four nuclei, each differing from the others, in which each chromosome of the parent is represented once. As a result of *chiasmata* with crossing over, the chromosomes usually do not consist of either completely maternal or paternal material, but of alternating segments of each. For example, in Figure 14–17 all segments of chromosome A, between the centromere and the chiasma, effect a reduction or segregation division in anaphase I and an equational division in anaphase II. On the other hand, the segments located between the distal end of the chromosome and the chiasma effect a reduction in anaphase II.

Meiosis is thus a mechanism for dis-

tributing the hereditary units (genes), permitting their random independent recombination. Crossing over provides a means whereby genes of different chromosomes can be brought together and recombined. If this process did not take place, the evolution of the species would be suspended by unalterable chromosomes and living nature would not have its characteristic diversity.

The study of meiosis is a prerequisite for the understanding of the chromosomal bases of genetics. At this moment the true significance of meiosis in hereditary phenomena will become apparent (see Chap. 15).

GENERAL REFERENCES

Anderson, N. G. (1956) Cell division. *Quart. Rev. Biol.*, 31:169; 243; 269.

Dan, K. (1963) Force of cleavage of the dividing sea urchin egg. In: *Cell growth and cell division. Symposia of the Internat. Soc. Cell Biology,* vol. 2. (Harris, R. J. C., ed.) Academic Press, New York.

Fautrez, J. (1963) Dynamisme de l'ana-telophase et cytodiérèse. In: *Cell growth and cell division. Symposia of the Internat. Soc. Cell Biology,* Vol. 2. (Harris, R. J. C., ed.) Academic Press, New York.

Gross, P., and Mazia, D., eds. (1960) Second conference on the mechanisms of cell division. *Ann. N.Y. Acad. Sci.,* 90, art. 2, 345.

Harris, R. J. C., ed. (1963) *Cell growth and cell division. Symposia of the Internat. Soc. for Cell Biology,* vol. 2. Academic Press, New York.

Hoffmann-Berling, H. (1960) Other mechanisms producing movements. *Comp. Biochem. Physiol.,* 2:341.

Hughes, A. (1952) *The mitotic cycle.* Academic Press, New York.

Hughes, A. F., and Swann, M. M. (1948) Anaphase movements in the living cells. *J. Exp. Biol.,* 25:45.

Kopac, M., ed. (1951) The mechanisms of cell division. *Ann. N.Y. Acad. Sci.,* 51:1279.

Mazia, D. (1956) The life history of the cell. *Amer. Scient.,* 44:1.

Mazia, D. (1961) Mitosis and the physiology of cell division. In: *The cell,* Vol. 3, p. 77. (Brachet, J., and Mirsky, A. E., eds.) Academic Press, New York.

Mazia, D. (1961) How cells divide. *Scient. Amer.,* 205:100.

Ris, H. (1957) Chromosome structure. In: *The chemical basis of heredity.* (McElroy, W. D., and Glass, B., eds.) Johns Hopkins Press, Baltimore, p. 23.

Scharer, F. (1944) *Mitosis.* Columbia University Press, New York.

Stern, H. (1956) The physiology of cell division. *Ann. Rev. Plant Physiol.,* 7:9.

Swann, M. M., and Mitchison, J. M. (1958) The mechanism of cleavage in animal cells. *Biol. Rev.,* 33:103.

Wolper, L. (1960) The mechanics and mechanism of cleavage. *Internat. Rev. Cytol.,* 10:163.

CITED REFERENCES

1. Swann, M. M., and Mitchison, J. M. (1958) *Biol. Rev.,* 33:103.
2. Cleveland, L. R. (1953) *Trans. Amer. Phil. Soc.,* new series 43:809.
3. Bessis, M., Breton-Gorius, J., and Thiéry, J. P. (1958) *Rev. hématol.,* 13:363.
4. Bernhard, W., and de Harven, E. (1958) L'ultrastructure du centriole et d'autres elements de l'appareil achromatique. *Proc. 4th Internat. Conf. Electron Microscopy,* 2:217.

5. Gall, J. G. (1961) *J. Biophys. Biochem. Cytol.,* 10:163.
6. Mazia, D., Harris, P. J., and Bibring, T. (1960) *J. Biophys. Biochem. Cytol.,* 7:1.
7. Fawcett, D. W., and Porter, K. R. (1954) *J. Morph.,* 94:221.
8. Burgos, M., and Fawcett, D. W. (1955) *J. Biophys. Biochem. Cytol.,* 1:287.
9. Fawcett, D. (1961) Cilia and flagella. In: *The cell,* Vol. 2, p. 217 (Brachet, J., and Mirsky, A. E., eds.) Academic Press, New York.
10. De Robertis, E. (1956) *J. Biophys. Biochem. Cytol.,* 2:suppl. 209.
11. Mazia, D., and Dan, K. (1952) *Proc. Nat. Acad. Sci.* (Wash.), 38:826.
12. Inoué, S. (1951) *Studies of the structure of the mitotic spindle in living cells with an improved polarization microscope.* Thesis, Princeton University.
13. Inoué, S. (1953) *Chromosoma,* 5:487.
14. Mazia, D. (1955) *Symp. Soc. Exp. Biol.,* 9:335.
15. De Harven, E., and Bernhard, W. (1956) *Ztschr. Zellforsch.,* 45:378.
16. Kawamura, N., and Dan, K. (1958) *J. Biophys. Biochem. Cytol.,* 4:615.
17. Swift, H. (1953) *Internat. Rev. Cytol.,* 2:1.
18. Stich, H. (1954) *Experientia,* 10:184.
19. Brachet, J. (1957) *Biochemical cytology.* Academic Press, New York.
20. Stich, H. (1954) *Chromosoma,* 6:199.
21. Gross, P. R. (1957) *Trans. N.Y. Acad. Sci.,* 20:154.
22. Ris, H. (1949) *Biol. Bull.* 96:90.
23. Hughes, A. F., and Swann, M. M. (1948) *J. Exp. Biol.,* 25:45.
24. Mazia, D. (1961) Mitosis and the physiology of cell division. In: *The cell,* Vol. 3, p. 77. (Brachet, J., and Mirsky, A. E., eds.) Academic Press, New York.
25. Sato, S. (1960) *Cytologia,* 25:119.
26. Hiramoto, Y. (1956) *Exp. Cell Res.,* 11:630.
27. Dan, K. (1963) Force of cleavage of the dividing sea urchin egg. In: *Cell growth and cell division. Symposia of the International Society for Cell Biology,* Vol. 2, p. 261. Academic Press, New York.
28. Swann, M. M. (1952) *Internat. Rev. Cytol.,* 1:195.
29. Selman, C. G., and Waddington, C. H. (1955) *J. Exp. Biol.,* 32:700.
30. Fautrez, J. (1963) Dynamisme de l'anatelophase et cytodiérèse. In: *Cell growth and cell division. Symposia of the Internat. Soc. Cell Biology,* Vol. 2. (Harris, R. J. C., ed.) Academic Press, New York, p. 199.
31. Hoffmann-Berling, H. (1954) *Biochim. Biophys. Acta,* 14:182; 15:226.
32. Hoffmann-Berling, H. (1956) *Biochim. Biophys. Acta,* 19:453.

CHAPTER 15

CYTOGENETICS. CHROMOSOMAL BASES OF GENETICS

Cytogenetics is a recent branch of biology that has emerged from the convergence of cytology and genetics (see Chap. 1). This discipline has great importance because it is concerned with the cytologic and molecular bases of heredity, variation, mutation, phylogeny, morphogenesis and evolution of organisms. Cytogenetics also deals with important problems applicable to medicine and agriculture.

This chapter is concerned with the cytogenetic aspects of heredity, mutation and evolution. The interpretation of genetic phenomena at a molecular level will be dealt with in Chapter 18.

LAWS OF HEREDITY

In 1865, Gregor Johann Mendel, while studying crosses between peas (*Pisum sativum*), discovered the laws of hered-itary transmission in the biologic world. Mendel selected several varieties of sweet peas that have pairs of differential or *contrasting* characteristics, which remain constant in the crossings. For example, he used plants that have white and red flowers, smooth and rough seeds, yellow and green seeds, long and short stems and so forth. After crossing the parental generation (P_1), he observed the resulting *hybrids* of the first filial generation, F_1. Then he crossed the hybrids (F_1) among themselves and studied the result in the second filial generation, F_2.

In a cross between parents with yellow and green seeds, in the first generation he found that all the hybrids had yellow seeds and thus the characteristic of only one parent. In the second cross (F_2), the characteristics of the parents reappeared in the proportion of 75 per cent to 25 per cent, or 3:1.

Law of Segregation

Mendel postulated that the color of the seeds was controlled by a "factor" that was transmitted to the offspring by means of the gametes. This hereditary factor, which we call the *gene*, could be transmitted without contamination or mixture with other genes. At the same time he postulated that the gene could be *segregated* in the hybrid into different gametes to be *distributed* in the offspring of the hybrid. For this reason this is called the *law* or *principle of segregation of the genes*. Later, Mendel found that the plants with yellow seeds in F_2, in spite of showing the yellow color, had different genetic constitutions. One-third of this group always gave yellow seeds, but the other two-thirds of the F_3 generation produced plants with yellow and green seeds in a 3:1 proportion. When the 25 per cent of plants in F_2 with green seeds were crossed among themselves, they always produced green seeds. This shows that they were a pure strain for this character. If we represent the genes in the crossing by letters, designating by *A* the gene with yellow character and by *a* the gene with green character, we have the following:

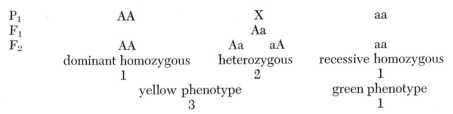

P$_1$ AA   X   aa
F$_1$ Aa
F$_2$ AA   Aa   aA   aa
        dominant homozygous   heterozygous   recessive homozygous
                    1   2   1
                    yellow phenotype   green phenotype
                            3   1

In the first generation (F$_1$) both *A* and *a* genes are present, but only *A* is revealed because it is *dominant;* gene *a* remains hidden and is called *recessive.* In the hybrid F$_1$ both genes are segregated and enter different gametes. Half of them will have the gene *A* and the other half *a*. Since each individual produces two types of gametes in each sex, there are four possible combinations in F$_2$. This gives as a result the proportion 1:2:1, corresponding to the 25 per cent of plants with pure yellow seeds (*AA*), 50 per cent with hybrid yellow seeds (*Aa*), and 25 per cent with pure green seeds (*aa*).

Mendel confirmed that F$_1$ hybrids produce two classes of gametes in equal numbers. Back-crossing the F$_1$ hybrid (heterozygous *Aa*) with the homozygous recessive *aa*, he obtained a 1 *Aa* : 1 *aa* ratio. Similar test crosses can be used whether a dominant organism of unknown ancestry is homozygous or heterozygous.

We can now explain Mendel's results in terms of the behavior of chromosomes and genes. We can label the gene for gray (*G*) and the gene for white (*g*) as shown in Figure 15–1. In this figure only one pair of chromosomes and of genes concerned are shown.

As mentioned, each chromosome has an identical mate (homologue); the genes present in the chromosomes are also found in pairs, called *allelic* pairs. In each homologous chromosome the gene for each trait occurs at a particular point called a *locus* (plural *loci*). In the case illustrated in Figure 15–1, the mouse will have two *GG* genes, one in each homologue. Since the two homologues separate (segregate) at meiosis, the two *GG* genes must also separate to enter the gametes. The mechanism is the same in a dominant as in a recessive. In the hybrid F$_1$, one chromosome bears gene

G and the homologous chromosome bears gene *g*. Since these chromosomes will separate or segregate during meiosis, they will enter different gametes.

When hybrids are self-fertilized, the gametes unite in the combinations shown by the checkerboard method illustrated in Figure 15–1. Figure 15–2 is a diagram of the segregation of a pair of genes contained in a pair of chromosomes that do not cross over during meiosis.

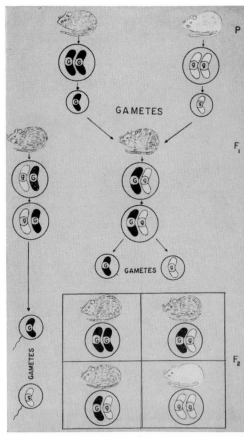

FIGURE 15–1. A monohybrid cross between a gray mouse (dominant) and a white mouse (recessive). The parallelism between distribution of genes and chromosomes is indicated, as well as the resulting phenotypes in the F$_1$ and F$_2$ generations.

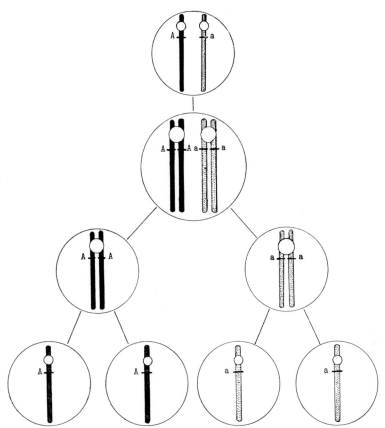

FIGURE 15–2.   Diagram of the segregation of a pair of genes localized in a pair of chromosomes in which crossing over does not occur during meiosis. Two classes of gametes result.

Genotype and Phenotype

In 1911, Johansen proposed the term *genotype* for the genetic constitution in which all the genes of the organism are represented, and the term *phenotype* for the visible characteristics shown by the individual. For example, in the case of the plants with green or yellow seeds there are two phenotypes in F₂: yellow seeds and green seeds in the proportion 3:1, respectively. However, according to the genetic constitution there are three different genotypes: 1 *AA*, 2 *Aa* and 1 *aa*. This means that there are two mendelian proportions, the phenotypic (3:1) and the genotypic (1:2:1). The phenotype includes all the characteristics of the individual that are an expression of the genes. These characteristics may be morphologic or physiological. For example, in the human the different hemoglobins or blood groups or some difference in taste toward thiourea are phenotypic characteristics.

In crossings of certain plants that have white and red flowers, such as *Mirabilis jalapa*, it is possible to find in F₂ three phenotypes (red, pink and white flowers), which correspond to the three genotypes. This is due to incomplete dominance. The rule of dominance and recessiveness is not always accomplished completely; dominance may be complete in most cases but incomplete in others. In this case there is a mixture of characteristics, called *intermediary heredity*.

Law of Independent Assortment

Whereas Mendel's first law, the law of segregation, applies to the behavior of a single pair of genes, the second law, the law of independent assortment, describes the simultaneous behavior of two or more pairs of genes located in different pairs of chromosomes. Genes that lie in separate chromosomes are independently distributed during meiosis. The resulting offspring is a hybrid at two loci, also called a dihybrid.

Figure 15–3 diagrams the cross between a black, short-haired guinea pig (*BBSS*) and a brown, long-haired guinea pig (*bbss*). The BBSS individual produces only *BS* gametes; the bbss guinea pig produces only *bs* gametes. At F₁ the offspring are heterozygous for hair color and hair length. Phenotypically they are all black and short-haired. However, when two of the F₁ dihybrids are mated, each produces four types of gametes (*BS, Bs, bS, bs*), which by fertilization result in 16 zygotic combinations. As shown in F₂ there are nine black, short-haired individuals, three black, long-haired, three brown, short-haired and only one brown, long-haired individual. This phenotypic proportion (9:3:3:1) is characteristic of the second generation of a cross of two contrasting pairs of genes.

Mendel's second law is less general than the first because the independent segregation of the genes is restricted by their linkage or localization along the length of the chromosomes (see the following section).

The independent separation of two or more pairs of homologous chromosomes can be detected cytologically only if the two homologues are morphologically different.

LINKAGE AND CROSSING OVER

The studies of Morgan and his collab-

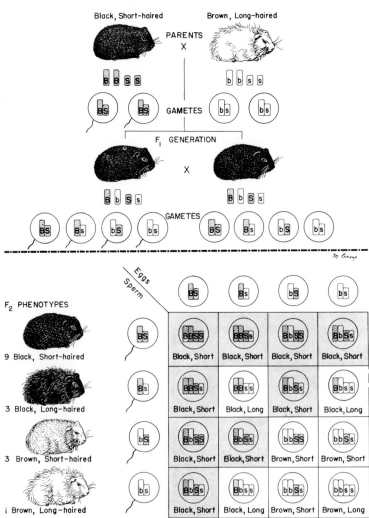

FIGURE 15–3. Diagram of a cross between black, short-haired (dominant) and brown, long-haired (recessive) guinea pigs. The independent assortment of genes is evident (see the description in the text). (From C. Villee.)

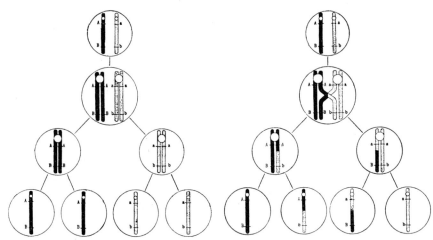

Figure 15–4.   Left, diagram of the segregation of two pairs of allelomorphic genes localized on the same pair of chromosomes without crossing over. The result is two types of gametes, AB and ab. A case of linkage. Right, diagram of the segregation of two pairs of allelomorphic genes on the same chromosome between which crossing over takes place during meiosis. Four types of gametes result: AB, ab, Ab, aB. A case of linkage with crossing over.

orators between 1910 and 1915 of the fly *Drosophila melanogaster* demonstrated that the law of independent assortment was not universally applicable and that in certain crosses of two or more allelic pairs of genes, there was a certain limitation of the free segregation. In each case there was a marked tendency for parental combinations to remain linked and to produce a lesser proportion of new combinations.

If two genes (A and B, or a and b) are in the same chromosome instead of in different chromosomes, only two classes of gametes will be obtained. In this case only two combinations are produced in the ratio 1:1, each corresponding to one of the parents:

ABab × abab = 1 ABab:1 abab

Figure 15–4 illustrates the mechanism of meiosis and the formation of the gametes in this hybrid, in which the two genes are in the same chromosome. The coexistence of two or more genes in the same chromosome is called *linkage*, which is defined as the tendency of two or more genes to be located together in the same chromosome during hereditary transmission.

After studying a considerable number of different crosses in *Drosophila*, Morgan reached the conclusion that all genes of this fly were clustered into four linked groups, each of which was contained in a single chromosome. In *Drosophila*

there are four pairs of chromosomes, each with one group of genes. The first chromosome has many hundreds of genes; the fourth chromosome, which is the smallest, has only a few. Further studies showed that the linkage is not absolute and that it may be broken with a certain frequency. For example, if a hybrid female F_1 of this insect with the genes "gray" and "long wings" (double dominant) is crossed with a male with the genes "black" and "vestigial wings" (double recessive), we have an unexpected result, and instead of two classes of descendants four are obtained (Fig. 15–5). The first two combinations are those expected from the linkage and appear in 83 per cent of cases; the other two are new combinations ("gray, vestigial wings" and "black, long wings") and appear in 17 per cent of cases. Calling *AB* the dominant genes and *ab* the recessive genes located respectively in each chromosome, the result is as shown in Figure 15–5.

Morgan hypothesized that the flies composing this 17 per cent are the product of a rupture of the linkage and that the recombination must come about through an interchange of parts between the two homologous chromosomes of the hybrid. This phenomenon was called *"crossing over,"* a term that has become a part of the general literature in all languages.

Morgan and his collaborators postu-

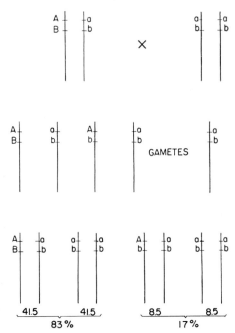

FIGURE 15–5. Cross involving two linked genes. Of the four types of offspring resulting, two are the expected combinations with a total of 83 per cent. The other two are new recombinations that occur in a total of 17 per cent of the individuals. (See the description in the text.)

lated that genes have a linear distribution in the chromosomes, that they are located in a constant and definite order and that they always occupy the same locus in the chromosome.

Thorough studies have been made of all the classes of combinations of a great number of genes. The results can be represented graphically by the construction of maps of each chromosome showing the topography and respective locations of the genes (Fig. 15–6). Corn (*Zea*), which is perhaps the most thoroughly studied of plants, has been mapped very completely with the localization of several hundred genes. Chromosome maps also have been constructed for the hen, mouse, sweet pea and so on. In the human species a series of genes have been localized in the sex chromosome (Fig. 15–6) and in the autosomes.

Crossing Over, Chiasmata and Genetic Maps

As indicated in the preceding section, genes that are linked may show inde-

pendent segregation through "crossing over." This phenomenon is explained in terms of the exchange of segments of chromatids that take place during meiosis by the formation of chiasmata (Fig. 15–4). The frequency of recombination of two linked genes is a function of the distance which separates them along the chromosome. When two genes are close to one another, the probability of crossing over is less than when they are far apart. If the distance between genes is estimated by linkage analysis, it is possible to construct a map indicating the relative locus of each gene along the chromosome (Fig. 15–6). This can be done in higher organisms as well as in bacteria and viruses.

The distance between genes is expressed in units of recombination, which is the percentage of the frequency from any particular cross that is different from either parent genotype. Since in crossing over only two of the four chromatids interchange (Fig. 14–18), the percentage of recombination will be half the average frequency of chiasmata (see Fig. 14–18). In the case of a cross experiment involving three genes (1, 2, 3), if the distance between 1 and 2 is x units and between 2 and 3 is y units, the distance between 1 and 3 will be $x + y$ units.

In general genetic maps represent the relative order of genes along the chromosome; however, the frequency of crossing over varies for different points of the chromosome and for different organisms. The concept of a linear arrangement of genes in specific loci is in accordance with our present knowledge of the structure of the DNA molecule and of its function in genetic phenomena (see Chap. 18).

Crossing Over and Recombination in Neurospora

Among the different organisms studied in genetics, the mold *Neurospora* occupies a special place. The advantage of this material is twofold: (a) it is possible to identify and to follow the fate of each of the four chromatids present in the bivalent meiotic chromosome and thus to determine whether the crossing over involves two, three or all four chro-

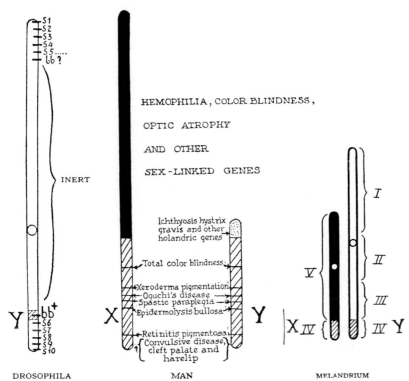

FIGURE 15–6. Schematic picture of the sex chromosomes of *Drosophila melanogaster*, man and *Melandrium*, showing the differential and homologous regions (shown by oblique lines) and the position of the genes. In the Y chromosomes of *Drosophila* there is a large inert segment, the bobbed genes in the homologous segment, and male fertility genes in the differential segment. (From Serra, 1949.) **Right,** the sex chromosomes of *Melandrium*. I, II, III, the differential segment of Y; IV, the homologous segments; V, the differential segment of X. Chromosome Y has lost segment I. (After Westergaard, 1958.)

matids; (b) it is possible to make a close correlation between genetic constitution and biochemical expression of genes. (The latter aspect is considered again in Chapter 18.)

As shown in Figure 15–7, the four cells resulting from the two meiotic divisions undergo a mitotic division, which gives rise to eight haploid ascospores. Each of these ascospores can be isolated by dissection and cultured separately, giving rise to haploid individuals having the genetic constitution carried in each of the four original chromatids of the bivalent chromosome.

The figure indicates a single crossing over between genes *a* and *b* and the resulting products. The analysis of the eight ascospores show that only two of the chromatids interchange segments while the other two remain intact. It can be also observed that the segregation of genes may occur either during the first or the second meiotic division, depend-

ing on the position of the locus concerned in relation to the point of crossing over and the centromere. Thus in Figure 15–7 genes aa^+ separate in the first meiotic division and genes bb^+ in the second meiotic division.

ALTERATION OF THE CHROMOSOMES AND THEIR MECHANISM OF REORGANIZATION

The normal functioning of the genetic system of an organism is maintained in alignment and distribution by the constancy of the hereditary material carried in the chromosomes. Sometimes changes may occur in chromosomes that are brought about spontaneously or by experimental accidents, producing structural disarrangements. Knowledge of such changes has been favored by experimental methods that increase the

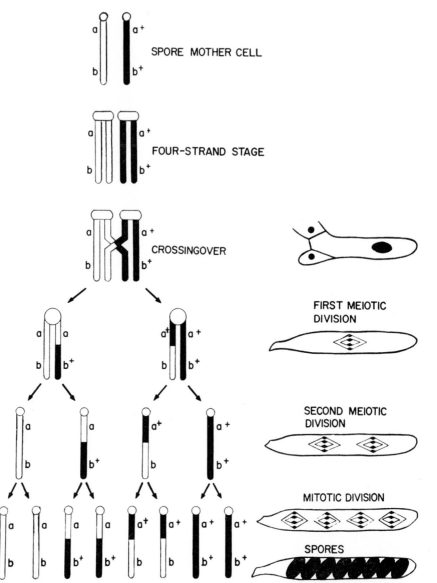

Figure 15–7. Diagram of the formation of ascospores in *Neurospora crassa*. A single crossover between genes *a* and *b*, the behavior of one pair of chromosomes during the first and second meiotic divisions, and the division by mitosis of each of the four products are shown.

frequency of changes and provide valuable means for analyzing the genetic and structural organization of the chromosome.

Structural changes in the chromosome may be:

A. *Submicroscopic* changes at the molecular level, i.e., *point mutation* or *gene mutation*.

B. *Microscopic changes* (also called aberrations), evidenced at the light microscope level. The aberrations comprise:

1. Loss of a chromosomal segment, i.e., *deficiency* or *deletion*.
2. Addition of a chromosomal segment, i.e., *duplication*.
3. Interchromosomal or intrachromosomal rearrangement by exchange of segments, i.e., *translocation*.
4. Intrachromosomal rearrangement by end for end rotation of a segment, which is in reverse genic order with relation to the rest of the chromosome, i.e., *inversion*.

Mutation

Although the gene is generally stable, it may change, which is called *mutation*. Mutation is a property of the genic material as important as stability. It takes place in all living organisms and is the origin of hereditary variations. The mutation of a gene may occur spontaneously, without apparent cause. The mutation becomes incorporated in the population and is transmitted by sexual reproduction. It will be eliminated only if the individual dies or cannot reproduce. Genetic mutations are changes localized at definite points in chromosomes and probably in individual genes. Mutation may occur in asexual unicellular organisms and also in somatic tissue. The frequency of mutation is different for each gene. Some alleles are stable. Some mutate with great frequency; for example, the normal allele of the recessive gene for hemophilia in man changes once in every 31,000 individuals in each generation. (The chemical bases of mutation will be studied in Chapter 18.)

It is now possible to induce mutation by means of ionizing and nonionizing irradiation, by chemicals and also by the action of temperature. The experimental production of mutations may increase their frequency, but there are no other differences between those induced artificially and those that appear spontaneously. The rate of spontaneous mutation is generally low. For example, in each generation of *Drosophila melanogaster* there are 1:100,000 to 1:1,000,000 mutations. Unicellular organisms are more appropriate for the study of the frequency of mutation because they produce a large number of organisms per generation.

Table 15–1 lists the frequencies of spontaneous mutation for certain genes.

Aberrations

Deficiency or Deletion

A *deficiency* is a chromosomal aberration in which a segment—either *interstitial* or *terminal*—is missing (Fig. 15–8). The deleted segment does not survive if it lacks a centromere. If it has a diffuse centromere, it survives and may be incorporated as a new chromosome. Terminal deficiency results from a single break in a chromosome. Interstitial deficiency results from two breaks followed by a union of the broken ends. Both types of deficiency can be observed during meiotic pachynema, or in the polytene chromosome. Terminal deficiencies have been reported in maize, but are rare in *Drosophila* and other organisms. In heterozygous deficiency, one chromosome is normal and its homologue has the deficiency (Fig. 15–8).

Animals with homozygous deficiency usually do not survive to an adult stage because a complete set of genes is lacking. This suggests that most genes are indispensable, at least in a single dose, for the development of a viable organism. Deficiencies are important in cyto-

TABLE 15–1. FREQUENCY OF SPONTANEOUS MUTATION OF SOME GENES*

ORGANISM	GENE	NUMBER OF GAMETES VERIFIED	FREQUENCY OF MUTATION FOR EACH 10,000 GAMETES
Corn	wx	1,503,744	0
	i	265,391	1.06
	rr	43,416	18.2
Drosophila melanogaster	white eye	70,000	0.29
	vestigial	60,000	0.3
Human	hemophilia		0.32
	chondrodystrophia		0.427
	retinoblastoma		0.23

* After Wagner and Mitchell.[2]

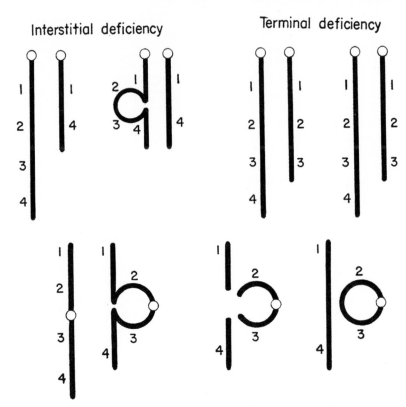

Formation of an acentric rod and deletion ring

FIGURE 15–8. Diagram illustrating the origin of different types of deficiencies.

genetic investigations of gene location and the presence and position of unmated genes.

Duplication

Duplication occurs when a segment of the chromosome is represented two or more times in the chromosome. This may be a free fragment with a centromere or a chromosomal segment of the normal complement. If the fragment includes the centromere, it may be incorporated as a small chromosome (extra-chromosome, Fig. 15–9). If the duplication occurs in an added segment, the disposition may be in tandem. An example of tandem duplication is the well-known *Bar* in *Drosophila*. Duplications make it possible to investigate the effects of an extra complement of genes in corresponding loci. Duplications are in general less deleterious to the individual than deficiencies.

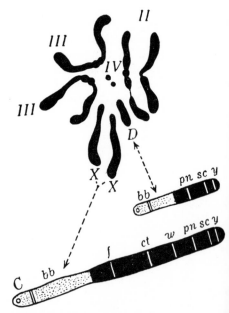

FIGURE 15–9. Duplication of a segment the X chromosome in *Drosophila melanogaste* The duplicated element (*D*) appears as a separate extra chromosome. *In black,* the euchromati region; *stippled,* the heterochromatic region.

Translocation

A translocation is a chromosomal rearrangement in which (1) segments are exchanged between nonhomologous chromosomes or (2) a segment of one chromosome is transferred to a different part of the same chromosome or to another chromosome. The first is a reciprocal translocation; the second is a simple translocation. When an interstitial segment is transferred from the arm of one chromosome to a different position in an arm of the same chromosome or to another chromosome, the rearrangement is called a *shift*. Such a shift requires three simultaneous breaks. Reciprocal translocations may be both homozygous and heterozygous (Fig. 15–10).

Cytologically a translocation homozygote cannot be distinguished from a normal pair of chromosomes, but it can be detected by genetic experiments. Heterozygote translocations give rise to special pairing configurations in meiosis.

In plants that have deficiencies and duplications the pollen grains are inviable and abortive. Consequently individuals heterozygous for translocations are half sterile. A cytologic examination of pollen in maize will show that about half the pollen grains are empty, contain little or no starch and are sterile.

An interesting result occurs when, during translocation, both chromosomes are broken very close to their centromeres. The fusion creates a metacentric chromosome with two arms in the form of **V** and a small fragment, which tends to be eliminated. Figure 15–11,*1* illustrates the mechanism of *centric fusion*, which has occurred during the phylogeny of *Drosophila*, grasshoppers, reptiles, birds, mammals and other groups. It is a process that establishes a new type of chromosome and reduces the somatic chromosome number of the species.

Inversion

An inversion is a chromosomal aberration in which a segment is inverted 180 degrees. Inversions are called *pericentric* when the segment includes the centromere and *paracentric* if the centromere is located outside the segment. When a crossing over (chiasma) occurs within the inverted segment of a paracentric inversion, dicentric and acentric chromatids are formed (Fig. 15–12). The dicentric chromatids form a bridge that breaks when the anaphase chromosomes

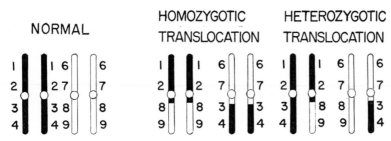

FIGURE 15–10. Schematic representation of homozygotic and heterozygotic reciprocal translocations compared with the normal arrangement.

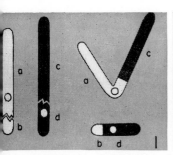
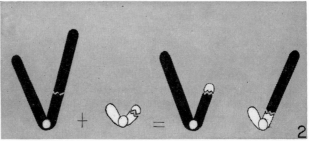

FIGURE 15–11. **1**, the origin of a new **V**-shaped (metacentric) chromosome by *centric fusion* of two nonhomologous acrocentric chromosomes. Segment *bd* is lost. **2**, *dissociation*. A metacentric and a small, supernumerary chromosomal fragment undergo a translocation, which results in two chromosomes (acrocentrics or metacentrics).

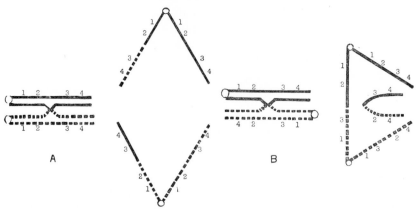

FIGURE 15–12. Diagram to show the occurrence (A) of normal crossing over between two chromatids and the result of this at anaphase. **B,** crossing over between two chromatids, one normal and the other inverted (4 2 3 1). The result of this crossing over is seen at anaphase with the production of a fragment (3 4 2 4) without a centromere and an anaphase (dicentric) bridge (1 2 3 1) with two centromeres. The fragment is lost.

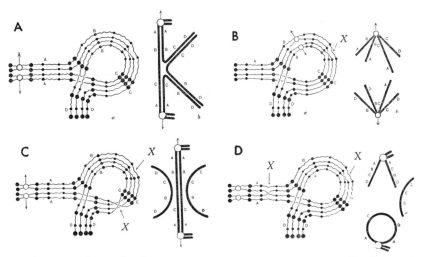

FIGURE 15–13. **A,** the results of crossing over in a paracentric inversion. **B,** when a chiasma is formed within a pericentric inversion, duplications and deficiencies result. **C,** two complementary chiasmata within an inversion and their results. **D,** ring formation in chromatids when one chiasma forms between the centromere and the inverted segment and the other forms within the inversion. (After White, 1945.)

separate toward the poles. The presence of this bridge or chromatid fragment furnishes a cytologic method for detecting inversions at meiotic divisions. If crossing over occurs within the loop of a pericentric inversion, the chromatids are produced with a deficiency and a duplication (Fig. 15–13B). Loop chromatids may be formed during anaphase I when chiasmata occur between the inverted region and the centromere as well as within the inversion. In this case a dicentric bridge may form at anaphase II (Fig. 15–13D).

Inversion has been produced in the evolution of some species of *Drosophila*

and in certain genera of Orthoptera. (An analysis of the chromosomal evolution of *Drosophila* is beyond the scope of this book.) In studies of inversion it has been demonstrated that racial groups in different geographic localities have resulted from successive rearrangement of the chromosomes during their phylogeny.

VARIATIONS IN CHROMOSOME NUMBER

Changes in chromosome number may involve:

1. The complete haploid set (n) as a whole. *Euploids* are organisms that have a balanced set or sets of chromosomes, in any number (Table 15–2).
2. The loss or gain of one or more chromosomes in a set. *Aneuploids* are organisms that have an unbalanced set of chromosomes.

Haploidy

Some exceptional plants and animals have a *monoploid* chromosome set, i.e., a chromosome set comprising a single genome (complete haploid set of genes). In these organisms meiosis is irregular because of the absence of homologous chromosomes with which to pair. As a result, gametes with varying number of chromosomes may be formed. Examples of haploids are found in *Sorghum, Triticum, Hordeum* and *Datura*. In animals, one sex may be normally haploid, as in the male of Hymenoptera.[3]

Polyploidy

A plant or animal that has more than two haploid sets of chromosomes is called a *polyploid* (Fig. 15–14). This change is common in nature, especially in the flowering plants. For example, in *Sorghum*, in which the haploid number (n) = 5, *S. versicolor, S. sudanense* and *S. halepense* have 10, 20 and 40 somatic chromosomes, respectively. These species constitute a series in which the latter two are polyploids. A diploid organism has two similar genomes (AA), an autotriploid has three (AAA), an autotetraploid has four (AAAA), and so on.

Autopolyploids may originate either by reduplication of the chromosome number in a somatic tissue with suppression of cytokinesis or by formation of gametes with an unreduced number of chromosomes.

Meiosis in an autotriploid is more irregular than in an autotetraploid. In general, the autopolyploids of uneven number are more sterile because the gametes have a more unbalanced number of chromosomes. In an autopolyploid there are three or more chromosomes that associate to form *multivalent* chromosomes. At pachynema only two chromosomes are always paired in a particular segment, whatever may be the number of homologues and whatever may be the place of contact during pairing.

Polyploidy in Animals. The scarcity of polyploids among animals is due to the bisexuality that characterizes the majority of animal species. This implies a special mechanism in which sex is determined by the segregation of a pair of differentiated sex chromosomes. Because one of the two sexes has two different types of gametes, XY or XO (O means the absence of the other sex chromosome), sterility or sexual abnormalities may result. If polyploidy occurs, the

TABLE 15–2. CHROMOSOME COMPLEMENTS IN EUPLOIDS AND ANEUPLOIDS

TYPE	FORMULA	COMPLEMENT*
EUPLOIDS		
Monoploid	n	(ABCD)
Diploid	2n	(ABCD)(ABCD)
Triploid	3n	(ABCD)(ABCD)(ABCD)
Tetraploid	4n	(ABCD)(ABCD)(ABCD)(ABCD)
Autotetraploid	4n	(ABCD)(ABCD)(ABCD)(ABCD)
Allotetraploid	4n	(ABCD)(ABCD)(A'B'C'D')(A'B'C'D')
ANEUPLOIDS		
Monosomic	2n − 1	(ABCD)(ABC)
Trisomic	2n + 1	(ABCD)(ABCD)(B)
Tetrasomic	2n + 2	(ABCD)(ABCD)(B)(B)
Double trisomic	2n + 1 + 1	(ABCD)(ABCD)(AC)
Nullisomic	2n − 2	(ABC)(ABC)

* A, B, C, D are nonhomologous chromosomes.

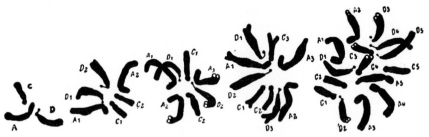

FIGURE 15–14.   Polyploid series in the plant *Crepis*. (After Nawashin.)

genic balance between the sex chromosomes and the autosomes is disturbed and the race or species may disappear because of sterility.

In amphibia, triploids, tetraploids, pentaploids and aneuploids induced experimentally by temperature shock have been studied.[4] A case of polyploidy in mammals is that of the hamster *Cricetus cricetus*.[5] Cells with reduplicated chromosome complexes are frequently observed in animals and in pathologic tissues.

At present it is possible to induce polyploidy by the use of substances such as colchicine, acenaphthene, heteroauxin and veratrine, and also by exposure to heat or cold. The most frequently employed is the alkaloid colchicine. Seeds are immersed in colchicine at the beginning of germination. This substance may also be injected into young plants.[6]

These substances inhibit the formation of the spindle; thus cell division is not completed. When some time has passed, the cells recover their normal activity, but have a double number of chromosomes. Innumerable possibilities are offered by the experimental production of polyploids from the standpoint of both scientific and applied work.

Allopolyploidy

This type of chromosome variation is produced in crosses between two species that have different sets of chromosomes. The resulting hybrid has a different number of chromosomes than the parents. For example, the argentine black *Sorghum* (*S. almum*) is an allotetraploid (2n = 4x = 40) originated in nature by an interspecific cross between *S. halepense* (2n = 4x = 40) with *S. sudanense* (2n = 2x

= 20) (Fig. 15–15). In this case the fertilization occurred between one abnormal diploid gamete and a normal gamete of the other species. In most cases crosses between distantly related species produce sterile diploid hybrids. However, as shown in Figure 15–16 sometimes a fertile organism results from a doubling of the chromosomes of the hybrid, which produces balanced gametes giving rise to an allotetraploid individual (AABB).

The study of meiosis in allopolyploids is of importance in determining the species which have taken part in the formation of the hybrid, and may furnish a key to the probable phylogeny.

Aneuploidy

When one or more chromosomes reduplicate, the organism is said to be *polysomic*. This is a special kind of aneuploidy caused by a faulty separation of chromosomes during meiosis. One of the chromosomes, together with its homologue, passes to the same pole and is contained in the same gamete. This phenomenon is also called *nondisjunction*. Such a gamete, upon union with any normal gamete, gives rise to a *trisomic* individual (2x + 1). This type of aberration produces *mongolism* in humans (see Chap. 16). Table 15–2 indicates other types of aneuploidy, such as *monosomic* and *nullisomic* organisms.

From the genetic point of view monosomic organisms are interesting because they have genes without mates (the genes lack a homologue). This allows one to follow the distribution of the recessive gene located in the unpaired element and to determine the values of linkages and of crossing over in the progeny

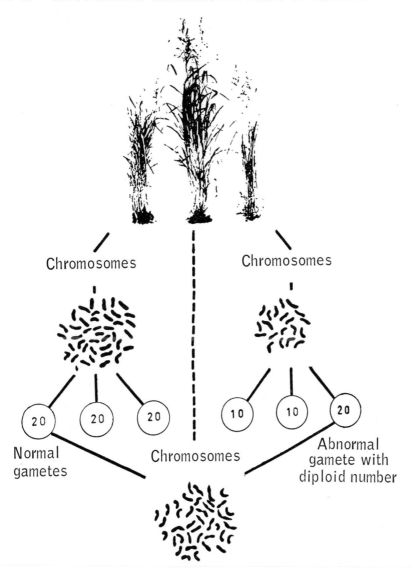

Chromosomes

Chromosomes

Chromosomes

Normal gametes

Chromosomes

Abnormal gamete with diploid number

FIGURE 15–15. The origin of the argentine *Sorghum almum* by crossing *Sorghum halepense* ($2n = 4x = 40$) with a diploid *Sorghum* ($2n = 2x = 20$) in which the fertilization occurred between one gamete not reduced ($x = 20$) and a normal gamete of *S. halepense*. Somatic chromosomes of the parents and the hybrid allopolyploid are illustrated. (After Saez and Nuñez, 1949.)

Endomitosis, Polyteny, Polysomaty and Somatic Reduction

Processes in nondividing cells during differentiation and development have attracted a great deal of interest. In the water strider *Gerris lateralis*, Geitler found chromosomal reduplication and subsequent separation without formation of a spindle and without disappearance of the nuclear membrane. He called this process *endomitosis*. Reduplication may be so marked that the diploid chromosome number (normally 21), may reach 1024 or 2048. In the epithelial sheath of the testis of Orthoptera there are endopolyploid or polysomic nuclei with a high degree of ploidy.

In tumor cells of mammals, such as in ascites and in solid tumors, reduplication and polyploidy are common. Reduplication of chromosomes may take place by two mechanisms, *polyteny* and *polysomaty*. In polyteny the sister chromatids do not separate and thus a multi-

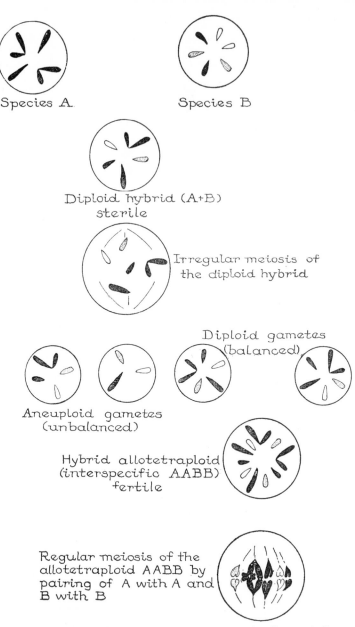

Figure 15–16. The formation of an interspecific allotetraploid.

stranded polytene chromosome is formed (Chap. 13). In polysomaty, the separation of the sister chromatids results in a somatic polyploid with chromosomes that have normal strands. Between these extremes the differences are only of degree, since polyteny is a special case of the general phenomenon of *endopolyploidy*. There are cases in which polyteny and polysomaty coexist in the same cell, as, for example, in the genus *Lestodisplosis*.[3]

As a result of the study of polysomaty in relation to differentiation, it can be demonstrated that tissues having a high mitotic activity have also a constant chromosome number. If cell division is slower than reduplication, polyteny and polysomaty may occur. On the other hand, if cell division is faster than reduplication or occurs after polyploidy, *somatic reduction* may take place, in which the chromosome number of somatic cells is reduced. This type of change has been observed in higher plants and in some insects. Somatic re luction is not infrequent in nature, and ts frequency can be increased experimentally by various treatments.[7]

Somatic Variation in Chromosome Number

A problem that is being studied with considerable interest is related to the variability in the chromosome number of somatic cells in different organisms, particularly in mammals. These studies can also be applied to human pathology. This variation, also called *somatic aneuploidy,* has been observed in different tissues of vertebrates, including man.

An example of chromosomal variation is the so-called *somatic segregation,* in which two cytologically or genetically different daughter cells arise from a somatic mitosis. This process may lead to individual cells in different tissues or parts of the body that have different chromosome numbers, e.g., in mosaic individuals, variegations, gynandromorphs and so forth. There are several causes for this curious change, including endomitosis, somatic reduction, somatic crossing over, fragmentation or deletion of chromosomes and so forth.

Chromosomal Variations in Cancer. In tissue cultures of normal cells, chromosomal variations are common, particularly after several transplants. These changes may lead to malignancy, but this is not the case in all cultures.

The study of chromosomal variations that take place in tumor cell populations has only begun. The cytogenetic analysis of different mammalian tumors has led investigators to consider them as altered karyotypes, which are genetically and cytologically unstable. Most ascitic tumors of rats have been found to consist of a mixture of cell types. The chromosomal content of these cell populations is variable, and the *modal number* is different from the diploid number of the species. Since cells having the same chromosome mode can be perpetuated by transplantation, it was thought that these were the stem lines of the tumor, and the cell populations were considered as variants of this "stem line."[8, 9]

This concept of stem lines has been extended to primary tumors of mice.[10] Serologic methods[11] and cultures of isolated cell clones have been also used in this problem.[12]

CYTOGENIC EFFECT OF RADIATION

In the section on chromosomal alteration the concept of mutation was presented. It was then said that mutation is a change in the genetic material that gives rise to hereditary variations and that it may occur "spontaneously" in nature. It was also mentioned that different agents, such as radiations and chemicals, may increase considerably the frequency of mutation.

Muller, Stadler and Altenburg[13-16] independently discovered the mutagenic affect of radiation. Experimenting with x-rays on *Drosophila melanogaster,* barley and maize, they found a considerable increase in the frequency of mutation. Radiation—i.e., x-rays, λ-rays, β-rays, fast neutrons, slow neutrons and ultraviolet rays—and any other kind of mutagenic agents can induce true point (intragenic) mutations and breakage and rearrangements of chromosomes (chromosomal aberrations).

In different organisms it was demonstrated that the number of mutations induced by radiation is proportional to the dose, i.e., the amount of irradiation. Figure 15–17 shows, in the case of *Drosophila,* that the relation is a linear function over the range 25 to 9000 roentgen units (r).* In *Escherichia coli,* at low doses of radiation, the number of induced mutations follows the linear relationship observed at higher doses.[17]

The effects of radiation are cumulative over long periods of time. For example 0.1 r per day in 10 years is enough to increase the mutation rate to about 150 per cent of the spontaneous level.

In mammals the effects of "acute" (i.e., a period of seconds or minutes) and "chronic" (i.e., a fractioned or con-

---

* The roentgen r is an amount of radiation sufficient to produce two ions per μ^3 and is defined as the radiation required to liberate one electrostatic unit in 0.001293 gm of air.

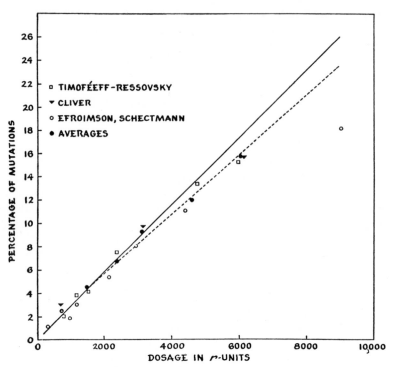

FIGURE 15–17. Relationship between doses of x-rays and frequency of lethal mutations in *Drosophila melanogaster*. (From Timoféeff-Ressovsky, Zimmer and Delbrück.)

tinuous slow exposure separated for days or weeks) irradiation show different rates of mutation. An acute exposure of 20 r to human cells in culture is sufficient to induce one chromosome break in each cell. Chronic irradiation of the mouse testis produces fewer mutations in the spermatogonia than an acute dose at high intensity.[18, 19] In *Drosophila*, the mutagenic effects of chronic and acute irradiation are equivalent.

The mutagenic differences between chronic and acute radiation in mouse spermatogonia may be a clue to what happens in man. It shows the need of considering separately the effect of acute and chronic irradiation to establish the relation between intensity and mutation frequency.

Chromosomal Aberrations

Radiations may induce chromosomal fragmentation and thus alter the structure of chromosomes. In contrast to gene mutations, chromosomal aberrations do not increase in direct proportion to the dose but rather increase exponentially (Fig. 15–18). More chromosomal aberrations are produced by continuous than by intermittent treatment.

A low dose of radiation is not intense enough to make two fractures in one chromosome or in one nucleus. As the dose increases, the number of breaks increases and "aberrant" fusions become more and more likely. If the dose is intermittent or of low intensity, there is a greater chance that the broken ends of the chromosome will rejoin, or "heal," in the original chromosome structure, before a second break could cause aberration.

If only one break is induced in one chromosome, only a slight deficiency is observed. Aberrations resulting from two breaks (translocations, inversions and large deletions), depend on an exponential dose (Fig. 15–18). The frequency of two simultaneous breaks is proportional to the square of the dose of radiation.[20, 21]

At high doses chromosomal aberrations that require more than one break are more numerous than aberrations depending on single breaks. Thus in *Tradescantia* the curve of the frequency of translocations remains close to zero for ow doses and rises rapidly at higher doses.[22, 23]

As mentioned in the section on chromosomal aberrations, when a chromosome breaks, the two fragments may either reunite or may remain separated permanently. Usually one broken end meets the other broken end in a process of *restitution*. In this case there is no lasting effect in the structure and in genetic function of the chromosome.

If, instead of restituting at once, the broken ends reduplicate to form two chromatids, the fragments with the centromere become distributed into different poles and the fragments without a centromere (acentric) are eliminated in the cytoplasm (Fig. 15–19A). Sometimes the sister fragments reduplicate and unite, forming a dicentric chromosome (with two centromeres) and another acentric chromosome (without a centromere). During mitosis the centromeres of the dicentric chromosome move to opposite poles and form a "bridge" between the daughter nuclei that finally breaks at some point (Fig. 15–19B). Thus the two daughter cells receive unbalanced chromosomes with deficiencies

and duplications. At the next mitosis the same cycle may be repeated with production of chromosomal aberrations comprising new "breakage-fusion bridges" that give rise to new genotypes.[24, 25]

In man double or multiple chromosome breaks are induced by acute exposures, e.g., heavy medical irradiations, atomic accidents or atomic warfare), whereas single breaks are produced at low doses. Chromosomal aberrations have been observed in blood cultures of humans who have been given radiation treatments or have had injections of radioactive substances.[26–28]

Somatic Cell and Germ Cell Mutations

The mutagenic action of radiations can be produced in any part of the organism, in either somatic or germ cells.

Somatic mutations are not transmitted from generation to generation but produce severe changes in the individual, depending on the type of cell affected and when in the life of the individual the mutation occurs. Radiation can affect tissues that undergo mitosis as well as tissues in which cell division no longer takes place. If mutation occurs during early embryonic development, a large number of cells are affected. The majority of mutated genes are recessive and thus have no effect as long as the individual is heterozygous. However if, in a descendant cell, it becomes homozygous, its phenotype will be immediately manifested.

It is probable that some cases of cancer produced in irradiated individuals are caused by somatic mutation. In contrast to somatic mutation, mutations in the germ cells may be transmitted to the offspring. However, in most cases of mutation caused by irradiation both somatic and germ cells are frequently affected.[25]

Even the lowest doses of radiation are genetically harmful and the effects are equally dangerous from the simplest organisms to man.[29–35] However, in microorganisms and plants, for many deleterious mutations a few useful ones may be obtained by irradiation. For example, irradiation is a method of producing new

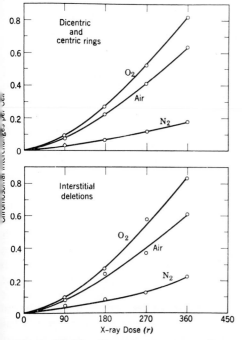

FIGURE 15–18. X-ray dosage curves, showing chromosomal aberrations induced in *Tradescantia* in the presence of oxygen, air and nitrogen. (From Giles and Riley.)

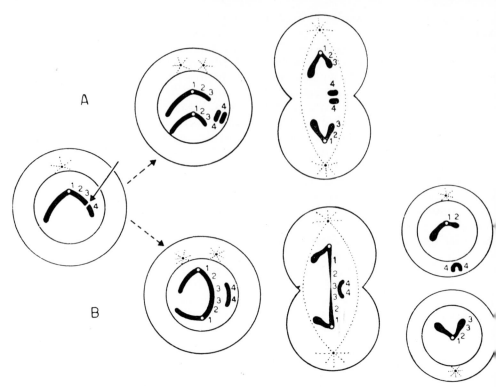

Figure 15–19. A single break in a chromosome between loci 3 and 4. **A,** the two parts of the broken chromosome reduplicate. The fragments with the centromere go to opposite poles. The fragments without the centromere remain in the equatorial region and are eliminated. **B,** the two parts of the broken chromosome reduplicate and the broken ends unite, forming a chromosome with two centromeres and another chromosome without a centromere. During mitosis the two centromeres move to opposite poles and the chromosome section between them breaks. The two daughter cells receive chromosomes with different constitutions. The fragment without a centromere is eliminated in the cytoplasm. (From Stern, 1960.)

antibiotics and plants with high economic value.

At present it is known that in the process of mutation there may be a series of interferences between the ionization produced in the tissue by radiation and the final mutation. For example, in an atmosphere of oxygen, mutations are frequent, whereas in one of helium or nitrogen the frequency diminishes. The biologic effects of radiation can be diminished in the presence of appropriate chemical protectors.

Mutation is essentially a biochemical change in the gene (see Chap. 18) and can now be explained in molecular terms.[36, 37]

CYTOGENETIC ACTION OF CHEMICAL AGENTS

The discovery of the effects of colchicine on cell division in animals (Lits,

1934) and in plants (Dustin, Havas and Lits, and Gavaudan [P. and N.] and Pompriaskinsky-Kabozieff, 1937) increased interest not only in colchicine itself but in the effects of chemical agents in general. From the cytogenetic point of view, the first production of polyploids by colchicine opened up new possibilities in applied and theoretical genetics.[38]

The effect of colchicine on the mechanism of mitosis has led to experimentation with many other substances in the hope of elucidating the physiology of normal and abnormal mitosis as well as the mechanism of mutagenesis (induction of genetic mutation). The most frequent effect of chemical agents is inhibition of mitosis and meiosis, but in a few cases chemical agents have a stimulating effect.

The inhibitory action may result in (1) chromosomal configurations that facilitate the counting and analysis of the karyotype; (2) polyploidy having innumerable practical applications; (3) the discovery of mutagens and anticancer substances; and (4) information about the basic mechanisms of inhibitory actions.[39] Similar studies of meiosis have provided indirect information about the physiology of pairing and "crossing over." In general, the specimen is observed immediately after the chemical action takes place. If the specimen survives, it can be maintained in a physiologic medium for a certain time for a study of residual effects or recuperation.

Inhibitors of the mitotic and meiotic processes are generally called "mitotic poisons."[40] Since the mitotic poison acts on a certain material and under certain experimental conditions, it must be qualified. These active agents can be endogenous (naturally occurring in tissues) or exogenous (developed or originating outside the organism).[41]

Mitotic poisons can be grouped according to their chemical structure, but, more advantageously, according to their actions and the possible mechanisms involved. The substance may inhibit different phases of mitosis or all phases of mitosis with different intensity. One or several mitotic mechanisms may be involved, e.g., the nuclear membrane cycle, chromosomal spiralization, behavior of the centromere, formation of the spindle and chromosomal movement, chromosomal duplication, nuclear cycle, metabolism of nuclear DNA and nuclear and cytoplasmic RNA and proteins and the energy-producing processes for mitosis and meiosis. The effects of mitotic poisons on the biochemical aspects of mitosis are less known, but progress is being made through different cytochemical techniques, including the use of radioisotopes.

The chemical agents that inhibit mitosis can be grouped according to (1) those that act at prophase and interphase and (2) those that act at metaphase and the following phases.

Chemical Agents That Act at Prophase and Interphase

Some substances produce a change at the critical stages during which the chromosomes duplicate (see Chap. 17).

Certain chemicals inhibit oxidation (cyanide and azide) and oxidative phosphorylation (2,4-dinitrophenol), processes that provide the energy for mitosis. Therefore, they prevent the mitotic process but not chromosomal duplication. The mitotic phase does not take place but the nuclear volume increases.[42]

Other agents affect carbohydrate metabolism (e.g., the adrenal glucocorticoids), or interfere with chromosomal replication by changing the metabolism of DNA and protein.

Important substances are those that produce a chromosomal fragmentation similar to that caused by ionizing radiation. These are called *radiomimetic* substances. Well-known examples are nitrogen mustards. In general, the morphologic and genetic results of all these agents are better known than the mechanism of action.

A frequent observation is a chromosomal fracture followed by reorganization, as in the case of irradiation. The results can be observed best in early mitotic metaphase and anaphase or in meiotic diplonema, metaphase and anaphase. In early mitotic metaphase pseudochiasmata can be observed, which result in fragmentation and interchange of the same chromosome. Translocations are indicated by the presence of dicentric bridges. In meiotic diplonema one can demonstrate the fracture and reorganization of the different chromosomes.

It has been suggested that fracture and fusion can be produced between bridges of the same chromosome or of neighboring chromosomes.[43] Breakage and fusion are probably produced simultaneously, as in crossing over. Research with chemical agents indicate that some areas of a chromosome are more sensitive than others, and the more sensitive areas are frequently located in the heterochromatin. Among these, the centromere is the area that is more frequently broken. (This effect has not been observed in similar research with radiation.[44, 45]) A highly active chemical agent can cause nuclear disintegration. In this process "DNA droplets" are forced out of the nucleus into the cytoplasm, and nuclear vacuolation and finally nuclear lysis take place[46] (Fig. 15–20).

*Chemical Agents That Act at
Metaphase and the Following
Phases*

This action is called *mitosis C* because
it is mainly produced by colchicine. This
is an alkaloid whose effect has great
practical importance. Colchicine mainly
affects the formation and physiology of
the spindle, but also acts on the chromosomes.

Action on the Spindle. The action on
the spindle leads to different degrees of
blockage of chromosomal division in
metaphase and anaphase. Since chromosomal duplication is not affected, polyploidy may result. In more advanced
cases it may produce multipolar spin-
dles, death of the daughter nuclei, or
aneuploidy (an unbalanced set of chromosomes). Under colchicine chromosomes may continue the spiralization
cycle, and the two chromatids are contracted and repel one another but remain
united by the centromere (ski configuration).

The mechanism of colchicine activity
on the spindle has not been discovered.
The substance may act on the –SH
groups, on protein synthesis or on the
molecular architecture (see Chap. 14).
It may also affect the RNA metabolism
of the spindle or the energy for its movements. Antagonism between ATP and
colchicine indicates that colchicine may
affect the ATP mechanism.

Mutagenic Action of Chemicals

The first observations of the mutagenic action of chemical agents were
made with nitrogen mustard in *Drosophila melanogaster* by Auerbach in
1942 (see reference 47) and with
urethan in plants by Oehlkers.[48, 49]

It has been shown that numerous agents
such as carcinogens, peroxides, formaldehyde, alkylating agents, phenol and
nucleotide analogues produce mutation
in plants and animals. In microorganisms
more precise data on the mutation rate
have been obtained. In this case the use
of a special device called a *chemostat*
has proved valuable.[50] It consists of a
container with a suspension of bacteria
in which the culture medium is con-

tinuously added together with the mutagen. It has been observed that purines
such as caffeine and adenine, increase
the spontaneous mutation rate when they
are continually supplied to the medium
whereas some purine ribosides, such as
adenosine, guanosine and inosine, decrease the spontaneous mutation rate.
The latter are known as *antimutagens*.
Pyrimidines are not mutagens and de-
oxyribosides are not antimutagens.

It has been suggested that spontaneous mutation is determined by the balance of mutagens and antimutagens,
such as adenine and adenosine, which
are naturally occurring metabolites.

The thymidine analogue *5-bromode-
oxyuridine* damages certain specific regions in mammalian chromosomes, one
of which is the telomere. The regions
affected are assumed to be rich in adenine-thymine (A–T) pairs (see Chap.
17).[51]

Another mutagen, *hydroxylamine*,
probably deaminates cytosine, and has a
special effect on the centromere and
other areas of some chromosomes in the
hamster. It has been assumed that these
regions are rich in the guanine-cytosine
(G–C) pairs. Both the regions affected
by 5-bromodeoxyuridine and hydroxylamine are specific for each pair of chromosomes.[52]

Radiation has a different effect from
these chemical agents. In fact, breakage
and other chromosomal damage caused
by radiation are distributed at random,
whereas the action of chemicals is specific for certain regions. Bromodeoxyuri-
dine acts on cells only during the synthetic, or S, period (see Chap. 17). The
drug does not affect the G_2 period. Similarly, 5-fluorodeoxyuridine, an inhibitor
of the enzyme thymidylate synthetase,
acts only on cells replicating DNA.

Stimulating Agents

An interesting problem is that of dis-
covering the factors that initiate cell division. It has been suggested that a
stimulating substance starts the division,
and in 1955 a substance called *kinetin*
(6-furfurilaminopurine) from DNA of
different origin was isolated. This substance increases the mitotic rate in meri-

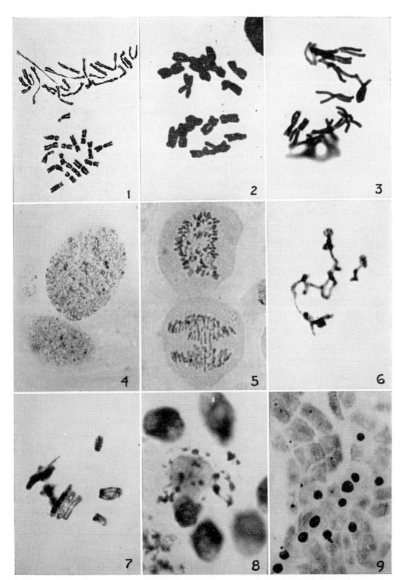

FIGURE 15-20.   Cytologic alterations produced by Actidione (2) and gonileptidine (1, 4–9).

1, above, a normal metaphase of *Allium cepa;* below, a metaphase of the same material showing the linear contraction of the chromosome.

2, metaphase with somatic chromosomes separated into two groups of equal number.

3, metaphase of segregative type showing the "ski" configuration of chromosomes induced by dinitrophenol in onion root tip.

4, giant prophase chromosomes induced by gonileptidine.

5, polyploid metaphase.

6, coalescence of chromosomes in a primary spermatocyte.

7, coalescence of all chromosomes except the sex chromosome (notice that the chromosomes show clear regions due to depolymerization of nucleoproteins).

8, fragmentation and expulsion of DNA to the cytoplasm, forming Feulgen-positive droplets in cells of *A. cepa.*

9, cells in which DNA has diffused through the entire cytoplasm.

(2, from Hawthorne and Wilson, 1952; 3, after Solari and Díaz, 1960; 1, 4–9, from Saez and Drets, 1954.)

stems of *Allium*. At low concentrations, this substance reduces the interphase rate and increases the mitotic rate. Certain hormones may also act as stimulating agents in certain experimental conditions (e.g., insulin and adrenocorticotropin). These hormones probably affect carbohydrate metabolism in mitosis.

CYTOGENETICS AND EVOLUTION

Great progress has been made in the study of evolution, owing to the development of comparative cytology and cytogenetics. McClung and S. Navashin were the first to emphasize the importance of cytogenetics to taxonomy and the study of evolution by comparing genomes of related species. Systematics have been greatly advanced by cytogenetic investigation, which now provides many of the best methods for elucidating intercorrelations between different taxonomic categories. In general, families, genera and species are characterized by different genetic systems.

The study of the karyotype of different species has revealed interesting facts about both the plant and animal kingdoms (see Chap. 13 and Table 13–1). It has been demonstrated that individuals in wild populations are to some extent heterogeneous cytologically and genetically. In some cases, even if the genes are identical they may be ordered in a different way, owing to alterations of the chromosomal segments. These changes have an important bearing on the evolution of species.

It was shown above that chromosomes may suffer spontaneous alterations, most of which are due to fractures followed by rearrangements that may change the order of the genes and that may even give rise to chromosomes with different genetic systems. These alterations in the karyotype can be related to the process of formation and evolution of species.

The majority of plant species originate from an abrupt and rapid change in nature, and aneuploidy or polyploidy are the main sources of variation. In the animal kingdom polyploidy is not so important. Among vertebrates, different species of fishes have a different number

of chromosomes. Amphibians are characterized by a special number for each family, especially in anurans. Reptiles and birds have large chromosomes (macrochromosomes) and small chromosomes (microchromosomes), which serve to differentiate them cytologically (see Chap. 13).

Owing to structural alterations, the number of centromeres may increase or decrease. Navashin's hypothesis that the variation in chromosome number is due to the fact that centromeres cannot originate *de novo* has been confirmed by experiments in both kingdoms. Furthermore, a reduction in the basic number of chromosomes involves the loss of one centromere and a gain (by duplication) of a chromosome and a centromere. Matthey distinguishes between the basic chromosome number and the number of chromosomal arms, also called fundamental number (FN). According to this concept, the metacentric chromosome has *two* arms and the acrocentric chromosome has *one*. This is an important distinction in a group having both acrocentric and metacentric chromosomes, and the number of arms in each of the different species can be compared.

Two opposite changes in the number (and configuration) of chromosomes are of particular importance in evolution (Fig. 15–11): In *centric fusion*, a process that leads to a decrease in chromosome number, two acrocentric chromosomes join together to produce a metacentric chromosome (Fig. 15–11,*1*). In *dissociation*, a process that leads to an increase in chromosome number, a metacentric (commonly large) and a small, supernumerary metacentric fragment became translocated so that two acrocentric or submetacentric chromosomes are produced (Fig. 15–11,*2*).

Fusion and dissociation are the main mechanisms by which the chromosome number can be decreased and increased during evolution of the majority of animals and in some groups of plants.

When the chromosome number increases or decreases, owing to an unequal translocation, one must study the segments carried by the centromere to determine whether they are genetically active or inert, i.e., euchromatic or heterochromatic. By such investigations the mechanism of chromosomal evolution in several groups of plants and animals has been explained. Studies of somatic and polytene chromosomes in several hundred species of *Drosophila* have elucidated the formation and evolution of this genus, which has been thoroughly analyzed from genetic, ecologic and geographic viewpoints. (A discussion of these problems is beyond the limits of this book.)

Observation of chromosomal organization and the different karyotypes in the individual, the species, the genera and the major systematic groups indicate that a chromosomal mechanism is involved in the process of evolution.

The problem of evolution should be considered from the different biochemical, cytologic, genetic, ecologic and experimental viewpoints. All these methods and approaches should be used to analyze the intricate relationships between groups of organisms, particularly those that show marked variations. These groups may serve to orient the taxonomist and to give him a firmer basis for interpreting the evolution and phylogeny of living organisms.

A modern view of the magnitude of the great problem of cytogenetics and evolution has been condensed by White as follows: "When we consider the varied types of life cycles and the many different kinds of population structure met with in plants and animals, the great variety of chromosomal mechanisms, although still very imperfectly understood as genetic systems, begins to take on meaning."

GENERAL REFERENCES

Beatty, R. A. (1954) How many chromosomes in mammalian somatic cells? *Internat. Rev. Cytol.*, 3:177.

Biesele, J. J. (1958) *Mitotic poisons and the cancer problem.* Elsevier Pub. Co., New York.

Brachet, J., and Mirsky, A. E., eds. (1959) *The cell*, Vol. 1. Academic Press, New York.

Darlington, C. D., and Bradshaw, A. D. (1964) *Teaching genetics.* Oliver & Boyd, Edinburgh.

Darlington, C. D., and Mather, K. (1949) *The elements of genetics.* Allen & Unwin, London.

Dobzhansky, T. (1958) *Genetics and the origin of species.* 3rd Ed. Columbia University Press, New York.

Eigsti, O. J., and Dustin, P. (1955) *Colchicine.* Iowa State College Press, Ames, Iowa.

Elliot, F. C. (1958) *Plant breeding and cytogenetics.* McGraw-Hill Book Co., New York.

Genetics and Twentieth Century Darwinism (1959) *Cold Spr. Harb. Symp. Quant. Biol.*, 24.

Goldschmidt, R. B. (1955) *Theoretical genetics.* University of California Press, Berkeley and Los Angeles.

Hayes, W. (1964) *The genetics of bacteria and their viruses.* Blackwell Scientific Publications, Oxford.

Hollaender, A. (1954) *Radiation biology.* 3 volumes. McGraw-Hill Book Co., New York.

Lea, D. E. (1955) *Actions of radiations on living cells.* 2nd Ed. Cambridge University Press, London.

Lewis, K. R., and John, B. (1963) *Chromosome marker.* J. & A. Churchill, London.

Makino, S. (1951) *An atlas of the chromosome number in animals.* Iowa State College Press, Ames, Iowa.

Matthey, R. (1949) *Les chromosomes des vertébrés.* Lausanne.

McElroy, W. D., and Glass, B., eds. (1957) *The chemical basis of heredity.* Johns Hopkins Press, Baltimore.

Muller, H. J. (1950) Our load of mutations. *Amer. J. Hum. Genet.*, 2:111.

Muller, H. J. (1956) Further studies bearing on the load of mutations in man. *Acta Genet. Stat. Med.*, 6:157.

Neel, J. V. (1963) *Changing perspectives on the genetic effects of radiation.* Charles C Thomas, Springfield, Ill.

Neel, J. V., and Schull, W. J. (1954) *Human heredity.* University of Chicago Press, Chicago.

Rhoades, M. M. (1955) *The cytogenetics of maize, corn and corn improvement.* Academic Press, New York.

Sager, R., and Ryan, F. J. (1961) *Cell heredity.* John Wiley & Sons, New York.

Simpson, G. G. (1950) *The meaning of evolution.* Yale University Press, New Haven, Conn.

Sinnott, E. W., Dunn, L. C., and Dobzhansky, T. (1958) *Principles of genetics.* 5th Ed. McGraw-Hill Book Co., New York.

Stern, C. (1960) *Principles of human genetics.* 2nd Ed. Freeman & Co., San Francisco.

Swanson, C. P. (1957) *Cytology and cytogenetics.* Prentice-Hall, Englewood Cliffs, New Jersey.

Taylor, J. H. (1963) *Molecular genetics*, part I. Academic Press, New York.

Wagner, R. P., and Mitchell, H. K. (1955) *Genetics and metabolism.* John Wiley & Sons, New York.

White, M. J. D. (1961) *The chromosomes.* 5th Ed. Methuen & Co., London.

Wilson, E. B. (1925) *The cell in development and heredity.* The Macmillan Co., New York.

Wilson, G. B., and Morrison, J. H. (1961) *Cytology.* Reinhold Publishing Corp., New York.

CITED REFERENCES

1. Dobzhansky, T. (1958) *Genetics and origin of species.* 3rd Ed. Columbia University Press, New York.
2. Wagner, R. P., and Mitchell, H. K., (1955) *Genetics and metabolism.* John Wiley & Sons, New York.
3. White, M. J. D. (1954) *Animal cytology and evolution.* Cambridge University Press.
4. Frankhauser, G. (1945) *Quart. Rev. Biol.,* 20:20.
5. Sachs, L. (1952) *Heredity,* 6:357.
6. Eigsti, O. J., and Dustin, P. (1955) *Colchicine.* Iowa State College Press, Ames, Iowa.
7. Huskins, C. L., Steinitz, L. M., Duncan, E., and Leonard, R. (1947) *Rec. Soc. America,* 16:38.
8. Levan, A. (1956) *Am. Acad. Sci.,* 63:774.
9. Makino, S. (1956) *Am. Acad. Sci.,* 63.
10. Ford, C. E., Hamerton, J. L., and Mole, R. H. (1958) *J. Cell. Comp. Physiol.,* 52:235.
11. Hauschka, T. S. (1958) *J. Cell. Comp. Physiol.,* 52:197.
12. Puck, T. T. (1959) Quantitative studies on mammalian cells "in vitro." *Biophysical science.* (Oncley, J. L., ed.) John Wiley & Sons, New York, p. 433.
13. Muller, H. J. (1927) *Science,* 66:84.
14. Muller, H. J. (1928) *Ztschr. Abstam. Vererbungsl.* suppl. 1:234.
15. Stadler, L. J. (1928) *Science,* 68:186.
16. Altenburg, E. (1928) *Amer. Nat.,* 62:540.
17. Demerec, M., and Sams, J. (1960) Proc. Symp. Venice. *Internat. J. Radiat. Biol.,* 283.
18. Russell, W. L. (1954) In: *Radiation biology,* Vol. 1, p. 825. (Hollaender, A., ed.) McGraw-Hill Book Co., New York.
19. Russell, W. L., Russell, L. B., and Kelly, E. M. (1958) *Science,* 128:1546.
20. Giles, N. H., and Riley, H. P. (1949) *Proc. Nat. Acad. Sci.* (Wash.), 35:640.
21. Giles, N. H. (1955) *Brookhaven Symp. Biol.,* 8:103.
22. Sax, K. (1940) *Genetics,* 25:41.
23. Sax, K. (1941) *Cold Spr. Harb. Symp. Quant. Biol.,* 9:93.
24. McClintock, B. (1938) *Missouri Agric. Exp. Sta. Res. Bull.,* 240:48.
25. Muller, H. J. (1954) In: *Radiation biology.*

(Hollaender, A., ed.) McGraw-Hill Book Co., New York.
26. Tough, I. M., et al. (1960) *Lancet,* 2:849.
27. Bender, M. A., and Gooch, P. C. (1962) *Radiat. Res.,* 16:44.
28. Boyd, E., Buchanan, W. W., and Lennox, B. (1961) *Lancet,* 1:977.
29. Muller, H. J. (1950) *Amer. J. Hum. Genet.,* 2:111.
30. Muller, H. J. (1950) *Amer. Scient.,* 38:35.
31. Muller, H. J. (1956) *Acta Genet. Stat. Med.,* 6:157.
32. Neel, J. V. (1958) *Amer. J. Hum. Genet.,* 10:398.
33. Turpin, R., Lejeune, J., and Rethore, M. O. (1956) *Acta Genet. Stat. Med.,* 6:204.
34. Puck, T. T. (1959) *Rev. Mod. Physics, 31:* 433.
35. Stern, C. (1962) *Principles of human genetics.* Freeman & Co., San Francisco.
36. Sager, R., and Ryan, F. J. (1963) *Cell heredity.* John Wiley & Sons, New York.
37. Freese, E. (1963) Molecular mechanism of mutations. In: *Molecular genetics,* Vol. 1, p. 207. (Hollaender, A., ed.) Academic Press, New York.
38. Blakeslee, A. F., and Avery, A. G. (1938) *J. Hered.,* 28:392.
39. Wilson, G. B., and Morrison, J. H. (1958) *Nucleus, 1:*45.
40. Biesele, J. J. (1958) *Mitotic poisons and the cancer problem.* Elsevier Publishing Co., New York.
41. D'Amato, F., and Hoffman-Ostenhof, O. (1956) *Advanc. Genet.,* 8:1.
42. Brachet, J. (1954) *Arch. Biol.* (*Liège*), 65:1.
43. Revell, S. H. (1953) *Heredity,* suppl. 6:107.
44. Darlington, C. D., and Koller, P. C. (1947) *Heredity, 1:*187.
45. Kihlmann, B. (1955) *Exp. Cell Res.,* 8:345.
46. Saez, F. A., and Drets, M. (1958) *Port. Acta Biol.,* ser. A, 5:287.
47. Auerbach, C. (1951) *Cold Spr. Harb. Symp. Quant. Biol.,* 16:199.
48. Oehlkers, F. (1943) *Ztschr. Indukt. Abstamm.-u.Vererb.-L.,* 81:313.
49. Oehlkers, F. (1953) *Heredity,* 6:95.
50. Novick, A. (1956) Mutagens and antimutagens. *Brookhaven Symp. Biol.,* 8:201.
51. Shu, T. C., and Somers, C. E. (1961) *Proc. Nat. Acad. Sci.* (Wash.), 47:396.
52. Somers, C. E., and Shu, T. C. (1962) *Proc. Nat. Acad. Sci.* (Wash.), 48:937.

CHAPTER 16

SEX DETERMINATION

AND

HUMAN

CYTOGENETICS

SEX DETERMINATION

The generally observed fact that male and female individuals are found in more or less equal proportions was the point of departure for thinking that sex determination is directly related to heredity. Studies of sex determination have demonstrated that the male and female characteristics are transmitted from one generation to the next in the same way as any other hereditary character.

It has now been demonstrated that sex is determined as soon as the egg is fertilized and that it depends on the gametes. Proof for this is twofold: physiologic and cytologic. Among the physiologic evidence is the finding that identical twins, which originate from a single zygote, are always of the same sex. Furthermore, in certain species having polyembryonic development (e.g., armadillo) all the embryos, which have developed from a single fertilized egg, are of the same sex. Cytologic evidence was first obtained by McClung,[1] who demonstrated that the chromosome complex

(karyotype) of a cell is composed of not only common chromosomes (*autosomes*) but one or more special chromosomes that are distinguished from the autosomes by their morphologic characteristics and behavior. These were called *accessory chromosomes, allosomes, heterochromosomes* or *sex chromosomes*.

In certain species the gametes are not identical with respect to the sex chromosomes. One of the sexes is heterozygous, producing two types of gametes. The other is homozygous, producing only one type of gamete. Therefore only two combinations of gametes are possible in fertilization, and the result is 50 per cent males and 50 per cent females (Figs. 14–12 and 16–1).

Sex Chromosomes

The majority of diploid sexual organisms (i.e., gonochoric) have a pair of sex chromosomes, which, in the course of evolution, has been specialized for sex determination. One of the sexes has a pair of identical sex chromosomes (XX) and the other sex has a single chromosome, which may be unpaired (XO) or paired with a Y chromosome (XY) (Fig. 16–1).

With respect to the sex chromosomes, in many species spermatogenesis produces two kinds of gametes (spermatozoa) in similar proportion. On the other hand, oögenesis produces only one kind of gamete (ova) (see Fig. 14–12). This type of sex determination is found in mammals, including the human, and in certain insects, such as *Drosophila*. In all these cases the male is heterogametic whereas the female is homogametic.

In other vertebrates (birds, some reptiles and fishes) and invertebrates (e.g., the insects of the order Lepidoptera), the female is heterogametic and the male is homogametic. In this case there are two kinds of ova (X and Y) and only one kind of spermatozoa (X). In Orthoptera, males are XO and females XX. Finally, in some cases sex is determined by the Y chromosome. For example, in the axolotl the sex depends on the presence or absence of this chromosome.[2, 3]

In some cases of parthenogenesis, as in Hymenoptera (bees, wasps and ants),

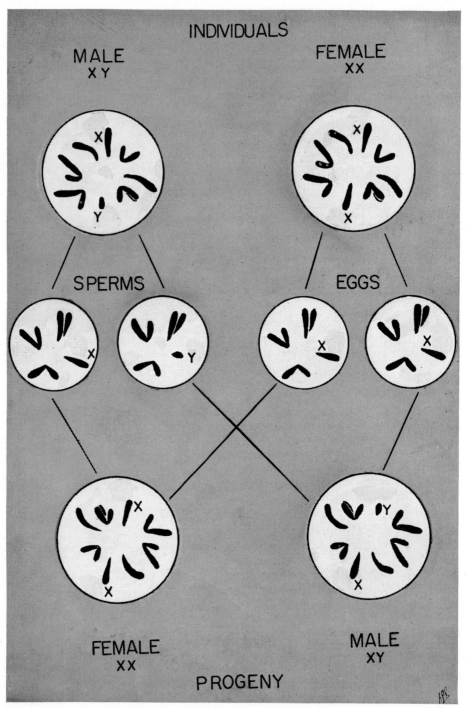

FIGURE 16–1.   Diagram of sex determination according to the XX-XY mechanism in the South American grasshopper *Dichroplus silveira guidoi* with four pairs of chromosomes (2n = 8).

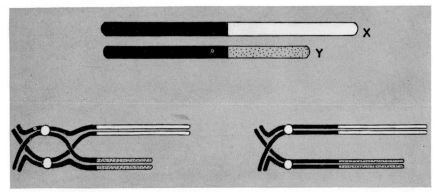

FIGURE 16–2.   Diagram of a pair of XY sex chromosomes of a mammal. In black, the pairing or homologous segments; in white, the differential segments of the X chromosome; stippled, the differential segments of the Y chromosome. The configuration of the bivalent depends on the position of the chiasmata, which is produced only in the homologous segment.

sex is determined by a haploid-diploid mechanism. If fertilization takes place, the individual is female and if it does not, a male results. Since all males are haploids, meiosis is anomalous (an anucleate polar body is eliminated), and does not reduce the chromosome number.

In the human the Y chromosome determines the male sex. Thus an XO individual (lacking the Y chromosome) resembles a female but lacks ovaries (Turner's syndrome). On the other hand, an XO mouse is a normal female. Probably in all mammals the Y chromosome determines the male sex.

Although in all animals there is a genetic mechanism of sex determination, sex chromosomes are not distinguishable in some animals. In such cases, the sex determining genes are probably confined to a short region of a pair of chromosomes.

The sex chromosomes can be thought of as composed of a *homologous* and a *differential region* (Fig. 15–6). The homologous region corresponds to the pairing segment, and when crossing over takes place, it is limited to this part (Fig. 16–2). The differential region influences sex determination.

Sex Chromatin and Sex Chromosomes

Barr and Bertram[5] opened an important field by their discovery in 1949 of a small chromatin body (i.e., a chromocenter) in nerve cells of the female cat, which was absent in the male. These observations were then made in other tissues and animals, including the human. In nuclei of the epidermis of females, this chromatin body, called the sex chromatin or Barr body, is found in much higher proportion than in males (Fig. 16–3C, D).[4–6]

Sex chromatin appears in the interphase nucleus as a small chromocenter heavily stained with basic dyes, which gives a positive Feulgen reaction (Fig. 16–3C) and has a relatively constant position in each tissue and species. It can be found in four positions: attached to the nucleolus, as in nerve cells of certain species (Fig. 16–3A); attached to the nuclear membrane, as in cells of the epidermis or of the oral mucosa; free in the nucleoplasm, as in neurons after electric stimulation (Fig. 16–3B); and as a nuclear expansion, the best-known example being that of the neutrophil leukocyte in which it appears as a small rod called the drumstick (Fig. 16–3D). This characteristic of the leukocyte has been utilized as a test of sex determination, along with the investigation of the basal cells of the epidermis and smears of the oral mucosa (Fig. 16–3).

The study of sex chromatin has a wide field of medical applications and offers the possibility of relating the origin of certain congenital diseases to chromosome anomalies. Among these applications are the diagnosis of sex in intersexual states in postnatal and even in fetal life (see Human Cytogenetics).

The relationship between sex chroma-

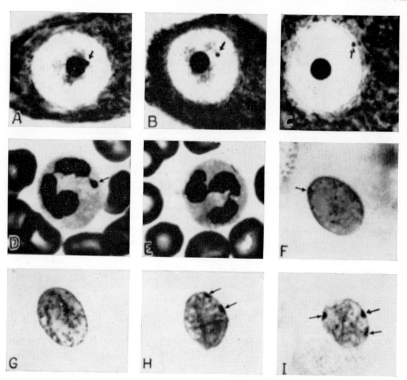

FIGURE 16–3.   Sex chromatin in a nerve cell of a female cat. **A**, near the nucleolus. **B**, in the nucleoplasm. **C**, under the nuclear membrane. (From M. L. Barr.) **D**, normal leukocyte from a human female with a drumstick nuclear appendage. ×1800. **E**, same as D in a male. Remember that 90 per cent of females also lack the drumstick, as in the male. ×1800. **F**, one sex chromatin corpuscle (*arrow*) in a nucleus from an oral smear. ×2000. **G**, same, from a male. Notice the lack of sex chromatin. ×1800. **H**, nucleus from the XXX female with two sex chromatin bodies. Vaginal smear. ×2000. **I**, similar, from an XXXX female. The three Barr bodies are indicated by arrows. ×2000. (From M. L. Barr and D. H. Carr, in J. L. Hamerton, ed., 1963.)

tin and sex chromosomes has recently been elucidated.[7] It has been demonstrated that the sex chromatin is derived from only one of the two X chromosomes. The other X chromosome behaves as an autosome and is not heteropyknotic at interphase (Fig. 16–4).

The number of corpuscles of sex chromatin at interphase is equal to $nX - 1$. This means that there is one Barr body less than the number of X chromosomes. This relationship between sex chromatin and sex chromosomes is particularly evident in some humans who have an abnormal number of sex chromosomes (see Table 16–1). Thus an XXX individual (superfemale or metafemale) has two sex chromatin bodies and an XXXX individual has three sex chromatin bodies (Fig. 16–3H, I), whereas an XO individual (Turner's syndrome) has no sex chromatin, as in the male (XY).

The X chromosome forming the sex chromatin is considered to be genetically inactive. This has been confirmed in mice.[8] DNA replication in sex chromosomes occurs at different times during the period of synthesis than that in most autosomes (see Chap. 17 and Fig. 17–3).

Sex Vesicle

In most mammalian species the sex bivalent formed by the XY chromosomes is embedded in a vesicle called the "sex vesicle," which is rich in RNA (Fig. 16–4,1). This vesicle is apparent mainly during the zygotene and pachytene stages of meiosis, at which time the XY chromosomes are not heteropyknotic. At the end of prophase, when the vesicle disintegrates, the XY bivalent becomes heteropyknotic again.

Some investigators[9] considered the sex

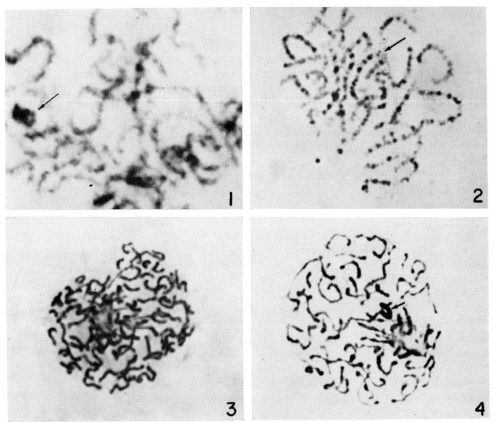

FIGURE 16–4.   1, pachytene from a spermatocyte of the Mulita (*Dasypus hybridus*), showing the sex vesicle containing the XY bivalent. (After Saez, Drets and Brum, 1962.) 2, pachytene stage in an oöcyte of a newborn female rat. The arrow indicates the region of the XX chromosomes. (Courtesy of S. Ohno.) 3, male somatic prophase from regenerating rat liver. (Courtesy of S. Ohno.) 4, hetero-pyknotic X chromosome (*arrow*) of the female somatic nucleus of regenerating rat liver. (Courtesy of S. Ohno.)

vesicle as a nucleolus associated or attached to the XY bivalent. However, this has been disproved by studies showing that the sex vesicle persists as long as the XY bivalent remains heteropyknotic, whereas the nucleolus disappears before or during the pachytene stage.

SEX-LINKED INHERITANCE

Sex-linked genes are those genes carried by the sex chromosomes except for those involved in sex determination. Morgan and his collaborators demonstrated sex-linked inheritance in *Drosophila*, a species that has hundreds of so-called sex-linked genes, which are carried on the sex chromosome.

The following is an example of this kind of inheritance: When a homo-zygous red-eyed female (dominant) is crossed with a white-eyed male (recessive), all individuals in the F_1 are red-eyed (Fig. 16–5,1), but when the cross is between a white-eyed female and a red-eyed male, male offspring in the F_1 have white eyes (Fig. 16–5,2). When heterozygous red-eyed females are crossed with white-eyed males, both sexes segregate 1:1, rather than 3:1, for eye color. These experiments demonstrate that the gene in this case is carried by the X chromosome, but not by the Y.

In organisms with an XY type of sex determination, genes may be present in the differential segments of the X and Y (Fig. 15–2). Such genes are not alleles, since they are in a nonhomologous section of the chromosome. They are completely linked and crossing over cannot occur.

There are three types of sex-linked inheritance: (1) *X-linked,* by genes localized in the nonhomologous section of X and that have no corresponding alleles in Y; (2) *Y-linked,* by genes localized in the nonhomologous section of Y and that have no alleles in X; and (3) *XY-linked,* by genes localized in one chromosomal segment that is homologous in both X and Y (the so-called incomplete linkage).

Genes Linked to the X Chromosome

The classic example of this is that of eye color in *Drosophila* given in the preceding section. In man the genes that determine *daltonism* (i.e., red-green color blindness) and hemophilia are linked to the X chromosome. Eight per cent of males have daltonism, whereas this is found in only 0.5 per cent of females. In the latter, both X chromosomes are altered at the same locus. Hemophilia (a defect of blood clotting) is inherited as a sex-linked recessive gene. Rarely, a female is a hemophiliac.

In this case the father is a hemophiliac and the mother is a carrier of hemophilia.

Other genes produce the following conditions in the human: ichthyosis, myopia, Gower's muscular atrophy and one type of color blindness. All these anomalies are transmitted in the same way as the "white-eyed" trait in *Drosophila,* and the same reasoning can be followed to obtain F_1 and F_2.

Genes Linked to the Y Chromosome

Genes in the nonhomologous region of the Y chromosome pass directly from father to son. There are 150 such genes in *Drosophila* and in man only a few are known. For example, ichthyosis hystrix, ichthyosis congenita and other skin diseases follow the male line (Fig. 15–6).

Genes Localized in the Homologous Segments of Both X and Y Chromosomes

Since these genes are in a homologous

TABLE 16–1.   SEX ANEUPLOIDS IN MAN

X \ Y	O	Y	YY	SEX CHROMATIN
x	Monosomic XO Turner's syndrome 2X − 1 2n = 45	Disomic XY Normal 2X 2n = 46	XYY	0
xx	Disomic XX Normal 2X 2n = 46	Trisomic XXY Klinefelter's syndrome 2X + 2 2n = 47	Tetrasomic XXYY Klinefelter's syndrome 2X + 2 2n = 48	1
xxx	Trisomic XXX Metafemale 2X + 1 2n = 47	Tetrasomic XXXY Klinefelter's syndrome 2X + 2 2n = 48		2
xxxx	Tetrasomic XXXX Metafemale 2X + 2 2n = 48	Pentasomic XXXXY 2X + 3 2n = 49 Klinefelter		3
PHENOTYPE	♀	♂	♂	

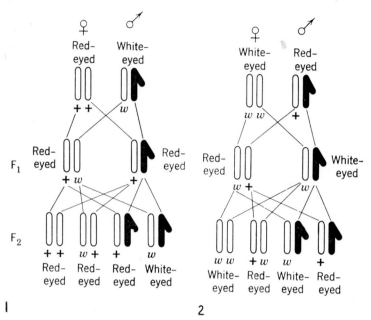

FIGURE 16–5.   Sex-linked inheritance of eye color in *Drosophila*. Reciprocal crosses of: **1**, a wild-type, red-eyed female to a white-eyed male and **2**, a white-eyed female to a wild-type, red-eyed male. (See the description in the text.) (From Morgan, Sturtevant, Muller and Bridges, 1919.)

locus they are inherited as the autosomal genes. They are *partially sex-linked.* In the human there are eight defects of this type, among which are: total color blindness, a night blindness, two skin diseases (*xeroderma pigmentosum* and *epidermolysis bullosa*), retinitis pigmentosa, spastic paraplegia, and one disease producing bleeding from the nose, uterus and other mucosae (see Fig. 15–6).

Neo-XY System of Sex Determination

In addition to the common type of sex determination based on XY chromosomes, in several species a special type of sex determination has been observed and called the *neo-XY system*. As shown in Figure 16–6, this arises from the fracture of the X chromosome followed by fusion of the main fragment to form one autosome. This association constitutes the *neo-X* chromosome. At meiosis the other autosome of the pair (AA′) forms the so-called *neo-Y* chromosome and remains confined to the male sex.

There is evidence that the neo-Y chromosome gradually becomes heterochro-matic. This conversion of euchromatin into heterochromatin is followed by genetic isolation and loss of homology between former partners. This sequence of stages is called the *gradient of hetero-chromatinization*.[10]

Gynandromorphs

A gynandromorph forms a mosaic of male and female sexual characters with chromosomes of both sexes in different parts of the body. It can be thought of as a genetic mosaic in space.

In *Drosophila* a gynandromorph is produced by the elimination of one of the X chromosomes during the development of the egg (Fig. 16–7). The earlier this is produced, the greater are the differences between the female and male parts in the same individual. Figure 16–7 shows an individual in which the right half is male and the other half female. Gynandromorphs are common among silkworms and bees. The occurrence of gynandromorphism in vertebrates is difficult to assess because it depends on the hazardous distinction between gynandromorphism and intersexuality due to hormonal effect.

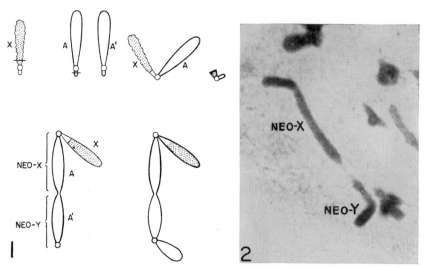

FIGURE 16–6.   1, the mechanism of centric fusion in between a member (A) of a pair of autosomes (AA') and the sex chromosome (X). The small fragment with the centromere at the right is lost. *Below, left,* the neo-X–neo-Y chromosome at metaphase I; *right,* the same element, showing the neo-Y with a submedian centromere. 2, the neo-X–neo-Y chromosome during the first meiotic metaphase in *Aleuas lineatus.* (After F. A. Saez.)

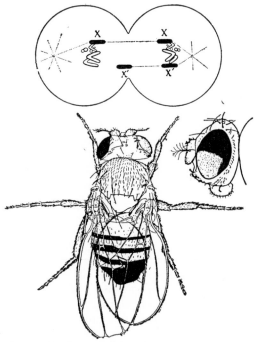

FIGURE 16–7.   Gynandromorph of *Drosophila.* **Above,** first division in the segmentation of the egg, showing the elimination of an X chromosome. **Below,** the resulting gynandromorph individual, the left side of which is female (XX) and the right side male (XO). **Right,** head of a fly. The X chromosome has been eliminated in one of the last somatic mitoses, showing a red color spot in the eye. (After Morgan, Bridges and Sturtevant; taken from Waddington, 1939.)

HUMAN CYTOGENETICS

In recent years the advances in genetics and cytology have been carried to the human, opening new fields with important biologic and medical implications. These advances have resulted from the use of more refined techniques for studying chromosomes, by which the human karyotype in normal and abnormal conditions has been studied in detail. These techniques, mentioned in Chapter 6, include the culture of leukocytes, bone marrow, fibroblasts and other tissues.

The individualized pairs of human chromosomes can be distinguished by their morphologic features, relative size, degree of chromatin concentration (heteropyknosis), presence of secondary constrictions and satellites and other structural characteristics (see Chap. 12).

The Normal Human Karyotype

In 1912, Winiwarter[11, 12] counted 47 chromosomes in the human male (46 autosomes + X) and 48 chromosomes in the human female (46 autosomes + XX). In 1923, Painter[13] found 48 chromosomes with the sexual types XX and XY. From 1923 to 1956 several studies indicated that the normal karyotype contained 48 chromosomes, i.e., 46 autosomes and two sex chromosomes (XX in the female and XY in the male). After that time, with improved culture techniques and the use of hypotonic solutions prior to making smears, it became evident that the actual normal number is 46 (44 autosomes + XY in the male and 44 autosomes + XX in the female).[14-16] (See Figure 16-8.) The 22 pairs of autosomes are numbered in descending order of length and are further classified according to the position of the centromere, e.g., metacentric, submetacentric and acrocentric chromosomes.

In 1960, a number of specialists at a convention in Denver, Colorado, adopted a classification and order of chromosomes that coincided with that proposed by Patau.[17] They classified the 22 pairs of autosomes into seven groups as follows (Fig. 16-9):

Group	Pairs	
I	1–3	(metacentrics)
II	4–5	(submetacentrics)
III	6–12	(submetacentrics)
IV	13–15	(acrocentrics)
V	16–18	(submetacentrics)
VI	19, 20	(metacentrics, approx.)
VII	21, 22	(acrocentrics)

Special characteristics are found in pair 13, which has a prominent satellite on the short arm, and in pairs 14 and 21, which have a small satellite on the short arm. In females, pair 22 has satellites (Fig. 16-9).

Abnormal Human Karyotypes

The study of abnormal human karyotypes began in 1959. Since then numerous types that are related to different diseases or clinical syndromes have been observed. Deviations from the normal karyotype are found in autosomes, sex chromosomes or in both kinds of chromosomes. They generally consist of aneuploidy, such as monosomy or trisomy. Structural aberrations, such as translocations, deficiency, duplication and so forth, and other more complex alterations have also been observed (see Chap. 15).

Various mechanisms are involved in the production of abnormal karyotypes. A frequent one, which may give rise to different types of aneuploidy, is *nondisjunction.*

Mitotic nondisjunction may occur at the mitotic division that precedes the formation of gonial cells or during cell division of the zygote. In the first case the effects are similar to those occurring in meiotic nondisjunction, but in the second case—since the alteration occurs early in embryonic development—a *mosaic* of different cell lines occurs.

The immediate cause of nondisjunction is the lagging of one sister chromatid in anaphase, which, at telophase, remains in one of the cells together with the other sister chromatid (Fig. 16-10). This change gives rise to a cell line that lacks one chromosome or has one chromosome in excess in the pair (monosomy and trisomy).

Meiotic nondisjunction, in which the pair of homologous chromosomes fails to separate during meiosis, may give rise to an aneuploid ovum, which, when fertilized by a normal spermatozoon, results in a zygote with chromosomal abnormality (Fig. 16-11). In some cases fertilization may take place between abnormal gametes from both parents, which produces more complex types of aberrations. Chromosomal aberrations

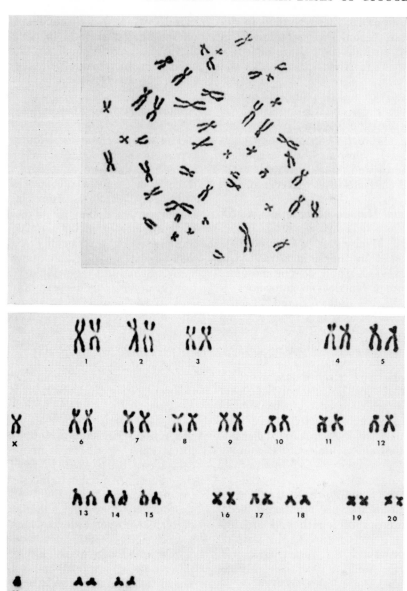

FIGURE 16–8. Human chromosomes from cultured leukocytes. **Above,** karyotype in the normal male. (From U. Mittwoch.) **Below,** idiogram in the normal male. ×1350. (From J. A. F. Roberts.)

can be produced in the autosomes, in the sex chromosomes or in both.

Autosomal Aberrations.
Mongolism

Among the most important autosomal aberrations is *mongolism,* which is characterized by mental retardation and markedly defective development of the central nervous system. Since in identical twins both individuals are affected,

but in fraternal twins only one is affected, mongolism originates from defective gametes. In general, the incidence of mongolism increases greatly with maternal age.

In 1959 it was discovered that the mongoloid has an extra chromosome. Pair 21 is trisomic instead of normal. This aberration probably originates from nondisjunction of pair 21 during meiosis.

The extra chromosome attached to pair 21 in some cases may become at-

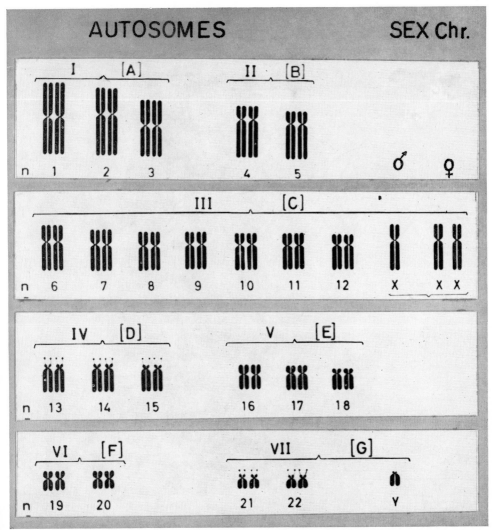

FIGURE 16–9.   Idiogram of human chromosomes according to the classification and nomenclature of the Denver convention held in 1960.

tached to another autosome (translocation). Less frequent trisomes are found in the pair 16–18, and result in the following abnormalities: skull deformation, malformation of the ears, micrognathia and mental retardation. When pair 13–15 is trisomic, the results are numerous malformations of the palate, eye, lips, fingers, etc. Also, mental retardation and anomalies of the interventricular septum are observed. Cultures of the epidermis show 47 chromosomes and a trisomic pair 13.

In the Sturge-Weber syndrome, which is also characterized by mental retardation, chromosome 17 is trisomic. Deficiencies and duplications are found in Marfan's syndrome and in chronic myeloid leukemia.

Aberrations of Sex Chromosomes

Anomalies of the *sex chromosomes* are best known and include the simplest aneuploidy produced by nondisjunction to the more complex aberrations produced by secondary nondisjunction in aberrant karyotypes. Table 16–1 shows some of the most common abnormalities found in sex chromosomes together with the clinical syndromes and presence or absence of sex chromatin.

Double and triple mosaics of sex chro-

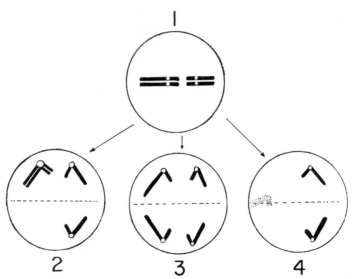

Figure 16–10. Mitotic nondisjunction and chromosome loss. **1,** normal metaphase. **2,** nondisjunction anaphase giving rise to monosomic and trisomic nuclei. **3,** normal anaphase. **4,** a chromosome loss results in two monosomic nuclei.

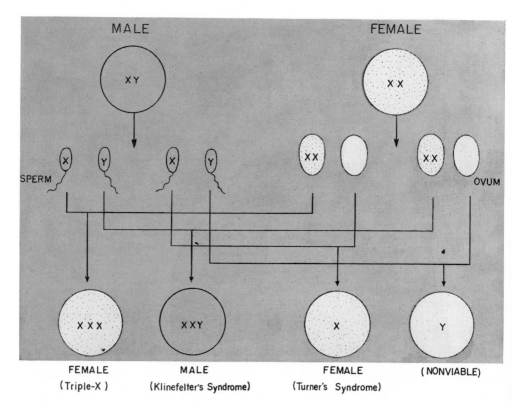

Figure 16–11. Diagram showing nondisjunction in mother gametes. Notice that while male gametes are normal, eggs are abnormal, lacking X or having two X. Fertilization of such eggs gives four possible constitutions, three abnormal and one nonviable. (From U. Mittwoch.)

mosomes produced by alterations during meiosis (nondisjunction or loss of chromosomes) may give a broad variety of combinations in the female as well as in the male (Table 16–2).

Figure 16–11 shows the possible mechanism involved in the production of sex chromosome aberrations. The female gamete is probably more involved than the male gamete in these aberra-

TABLE 16–2.   SEX CHROMOSOME MOSAICS

	CLINICAL SYNDROME	SEX CHROMATIN
Females		
XO/XY	Turner	—
XO/XX	Turner	—
XO/XYY	Turner	—
XO/XXX	Variable	—
Males		
XX/XXY	Klinefelter	+
XY/XXY	Klinefelter	+
XXXY/XXXXY	Small gonads and immature sexual characteristics, mental disorder	3+
XO/XY	Hermaphrodite	—

tions, since for each ovum millions of spermatozoa are produced. The most important aberrations of this type are:

Turner's Syndrome (Gonadal Dysgenesis). In Turner's syndrome the person has a female appearance, a short stature, a webbed neck and generally infantile internal sexual organs. The ovary does not develop and the uterus and oviduct are small. Menstruation does not occur and secondary sexual characteristics do not develop. The karyotype shows 45 chromosomes (44 autosomes + X), and there is no sex chromatin (Fig. 16–12).

Klinefelter's Syndrome. A person who has this condition appears to be a nearly normal male, but has small testes and usually gynecomastia (a tendency for formation of female-like breasts). Spermatogenesis does not occur. Most of these persons have a positive sex chromatin and 47 chromosomes (44 autosomes + XXY). The testes show abundant Leydig cells and atrophic tubules, which contain only Sertoli cells.

Males with Multiple Corpuscles of Sex Chromatin. These males are mentally deficient, and have small testes and two Barr corpuscles. The karyotype contains 48 chromosomes (44 autosomes + XXXY). In one case of similar somatic alterations and 49 chromosomes, 44 autosomes + XXXXY were found.

Super- or Metafemales. These individuals have normal sex organs but do not menstruate. Intelligence is slightly impaired, but there are no somatic anomalies. In the oral mucosa two sex chromatin bodies are found. The chromosome number is 47 (44 autosomes + XXX). In two cases with mental retardation three Barr corpuscles and 44 autosomes + XXXX were found.

Mixed Chromosomal Aberrations and Sex Mosaics. Klinefelter's syndrome can be found combined with mongolism.

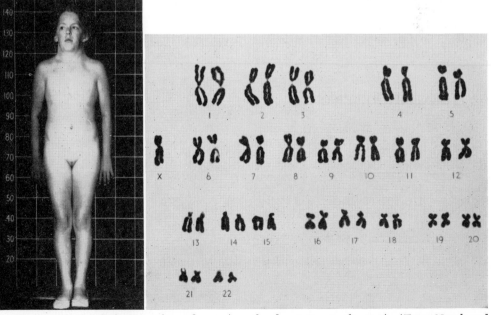

FIGURE 16–12.   **Left,** Turner's syndrome (see the description in the text). (From Novak and Seegar.) **Right,** idiogram of Turner's syndrome, showing 44 + XO chromosomes. (From P. E. Polani, in J. L. Hamerton, ed., 1963.)

Such a person has 48 chromosomes: 45 autosomes (including a trisomic pair 21) + XXY. Since sex mosaics with the constitutions YO/XXY, YO/XY/XXY and YO/XY have not been found, it seems possible that the combination YO is not viable.

In contrast to *Drosophila,* in man the presence of a Y chromosome suffices to produce male organs, even in the presence of several X chromosomes. The absence of Y, as in Turner's syndrome, produces a female but with gonadal disgenesis.

In *Drosophila melanogaster* the Y chromosome does not carry sex genes. Therefore YO flies are normal males and XXY are females. In this species the sex depends on the ratio between autosomes and sex chromosomes. In females the ratio is $X/A = 1$; in males it is $X/2A = 0.5$. In an intersexual individual the ratio is $2X/3A = 0.67$. The ratio $3X/2A = 1.5$ is a metafemale and $X/3A$ is a metamale.

In man an XXY is a sterile male (Klinefelter's syndrome) and an XO is a sterile female (Turner's syndrome) (Table 16–1), but in the mouse XO is a fertile female. The so-called superfemales or metafemales in the human have $3X/2A$ and $4X/2A$. The X chromosome is strongly feminizing in mammals, including the human, and probably has genes that are indispensable for development. So far, an individual who has no X chromosome has not been found.

GENERAL REFERENCES

Ford, C. E., Jones, L. W., Miller, O. J., Mittwoch, U., Penrose, L. S., Ridler, M., and Shapiro, A. (1959) The chromosomes in a patient showing both mongolism and the Klinefelter syndrome. *Lancet,* p. 709, April 9.

Gallien, L. (1959) Sex determination. In: *The cell,* Vol. 1, p. 399. (Brachet, J., and Mirsky, A. E., eds.) Academic Press, New York.

Gardner, L. I. (1961) *Molecular genetics and human disease.* Charles C Thomas, Springfield, Ill.

Gowen, J. W. (1961) Genetic and cytologic foundations for sex. In: *Sex and internal secretions.* (Young, W. C., ed.) 3rd Ed. The Williams & Wilkins Co., Baltimore.

Hamerton, J. L. (1963) *Chromosomes in medicine.* Medical Advisory Committee of the National Spastics Society in association with Wm. Heinemann. Little Club Clinics in Developmental Medicine, No. 5.

Jacobs, P. A., Baikie, A. G., Court Brown, W. M., and Strong, J. A. (1959) The somatic chromosomes in mongolism. *Lancet,* p. 710, April 4.

Kerr, W. E. (1963) Genética da determinacao do sexo. In: *Genetica.* (Pavan, C., and Da Cunha, B., eds.) University of São Paulo, Brazil.

Kihlman, B. A., Nichols, W. W., and Levan, A. (1963) The effect of deoxyadenosine and cytosine arabinoside on the chromosomes of human leukocytes in vitro. *Hereditas, 50:* 139.

Lejeune, J., Gautier, M., and Turpin, R. (1959) Les chromosomes humaines en culture. *C. R. Acad. Sci., 248:*602.

Luning, K. G. (1963) Studies of irradiated mouse populations. II. Dominant effects on productivity in the 4th–6th generation. *Hereditas, 50:*361.

Melander, Y. (1962) Chromosomal behavior during the origin of sex chromatin in the rabbit. *Hereditas, 48:*646.

Melander, Y., and Hansen-Melander, E. (1962) Sex chromosome allocycly in the male rabbit. *Hereditas, 48:*662.

Moore, K. L., Graham, M. A., and Barr, M. L. (1953) The detection of chromosomal sex in hermaphrodites from skin biopsy. *Surg. Gynec. Obstet., 96:*641.

Ohno, S. (1964) The sex chromatin: Its origin and nature. *Symposium on mammalian tissue culture and cytology.* University of São Paulo, Brazil.

Saez, F. A., Drets, M. E., and Brum, N. (1962) The chromosomes of the mulita (*Dasypus hybridus Desmarest*). A mammalian edentata of South America. *Symposium of mammalian tissue culture and cytology.* São Paulo, Brazil.

Valencia, J. I. (1963) Genética y gónadas. *Pren. Méd. Argent., 50:*1303.

Wennstrom, J., and Chapelle, A. (1963) Elongation as the possible mechanism of origin of large human chromosomes. An autoradiographic study. *Hereditas, 50:*345.

Westergaard, M. (1958) The mechanism of sex determination in dioecious flowering plants. *Advanc. Genet., 9.*

White, M. J. D. (1960) Are there mammal species with XO males and if not, why not? *Amer. Nat., 94:*301.

CITED REFERENCES

1. McClung, C. E. (1902) *Biol. Bull., 3:*43.
2. White, M. J. D. (1954) *Animal cytology and evolution.* Cambridge University Press.
3. White, M. J. D. (1961) *The chromosomes.* 5th Ed. Methuen & Co., London.
4. Barr, M. L. (1955) *Anat. Rec., 121:*387.

5. Barr, M. L., and Bertram, E. G. (1949) *Nature* (London), *163*:676.
6. Barr, M. L., Bertram, E. G., and Lindsay, H. A. (1950) *Anat. Rec., 107*:283.
7. Ohno, S., Kaplan, W. D., and Kinosita, R. (1959) *Exp. Cell Res., 18*:415.
8. Ohno, S., and Cattanach, B. M. (1962) *Cytogenetics, 1*:129.
9. Ohno, S., Kaplan, W. D., and Kinosita, R. (1956) *Exp. Cell Res., 11*:520.
10. Saez, F. A. (1963) *Port. Acta Biol. A, 7*:111.
11. Winiwarter, H. (1912) *Arch. Biol., 5*:27.
12. Winiwarter, H., and Oguma, K. (1930) *Arch. Biol., 40*:541.
13. Painter, T. S. (1923) *J. Exp. Zool., 37*:291.
14. Tjio, J., and Levan, A. (1956) *Hereditas, 42*:1.
15. Tjio, J. M., and Puck, T. T. (1958) *J. Exp. Med., 108*:259.
16. Ford, C. E., Hamerton, J. L., and Mole, R. H. (1958) *J. Cell. Comp. Physiol., 52*:235.
17. Patau, K. (1960) *Amer. J. Hum. Genet., 12*:250.

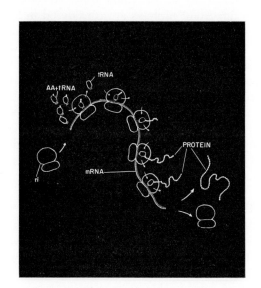

PART SIX

MOLECULAR

BASES

OF

CYTOGENETICS

In the following chapters the most recent advances in nuclear physiology from chemical and molecular viewpoints are discussed. Studies in the field of molecular genetics are attempts to explain hereditary phenomena as resulting from specific chemical components that are localized or formed in the chromosomes. These studies have provided conclusive evidence that genetic information is initially dictated by the disposition of bases in deoxyribonucleic acid (DNA) and that this information is then transcribed in the different molecules of ribonucleic acid (RNA) (i.e., messenger RNA, transfer RNA and ribosomal RNA), and finally translated phenotypically into the different specific proteins and enzymes. Knowledge of the Watson-Crick model of DNA presented in Chapter 3 and the exact disposition of the base pairs in its molecule is requisite to this chapter.

The duplication of the DNA molecule can now be studied not only with methods of ultracentrifugation, but also at the cellular level in bacteria and higher cells. It will be shown that in higher cells DNA duplication takes place in a specific period of interphase called the synthetic or S-phase, which is preceded and followed by two gaps called G_1 and G_2 in which DNA synthesis does not take place.

Using tritiated thymidine, which specifically labels synthesized DNA, it is possible to observe by radioautography the duplication of the single chromosome which, in this case, is made of a single, circular DNA molecule. This result is extraordinarily simple, and, amazingly, during DNA duplication, the unwinding of the two polynucleotide chains and the corresponding rupture of hydrogen bonds must occur at 10,000 revolutions per minute. In higher cells, DNA synthesis is not produced simultaneously in all chromosomes and in some cases even certain parts duplicate early or late in the S-phase.

The cycle of the different RNA molecules, all of which are synthesized in the nucleus, as well as that of certain important proteins are considered in light of the microfibrillar structure of the chromosome shown by electron microscopy.

The nucleolus is interpreted as the site of accumulation of ribosomal RNA and proteins that are to be utilized in the cytoplasm for protein synthesis.

Chapter 18 on molecular genetics proper treats in a simplified way the molecular bases of the action of genes in the control of biochemical reactions. The one-gene–one-enzyme concept is presented in relation to the genetic code and the mechanism of protein synthesis. New concepts, such as muton, recon, codon, cistron, complon, operon, replicon, and transcripton, are introduced as genetic units of different complexity and function. Finally the mechanisms of enzymatic induction and repression that regulate the expression of genes are discussed briefly.

Thus Chapters 17 and 18, on the physiology of the nucleus, illustrate the continuous interrelationships that exist between the nucleus and the cytoplasm, as well as the way that they are integrated in the regulation of cellular activity. Chapter 19 applies these concepts to the study of the differentiation, growth, renewal and aging of cells. The study of the life cycle of the different cell types that constitute a higher organism is of considerable theoretical and practical interest, and is related to that of embryonic and cancerous cells. These concepts are valuable as an introduction to the study of the different tissues, each of which has a different cycle of division and differentiation.

CHAPTER 17

CHEMICAL

AND

MACROMOLECULAR

ORGANIZATION

OF THE

CHROMOSOMES

AND NUCLEOLUS.

DNA DUPLICATION

After having studied the nucleus and chromosomes with the classical cytologic and cytogenetic methods, we can now discuss the physiology of the nucleus from the point of view of its chemical and macromolecular organization. This is the introductory chapter of an elementary discussion of the field now known as *molecular genetics*, in which control and regulation of cellular functions are investigated. (An extended treatment of these concepts can be found in specialized textbooks and articles.) In these new fields—nuclear physiology and molecular genetics—the principal investigations concern the role of nucleic acids in genetic functions. Some of the early evidence comes from the work on *bacterial transformation*, by which a strain of bacteria is changed genetically by the action of extracts of another strain.[1] Avery and his collaborators[2] demonstrated in 1944 that the substance responsible for this transformation is deoxyribonucleic acid (DNA).

DNA can now be considered as the main genetic constituent of cells, carrying in a coded form information from cell to cell and from organism to organism. Ribonucleic acid (RNA) can also carry genetic information, replacing DNA in some plant viruses or serving as an intermediary in the transcription of genetic information, which is finally expressed in the formation of the different specific proteins of the cells. Figure 17–1 introduces these concepts. According to the diagram, genetic information is transferred in three steps: (1) *duplication* of the DNA molecule and thus of its genetic information by a template mechanism; (2) *transcription* of this information into different RNA molecules; and (3) *translation* of this information into the different protein components (including the enzymes) of a cell. The problem of DNA duplication in relation to the chemical and macromolecular organization of the nucleus is discussed in this chapter. (Steps 2 and 3 will be analyzed in Chapter 18.)

These fundamental problems are usually studied in bacteria and viruses, in which these mechanisms follow a similar although much simpler pattern than those of higher plant and animal cells. For this reason, reference is made in this and other chapters to hypotheses and discoveries based upon studies of these simple microorganisms.

CYTOCHEMICAL STUDY OF THE NUCLEUS

The study of the chemical organization of the nucleus has followed two main lines. The first, which is essentially biochemical, consists of isolating a large enough number of nuclei to permit analysis by biochemical methods. The second approach, which is essential-

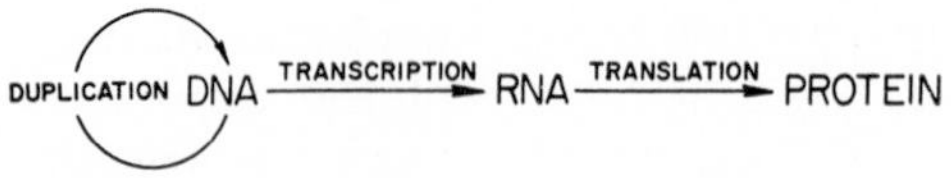

DUPLICATION DNA ——TRANSCRIPTION——▶ RNA ——TRANSLATION——▶ PROTEIN

FIGURE 17–1.   Diagram of the flow of information from the genome (DNA). (See the description in the text.) (From S. Spiegelman.)

ly cytologic and cytochemical, uses the cytophotometric, cytochemical and autoradiographic methods described in Chapter 6. The results of both approaches are complementary and should be integrated within the discussion of the chemical organization and physiology of the nucleus.

This fundamental field was started in 1869 by the studies of Miescher, who analyzed the chemical composition of pus cells, spermatozoa, hemolyzed nucleated red cells of birds, etc., and demonstrated that nucleic acids are one of the main components of the nucleus. In Chapter 6 we described the methods of cell fractionation, and Figure 17–2 illustrates with the electron microscope the degree of purity that can now be achieved in the isolation of nuclei and nucleoli of liver cells. These methods are of considerable importance not only for the chemical analysis of the nucleus, but also for the study of growth and related problems. The number of nuclei isolated from a growing tissue (for example, in an embryo or tissue culture) can be measured easily in a chamber similar to that used for blood counts. The amount of a chemical substance per nucleus (viz. DNA) can then be determined.

The main result of these biochemical studies is the finding that the nucleus has a complex chemical organization in which the *nucleoproteins* are the most important components. Nucleoproteins result from the combination of nucleic acids and proteins, and in certain cells constitute the major part of the solid material (96 per cent of the trout spermatozoon, and almost 100 per cent in certain erythrocyte nuclei.[3]

The protein part of the nucleus is complex and has several components. Of these, the best known are two strongly basic and simple proteins: the protamines and the histones. In addition to these there are several acidic proteins, the so-called nonhistone proteins, which

may constitute the most abundant component of the interphase nucleus.

Early studies indicated that DNA was the only nucleic acid present in the nucleus. Later, RNA was demonstrated both in the nucleolus and as a component of chromatin.

To summarize, the chemical composition of the nucleus includes:

deoxyribonucleic acid (DNA).
ribonucleic acid (RNA).
basic proteins: protamine or histone.
nonhistone acid proteins (residual protein, chromosomin and enzymes).
other nuclear components.

Deoxyribonucleic Acid (DNA)

The chemical and stereochemical structure of DNA was studied in Chapter 3 in the discussion of the Watson-Crick molecular model of DNA. The high degree of polymerization of DNA and the sequence of the bases gives rise to an enormous number of structurally different DNA molecules, and thus an extraordinary amount of genetic information can be recorded. Remember that since the other two components of DNA (phosphoric acid and deoxyribose) are constant, the information is coded only by the sequence of the four bases (adenine, guanine, cytosine and thymine). Thus the *genetic "dictionary" has only a four-unit "language."*

From the physicochemical viewpoint, DNA is a fibrous material that has a molecular weight that may run into several millions. As will be shown later, in bacteriophages and bacteria, DNA may be a single molecule many microns or even millimeters in length (Fig. 17–8).

Isolated DNA forms fibers that have a strong negative birefringence and dichroism in ultraviolet light.[4] Under the electron microscope, DNA appears as long, unbranched microfibrils with a diameter of 20 Å. Figure 17–3 shows the entire DNA molecule contained in the head of a bacteriophage. DNA fibers can be oriented so as to give coherent x-ray diffraction patterns from which the atomic organization of the two polynu- cleotide strands can be determined. Along the molecule each nucleotide oc- cupies 3.4 Å, and a complete turn of the two strands of DNA in the Watson- Crick model is made of 10 such intervals, i.e., 34 Å (Fig. 3–15).

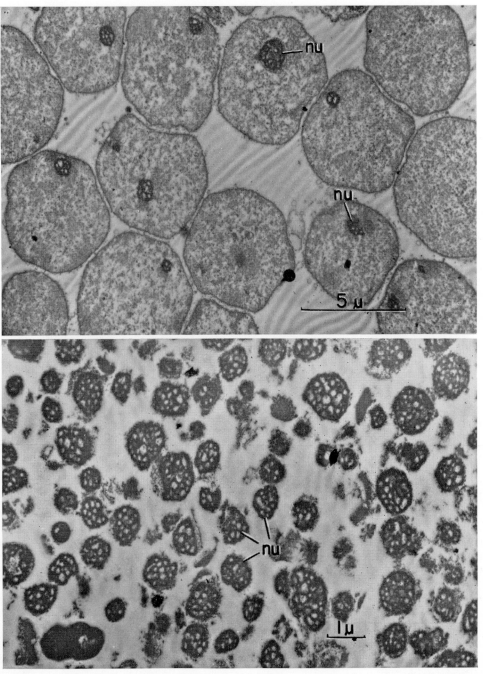

FIGURE 17–2.   Above, isolated nuclei (*nu*) from guinea pig liver observed under the electron microscope. ×3000. Below, isolated nucleoli (*nu*) from guinea pig liver. ×16,000. (Courtesy of R. Maggio, P. Siekevitz and G. E. Palade.)

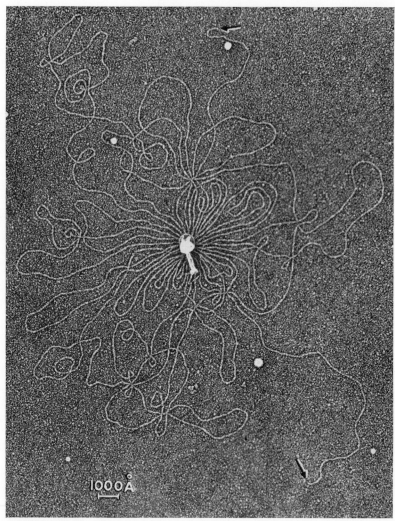

Figure 17–3. Electron micrograph of a bacteriophage (*in the center*) that has undergone an osmotic shock. The DNA molecule that was contained in the "head" of the bacteriophage is now dispersed. Arrows indicate the extremes of the single, unbranched DNA molecule. Preparation shadowcast with platinum. ×76,000. (Courtesy of A. K. Kleinschmidt.)

Ribonucleic Acid (RNA)

In recent years the study of nuclear and cytoplasmic RNA has become of primary importance because of its role in the transcription of genetic information contained in the DNA molecule (Fig. 17–1) and in protein synthesis. Three main types of RNA are now recognized and all of them apparently originate from the nucleus (see Table 17–1).

Ribosomal RNA (rRNA) was studied

TABLE 17–1. TYPES OF RNA IN CELLS*

	rRNA	mRNA	tRNA
Molecular weight	1,200,000 to 500,000	$\sim$ 150,000 to $\sim$ 2,000,000	24,000
Sedimentation constant	23 and 16 S	< 30 S	4 S
Percentage of total RNA	75 to 85%	5 to 10%	5 to 10%

* *r*, ribosomal; *m*, messenger; *t*, transfer (soluble) RNA.

in Chapter 9. It is contained mainly in the cytoplasmic ribosomes, but, as will be shown later, is formed in the nucleus and probably accumulates in the nucleolus. As shown in Table 17–1, it is present in two sizes (23 and 16 S) in the 60 S and 40 S ribosomal subunits (see Chap. 9). This is the largest RNA fraction of the cell and may constitute 75 to 85 per cent of the total RNA.

Messenger RNA (mRNA) is recognized among other properties by its rapid turnover. When a cell is given radioisotope precursors of RNA (e.g., cytidine, uridine) for a few minutes, the first RNA formed is mRNA. This is a highly dispersed fraction formed by molecules of different sizes, which, starting in the few hundred thousands, may reach a molecular weight of 2,000,000. The base composition is complementary to that of DNA. The name "messenger" comes from its function of transcribing the information from the DNA molecule and carrying it to be translated into protein (Fig. 17–1). The longer mRNA is, the longer the message it carries and the protein it can form. In Chapter 9 it was stated that for proteins of molecular weight 35,000 and 70,000, mRNAs of 300,000 and 600,000, respectively, were needed.

Transfer (soluble) RNA (tRNA) is of low molecular weight (24,000) and formed by about 67 nucleotides, which contain some methylated bases (e.g., methylcytosine). The name "soluble" is self-explanatory and that of "transfer" (also called adapter by some persons) is based on the role of this type of RNA in protein synthesis. Each tRNA molecule carries one amino acid to the site of protein synthesis (i.e., the ribosomes), as will be shown in Chapter 18. Since there are 20 different amino acids, there should be one kind of tRNA for each one.

Basic Proteins: Protamine and Histone

Protamines are simple, have a molecular weight of only about 2000 and are rich in arginine. They are found mainly in fish spermatozoa. *Histones* may have a molecular weight of 12,000 and are found in all nuclei of higher plants and animals. They contain mainly lysine and arginine. In erythrocytes of birds histones constitute 40 per cent of the dry weight of the nuclear material.

In general, the content of basic proteins is proportional to that of DNA, with which they are intimately related. The association between DNA and histone can be demonstrated cytochemically by the use of the Feulgen technique for DNA and the fast green technique for histones on the same material.[5] The chemical and physical properties of protamines and histones overlap, and there are transitions between them.

The combination of histones and protamines with DNA is ionic; salt linkages are made with the phosphate groups of the nucleic acid.[6]

Although several histone fractions of different composition have been isolated, histone is relatively constant in cells of the same type. Several investigators have expressed the concept that histone, by its close association with DNA at certain stages of the cell cycle, may regulate genetic activity (see below).[7, 8]

Nonhistone Acid Proteins

The nonhistone proteins are acidic and contain tryptophan, but there is limited information about them.[9] A so-called *residual protein* has been isolated from chromosomal threads after extraction of the nucleohistones by salt solutions. This insoluble fraction retains some of the morphologic aspects of chromosomes but it now contains more RNA than DNA. A large part of the nonhistone proteins of the nucleus is lost in the process of isolation and purification.[10] It has been found that in an aqueous medium 35 percent of the protein diffuses out of the nucleus. To prevent the loss of nuclear protein and the diffusion of soluble cytoplasmic components into the nucleus, the importance of isolating the nuclei in a nonpolar medium has been emphasized.[11, 12]

The probable composition of the interphase nucleus of mammalian liver is as follows: DNA, 9 per cent; RNA, 1 per cent; histone, 11 per cent; residual protein, 14 per cent; other nonhistone proteins, 65 per cent.[13]

The considerable amount of nonhistone protein present in a metabolically active cell contrasts markedly with the composition of the spermatozoon, which is much less active. In the spermatozoon the nucleus is almost entirely made up of nucleoprotamine or nucleohistone, indicating that the other proteins have left the nucleus. The volume of the nucleus is proportional to the protein content; for example, in neurons, the large nucleus contains 20 times more protein than the sperm head. Interesting studies are now being carried out on the turnover of nuclear proteins (see below).

Nuclear Enzymes

The cell nucleus lacks essential respiratory enzymes, such as cytochrome oxidase and succinic dehydrogenase. On the other hand, some glycolytic enzymes, such as aldolase, enolase and 3-phosphoglyceraldehyde dehydrogenase have been found in the nucleus. These findings suggest that the cell nucleus has a predominantly anaerobic metabolism, using glycolysis as the main source of energy. However, it has been found that isolated nuclei can synthesize ATP by an aerobic process accompanied by the uptake of oxygen.[14]

The most important nuclear enzymes are those involved in the metabolism of nucleic acids. Thus *DNA polymerase* can synthesize DNA using a primer (i.e., a short chain of DNA) and the triphosphates of the four deoxyribonucleotides.[15] RNA-polymerase can form specific or mRNA from the four ribonucleotide triphosphates using DNA as template.[16-18]

Some enzymes related to nucleoside metabolism are found in high concentration (e.g., adenosine diaminase, nucleoside phosphorylase and guanase).

Some special enzymes appear to be concentrated in certain nuclei but absent in others (e.g., catalase and arginase).[19, 20] These and other findings may be an indication that some nuclei are biochemically differentiated.

Other Nuclear Components

The *lipid* content of the nucleus has been investigated in isolated nuclei.[21, 22] Direct staining of the nuclei with lipid reagents, such as Sudan black, is generally negative. Sudanophilic lipids have been unmasked from lipoprotein complexes by the action of carboxylic acids, such as acetic, citric, formic or oxalic acid.[23]

The distribution of *minerals* can be studied by microincineration. The spodogram (ash picture) shows that the ash of the nucleus is more concentrated than that of the cytoplasm. (The ash is composed of phosphorus, potassium, sodium and, particularly, calcium and magnesium.) Apparently, minerals are found in greater proportion in chromatin. Calcium and magnesium have been localized in the nucleus by means of the emission electron microscope.

Calcium may play a significant structural role.[24] By the action of the enzyme deoxyribonuclease in the nucleus, 80 per cent of the DNA can be depolymerized, and calcium is liberated in stoichiometric amounts. This calcium has not been separated by other means, and it has been suggested that it is combined with DNA.

DNA Content of the Nucleus

If a set of chromosomes of a species contains all the genetic information within the DNA molecule, it can be postulated that this component should be constant in all diploid cells of the individual.

TABLE 17–2.   DNA CONTENT OF VARIOUS NUCLEI OF THE FOWL (expressed as mg $\times$ 10^{-9} per nucleus)

	ERYTHROCYTE	LIVER	KIDNEY	SPLEEN	HEART	PANCREAS	SPERM
Mirsky and Ris, 1949	2.34	2.39	—	—	—	—	1.26
Davidson et al., 1950	2.49	2.56	2.20	2.54	2.45	2.61	

The use of biochemical methods to isolate nuclei has given the first information on the *DNA constancy* of the cell.[25, 26] As shown in Table 17-2, diploid cells of different tissues of the fowl contain approximately 2.5×10^{-9} mg of DNA, whereas the haploid sperm has half that amount. Analyses of DNA content in several different mammalian species have shown that the variations in DNA content, although definite, are small; in the species of birds and fishes studied, there is more variation.[27, 28]

Among invertebrates, the lowest DNA values are found in the most primitive animals, such as sponges and coelenterates. In fishes, the DNA content per cell tends to remain constant within the different species of a family. The values of DNA in lung fishes, amphibians, reptiles and birds suggest that during evolution the DNA content has declined.[29] This is particularly striking in amphibians, in which DNA varies from 168×10^{-9} mg in *Amphiuma* to 7.33×10^{-9} in the toad.

Whereas biochemical data are statistical expressions of a large number of nuclei found in a tissue, which may differ in size, cell type or physiologic state, by the cytophotometric method (see Chap. 6), individual nuclei can be analyzed. Cytophotometry has made possible the investigation of a number of problems, and has led to interesting correlations. One of these is the relationship of DNA content to the changing cellular volume. This is particularly well illustrated by the spermatid nucleus, which shrinks continuously during spermiogenesis until maturity of the spermatozoon, but the haploid DNA content of the cell remains constant.[30]

Measurements in a large variety of cell types of a species have shown that the DNA content is practically constant.[31] This is certainly related to the number of chromosome sets (n), which is 2n in most somatic cells. This is not always the case. In the liver there are large nuclei which contain two and four times as much DNA as the diploid nuclei (Table 17-3). This duplication or quadruplication of DNA content obviously corresponds to polyploidy (see Chap. 15 and Table 17-3).[31, 32]

TABLE 17-3.   DNA Content and Chromosome Complement[*]

CELLS	MEAN DNA-FEULGEN CONTENT	PRESUMED CHROMOSOME SET
Spermatid	1.68	haploid (n)
Liver	3.16	diploid (2n)
Liver	6.30	tetraploid (4n)
Liver	12.80	octoploid (8n)

[*] From Pollister, Swift and Alfert.[30]

In the case of the liver cell, it can be observed that the increase in DNA content is correlated with the age of the animal. In young rats most nuclei are diploid, but in adult rats tetraploids and octoploids predominate. The reduplication of DNA in this case is mainly by endomitosis.

Another interesting example is found in the study of spermatogenesis (Table 17-4). Previous to meiosis (see Chap. 14), there are two classes of cells (spermatogonia) having different DNA content (2n and 4n). The early primary spermatocyte is 4n (tetraploid). After the first maturation division, the secondary spermatocyte contains half the DNA content, corresponding to 2n (diploid). Finally the second maturation division results in four spermatids; these have the DNA of only one chromosomal set (haploid cell) (Table 17-4). Similar results have been observed in oögenesis during maturation of the oöcytes.[33]

All these findings are consistent with the general conclusion that DNA content is directly connected with the chromosomes and thus with the genic (hereditary) content of the cell. Although small functional variations in

TABLE 17-4.   DNA Content at Different Stages in Spermatogenesis[*]

CELL TYPE		DNA-FEULGEN
Premeiotic	Class 2n	3.28 ± 0.07
	Class 4n	5.96 ± 0.07
Primary spermatocyte		6.28 ± 0.07
Secondary spermatocyte		3.35 ± 0.04
Spermatid		1.68 ± 0.02

[*] From Pollister, Swift and Alfert.[30]

DNA content have been observed in a variety of tissues, this does not disprove the concept of a DNA constancy related to a constant genic constitution.

DNA Duplication and the Life Cycle of the Cell

Even more interesting than the study of the DNA content of the interphase nucleus is that of the changes in DNA during the life cycle of the cell. Among other aims, investigators are trying to determine the exact timing of DNA reduplication during the life cycle of the cell. This can be investigated by cytophotometric analysis of individual nuclei during cell division or during other phases of the cell cycle. However, in this case another cytochemical technique, *autoradiography* (Chap. 6), which is based on the use of labeled compounds, has been of great importance and has permitted investigators to follow the incorporation of DNA precursors and to analyze the mechanism of DNA duplication.

As shown in Figure 17–4, the diploid

DNA content (2c) duplicates (4c) and then is reduced to the haploid conten (1c) by the two meiotic divisions. The the DNA content increases again prio to the mitotic division and formation o pollen grains. The time at which P^{32} i incorporated is also indicated.

If we study cells that are dividing con tinuously with a certain rate (see Tabl 17–5), it is possible to find that the pe riod of DNA synthesis (S) does not oc cupy the entire interphase (intermitoti period), but only a certain part of it. A shown in Figure 17–5, after separatio of the daughter cells at telophase, ther is first a certain period or gap (G_1) i which the DNA content is kept constan (at 2n). Suddenly, some unknown caus determines the beginning of DNA bio synthesis and this is completed along th S-period. When duplication is complete and before the next division there is second gap or blank period (G_2) i which the DNA content is kept constan at 4n (Fig. 17–5).

A typical experiment consists of ex posing cultured cells for 10 minutes t H^3-thymidine (a nucleoside that enter

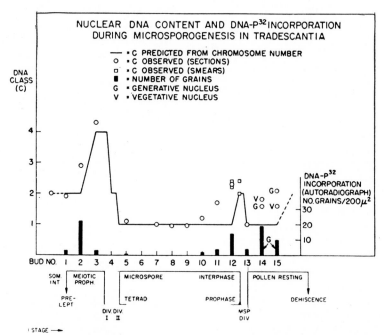

FIGURE 17–4. Diagram indicating the DNA content in different phases of meiosis in the micro sporogenesis of *Tradescantia* measured by cytophotometry. At the same time incorporation of P^{32} i DNA is measured by the number of grains shown in the autoradiograph. In the lower part of th figure the different stages are indicated. The tetraploid cell (4c) after mitotic prophase undergoe a double division, which gives haploid microspores. Note that fixation of P^{32} occurs only in period of reduplication. (From Moses and Taylor, 1955.)

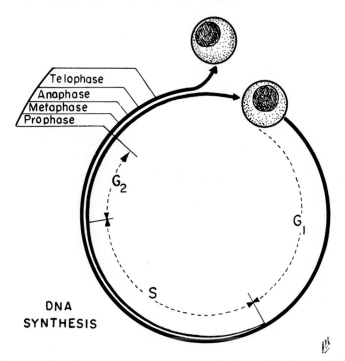

Figure 17–5. Diagram showing the DNA cycle in a dividing cell. After mitosis a diploid cell containing 2c DNA enters the G_1-period during which there is no DNA synthesis. This takes place during the S-period and, as shown by the increasing thickness of the line, is produced all along the period (see the text). During the G_2-period the cell contains 4c DNA. During mitosis the two daughter cells, each having 2c DNA, separate.

the DNA molecule only). Then the culture is washed thoroughly and samples are fixed for autoradiographic studies at one- to two-hour intervals for 24 hours. In this experiment the first mitotic chromosomes that become labeled appear after four hours. This indicates that the G_2-period is about that long. The proportion of labeled divisions in this particular case permit one to calculate an S-period of eight and a half hours and a G_1-period of four hours.[34]

DNA synthesis is sometimes tacitly equated with chromosomal duplication (see reference 35). In fact, during this entire growth-duplication cycle the chromosome participates in at least three different activities: (a) self-duplication,

Table 17–5. Mitotic and Intermitotic Times in Various Cell Types*

CELL	TIME IN MINUTES	
	INTERMITOTIC	MITOTIC
Vicia faba root meristem (19° C.)	1300	150
	1400	186
Pisum sativum (peas) root meristem (20° C.)	1350	177
Chick fibroblasts (38° C.)	660–720	23
Mouse spleen cultures	480–1080	43–90
Rat jejunum (in animal)	2000	28
Jensen's sarcoma (in animal)	720	27
Rat corneal epithelium (in animal)	14,000	70
Chrotophaga (grasshopper) neuroblast	27	181
Drosophila egg	2.9	6.2
Psammechinus (sea urchin) embryo, two to four cell stage (16° C.)	14	28

* From Mazia, 1961.

(b) transfer of genetic information to the rest of the cell, and (c) the coiling-uncoiling cycle associated with the separation of the duplicated chromosomes or daughter chromatids (see Chap. 13 and Fig. 13–6). Functions *a* and *b* (duplication and information transfer) probably occur at the moment when chromosomes are most dispersed (uncoiled).

Molecular Mechanism of DNA Duplication

The molecular mechanism of DNA duplication postulated by Watson and Crick in 1953[36] involves the unwinding of the two polynucleotide strands (Fig. 17–6) and the copy of two complementary new strands by a template mechanism (Fig. 17–6); each strand acts as a mold for the newly synthesized molecule. Each DNA molecule replicates only once in the course of a cycle, and the immediate stimulus to DNA synthesis could be the unwinding of the double helix of the DNA molecule at a certain point. The mechanism could be set into action simply by the separation of

the two DNA strands; the nucleotides fall into phase and are linked by the action of the enzyme DNA-polymerase (Fig. 17–6).

This mechanism also suggests that in DNA replication half of the DNA is conserved at the molecular level (i.e., only half of the original DNA is synthesized; half is retained) (Fig. 17–7). This has been verified by several demonstrations. For example, *Escherichia coli* bacteria are grown in a medium containing N^{15} and are then passed to another medium containing N^{14}. The DNA is then isolated and analyzed with the ultracentrifuge at different intervals, and the following results are obtained:[37] After the first division cycle there is only one DNA peak corresponding to the hybrid molecule (i.e., one strand is labeled with N^{14}, the other with N^{15}). At the second generation (as in Mendel's law, see Chap. 15), two peaks of DNA appear, one in which the two DNA strands contain N^{14} and the other still corresponding to hybrid molecules (Fig. 17–7). Recently the semiconservative nature of DNA replication has been well demonstrated both at the molecular and cellu-

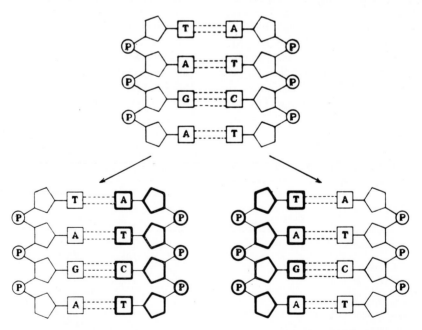

Figure 17–6. Diagram showing the mechanism of DNA duplication. **Above,** the two standard parent molecules which separate by opening of hydrogen bonds. **Below,** the two new strands that have been synthesized and that have a complementary base composition with respect to the parent DNA strands are indicated by bold outlines. (From Kornberg, A., 1962: Ciba Lecture in Microbial Biochemistry, John Wiley & Sons, New York.)

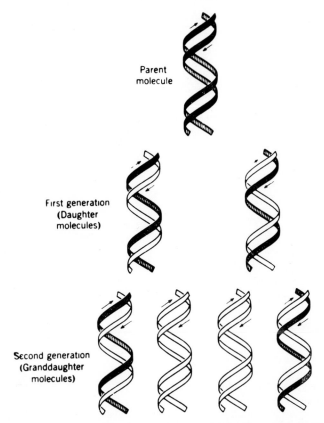

Parent
molecule

First generation
(Daughter
molecules)

Second generation
(Granddaughter
molecules)

FIGURE 17-7. Diagram interpreting the experiment of Messelson and Stahl described in the text. **Above,** parent DNA molecule with both strands labeled with N^{15}. **Middle,** first generation shows the daughter molecules (in white) synthesized in a medium containing N^{14}. (Note that the DNA molecules are hybrids of N^{15} and N^{14} DNA strands.) **Below,** at the second generation (granddaughter molecules) two molecules are hybrids and two are not.

lar levels,[38] also in the bacterium *E. coli.* In contrast to higher cells, in *E. coli* DNA synthesis is almost continuous and DNA duplication takes place every 20 to 30 minutes. After treatment with H^3-thymidine and using a special autoradiographic technique, it has been possible to demonstrate that: (a) the entire chromosome is made of a single, two-stranded, circular DNA molecule, 1 to 1.5 mm long (Fig. 17–8); (b) the duplication starts at a fixed point of the circle and proceeds from that point in one direction (Fig. 17–9); and (c) at the site of duplication the two parent strands separate and the daughter molecules lie alongside. During the entire duplication period the daughter molecules remain attached to each other and to the far end of the parent molecule. Finally the two circular DNA molecules separate and a new cycle begins (Fig. 17–9).

Since the entire process of DNA duplication in *E. coli* takes place in 20 to 30 minutes, the molecule should unwind at the extraordinary rate of 10,000 revolutions per minute!

The semiconservative replication of DNA had previously been demonstrated in higher cells.[39] For example, plant cells were grown in a medium containing radioactive thymidine and then passed to a normal medium. It was found that the nuclei that were in the synthetic phase incorporated the tracer (Fig. 17–10A), whereas those that had completed DNA duplication previously were not tagged (Fig. 17–10B). To stop mitosis, colchicine was used. This drug prevents cell division, but allows chromosome duplication, thus permitting sequestration of the new chromosomes (polyploidy) of the first and second generations within the original cell (Figs. 17–10C, D).

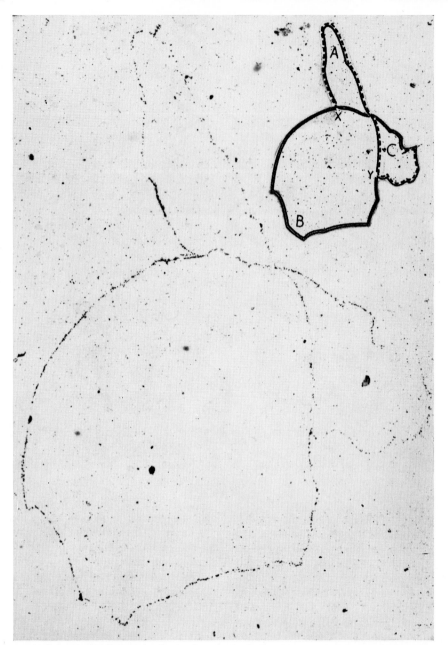

FIGURE 17–8. Autoradiograph observed with the light microscope of a chromosome of *E. coli* K 12 *Hfr* labeled with tritiated thymidine for two generations. The bacterium has been gently lysed and the entire duplicating chromosome is observed. Notice the circular disposition of the single DNA molecule that constitutes the chromosome and that is being duplicated. This figure corresponds to the last diagram of Figure 17–9. It can be demonstrated that in segment *B* of the molecule there are about twice the number of grains/μ than in segment *A*. (See the inset and Fig. 17–9.) (Courtesy of J. Cairns.)

These results are interpreted in Figure 17–11. It was concluded that prior to replication each chromosome is doubled and behaves as if it consisted of two units of DNA along its length. At the time of duplication (S), two new units (now labeled) are built alongside. Therefore each chromatid includes an original nonlabeled strand and a new labeled one. When the second duplication occurs, in the absence of labeled precursor, the labeled and unlabeled

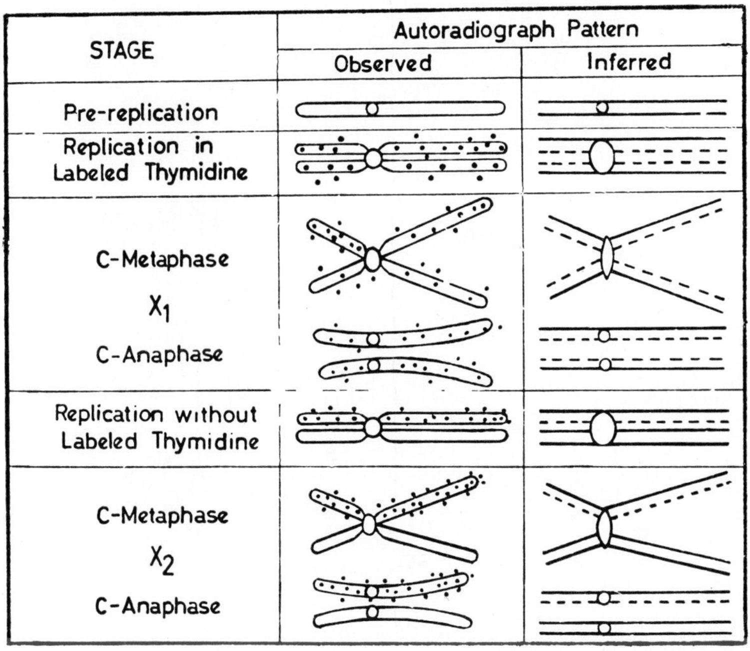

STAGE	Autoradiograph Pattern	
	Observed	Inferred
Pre-replication		
Replication in Labeled Thymidine		
C-Metaphase X_1 C-Anaphase		
Replication without Labeled Thymidine		
C-Metaphase X_2 C-Anaphase		

FIGURE 17–11. Diagram interpreting the experiment of Taylor shown in Figure 17–10. In the inferred autoradiograph pattern, the broken lines correspond to the tritiated DNA strands. (From K. R. Lewis and B. John, 1963, *Chromosome markers*, J. & A. Churchill, London.)

ably a range of fibers of different sizes. In lampbrush chromosomes, fibrils of 500 Å have been observed, each consisting of two subunits of 200 Å, and the basic structure of chromosomes has been considered by some authors to be of this order of magnitude.[45]

In high resolution electron micrographs of meiotic chromosomes of the locust a filamentous macromolecular component has been described as the basic unit of structure.[46] The thinnest microfibrils observed have been of the order of 30 Å, and it has been postulated that they represent single nucleoprotein molecules. These microfibrils vary between 30 and 170 Å with a tendency to increase in size from early prophase to metaphase of the spermatocyte.

In the same tissue, during the development of the spermatid, the macromolecular structure of the nuclear material changes considerably. In early stages microfibrils of about 50 Å are uniformly distributed and randomly oriented within the nucleus. Later, from the region of the so-called ring centriole orientation of the microfibrils (Fig. 17–15) starts and progresses along with the

thickening of the microfibrils. In later stages, the microfibrils are parallel to the axis of the spermatid and about 150 Å thick. Also, in the bands of polytene chromosomes there are tightly packed microfibrils with a mean diameter of 130 Å.

The most general conclusion that can be made from these and other electron microscope observations is that, although the chromosomal structure undergoes complex cyclic rearrangements during mitosis, meiosis and spermiogenesis, in all stages the basic structural unit is a filamentous nucleoprotein macromolecule.

In the DNA duplication of a chromosome a model based on a single double helix extending along the entire chromosome seems to be difficult in view of the long distances which should unwind and fold during this process and also of the above mentioned data of an intrachromosomal asynchrony in DNA replication. To explain this difficulty, models provided with intermediary linkers have been proposed.[44, 47] In one of them, shown in Figure 17–16, several linkers, some of which could be open at certain

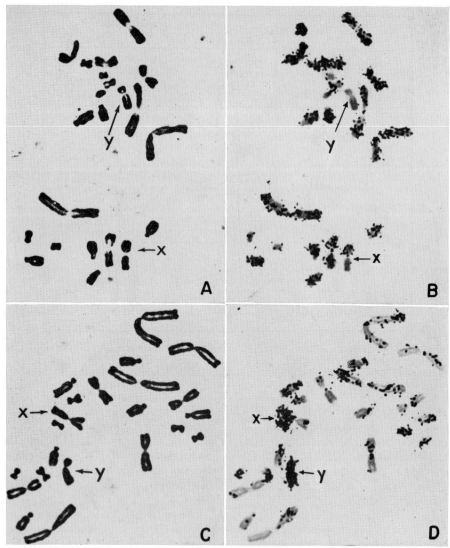

FIGURE 17–12. Autoradiographs with tritiated thymidine of cultured cells from the Chinese hamster. **A** and **B,** chromosomal complex showing the early replicating chromosomes (first half of the S-period). Notice that Y and the long arm of X have not duplicated. **C** and **D,** chromosomes replicating late (second half of the S-period). Notice that Y and the long arm of X replicate at this time. (Courtesy of T. C. Hsu.)

operator sites for the control and order of the sequence of nucleotides, are indicated.

In addition to linkers joining the ends of the phosphate groups of the polynucleotide chains, other linkers would be polymers, probably polypeptides, involved in stabilizing the structure during replication. Each H-linker would represent half a chromatid and a new set of H-linkers would be formed at prophase when each chromatid is doubled. There is little or no morphologic evidence for the existence of linkers. However, the structure that will now be described in meiotic chromosomes could be interpreted within this concept.

Synaptinemal Complex or Meiotic Chromosomal Cores

In meiotic chromosomes of many species it is possible to observe an axial differentiation that appears as dense lines that are twisted about each other and flank an indistinct central line.[48, 49] Each

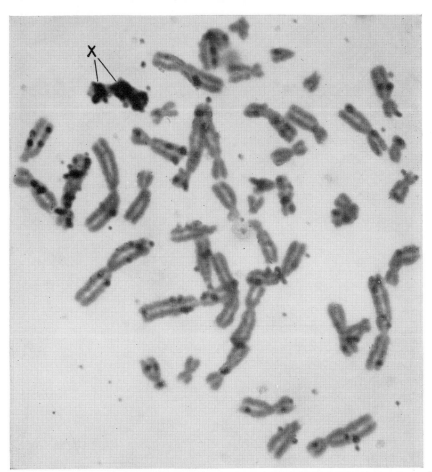

X

FIGURE 17–13.   Human karyotype from a normal female showing one late replicating X chromosome. This is the chromosome that gives the sex chromatin body (see Chap. 16). (Courtesy of C. W. Gilbert, L. G. Lajtha and J. Rowley.)

lateral element of the synaptinemal complex is a part of a single chromosome of a homologous pair. If the pairing is not complete, the lateral parts of the axial complex may be seen to diverge. All around the axial complex a fibrillar material is found, which constitutes the main bulk of the chromosome. This synaptinemal structure probably represents an axial differentiation, which appears during meiotic prophase and is probably involved in the linear pairing and interchange of homologous chromatids during crossing over.

Nuclear RNA in the Life Cycle of the Cell

The studies of chromosomal DNA using labeled precursors have demon-strated that DNA segregation among the chromatids is semiconservative (see above). These studies have also shown that DNA labeling is permanent, remaining for several cell generations. Also, the *DNA molecule is stable,* as it should be to perform its primary function of storing genetic information. We will now see that chromosomal RNA and proteins behave differently.

When an RNA radioactive precursor is incorporated into a cell, the precursor is consistently found first in the nucleus and then in the cytoplasm. This has been interpreted as a demonstration that RNA synthesis takes place in the nucleus and then this molecule is transferred to cytoplasm. For example, if the protozoa *Tetrahymena* is incubated in H^3-cytidine for 1.5 to 12 minutes, all the labeled RNA appears in the nucleus (Fig.

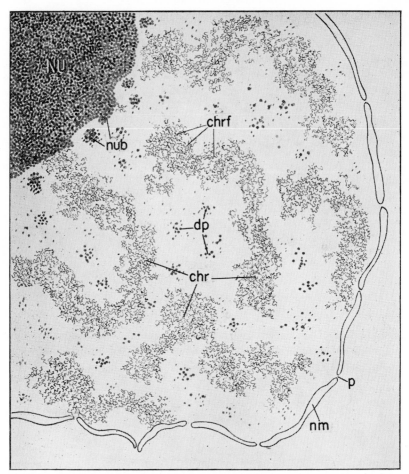

FIGURE 17–14.   Diagram of the ultrastructure of the nucleus, showing the nucleolus, the daughter nucleoli and the dense particles situated in the nucleoplasm. The chromosomes are built of microfibrils. *chr,* chromosomes; *chrf,* chromosome fibrils; *dp,* dense particles of nucleolar origin; *nm,* nuclear membrane with pores; *Nu,* nucleolus; *nub,* nucleolar bodies; *p,* pore. (From De Robertis, 1956.)

17-17A). After 35 minutes both the nucleus and cytoplasm contain about the same amount (Fig. 17–17B). Finally if the cell is given H³-cytidine for a few minutes and then incubated in a nonradioactive medium (a chase) for a longer period, the cytoplasm is labeled, but the nucleus is not (Fig. 17–17C). In the same organism an anucleated fragment does not incorporate the cytidine, whereas a nucleated fragment does.[50] These and other results clearly show that cytoplasmic RNA is of nuclear origin.

Similar studies carried on in dividing cells show that whereas at interphase the nucleus concentrates more labeled RNA than the cytoplasm, at late prophase almost all nuclear RNA (including the nucleolar RNA) is lost to the cytoplasm and the metaphase chromosomes have little RNA.[41] These and other studies demonstrate that the turnover of chromosomal RNA is so high that labeled RNA is practically lost after the first cell generation.

Proteins in the Life Cycle of the Cell

The study of the protein cycle with labeled amino acids (e.g., H³-leucine, H³-histidine, H³-lysine and H³-proline), also shows that the metaphase chromosomes contain small amounts of protein, whereas shortly before proteins are released into the cytoplasm in large quantity.

The histones, as well as other nuclear proteins, are synthesized continuously

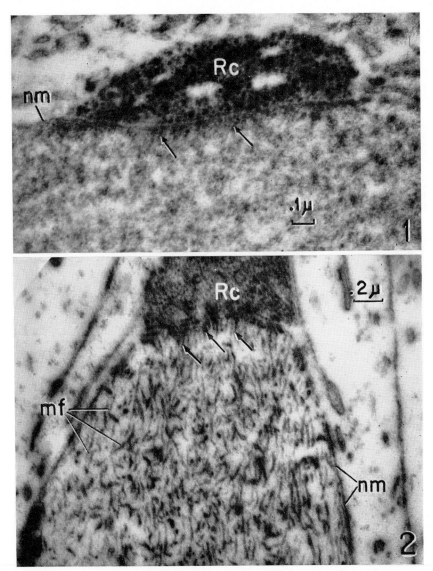

FIGURE 17–15. *1*, electron micrograph of one region of the nucleus of a young spermatid from the locust. *Rc*, region near the ring centriole; *nm*, nuclear membrane. The nucleus has a fibrillar, dispersed, fine structure. The microfibrils (indicated by arrows) are oriented in the vicinity of the ring centriole. ×60,000. *2*, later stage in the development of the spermatid. The microfibrils (*mf*) are thicker and oriented in the axis of the spermatid head. ×40,000. (From De Robertis, 1955.)

during interphase. An important occurrence at late telophase is the return of some labeled proteins from the cytoplasm into the nucleus. In nuclei of amebae, two types of nuclear proteins have been demonstrated.[51] One of them migrates continuously between the nucleus and the cytoplasm and the other is apparently nonmigratory and remains in the nucleus. During mitosis both these nucleus-specific proteins are released into the cytoplasm and return to the nucleus when division is over. The

site of synthesis of both groups of nuclear proteins seems to be at least in part the cytoplasm. These findings are of great interest in dealing with the general problem of the nucleocytoplasmic relationship and the nature of the agents that may bring messages from the nucleus to the cytoplasm and vice versa (see Chap. 18).

In certain human diseases, such as disseminated lupus, auto-antibodies are produced against certain components of a person's own cells. If these antibodies

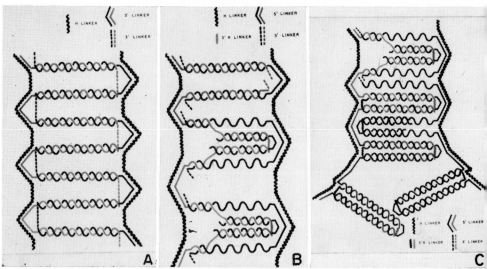

FIGURE 17–16. Several types of linkers proposed to explain DNA duplication in a chromosom of a higher cell. **A,** 3' and 5' linkers between phosphate groups in DNA. H linkers probably of pro tein nature. **B,** beginning of DNA duplication by the breakage of 3' linkers. **C,** duplication is com pleted at some segments and the two chromatids start to separate. (From J. H. Taylor.[44])

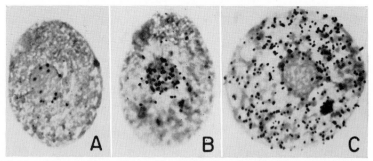

FIGURE 17–17. **A,** autoradiograph of a *Tetrahymena* incubated in H³-cytidine for 1.5 to 12 min utes. Notice that all labeled RNA is restricted to the nucleus. **B,** the same after 35 minutes. RNA begins to enter the cytoplasm. **C,** the same incubated for 12 minutes in H³-cytidine and then fo 88 minutes in a nonradioactive medium. Notice that while the nucleus has lost all labeled RNA, the cytoplasm is heavily labeled. (Courtesy of D. M. Prescott.)

are labeled with a fluorescent dye they may serve to localize the intracellular antigen (see Chap. 6). With this method an antibody for deoxyribonucleoprotein that "stains" the chromosome is obtained. In addition there are two other antigens in the nucleus, one belonging to a soluble protein and the other to a component of the nucleolus. During cell division these two antigens enter the cytoplasm and return to the nucleus during telophase.[52]

Also related to the cycle of the nuclear proteins are the observations that during spermiogenesis (in the grasshopper) histone is replaced by a protamine-like histone richer in arginine and more basic. Studies with labeled amino acids (H³-arginine) have shown that this basic protein is synthesized in the cyto plasm using the ribosomal machinery (see Chap. 9) and then migrates into the nucleus and combines with DNA. The histone-DNA association is appar ently nonspecific, but, as proposed by some investigators, it may control the phenotypic expression of genes.[53]

THE NUCLEOLUS. STRUCTURE AND FUNCTION

Since its discovery by Fontana in 1781 the nucleolus has been the subject of much discussion.[54] In the living cell, nu cleoli are highly refringent bodies (Fig.

2–2). This is related to a large concentration of solid material, which can be measured by interference microscopy (see Chap. 5) and may constitute 40 to 85 per cent of dry mass.[55] Under the light microscope the nucleolus generally appears to be structurally homogeneous, although small corpuscles or vacuoles are sometimes observed.

Studies of living cells with phase microscopy and time-lapse cinematography show that vacuoles formed inside the nucleolus may move toward the periphery, forming clear areas. The nucleolus is frequently attached to the nuclear membrane, and some of these vacuoles and material of the dense part of the nucleolus seem to pass into the cytoplasm.[56]

After fixation, the nucleolus is Feulgen-negative, which is indicative of the lack of deoxyribonucleic acid. The nucleolus stains with pyronine and other stains and absorbs ultraviolet light at 2600 Å (see Fig. 12–14). Treatment with ribonuclease shows that this basophilic stain and ultraviolet absorption depend on the presence of RNA.

The nucleolus may be surrounded by a ring of Feulgen-positive chromatin (Fig. 6–7), which represents heterochromatic regions of one or more chromosomes associated with the nucleolus. In large nucleoli some Feulgen-positive granules can be observed in portions of the chromosomes that penetrate the nucleolus. Also, in plant roots treated with ribonuclease, the nucleolus is no longer basophilic, which indicates that this enzyme may penetrate into the living cell (Fig. 17–18).

In some living cells, particularly after silver staining, a filamentous structure called a *nucleoloneme* has been described (Fig. 17–19).[57] Electron microscopy has revealed the existence of a definite submicroscopic organization within the nucleolus. In some cells an irregularly fibrillar structure similar to the nucleoloneme can be observed,[58, 59] but in others the structure appears to be compact and relatively homogeneous (see Fig. 17–14). In these cases it appears as a dense mass made up of closely aggregated round particles of about 150 Å.

The macromolecular particulate component is constant in all nucleoli having a compact or a more or less open or vacuolar structure. Sometimes surrounding the main mass of the nucleolus are smaller bodies having the same struc-

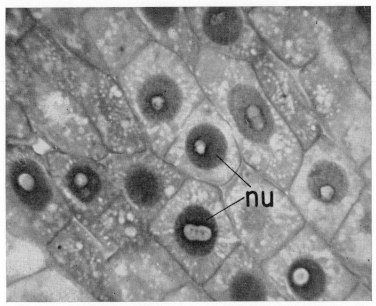

FIGURE 17–18.   Cells of the root of *Allium cepa* treated in vivo with ribonuclease for three hours. Note disappearance of the nucleolar basophilia; that of chromatin is maintained. *nu,* nucleus. Staining with toluidine blue at pH 4.6. (Courtesy of M. Perez del Cerro and A. Solari.)

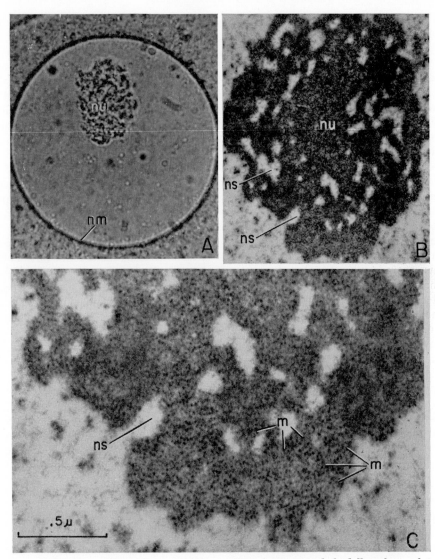

FIGURE 17–19. A, nucleus of an immature oöcyte of *Heteropachyloidellus* observed in vivo. Note the structure of the nucleolus (*nu*). *nm*, nuclear membrane. (Courtesy of C. Estable and J. R. Sotelo, 1951.) B, nucleolus of a young neuron. *ns*, nucleoplasm. C, same, at higher magnification. Note the macromolecular structure (*m*) of the nucleolus. ×70,000.

ture; these can be interpreted as nucleolar material derived by fragmentation of the outer portion of the nucleolus. Also, in the nuclear sap, in between the chromosomes, are dense particles with dimensions similar to those of the nucleolus.[46] These dense particles may be nuclear ribosomes (see Chap. 9), but whether they are identical to cytoplasmic ribosomes is not certain. In a study with different staining methods and enzymatic treatment, two types of granular structures have been recognized: one corresponds in size to ribosomes (150 to 250 Å) and the other is formed by smaller grains of 50 to 100 Å. Both types are attacked by ribonuclease.[60] In nucleoli that have an open structure (nucleoloneme), the less dense parts should be interpreted as nucleoplasm that pervades throughout the nucleolar mass.

In addition to the observation of the passage of nucleolar material into the cytoplasm in living cells, are similar observations in fixed cells examined with the light microscope and, more recently, the electron microscope. This phenomenon is particularly evident in am-

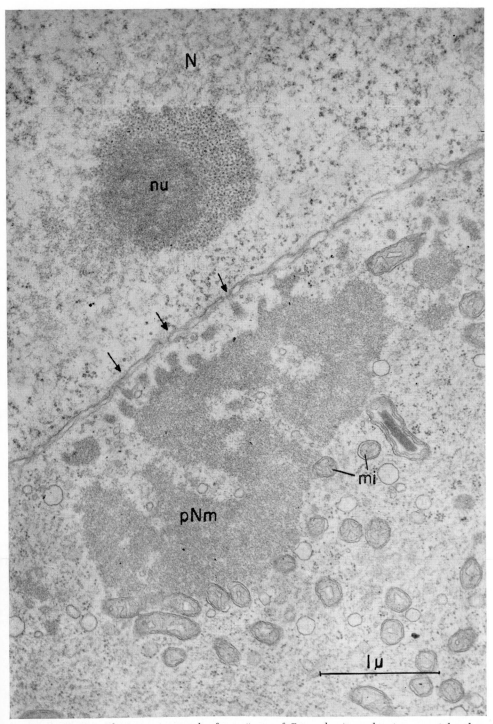

Figure 17–20. Electron micrograph of an oöcyte of *Rana clamitans* showing a peripheral nucleolus (*nu*) and material entering the cytoplasm through nuclear pores (*arrows*). *mi*, mitochondria; *N*, nucleus; *pNm*, passing nuclear material. (Courtesy of O. L. Miller.)

phibian oöcytes, in which nearly 1000 nucleoli are at the periphery of the nucleus after the pachytene stage. A material of probably nucleolar origin may be seen to pass through the pores of the nuclear envelope and to penetrate the cytoplasm (Fig. 17–20).[61]

During mitosis, nucleoli undergo cyclic

changes. Early studies revealed that: (1) nucleoli seem to disappear at the beginning of cell division (prophase), while the chromosomes stain more deeply, and (2) nucleoli reappear at the end of division (telophase). The relation between the nucleolar and chromosomal cycles has been clarified in part by the demonstration in plant cells that nucleoli are intimately related to certain chromosomes: Each nucleolus lies in contact with a chromosome; the point of union is a special region called the organizer of the nucleolus (see Chap. 13). At telophase the nucleolar substance may originate from the fusion of small "prenucleolar bodies," which are collected in relationship with the nucleolar organizer.[62]

With silver staining, a material believed to be a protein or lipoprotein[63, 64] has been seen to shift from the prophase nucleus into the cytoplasm and then to return to the daughter chromosomes at telophase.[65] Other experiments with H[3]-valine also suggest that some protein of the nucleolus may be carried over to the reforming nucleolus after division.[66]

Isolation of the Nucleolus

The nucleolus has been isolated in oöcytes of marine animals[67, 68] and also in liver cells (Fig. 17–2). Isolated nucleoli were found to contain 3 to 5 per cent RNA. This is lower than cytochemical observations have indicated, but there may be a certain loss during extraction.[69–71] The protein content of the nucleolus is high, and according to some investigators the main protein components are phosphoproteins.[67] No histones have been found in isolated nucleoli, and the fast green staining test is negative. There is cytochemical evidence for the existence of a high concentration of orthophosphate in the nucleolus, which may serve as a precursor of the RNA phosphorus.[72]

Little is known about the enzyme content of the nucleolus. By isolation techniques, acid phosphatase, nucleoside phosphorylase and DPN-synthesizing enzymes have been found. These last two enzymes are important because they act in nucleotide and coenzyme synthesis.[68] RNA methylase, an enzyme that transfers methyl groups on the RNA bases, has been localized in the nucleolus of certain cells.[73]

Nucleolar Functions and Sites of Origin of rRNA, mRNA and tRNA

A possible relationship of the nucleolus with protein synthesis was first suggested by Caspersson in 1939.[4] However, early cytologic observations had already demonstrated large nucleoli in rapidly growing tissues, including tumor cells (Fig. 2–2), growing oöcytes (Fig. 17–20), plant meristems (Fig. 17–18), protein-secreting cells, early erythroblasts and so forth. When protein synthesis slows down (e.g., in full-grown eggs, more mature erythroblasts or glands secreting nonprotein substances) nucleoli are small or inconspicuous. All these observations indicate that the nucleolus probably has an important role in protein synthesis. Furthermore, a large part of nuclear RNA is localized in the nucleolus, which indicates that the nucleolus may intervene in RNA metabolism.

By isolation experiments it has been found that the RNA of the different parts of the cell, including the nucleolus, has a distinct base composition, and that the nucleolar RNA behaves differently from the cytoplasmic RNA[74, 75] or from the chromosomal RNA with regard to the uptake of different labeled nucleosides and to the action of inhibitors of RNA synthesis, such as *actinomycin*.[76, 77] In fact, low concentrations of actinomycin suppress the incorporation of nucleosides into the nucleolar and ribosomal (cytoplasmic) RNA, whereas chromosomal RNA is not affected.

There is other evidence that the major portion of ribosomal (cytoplasmic) RNA is derived from nucleolar RNA. In addition, extranucleolar (chromosomal) RNA appears to be synthesized independently of nucleolar RNA.

In a study of cultured fibroblasts exposed to H[3]-cytidine for short periods and then to unlabeled cytidine (i.e., a chase),[77, 78] both normal and actino-

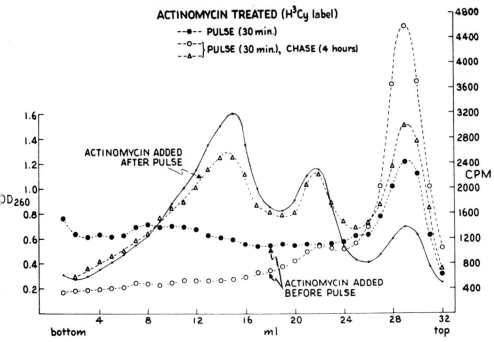

FIGURE 17–21. In the experiment represented in this diagram, cultured fibroblasts were treated with a pulse of H³-cytidine for 30 minutes and others with a similar pulse followed by a chase in cold cytidine for four hours. In other experiments actinomycin was added before or after the pulse. The RNA was extracted and ultracentrifuged on a sucrose gradient. The optical density at 2600 Å (OD 260) and the counts per minute (CPM) of the different fractions are indicated. Three peaks are observed, two of which (26 S and 16 S) at the left are characteristic of ribosomal RNA and one at 4 S (left) corresponds to transfer or soluble RNA. The 26 S and 16 S peaks disappear when actinomycin, which inhibits rRNA synthesis, is added before the pulse. (From R. P. Perry.)

mycin-treated cells were compared. In both the normal and treated cells the RNA was extracted and ultracentrifuged for sedimentation analysis (Fig. 17–21). After four hours of chase incubation the bulk of RNA was distributed in three peaks, of which two (26 S and 16 S) were characteristic of ribosomal RNA and one (4 S) was characteristic of transfer (soluble) RNA (see Table 17–1). When only a short pulse of 30 minutes is used, RNA is polydisperse; this as well as the two ribosomal peaks disappear when actinomycin is added before the pulse. These and other results are interpreted in Figure 17–22.

The following are the postulated sites of origin of the different types of RNA[79–81] (see Table 17–1): mRNA would be synthesized in the chromosomes at each special genic locus of the genome; tRNA would also be synthesized in the chromosomes; and rRNA would also be derived from the chromosomes (DNA), but in a special region related to the nucleolus (nucleolar organizer), in which numerous copies of rRNA would be formed.

According to this theory rRNA represents a homogeneous transcription of a restricted region of DNA which is accumulated in the nucleolus prior to its penetration into the cytoplasm. The nucleolar organizer of chromosomes would be the site or locus primarily devoted to the large-scale production of cytoplasmic ribosomes. Thus the presence of large nucleoli in all rapidly synthesizing cells would be explained on the bases of the large number of copies of rRNA needed for protein synthesis. This explanation is apparently contradicted by experiments in a chironomid (Smittia spp.) in which the nucleolar organizer shows practically no labeling as compared to the nucleolus (Fig. 17–23). Similarly, in amphibian oöcytes there are numerous nucleoli which lack an organizer but can synthesize RNA autonomously.[82]

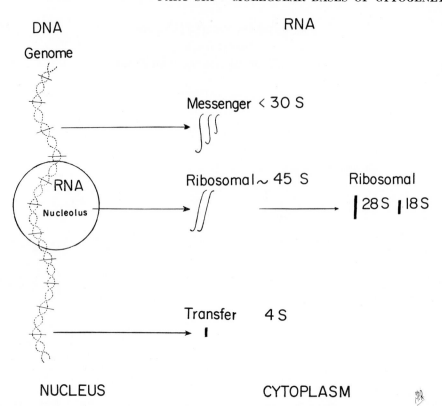

FIGURE 17–22. Diagram indicating the possible sites of origin of the different RNA molecules according to the experiments shown in Figure 17–21. (See the description in the text.) (Modified from R. P. Perry.)

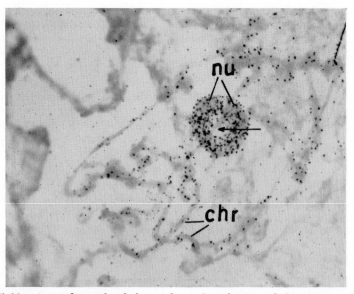

FIGURE 17–23. Autoradiograph of the nucleus of a chironomid (*Smittia* spp.) labeled with H³-cytidine. Notice that the main labeling is in the nucleolus (*nu*) while the giant chromosomes (*chr*) show lesser labeling. The arrow indicates the region of the nucleolar organizer that shows no labeling. (Courtesy of J. Tandler and J. Sirlin.)

NUCLEOCYTOPLASMIC INTER-RELATIONS

Throughout this and previous chapters numerous examples of nucleocytoplasmic interrelations have been given. The nucleus and the cytoplasm are interdependent; one cannot survive without the other. Whereas the cytoplasm provides most of the energy for the cell through oxidative phosphorylation (mitochondria) and anaerobic glycolysis and has part of the "machinery" for protein synthesis (ribosomes), the nucleus provides templates for specific synthesis (mRNA) and also the other important RNA molecules (rRNA and tRNA). Any discussion of nucleocytoplasmic interrelations must consider (a) the mechanisms by which the genes contained in the chromosome exert their control on the metabolic processes of the cytoplasm, and (b) the mechanisms by which the cytoplasm influences gene activity. (This is discussed further in the following chapter.)

This problem was first considered in the last century by Balbiani in the so-called merotomy experiments (Gr. *meros* part) in which protozoa were enucleated and studied. Such fragments can carry out most cellular activities; e.g., they can react to stimuli and ingest food (amebae), form a cellulose membrane, carry on photosynthesis (plant cells), move cilia (ciliated cells), undergo cytoplasmic streaming and so forth. However, in general they survive only a short time and are incapable of growth and reproduction.

Within 5 to 10 minutes after being enucleated by micromanipulation, an ameba loses its surface tension and becomes spheroid and has numerous blunt pseudopodia. Its movements are slowed down and it can no longer digest foods. In this state an ameba may survive for about 20 days. If within three days a nucleus is successfully implanted, the ameba becomes extended, and starts to move normally and to digest foods. Finally, it may even divide and eventually produce a mass culture.[83] This "reactivation" produced by the implanted nucleus may take place in a few seconds or minutes. When a nucleus is transferred from one ameba to another of the same species (a homotransfer), activation of the cytoplasm, division and mass culture may occur readily. When a nucleus of another species is implanted (a heterotransfer), the cytoplasm is activated, but cell division occurs less readily.[84] Detailed analyses of cultured enucleate human cell fragments have been made.[85]

Nuclear Control in Acetabularia

The unicellular marine alga *Acetabularia* is a unique system for the study of nucleocytoplasmic relationships. The only nucleus of this giant cell is located in the basal or rhizoid end and can be easily amputated. In this case survival may be prolonged for months. During part of this time the enucleate cell can carry on synthetic and morphogenetic activities, which indicates that either the cytoplasm is autonomous or it stores a large pool of nuclear products. Protein synthesis in enucleate cells is essentially normal during the first week, but then declines and almost ceases by the third week. In contrast, photosynthesis and respiration are not affected for several months.

The synthesis of individual enzymes (e.g., phosphorylase and phosphatase) diminishes at different times, which indicates that the nuclear products may be specific for each protein. One can thus assume that in the cytoplasm there would be smaller or larger pools of different mRNA, which have come from the nucleus.[86, 87]

Nucleocytoplasmic Interrelations in Cells with Polytene and Lampbrush Chromosomes

In Chapter 13 we studied the special giant polytene chromosomes and mentioned the formation of "puffs" and Balbiani rings at certain stages of development of the larvae. This phenomenon can now be interpreted in light of nucleocytoplasmic interrelations. It is now generally accepted that the "puffs" represent genes in the active process of synthesis.[88] Two main groups of substances are produced at the "puffs": RNA and higher proteins.[79, 89, 90] DNA

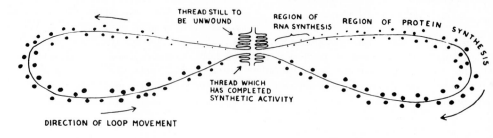

THREAD STILL TO BE UNWOUND

REGION OF RNA SYNTHESIS   REGION OF PROTEIN SYNTHESIS

THREAD WHICH HAS COMPLETED SYNTHETIC ACTIVITY

DIRECTION OF LOOP MOVEMENT

FIGURE 17–24.   Diagram of a loop of a lampbrush chromosome. Based on labeling with RN. precursors (H[3]-uridine), it is postulated that first RNA synthesis and then protein synthesis tak place along the loop. (Courtesy of J. G. Gall and H. G. Callan.)

and histone in general remain unchanged.

With H[3]-cytidine in short pulses the puffs and nucleoli are labeled almost exclusively.[79, 80] A study of the base composition of RNA from different cell components has shown that (a) chromosomal RNA differs from nucleolar or cytoplasmic RNA and (b) RNA from different chromosomes and different "puffs" differ among themselves.[91] These and other results seem to indicate that the substance synthesized at the "puffs" is mainly mRNA. The genetic message carried by these different mRNAs would be related to the special secretory activity of the salivary glands at the particular moment of "puffing."

Interesting studies of the mechanism by which the cytoplasm may control the phases of puffing in the larva of Diptera are being carried out. One of the main factors seems to be the hormone *ecdysone* secreted by the prothoracic gland, which induces molting in insects. After this hormone is injected in young larvae, some special puffs may appear in less than one hour. Also, the duration of puffing depends on the level of the hormone.[92, 93]

Some antibiotics that interfere with RNA metabolism (e.g., actinomycin) inhibit the formation of "puffs," whereas those that inhibit protein synthesis (e.g., puromycin) are ineffective. (In Chapter 18 we will study the regulator-operator genetic system of bacteria, which may elucidate the hormonal control of puffing.)

Cytochemical studies of lampbrush chromosomes have revealed considerable similarities with the polyten chromosomes and the phenomenon o puffing. Also in this case, RNA precursors (e.g., H[3]-uridine) are taken b some of the loops starting at the thir end and progressing in a few days to ward the thick end (Fig. 17–24). Thi RNA material is inhibited by actinomy cin and appears to be mRNA. Protei synthesis also takes place near the loop When the synthetic activity of the loo ceases, the RNA material is given of and the loop collapses.[94]

Nuclear Differentiation

Another important phenomenon re garding nucleocytoplasmic interrelation is that of the changes in somatic nucle in the course of embryonic differentia tion. In essence, a nucleus isolated from an amphibian blastula can promote nor mal development when transplanter into an enucleate amphibian egg;[95, 9] whereas a nucleus from an older em bryo no longer has this capacity. Thi ability of the nucleus to promote nor mal development diminishes progres sively in the course of differentiation For example, 4 per cent of nuclei iso lated at the neurula stage can produc normal embryos. These findings indicat that the nucleus, probably under the in fluence of the cytoplasm, undergoes certain change that restricts its ful genetic capacity.

GENERAL REFERENCES

Allfrey, V. G., Mirsky, A. E., and Stern, H. (1955) The chemistry of the cell nucleus. *Advanc. Enzymol.*, 16:411.

Anfinsen, C. B. (1959) *The chemical basis of evolution.* John Wiley & Sons, New York.

Benzer, S. (1962) The fine structure of the gene. *Scient. Amer.*, 206:70.

Bloch, D. P. (1958) Changes in the deoxyribonucleic complex during the cell cycle. In: *Frontiers in cytology.* (Palay, S. L., ed.) Yale University Press, New Haven, Conn.

Brachet, J. (1957) *Biochemical cytology.* Academic Press, New York.

Caspersson, T. (1950) *Cell growth and cell function.* W. W. Norton & Co., New York.

Chargaff, E., and Davidson, J. N. (1955) *Nucleic acids.* Academic Press, New York.

Crick, F. H. C. (1957) Nucleic acids. *Scient. Amer.*, 197:188.

Davidson, J. N. (1960) *The biochemistry of the nucleic acids.* 4th Ed. John Wiley & Sons, New York.

Gale, E. F. (1955–1956) Nucleic acids and protein synthesis. *Harvey Lect.*, ser. 51, p. 25.

Mazia, D. (1952) Physiology of the cell nucleus. In: *Modern trends in physiology and biochemistry.* (Barrón, E. S. G., ed.) Academic Press, New York.

McElroy, W. D., and Glass, B., eds. (1957) *The chemical basis of heredity.* Johns Hopkins Press, Baltimore.

Mitchell, J. S., ed. (1960) *The cell nucleus* (Symposium). Academic Press, New York.

Moses, M. J. (1952) Quantitative optical techniques in the study of nuclear chemistry. *Exp. Cell Res.*, suppl. 2:76.

Strauss, B. S. (1960) *An outline of chemical genetics.* W. B. Saunders Co., Philadelphia.

Taylor, J. H. (1958) The duplication of chromosomes. *Scient. Amer.*, 198(No. 6):36.

CITED REFERENCES

1. Griffith, F. (1928) *J. Hyg.*, 27:113.
2. Avery, O. T., McLeod, C. M., and McCarthy, M. (1944) *J. Exp. Med.*, 79:137.
3. Mirsky, A. E., and Pollister, A. W. (1946) *J. Gen. Physiol.*, 30:117.
4. Caspersson, T. (1950) *Cell growth and cell function.* W. W. Norton & Co., New York.
5. Alfert, M., and Geschwind, I. I. (1953) *Proc. Nat. Acad. Sci.* (Wash.), 39:991.
6. Felix, K., Fischer, H., and Krekels, A. (1956) *Progr. Biophys.*, 6:1.
7. Bloch, D. P. (1958) Changes in the desoxyribonucleoprotein complex during the cell cycle. In: *Frontiers in cytology.* (Palay, S. L., ed.) Yale University Press, New Haven, Conn.
8. Bloch, D. P. (1963) The DNA histone association as a basis for alternative hereditary gene states. *Proc. XIV Internat. Congress of Zool.* (Wash.), 3.
9. Mirsky, A. E., and Osawa, S. (1961) The interphase nucleus. In: *The cell,* Vol. 2, p. 677. (Brachet, J., and Mirsky, A. E., eds.) Academic Press, New York.
10. Pollister, A. W., and Leuchtenberger, C. (1949) *Nature,* 163:360.
11. Dounce, A. L., Tishkoff, G. H., Barnett, S. R. and Freer, R. M. (1950) *J. Gen. Physiol.,* 33:629.
12. Allfrey, V. G., Stern, H., Mirsky, A. E., and Saetren, H. (1951) *J. Gen. Physiol., 34:* 529.
13. Pollister, A. W. (1952) *Exp. Cell Res.,* suppl. 2, 59.
14. Allfrey, V. G., and Mirsky, A. E. (1961) In: *Protein biosynthesis.* (Harris, R. J. C., ed.) Academic Press, New York, p. 49.
15. Kornberg, A. (1957) In: *The chemical basis of heredity.* (McElroy, W. D., and Glass, B., eds.) Johns Hopkins Press, Baltimore, p. 579.
16. Weiss, S. B., and Nakamoto, T. (1961) *J. Biol. Chem.,* 236:PC18.
17. Hurwitz, J., Furth, J. J., Andres, M., Ortiz, P. J., and August, J. T. (1961) *J. Chim. Phys.,* p. 934.
18. Stevens, A. J. (1961) *J. Biol. Chem.,* 236: PC43.
19. Stern, H., Allfrey, V. G., Mirsky, A. E., and Saetren, H. (1951) *J. Gen. Physiol., 34:* 559.
20. Hogeboom, G. H., and Schneider, W. C. (1952) *J. Biol. Chem.,* 197:611.
21. Stoneburg, C. A. (1939) *J. Biol. Chem.,* 129:189.
22. Dounce, A. I. (1955) In: *The nucleic acids,* Vol. 2, p. 93. (Chargaff, E., and Davidson, J. N., eds.) Academic Press, New York.
23. Ackerman, G. A. (1952) *Science,* 115:629.
24. Barton, J. (1951) *Quantitative analysis of the results of the enzymatic digestion of nuclei.* Thesis, University of Missouri, Columbia, Mo.
25. Boivin, A., Vendrely, R., and Vendrely, C. (1948) *C. R. Acad. Sci.* (Paris), 226: 1061.
26. Mirsky, A. E., and Ris, H. (1948) *J. Gen. Physiol.,* 31:1.
27. Vendrely, R. (1954) *Internat. Rev. Cytol.,* 4:115.
28. Vendrely, R. (1955) In: *The nucleic acids,* Vol. 2, p. 155. (Chargaff, E., and Davidson, J. N., eds.) Academic Press, New York.
29. Mirsky, A. E., and Ris, H. (1951) *J. Gen. Physiol.,* 34:451.
30. Pollister, A. W., Swift, H., and Alfert, M. (1951) *J. Cell. Comp. Physiol.,* 38: suppl. 1, p. 101.
31. Swift, H. (1950) *Anat. Rec.,* 105:56.
32. Pasteels, J., and Lison, L. (1950) *Arch. Biol.,* 61:445.
33. Alfert, M. (1950) *J. Cell. Comp. Physiol.,* 36:381.

34. Prescott, D. M., and Bender, M. A. (1963) *Exp. Cell Res., 39:*430.

35. Prescott, D. M., and Bender, M. A. (1963) *J. Cell. Comp. Physiol., 62:* suppl. 1, p. 175.

36. Watson, J. D., and Crick, F. H. C. (1953) *Nature, 171:*737.

37. Messelson, M., and Stahl, F. W. (1958) *Proc. Nat. Acad. Sci. (Wash.), 44:*671.

38. Cairns, J. (1963) *J. Molec. Biol., 6:*208.

39. Taylor, J. H., Woods, P. S., and Hughes, W. L. (1957) *Proc. Nat. Acad. Sci. (Wash.), 43:*122.

40. Taylor, J. H. (1960) *J. Biophys. Biochem. Cytol., 7:*455.

41. Bender, M. A., and Prescott, D. M. (1962) *Exp. Cell Res., 27:*221.

42. Gilbert, C. W., Muldal, S., Lajtha, L. G., and Rowley, J. (1962) *Nature, 195:*869.

43. Hsu, T. C., and Somers, C. E. (1963) Structural and physiological heterogeneity of mammalian chromosomes. *Proc. XIV Internat. Congress of Zool. (Wash.), 4:*269.

44. Taylor, J. H., ed. (1963) *Molecular genetics,* Part I. Academic Press, New York.

45. Ris, H. (1957) Chromosome structure. In: *The chemical basis of heredity.* (McElroy, W. D., and Glass, B., eds.) Johns Hopkins Press, Baltimore, p. 23.

46. De Robertis, E. (1956) *J. Biophys. Biochem. Cytol., 2:*785.

47. Freese, E. (1963) In: *Molecular genetics,* Part I. (Taylor, J. H., ed.) Academic Press, New York.

48. Moses, M. J. (1956) *J. Biophys. Biochem. Cytol., 2:*215.

49. Moses, M. J. (1958) *J. Biophys. Biochem. Cytol., 4:*633.

50. Prescott, D. M. (1961) RNA and protein replacement in the nucleus during growth and division and the conservation of components in the chromosome. In: *Cell growth and cell division.* Internat. Soc. for Cell Biology, Vol. II. Academic Press, New York.

51. Goldstein, L. (1963) RNA and protein in nucleocytoplasmic interactions. In: *Cell growth and cell division.* Internat. Soc. for Cell Biology, Vol. II. Academic Press, New York.

52. Beck, J. S. (1962) *Exp. Cell Res., 28:*406.

53. Huang, R. C., and Bonner, J. (1952) *Proc. Nat. Acad. Sci. (Wash.), 48:*1216.

54. Sirlin, J. L. (1962) *Progr. Biophys., 12:*25.

55. Vincent, W. S. (1955) *Internat. Rev. Cytol., 4:*269.

56. Gonzáles Ramirez, J. (1963) Considerations on nucleolar physiology. In: *Cinemicrography in cell biology.* (Rose, G. G., ed.) Academic Press, New York, p. 429.

57. Estable, C., and Sotelo, J. R. (1950) *Inst. C. Biol.,* Montevideo, *1:*105.

58. Borysko, C., and Bang, F. B. (1951) *Bull. Johns Hopkins Hosp., 89:*468.

59. Bernhard, W., Hagenau, F., and Oberling, C. (1952) *Experientia, 8:*58.

60. Marinozzi, V. (1962) Premières observations sur la structure fine du nucléole revélés par des méthodes de cytochimie ultrastructurale. In: *Electron microscopy. Fifth Internat. Congress for Electron Microscopy.* Vol 2, p. NN-5. (Breese, S. S., Jr., ed.) Academic Press, New York.

61. Miller, O. L. (1962) Studies on the ultrastructure and metabolism of nucleoli in amphibian oocytes. *Fifth Internat. Congress for Electron Microscopy.* Vol. 2, p. NN-8. (Breese, S. S., Jr., ed.) Academic Press, New York.

62. Lafontaine, J. G., and Chouinard, L. A. (1963) *J. Cell Biol., 17:*167.

63. Tandler, C. J. (1954) *J. Histochem. Cytochem., 2:*165.

64. Tandler, C. J. (1959) *Exp. Cell Res., 17:* 560.

65. Das, N. K. (1962) *Exp. Cell Res., 26:*428.

66. Harris, H. (1961) *Nature, 190:*1077.

67. Vincent, W. S. (1952) *Proc. Nat. Acad. Sci. (Wash.), 38:*139.

68. Baltus, E. (1954) *Biochim. Biophys. Acta, 15:*263.

69. Monty, K. J., Litt, M., Kay, E. R. M., and Dounce, A. L. (1956) *J. Biophys. Biochem. Cytol., 2:*127.

70. Birstiel, M. L., and Chipchase, M. I. H. (1963) *Fed. Proc., 22:*473.

71. Maggio, R., Siekevitz, P., and Palade, G. E. (1963) *J. Cell Biol., 18:*267, 293.

72. Tandler, C. J., and Sirlin, J. L. (1962) *Biochim. Biophys. Acta, 55:*228.

73. Sirlin, J. L., Jacob, J., and Tandler, C. J. (1963) *Biochem. J., 89:*447.

74. Edström, J. E. (1960) *J. Biophys. Biochem. Cytol., 8:*47.

75. Edström, J. E., Grampp, W., and Schor, N. (1961) *J. Biophys. Biochem. Cytol., 11:* 549.

76. Sirlin, J. L., Jacob, J., and Kano, K. I. (1962) *Exp. Cell Res., 27:*355.

77. Perry, R. P. (1963) *Exp. Cell Res., 29:*400.

78. Scherrer, K., Latham, H., and Darnell, J. E. (1963) *Proc. Nat. Acad. Sci. (Wash.), 49:*240.

79. Pelling, G. (1959) *Nature, 184:*655.

80. Sirlin, J. L. (1960) *Exp. Cell Res., 19:*177.

81. Spiegelman, S. (1963) *Fed. Proc., 22:*1, 36.

82. Callan, H. C. (1963) *Internat. Rev. Cytol., 15:*1.

83. Fonbrune, P. (1949) *La technique de micromanipulation.* Masson et Cie, Paris.

84. Lorch, I. J., and Danielli, J. F. (1960) *Nature, 166:*329.

85. Goldstein, L., Cailleau, R., and Crocket, T. T. (1960) *Exp. Cell Res., 19:*332.

86. Hammerling, J. (1963) *Ann. Rev. Plant Physiol., 14.*

87. Keck, K. (1963) The nuclear control of synthetic activities in Acetabularia. *Proc. XIV Internat. Congress Zool. (Wash.) 3:*203.

88. Beerman, W. (1962) *Protoplasmalogia, VI.* D. Wien, Springer.

89. Pavan, C., and Breuer, M. (1955) *Symp. Cell Secretion,* Bello Horizonte, 90.

90. Swift, H. (1962) In: *Molecular control of cellular activity.* (Allan, J. M., ed.) McGraw-Hill Book Co., New York, p. 73.
91. Edström, J. E., and Beerman, W. (1962) *J. Cell Biol., 14:*371.
92. Clever, U., and Karlson, P. (1960) *Exp. Cell Res., 20:*623.
93. Clever, U., and Beerman, W. (1963) Studies of nucleo-cytoplasmic interrelations in giant chromosomes of Diptera. *Proc. XIV Internat. Congress of Zool.* (*Wash.*), 3:210.
94. Gall, J. G., and Callan, H. C. (1963) Structure and function of Lampbrush chromosomes. *Proc. XIV Internat. Congress of Zool.* (*Wash.*), 3:280.
95. Briggs, R., and King, T. J. (1952) *Proc. Nat. Acad. Sci.* (*Wash.*), 38:455.
96. King, T. J. (1963) The role of the nucleus in embryonic differentiation as revealed by nuclear transplantation studies in amphibia. *Proc. XIV Internat. Congress of Zool.* (*Wash.*), 3:208.

CHAPTER 18

MOLECULAR GENETICS

The cytologic analysis of genetics was presented in Chapter 15. In recent years the main emphasis has turned toward the study of the mechanisms of heredity at the molecular level. Structurally the interest has shifted from the chromosome to deoxyribonucleic acid (DNA), ribonucleic acid (RNA), and proteins, which constitute the fundamental molecular "machinery" of the cell.

Among other causes, this change is the result of genetic experiments with microorganisms, which have revealed finer mechanisms of genetic interchange. Large populations of microorganisms can be obtained by culture, and experimental conditions are precise and reproducible. Furthermore, changes in phenotype are easily discovered and easily related to changes in enzymes and metabolism. Bacteria and viruses are used most in these studies.

Although bacteria are usually haploid and multiply by simple division and in this way transmit the hereditary characters, they can multiply by other mechanisms that involve recombination. The diagram of Figure 18–1 indicates three ways by which genetic material can be transferred from one bacterium to another. In *transformation* the DNA extracted from a strain of bacteria pene-

trates another strain (Fig. 18–1A). This DNA in general is substituted for part of the original DNA of the genome, and as a consequence some new phenotypic characteristics may appear. In *transduction* the genetic material is carried from one bacterium to another by a bacteriophage (a bacterial virus) (Fig. 18–1B). In *conjugation* bacteria of different polarity (or sex) pair and recombine sexually (Fig. 18–1C). These and other mechanisms of recombination analysis are widely used in molecular genetics.

The knowledge gathered in studies of bacteria, bacteriophages and other viruses and in the molds *Neurospora* and *Aspergillus* is applicable to higher cells, since at the molecular level all living organisms have similar genetic mechanisms. To illustrate this point we will start this chapter with a discussion of some human diseases of genetic origin that can be explained as due to molecular changes in the genes and proteins.

Molecular genetics is a rapidly growing field that is of great interest to cell biology, particularly in relation to DNA replication and the organization of chromosomes (see Chap. 17), the biochemical expression of genic action, the mechanism of specific protein biosynthesis, the translation of the genetic code, and the genetic mechanisms of control and regulation and the nucleocytoplasmic interrelations in cell growth and differentiation. (Only a few topics are mentioned here. For further reading, refer to the selected references.)

MOLECULAR EXPRESSIONS OF GENIC ACTION

The concept of the *genotype* contained in the genome of the cell was first introduced in Chapter 13 in the discussion of cytogenetics at the chromosome level. This concept was considered again from the biochemical viewpoint in Chapter 17. We concluded that the genotype, which is the sum of all the hereditary potentialities of an organism, is contained in the chromosomes and essentially in the DNA molecule. The mechanism by which DNA information is duplicated was mentioned, but so far

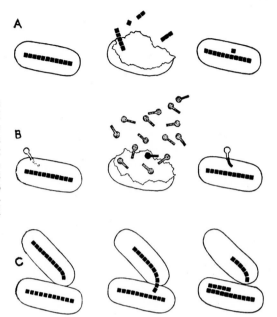

FIGURE 18–1. Diagram showing the three methods by which genetic material can be transferred from one bacterium to another. **A,** in *transformation* the bacteria are destroyed and the genetic material that is liberated penetrates another bacterium. **B,** in *transduction* the bacteriophage carries genetic material from one bacterium to another. **C,** in *conjugation* the genetic material is transferred directly by pairing and sexual recombination.

little has been said of the *mechanisms by which the genotype is expressed into the phenotype.* Therefore, we are going to analyze the chemical pathway by which a gene contained in DNA can produce visible changes, such as those observed by Mendel in his experiments with peas (e.g., red or white flowers, smooth or rough seeds), or in the crosses of rats or guinea pigs shown in Figures 15–1 and 15–3. This analysis of genic action in higher organisms is difficult because in most cases a mutation of a single gene can produce a number of other secondary changes which can mask the original change.

Phenylketonuria and other Human Diseases

A few examples of human diseases illustrate this point and show that the action of genes is essentially a biochemical mechanism.

By 1930, it was found that certain patients who had a severe mental disorder excreted an abnormal compound in the urine: *phenylpyruvic acid.* The disease was called *phenylketonuria* and was found to be associated with a recessive gene. In fact, this disease is manifest only in homozygous recessive individuals generally produced by consanguine-

ous unions (e.g., cousin-cousin or uncle-niece). In this disease *phenylalanine,* a normal amino acid of the diet, cannot by oxidized to tyrosine and is alternatively oxidized to phenylpyruvic acid (Fig. 18–2A). The mutated gene has resulted in the *lack of the enzyme* needed for normal metabolism. This is the primary action of the gene, but the mental disorder, which can lead to idiocy or imbecility in the organism, is due to the accumulation of phenylpyruvic acid. If the disorder is discovered early enough, the mental disease can be prevented to some extent by a special diet that is low in phenylalanine.

In humans there are several other "errors of metabolism" due to genic action, such as *tyrosinosis, alkaptonuria, goitrous cretinism* and *albinism,* in which blocks in the metabolism of phenylalanine and tyrosine are involved (see Fig. 18–2).

In *galactosemia,* another hereditary disease, the utilization of galactose is prevented by the lack of a special enzyme, and this sugar accumulates in the blood and poisons the organism. Elimination of galactose (and lactose) from the diet can improve the condition. These babies cannot be fed on milk.

In general, genes act mainly by producing enzymes, which are involved in

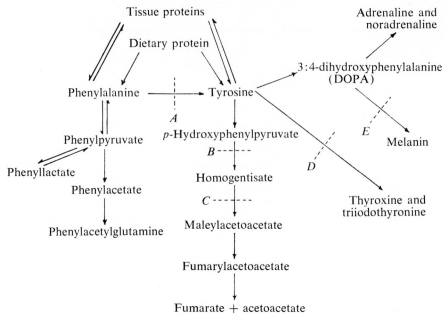

FIGURE 18–2. Possible genetic blocks in the normal metabolism of the amino acids phenylalanine and tyrosine in humans. These blocks lead to the production of the following genetic syndromes: A, phenylketonuria; B, tyrosinosis; C, alkaptonuria; D, goitrous cretinism; E, albinism. (From Harris.)

the different steps of metabolism. If a mutation occurs, the enzyme is no longer produced or the protein is inactive.

One-Gene–One-Enzyme Theory

These mechanisms of genic action can be studied better in the mold *Neurospora crassa*. (The advantages of using this mold in cytogenetics were considered in Chapter 15. See Fig. 15–7.) Normally this mold can grow in a "minimal medium" containing sucrose, nitrate, minerals and only one vitamin—biotin. This means that this organism can synthesize all the other vitamins, amino acids and so forth required for its metabolism. However, if spores of *Neurospora* are treated with a *mutagen* (i.e., an agent, such as x-rays, that produces gene mutations), some of the spores will become unable to reproduce in the "minimal medium" and will require the addition of some other substance, such as the amino acid arginine or tryptophan or the vitamin niacin. These mutants can then be crossed with the normal or wild type and the results may be analyzed in the eight ascospores resulting from meiosis (see Fig. 15–7).

For example, if an arginine-requiring specimen (A—) is crossed with a normal strain (A+), all eight ascospores can grow in a medium containing arginine, but only four can grow in the "minimal medium." This indicates that a single gene has been altered.

This particular case of arginine mutants may be more complex because, as shown in Figure 18–3, this amino acid results from a chain of reactions, i.e., *glutamic acid* → *ornithine* → *citrulline* → *arginine*, which are controlled by a series of genes. The mutation of a single gene leads to the suppression of one biochemical reaction, as can be demonstrated by supplementing the "minimal medium" with the compound that cannot be synthesized.

From varied studies of this kind Beadle and Tatum hypothesized that there is a one-to-one correlation between genes and enzymes (or proteins).

Genes and the Structure of Proteins. Sickle Cell Anemia

Enzymes are proteins, and from what has just been said, we must assume that genes determine the structure of the protein and thus the sequence of amino acids. An excellent example may also be taken from the human. An inherited disease that is apparently confined to Negroes is characterized by a change in shape of the red blood cells in the venous blood. Owing to a decrease in oxygen tension, these erythrocytes change from their normal configuration and become sickle-shaped (Fig. 18–4), which

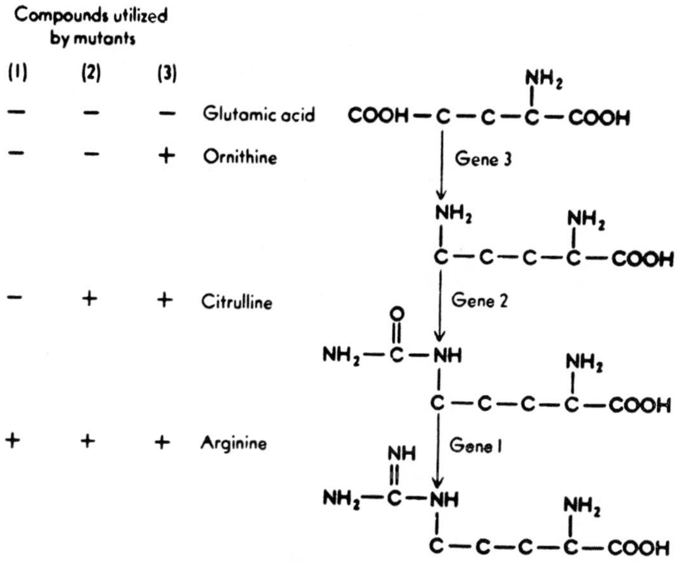

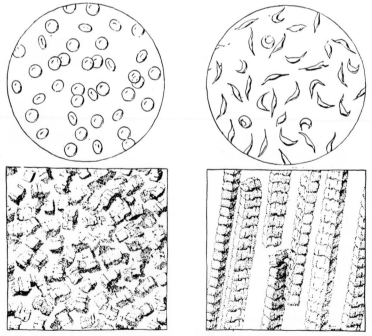

FIGURE 18–3. Diagram showing the genetic control of the biochemical reactions concerned with the formation of arginine. Left, the compounds in which the different mutants can grow. Notice that a chain of three genes corresponding to three enzymes is involved in the formation of arginine from glutamic acid. (From Bonner, 1961.)

FIGURE 18–4. Above, left, normal erythrocytes; right, erythrocytes from venous blood of a patient with sickle cell anemia. Below, left, the hemoglobin molecules are randomly distributed in a normal individual; right, disposition of molecules of the venous blood in sickle cell anemia. In this case the hemoglobin molecules are in a crystalline array, which produces birefringence and deformation of the erythrocytes. (From Pauling.)

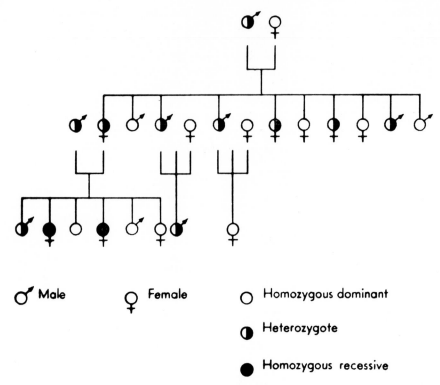

FIGURE 18–5. Pedigree of sickle cell anemia. Only the homozygous recessives show sickling and severe anemia. (See the text.) (After Neel, in Bonner, 1961.)

may cause rupture of the cell and severe hemolytic anemia. As shown in Figure 18–5, the family distribution of this disease shows that it is caused by a recessive gene. A homozygous recessive individual has sickle cells and suffers from anemia, whereas a heterozygous individual has sickling but no other symptoms of the disease.

The molecular bases of this genetic disease were discovered through studies of the hemoglobin (Hb) molecule.[1] Abnormal hemoglobin was found to have a different electrophoretic behavior (Fig. 18–6). Normal hemoglobin (HbA) and sickle cell hemoglobin (HbS) differ in their surface charge and thus move differently in an electric field. Notice in Figure 18–6 that a heterozygous individual has both HbA and HbS in about equal amounts.

Hemoglobin is a protein with a molecular weight of 64,000, containing 600 amino acids arranged in four polypeptide chains: two identical α-chains and two identical β-chains. The method called "finger printing" has been used

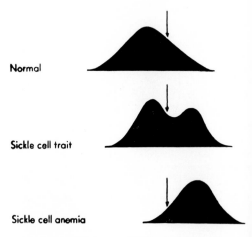

FIGURE 18–6. Electrophoretic behavior of various human hemoglobins. Normal homozygous dominant. Sickle cell trait heterozygous. Sickle cell anemia. The arrows indicate the reference point of origin of the electrophoretic pattern. (After L. Pauling, in Bonner, 1961.)

to demonstrate that HbA and HbS differ only in one amino acid. In a peptide number 4 from the β-chain, *glutamic acid* is replaced by *valine*. In another abnormal hemoglobin, HbC, glutamic

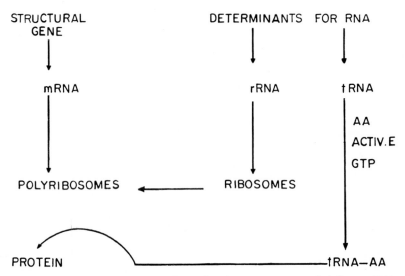

FIGURE 18–7. Diagram showing the relationship between genes and different RNA molecules in protein synthesis. (See the description in the text.)

acid is replaced by *lysine* in the same position (see Table 18–1).

GENES AND PROTEIN SYNTHESIS

Figure 18–7 shows the main components that are involved in protein synthesis at the cellular level. In summary, DNA, which contains the genetic information (genome), gives rise to the three types of RNA (messenger, ribosomal and transfer) that are involved in protein synthesis (see Chap. 17 and Table 17–1). mRNA is copied from the corresponding locus of the genome also called a *structural gene.* In the diagram of Figure 18–7 rRNA and tRNA are pictured as coming from special genes called *determinants for RNA.*

The 20 amino acids (*AA*) are activated by a similar number of soluble enzymes, which require the chemical energy supplied by ATP. Each activated

amino acid becomes linked to tRNA, and this AA-tRNA complex is carried on the ribosome. Guanosine triphosphate (GTP) appears to be necessary for the final polypeptide formation. For each amino acid, one specific activating enzyme (aminoacyl-tRNA synthetase) and one specific tRNA is postulated.

Molecular Structure of tRNA

The fact that a special tRNA is involved in protein synthesis was discovered with the use of an in vitro system, which included subcellular fractions containing ribosomes and a soluble supernatant with the addition of ATP and radioactive amino acids.[3]

In addition to the characteristics given in Chapter 17 (i.e., molecular weight of 24,000, about 67 nucleotides, sedimentation constant 4 S and presence of methylated bases), tRNA consists of a single polynucleotide chain, which is appar-

TABLE 18–1. CHEMICAL DIFFERENCES IN HEMOGLOBINS[*]

Hg	CHAIN	PEPTIDE	AMINO ACID SEQUENCE
A	β	4	Val · His$^+$· Leu · Thr · Pro · *Glu$^-$*· Glu$^-$ · Lys$^+$
S	β	4	Val · His$^+$· Leu · Thr · Pro · *Val* · Glu$^-$ · Lys$^+$
C	β	4	Val · His$^+$· Leu · Thr · Pro · *Lys$^+$*· Glu$^-$ · Lys$^+$

Glu, glutamic acid; *His,* histidine; *Leu,* leucine; *Lys,* lysine; *Pro,* proline; *Thr,* threonine; *Val,* valine.
* From Hunt and Ingram.[2]

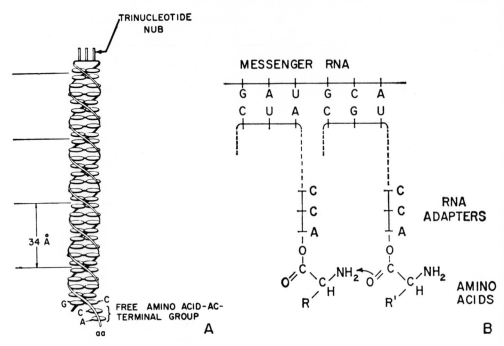

FIGURE 18–8.   **A,** diagram showing a proposed structure for soluble or transfer (adapter) RNA. This is composed of a short polynucleotide chain with a bend in the middle. A double helix structure is postulated. (However, another model may be possible, e.g., a hairpin with a region lacking hydrogen bonds.) At the bend the presence of three unpaired bases is postulated. These bases (trinucleotide nub) would be the ones involved in recognizing the triplet or codon on messenger RNA. See B. Notice the free end formed by G–C–A attached to the amino acid (aminoacyl-tRNA complex). The molecule of tRNA is about 100 Å long and 20 Å wide. **B,** diagram showing the function of tRNA in protein synthesis: *above,* messenger RNA with two codons; *below,* two tRNA (or RNA adapters) whose impaired triplet complements the codon forming hydrogen bonds. Notice at the bottom that two amino acids are linked to the C–C–A end of tRNA and are ready to form a peptide bond. (From Zubay.[4])

ently bent in the middle and the two arms coiled over one another. At the end of one of the chains is a guanosine residue and at the other the sequence: cytosine–cytosine–adenine, which carries the amino acid (see Fig. 18–8). This tightly coiled model does not explain the presence of a variety of methylated bases that could not pair, and other models may be possible (e.g., a hairpin model with an unwound portion).

At the bend of tRNA the existence of three unpaired nucleotides is postulated.[4] As will be shown later, it is presumed that these three nucleotides (also called an adapter nucleotide triplet) carry the specific information to pair with mRNA.

Molecular Structure of mRNA

Figure 18–7 shows that the information copied from the specific structural gene is transferred to the cytoplasm in the form of mRNA, and that this is deposited upon a certain number of ribosomes which constitute the synthetic "machinery," or *polyribosome.* The demonstration of the existence of a template RNA carrying the information from the DNA molecule came from the work of several laboratories that demonstrated the existence of a metabolically unstable RNA in bacteria infected with phages and later on also in uninfected organisms. The name "messenger" RNA was created in 1961 by Jacob and Monod in reference to the fact that it was an unstable template of DNA that has a high turnover.[5] mRNA was labeled with short pulses and was then found largely attached to the ribosomes[6] (Fig. 18–9).

Interesting studies have also been made with the technique of making hybrid molecules between mRNA and the corresponding complementary DNA. If

DNA molecules are heated to 100° C., the two polynucleotide strands separate because the hydrogen bonds holding the base pairs break (see Fig. 17–6). Under slow cooling the strands unite again, but by a rapid procedure it is possible to isolate each strand and to make hybrids with the corresponding mRNA, which will have the complementary bases. Several recent experiments indicate that *only one of the two strands of DNA is used as a template for mRNA synthesis.* Thus we can assume that each particular single-stranded mRNA molecule carries a base distribution that is the complement of that part of DNA from which

it was copied, with the only difference that thymine (T) in DNA is substituted by uracil (U) in mRNA (Fig. 18–8).

Recent experiments indicate that the fact that only one of the DNA polynucleotide chains is copied by the RNA-polymerase in synthesizing mRNA is due to the circularity of the chromosome (see Chap. 17). In fact, certain bacteriophages that have a circular chromosome as shown by electron microscopy make only a copy of mRNA, but when they are submitted to sonic vibrations that break the circular DNA, the two polynucleotide chains are copied. It is postulated that the circular arrangement

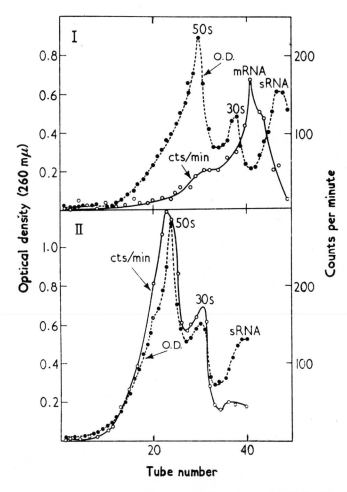

FIGURE 18–9. Diagram showing the rapid turnover of messenger RNA (*mRNA*). *E. coli* were incubated for 5 seconds with C^{14}-uridine and then washed in nonradioactive uracil. In **I** the cells were rapidly frozen and in **II** they were incubated for 15 minutes at 37° C. prior to freezing. Ribonucleic acids were extracted in both experiments and ultracentrifuged. The optical density at 260 mμ indicated the concentration of different RNA molecules, and the counts per minute indicated the incorporation of C^{14}-uridine. Notice in **I** that the only labeled RNA is mRNA, whereas in **II** radioactivity is found in two peaks of ribosomal RNA (*rRNA*) (50 S and 30 S) and in soluble RNA (*sRNA*). (From Gros et al.[6])

of DNA is not confined to bacteria and viruses, but may be found in chromosomes of higher cells forming units of transcription. This has been called *transcripton,* a name that corresponds to that of *replicon* (see Table 18–3).[8]

In summary, the following generally identify mRNA: it has a high turnover, it acts as a template for protein synthesis, it hybridizes with homologous DNA, and it binds reversibly to ribosomes, as in the case of forming polysomes. However in some cases, as in reticulocytes, the turnover is not high and mRNA is more stable.

Another important step in the study of mRNA was the discovery of the enzyme RNA-polymerase,[9, 10] which synthesizes RNA using DNA as a primer and the four ribonucleoside triphosphates. In this reaction DNA acts as a template and the RNA formed is complementary to the primer DNA.

The Genetic Code. Codon

Summarizing at this point, the synthesis of mRNA represents the *transcription* (see Fig. 17–1) of the information coded in DNA, which is now transferred to an RNA "tape" (mRNA). So far the four-character "language" of DNA has been transcribed into another (complementary) four-character "language" in mRNA.[11]

The next important step is the actual *translation* of the four-character code into the 20-character "language" of the proteins. This is called the "genetic code," which is the actual phenotypic expression of the genotype.

For some time speculations were raised about the actual number of nucleotides needed to specify (or code) a single amino acid. Since mRNA has only four different nucleotides (AGCU), a code consisting of two "words" (doublet) is insufficient for the 20 amino acids. A triplet code gives more than enough information for the amino acids:

$$4^2 = 16 \text{ combinations}$$
$$4^3 = 64 \text{ combinations}$$

On this basis it was postulated that the *genetic code* is made of triplets (see Table 18–2) and that the coding ratio nucleotide/AA is 3:1.

When synthetic RNAs with different known base compositions became available it was possible to test this hypothesis. These nucleotide polymers were made with the enzyme *polynucleotide phosphorylase,* which can link the nucleotides added to the medium.[12, 13] In the crucial experiment an in vitro system was used, which, as was indicated, consisted of ribosomes, supernatant containing the activating enzymes, tRNA, ATP and GTP and the different labeled amino acids. To this system a synthetic RNA composed only of polyuridylic acid (Poly U) was added. Under those circumstances the only amino acid incorporated was phenylalanine and the peptide formed was polyphenylalanine.[14, 15] This fundamental discovery demonstrated that the series of nucleotides UUU was the code for phenylalanine (Phe).

Similar work carried out in the Nirenberg and Ochoa laboratories using a variety of synthetic polynucleotides which act as artificial mRNAs has permitted the establishment of the probable genetic code for the different amino acids (see Table 18–2).

The group of nucleotide triplets in mRNA that determines each amino acid

TABLE 18–2.   GENETIC CODE*

AMINO ACID	CODON
Alanine	CUG, CAG, CCG
Arginine	GAA, GCC, GUC
Asparagine	UAA, CAA, CUA
Aspartic acid	GUA, GCA
Cysteine	GUU
Glutamic acid	AUG, AAG
Glycine	GUG, GAG, GCG
Histidine	AUC, ACC
Isoleucine	UUA, AAU, CAU
Leucine	UAU, UUC, UGU, CCU, AAU
Lysine	AUA, AAA
Methionine	UGA
Phenylalanine	UUU, UCU
Proline	CUC, CCC, CAC
Serine	CUU, UCC, ACG
Threonine	UCA, ACA, CGC, CCA
Tyrosine	AUU, ACU
Valine	UUG

* Data from Nirenberg and Ochoa.

is now called a *codon* and is one of the new genetic units that should be remembered. As shown in Table 18–2, in some cases more than one codon can be used for the same amino acid (e.g., leucine). This is also called a *degeneration of the code*. After having determined the code for each amino acid, we are still confronted with the problem of the mechanism by which the amino acid recognizes the particular codon. It is now generally accepted (and there are experimental proofs of this) that the tRNA-AA complex can detect the specific codon by means of the extremity that carries the three unpaired bases (see Fig. 18–8).

The recognition of the particular site in mRNA will be mediated by the adapter triplet of tRNA as shown in Figure 18–8B. Hydrogen bonds would be established between these adapter triplets and the codon triplets in mRNA.[4] Once two amino acids are put in the proper juxtaposition, the peptide bond between them will be formed by the action of a special enzyme.

Role of Ribosomes in Protein Synthesis

The evidence presented in Chapter 9 indicates that ribosomes and especially polyribosomes have an important role in protein synthesis. As stated, the thin filament connecting the individual ribosomes and seen under the electron microscope could be mRNA.

It is now known that the AA-tRNA complex becomes tightly fixed to the 70 to 80 S ribosome and that one molecule of this complex is attached to each ribosome. Also the growing polypeptide chain is seen to be attached to the 50 to 60 S component of the ribosome.

Studies in hemoglobin synthesis have shown that the polypeptide chain that is being formed grows sequentially from the free terminal amino group toward the carboxyl end.[16] It takes about one minute for one molecule to be synthesized.

The role of ribosomes in protein synthesis is not well understood. One hypothesis is that they provide a stabilizing surface to support mRNA and to maintain this molecule in register with the AA-tRNA complex for coding. This type of interaction is illustrated in the model depicted in Figure 18–10. For this mechanism to work the messenger "tape," which carries the message, must move over the ribosome or vice versa so that ribosomes can drop out from the "tape" and thus be replaced by new ribosomes. The discovery that several ribosomes (polyribosomes) are needed for the synthesis of a definite protein has elucidated this aspect of protein biosynthesis. The number of ribosomes appears to be related to the length of mRNA and this to the actual length of the polypeptide chain to be formed (see Chap. 9).

Genetic Code and Mutations. Universality of the Genetic Code

Although the genetic code is being studied mainly in in vitro systems derived from the bacteria *Escherichia coli*, similar findings have been obtained with reticulocytes from mammals and with mutants of tobacco mosaic virus. All these findings tend to demonstrate that the genetic code is universal, i.e., there is a single code for all living organisms.

Of particular interest is the relationship between the genetic code and mutation. In Chapter 15 we gave the classic definition of mutation. Now it is possible to discuss it at the molecular level. As shown from the work on hemoglobins (see above), a mutation results from a change in amino acid composition of a certain protein. (Remember that glutamic acid in normal hemoglobin [HbA] is replaced by valine in HbS and by lysine in HbC, Table 18–1.) From what has just been said, this amino acid change could result from the exchange of a single base for another in the codon.

This type of study can be made with mutagens that change nucleic acids chemically. Of these, one of the most interesting is nitrous acid (HNO_2), which can deaminate certain bases, thus altering the genetic code. It has been observed that there is a high correlation

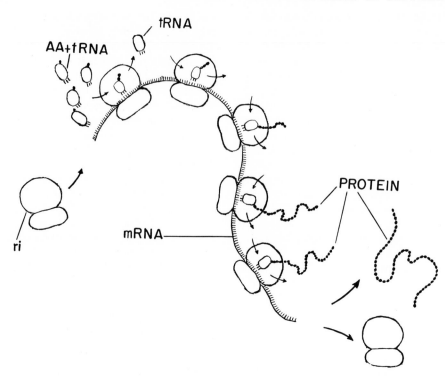

Figure 18–10. Diagram showing a possible interpretation of the mechanism of protein synthesis. A polyribosome of five units is held by a molecule of messenger RNA (*mRNA*) with the codons sticking to one side. The amino acid + transfer RNA (*AA + tRNA*) is depicted as a spheroid having a trinucleotide at one end and one amino acid at the other (black dot). The AA-tRNA complex comes in contact with the suitable codon on the surface of the ribosome (*ri*). When a second AA-tRNA complex is put at one side, polymerization takes place and one tRNA is liberated. The polypeptide grows until the end of mRNA is reached and the protein molecule is detached. Ribosomes are supposed to enter in contact with mRNA at one end and leave at the other end.

between this change in genetic code and the amino acid replacement in the mutant.[13, 17]

THE FINE STRUCTURE OF GENES

Since its postulation by Mendel, the concept of a hereditary "factor" or gene has been changed considerably. Its definition is an operational one and has different meanings according to different viewpoints. In the classic sense a gene is a *unit of function* that occupies a definite locus in the chromosome and is responsible for a specific phenotypic character, e.g., vestigial or long wings, white or yellow eyes in *Drosophila*. At the same time a gene is a *unit of transmission* or *segregation*, because it can be segregated and exchanged at meiosis by way of crossing over, and a *unit of muta-*

tion, because by a spontaneous or induced change it can give rise to a different phenotypic expression (see Chap. 15).

With advances in knowledge of the biochemical mechanisms underlying genetic phenomena, it became evident that these classic definitions of a gene were insufficient and that more precise correlations at the molecular level were needed. We have already seen that biochemically a structural gene is a certain length of a DNA molecule that contains enough information to produce a mRNA molecule and this in turn to produce a certain protein (or enzyme).

The ultimate goal of molecular genetics is to define the structure of genes as a definite sequence of nucleotides in the DNA molecule. As was indicated, a beginning has been achieved by the discovery of the *genetic code* and the codon, the gene subunit that is able to determine a certain amino acid. However, a protein molecule (see Chap. 3) has a complex architecture with a sequence of amino acids (primary structure), and a secondary, tertiary and even quaternary structure in addition to regions that are specially differentiated for activity (e.g., active groups of an enzyme, see Chap. 4). There is now convincing evidence that the sequence of amino acids determines the secondary, tertiary and quaternary structures.

Investigating the correlation between the molecular structure of genes and proteins is still a formidable task, but with the use of microorganisms some progress has been made in this direction.

Recombination in Bacteriophages

For an analysis of the fine structure of genes, bacteriophages (i.e., viruses that infect bacteria) are best suited (Fig. 17–3). The bacteriophage injects its DNA molecule into a bacterium and multiplies, producing hundreds of copies in a few minutes. The complex molecu-

lar structure of a phage particle is illustrated in Figure 18–11. (The details of the lytic infection and multiplication within the bacteria will not be considered here.)

Among other advantages, this material has a DNA molecule up to 100 μ long and about 200,000 nucleotides, a number which is enough to code only about 100 different proteins. The effect of phages on bacteria can be easily observed in agar cultures of bacteria. Each phage produces a region of lysis (plaque), which may show a special characteristic for different mutants and also when tried on different bacterial strains. With the methods now available, one recombination in 10^8 to 10^9 can be recognized.

A bacteriophage may be considered as a haploid organism with a single chromosome, and since a bacterium can be infected simultaneously with two mutant phages, a recombination between both DNA molecules can take place. With this type of fine analysis it has been possible to make genetic maps that approach the molecular level.[18, 19]

This analysis has led to the coining of

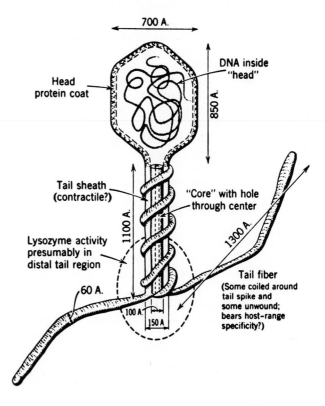

FIGURE 18–11. Diagram showing the macromolecular organization of a bacteriophage, indicating the probable function of each part.

700 A.

Head protein coat

DNA inside "head"

850 A.

Tail sheath (contractile?)

"Core" with hole through center

1100 A.

1300 A.

Lysozyme activity presumably in distal tail region

60 A.

Tail fiber (Some coiled around tail spike and some unwound; bears host-range specificity?)

100 A.

150 A.

new names to explain the relationship between different genetic phenomena and the DNA molecule. According to Benzer: (1) a *recon* is the unit of recombination, and in its minimal expression corresponds to the distance between adjacent nucleotides in the DNA chain. (2) A *muton* is the unit of mutation, and corresponds, in its smallest expression, to a change in a pair of nucleotides. This is easily understandable because a change in a base of the triplet may modify the message carried by the codon and may give rise to a different amino acid (see Table 18–2). (3) A *cistron* is a unit of function within a gene. For example, in the case of the gene that produces tryptophan synthetase in *E. coli*, two cistrons are involved (A and B), each producing a polypeptide chain of the enzyme.

More recently, some of the phenomena previously explained as due to different cistrons have been explained as due to intragenic complementation. There is a tendency to substitute the name "cistron" for *complon*. Some enzymes may be formed by two or more polypeptide chains, whose active groups are complements. Thus the deficiency or alteration in each polypeptide chain is canceled out by complementation.

Recently other names have been coined, such as the *operon*, which comprises several genes with the *operator* (see below) and the *replicon*, which is a larger unit of replication, several of which may constitute the chromosome. Thus a bacterial chromosome is a unit of replication (a replicon), but a larger

chromosome of a higher cell may have several replicating units.

The series of names in order of complexity shown in Table 18–3 are an aid to understanding and remembering the meaning of these different words, all of which indicate the complexity of our knowledge of the molecular structure of genes.

In the present concept a gene is a region in the chromosome that codes the formation of a specific enzyme. Such a genetic region is complex in terms of mutation and recombination, and can be subdivided into many recon-mutons and codons and at times into a few cistrons.

REGULATION OF GENIC ACTION

So far in this chapter only the concept of a "structural gene" has been introduced. We have seen that this designates a DNA molecule whose coded information can be translated into the specific structure of a protein molecule. The impression given so far is that of a unidirectional, stable phenomenon centrally controlled by DNA and started by the synthesis of a RNA template. Now we will consider how the action of these structural genes can be modified under the influence of other parts of the genome or of external (environmental) agents that may act by way of the cytoplasm (Fig. 18–12). This new field is as interesting as the other, since it concerns the different mechanisms by which genic action is regulated.

Regulation, a fundamental property of

TABLE 18–3. RELATIONSHIP BETWEEN GENOME, DNA, PROTEIN AND GENETIC UNITS

GENOME	DNA	PROTEIN	GENETIC UNITS
Recon	internucleotide distance		recombination
Muton	nucleotide (pair)		mutation
Codon	triplet	amino acid	translation
Cistron	segment of DNA molecule	polypeptide	partial function
Complon	segment of DNA molecule	polypeptide	complementation
Gene	segment of DNA molecule	protein	function
Operon	segment of DNA molecule	several related enzymes	function
Replicon	probably a DNA molecule or part of a chromosome	block of enzymes	replication
Transcripton	circular DNA	block of enzymes	transcription

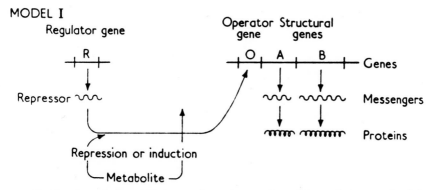

FIGURE 18–12.   One of the mechanisms of regulation of protein synthesis postulated by Jacob and Monod. (See the description in the text.) (From Jacob and Monod.[5])

living matter, is related to adaptation to the changing environment and to the phenomena of growth and differentiation.

Enzyme Induction and Repression

By 1900 it had been found that certain microorganisms could change their enzymatic machinery under the influence of specific substrates (foodstuffs added to the medium). For example, yeast cells grown on glucose do not contain the *galactozymase* system (e.g., Leloir's pathway or series of enzymes fermenting galactose). However if this sugar is added to the medium after a certain delay (lag period), galactozymase activity increases and the same yeast cells start to use galactose (Fig. 18–13). This phenomenon is produced both in the presence or absence of a nitrogen source (Fig. 18–13). If there is no nitrogen source, there is practically no cell division and thus no possibility of a special selection of cells. This phenomenon, designated *enzyme adaptation* or *induction,* is thus a true cellular change and not the result of a population shift by division of certain cells. Adaptation can be a reversible change, since in the absence of the *inducer* the enzyme content may decrease (*deadaptation*). Using radioactive amino acids it has been proved that enzyme adaptation involves the synthesis of a new protein.

One of the systems best studied is β-galactosidase in *E. coli.*[20] It has been demonstrated that the inducer of the enzyme and the substrate on which it

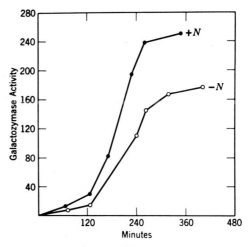

FIGURE 18–13.   Induction of galactozymase in yeast cells in the presence and absence of a nitrogen source (N). Yeast cells grown on glucose have no enzyme which appears following the addition of galactose. (After S. Spiegelman.)

acts may be identical or may differ. In fact, not all inducers are substrates and not all substrates are inducers. For example, methyl-β-D-thiogalactoside is an inducer but not a substrate and phenyl-β-D-galactoside is a substrate but not an inducer. Neither of these substances supports growth alone, but if put together growth takes place (Fig. 18–14). Because of these findings, the concept of enzyme adaptation has been changed to that of *induced enzyme synthesis.*

The opposite phenomenon—*enzyme repression*—has been known only for the last 10 years. It was found that the synthesis of the enzyme tryptophan synthetase in *E. coli* was inhibited selectively by tryptophan and certain ana-

	Inducer	Substrate
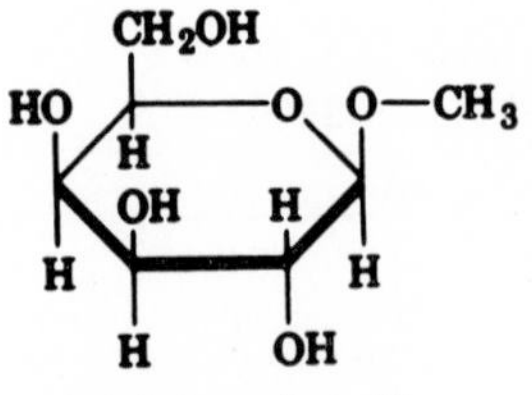 Methyl-β-D-galactoside	+	+
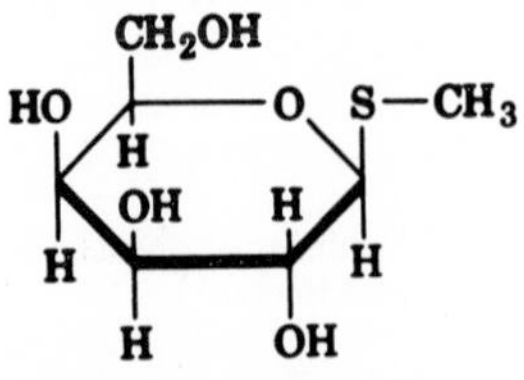 Methyl-β-D-thiogalactoside	+	-
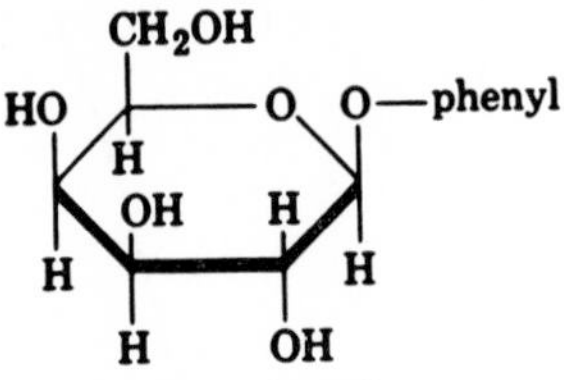 Phenyl-β-D-galactoside	-	+
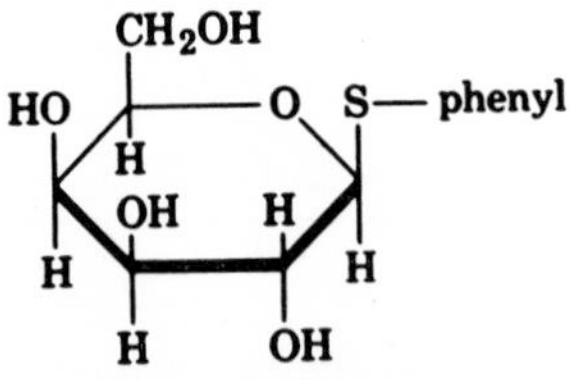 Phenyl-β-D-thiogalactoside	-	-

FIGURE 18–14. Different galactosides and thiogalactosides as inducers of β-galactosidase and as substrates of that enzyme in *E. coli*. (From Monod.)

logues. Enzyme repression, like induction, involves not a single enzyme, but a sequence of enzymes acting in successive metabolic steps. The importance of this phenomenon in the regulation of the cell is evident. In all cases studied the end product of a biosynthetic sequence represses the synthesis of the enzymes involved.

Regulator Genes

Recent studies on bacteria indicate that not all genes act by determining the structure of a given enzyme. Some "regulate" the action of other genes. These have been called *regulator genes,* which indicates that their activity is different than that of the "structural genes" (Fig. 18–12). A mutation in the regulator gene does not cause the disappearance or qualitative alteration of a definite enzyme, but it may change markedly the enzyme's activity or condition of synthesis. For example, the tryptophan synthetase and the β-galactosidase content of *E. coli* can be changed by special regulator genes. These genes appear to mediate the environmental signals in induction and repression.

As shown in the diagram of Figure 18–12, it is postulated that the regulator gene acts by way of the *repressor,* probably a macromolecule, which exerts its action on a special part of the genome that is designated the *operator gene.* These regulator genes control the rate of information sent to the protein.[5] A single regulator gene can affect the synthesis of different proteins, whereas a structural gene obeys the one-gene–one-enzyme principle. For instance, the gene that regulates the formation of tryptophan synthetase also regulates other enzymes required in the early steps of tryptophan biosynthesis.

Operator Genes. Operon

Whereas regulator genes need not be near the structural genes on which they act (in fact they may even be in another chromosome since they act by way of the repressor), another type of gene regulates the structural gene directly at the genome level without an intervening cytoplasm. This is the so-called *operator gene*, which in order to function requires a close linkage and a *cis* configuration with the structural gene. For example, if we call enzyme+ and enzyme− the alleles of the structural gene, and o+ and o− those of the operator gene, of the following two heterozygous diploid combinations only the *cis* configuration permits enzyme formation:

$$\frac{enz^-\quad o^+}{enz^+\quad o^-}\qquad \frac{enz^+\quad o^+}{enz^-\quad o^-}$$
$$\textit{trans}\qquad\qquad \textit{cis}$$

Another important characteristic is that the operator gene controls several related structural genes. For example, all of the genes involved in histidine biosynthesis are controlled by a single operator gene.[5] Jacob and Monod have created a new genetic unit, the *operon,* which comprises the *operator* and the group of genes that are under its control. The operon is larger than the gene and the cistron, because it comprises a few genes and may be several cistrons (Table 18–3). Both regulator and operator genes are carried in the chromosomes, can recombine and are composed of DNA.

The β-Galactosidase-Permease Operon. Another example of operon is the β-galactosidase-permease system in *E. coli,* which are two genes linked and regulated by the same operator gene:

operon

operator — β-galactosidase — permease

Permease is not an enzyme, but some kind of carrier protein related to the "uptake" of the substrate by the cell. If permease is lacking the cell cannot utilize galactose even though it has the proper enzyme. Both permease and the enzyme are thus needed for the normal functioning of this system, which is under the control of a single operator gene. Several cases are known in which, by changing the permeability of the cell membrane, genes can act not on enzymes but on the utilization of substrates (see Chap. 20).

Mechanisms of Gene Regulation

All the facts and concepts just mentioned concern the existence of subtle mechanisms of gene regulation. It is now interesting to refer again to the problem of induction and repression of enzyme synthesis. How can a metabolite act in these mechanisms of gene regulation? One method is hypothesized in the diagram of Figure 18–12. The metabolite may act by combining with the repressor produced by the regulator gene and thus blocking its action on the operator. The result would be an acceleration of the activity of the structural genes (started by the operator gene), followed by the production of more mRNA and more protein (enzyme). This metabolite could also join to an incomplete repressor and depress the action of the operator gene, thus stopping the action of the structural genes and the production of mRNA and protein.

Though enzyme formation is essentially cytoplasmic, it is controlled by several genes that determine its structure or accelerate or reduce its production. Also the cytoplasm may act on the genome through the interaction of metabolites with the repressor molecules.

According to the strictly structural concept, the genome is considered as a mosaic of independent molecular blueprints for the building of individual cellular constituents. In the execution of these plans, however, co-ordination is evidently of absolute survival value. The discovery of regulator and operator genes, and of repressive regulation of the activity of structural genes, reveals that the genome contains not only a series of blueprints, but a coordinated program of protein synthesis and the means of controlling its execution.[5]

Only the proper balance of the different genes can produce the normal development of a cell or an organism. In Chapter 16 we have seen that in the human the increase of a single chromosome (resulting in a trisomy) can result in abnormal development, such as mongolism with severe alteration of the nervous system. A genetic imbalance is produced in cancer cells, in which aneuploidy is frequent. This does not mean that cancer may not be induced by other factors—such as viruses, which can "penetrate" and change the genome of the cell. Certain bacteriophages in a state of *lysogeny* and other cellular elements called *episomes*, which have alternate cytoplasmic and chromosomal locations, also may regulate genes.

In cells of higher organisms the *histones* are considered to be involved in gene regulation. The addition of histones may inhibit RNA synthesis both in the nucleus and in an isolated RNA-polymerase system.[21]

Related to the problem of gene regulation are also the nucleocytoplasmic interactions and the existence of proteins that can shuttle between the nucleus and cytoplasm (see Chap. 17).

Recently it has been argued that as the nuclear system becomes more complex from the bacterial to the higher cells the number of regulator genes increases in relation to the structural genes. In a mammalian nucleus most of the RNA would be repressor. The nucleus is viewed as an effective device for the interaction of repressors, histones and operators with the structural genes.[22, 23]

"A cell must be visualized as a society of macromolecules, bound together by a complex system of communications regulating both their synthesis and their activity."[23] Living organisms could not survive and multiply if it were not for the operation of these and other complex regulatory networks that interconnect the different parts of its macromolecular architecture.

GENERAL REFERENCES

Anfinsen, C. B. (1961) *The molecular basis of evolution.* John Wiley & Sons, New York.

Beadle, W. (1957) The role of the nucleus in heredity. In: *The chemical basis of heredity.* (McElroy, W. D., and Glass, B., eds.) Johns Hopkins Press, Baltimore.

Bonner, D. M. (1961) *Heredity.* Prentice-Hall, Englewood Cliffs, New Jersey.

Braun, W. (1953) *Bacterial genetics.* W. B. Saunders Co., Philadelphia.

Gardner, L. I., ed. (1961) *Molecular genetics and human disease.* Charles C Thomas, Springfield, Ill.

McElroy, W. D., and Glass, B., eds. (1957) *The chemical basis of heredity.* Johns Hopkins Press, Baltimore.

Monod, J. (1958) In: *Enzymes: Units of biological structure and function.* (Gaebler, O. H., ed.) Academic Press, New York.

Ochoa, S. (1963) Synthetic polynucleotides and the genetic code. *Fed. Proc.,* 22:62.

Roberts, J. A. F. (1963) *An introduction to medical genetics.* 3rd Ed. Oxford University Press, New York.

Sager, R., and Ryan, F. J. (1963) *Cell heredity. An analysis of the mechanisms of heredity at the cellular level.* John Wiley & Sons, New York.

Spiegelman, S. (1963) Genetic mechanisms. Information transfer from the genome. *Fed. Proc.,* 22:36.

Wagner, R., and Mitchell, H. K. (1955) *Genetics and metabolism.* John Wiley & Sons, New York.

Watson, J. D. (1963) Involvement of RNA in the synthesis of proteins. *Science,* 140:3562.

Zubay, G. (1963) Molecular model for protein synthesis. *Science,* 140:1092, 3571.

CITED REFERENCES

1. Pauling, L. (1952) *Proc. Amer. Phil. Soc.,* 96:556.
2. Hunt, J. A., and Ingram, V. M. (1958) In: *Symposium on protein structure.* (Neuberger, A., ed.) Methuen & Co., London.
3. Hoagland, M. B., Zamecnick, P. C., and Stephenson, M. L. (1957) *Biochim. Biophys. Acta,* 24:215.
4. Zubay, G. (1963) *Science,* 140:1092, 3571.
5. Jacob, F., and Monod, J. (1961) *J. Molec. Biol.,* 3:318.
6. Gros, F., Hiatt, H., Gilbert, W., Kurland, C. G., Risebrough, R. W., and Watson, J. D. (1961) *Nature,* 190:581.
7. Hall, B. D., and Spiegelman, S. (1961) *Proc. Nat. Acad. Sci.* (Wash.), 47:137.
8. Hayashi, M., Hayashi, M. N., and Spiegelman, S. (1964) *Proc. Nat. Acad. Sci* (Wash.), 51:351.
9. Hurwitz, J., Bresler, A., and Dinger, R. (1960) *Biochem. Biophys. Res. Commun.,* 3:15.
10. Weiss, S. B., and Nakamoto, T. (1961) *Proc. Nat. Acad. Sci.* (Wash.), 47:694.
11. Spiegelman, S. (1963) *Fed. Proc.,* 22:36.
12. Grunberg-Manago, M., Ortiz, M. P. J., and Ochoa, S. (1956) *Biochim. Biophys. Acta,* 20:269.

13. Ochoa, S. (1963) *Fed. Proc., 22*:62.
14. Nirenberg, M. W., and Matthaei, J. H. (1961) *Proc. Nat. Acad. Sci. (Wash.), 47*:1588.
15. Nirenberg, M. W., Matthaei, J. H., Jones, O. W., Martin, R. G., and Barondes, S. H. (1963) *Fed. Proc., 22*:55.
16. Dintzis, H. M. (1961) *Proc. Nat. Acad. Sci. (Wash.), 47*:247.
17. Freese, E. (1963) Molecular mechanism of mutations. In: *Molecular genetics*, Part 1. (Taylor, J. H., ed.) Academic Press, New York, p. 207.
18. Benzer, S. (1957) In: *The chemical basis of heredity.* (McElroy, W. D., and Glass, B., eds.) Johns Hopkins Press, Baltimore, p. 70.
19. Benzer, S. (1963) *Internat. Congress of Zoology. Symposium.* (In press).
20. Monod, J. (1956) In: *Enzymes: Units of biological structure and function.* (Gaebler, O. H., ed.) Academic Press, New York, p. 728.
21. Allfrey, V. G., and Mirsky, A. E. (1963) *Cold Spr. Harb. Symp. Quant. Biol., 28*: 247.
22. Pontecorvo, G. (1963) Microbial genetics: retrospect and prospect. *Proc. Roy. Soc. London, ser. B, 158*:1.
23. Sirlin, J. L. (1963) *Internat. Rev. Cytol., 15*:35.

CHAPTER 19

DIFFERENTIATION, GROWTH, RENEWAL AND SENESCENCE OF CELL POPULATIONS

DIFFERENTIATION

In the preceding chapters we have studied the general morphologic, cytochemical and cytogenetic aspects of the cell. Although several types of cells have been used as examples (eggs, blastomeres, germ cells, epithelial cells and so on), in all of them the fundamental characteristics are similar. We have dealt with elements that are little differentiated morphologically (i.e., little specialized). Nevertheless, the multiplicity of functions of an organism necessitates a greater or lesser degree of cellular specialization and differentiation. Certain cells are adapted to specialized functions, and their morphology is therefore modified. For example, nerve cells assume a shape and structure adapted to the functions of *irritability* and *conductivity*, which enable them to react to stimuli and to transmit signals from one part of the organism

to another. In muscle cells, which contain *myofibrils, contractility* has reached its highest development, although this is also a fundamental property of all cells.

This progressive specialization in structure and function constitutes, in a restricted sense, *cellular differentiation*. (Differentiation is always the transformation of something more general and homogeneous into something more specialized and heterogeneous, and is reflected in both morphologic and physiologic characteristics.) Cellular differentiation occurs continuously throughout the life of the organism. However, during the embryonic period it reaches its maximum and is one of the most important processes. Most organisms develop from a single cell—the *fertilized ovum*—which gives rise to all the tissues and organs. This cell divides actively to form the embryonic structure known as the *blastula*, in which the tissues and organs are not yet defined. In many species, up to this time, this process is mainly quantitative (increase in the number of cells), but after the blastula is formed the process becomes qualitative also. The cells of the blastula begin to rearrange themselves, a process called *gastrulation*, during which the three germ layers are formed and the future organs are determined. At this time and later, *cellular differentiation* takes place with the formation of the various tissues (*histogenesis*) and the separation of portions of some of these tissues to form the organs (*organogenesis*).

The fundamental processes of embryonic development are *growth, differentiation* and *metabolism*. Growth is an increase of the spatial dimensions and depends on the multiplication of cells, the increase in cell size, or the addition of nonliving substances (cell inclusions or paraplasm and intercellular substances). Differentiation is characterized by the increase in complexity and degree of organization and includes histogenesis and organogenesis. Metabolism is the name given to all chemical changes in the embryo that supply part of the energy needed for the other activities.

Determination and Embryonic Organizers

The study of the causes of differentiation is beyond the limits of cytology. It is a special field of embryology—causal embryology, also called developmental mechanics. This science has demonstrated that cellular differentiation of any region of the gastrula is preceded at a particular period by embryonic *determination,* a process *that fixes its destiny* in regard to future development.

This concept is demonstrated by the following experiment:[1] If in an early amphibian gastrula a portion of the dorsal ectoderm is removed (a part which in normal development would become a portion of the nervous system), and if this is implanted into the ventral region of another gastrula of equal age, instead of differentiating into nervous tissue it develops *in accordance with the region* and forms epidermis. If the same experiment is repeated with amphibian gastrulas at a later stage of development, the grafted part develops *in accordance with its site of origin,* i.e., it becomes a part of the nervous system in strange surroundings.

The experiments of Spemann and his school show that a considerable part of embryonic development, and therefore the differentiation of tissues and organs, results from the coordinated action of *organizers,* special regions of the embryo that determine the differentiation of other regions. For example, the dorsal lip of the blastopore of the gastrula, which is the *primary organizer,* determines the differentiation of the nervous system. In turn, after its own determination, the diencephalon acts as an organizer and determines the formation of the optic vesicle. The latter (secondary organizer) induces the differentiation of the crystalline lens, which in turn induces the formation of the cornea. This whole series of integrated processes is thought to depend on substances ("evocators")[2] that are produced by the organizers and that are capable of bringing about the differentiation of neighboring regions when these are in a state of reactivity or appropriate *competence.*

Cellular Differentiation

If we now limit the problem to its cytologic aspects, differentiation may be defined as the process that results in the specialization of the present and potential functions of the cell.[3] As the cell differentiates, it adapts progressively to a specified function and at the same time loses, in general, the capacity (potency) to carry out other functions. In certain cases, differentiation is temporary and reversible and is called *modulation;* in others it is permanent and irreversible.

It is generally accepted that there is a certain antagonism between cell division and differentiation, but this is not always the rule, and differentiated cells, such as those of the pancreatic acinus, liver and kidney may undergo mitosis (see below). Differentiation generally takes place during interphase, between mitoses or in nerve cells after cell divisions have definitely ceased. The neuroblasts, which originate from undifferentiated cells of the embryonic neural tube and neural crest, reach a high degree of differentiation, so that the nerve cell loses not only its capacity to transform into other types of cells but also its capacity to divide. On the other hand, some other cells in the adult organism have acquired a lesser degree of differentiation, and under certain conditions can be transformed into different cell types. For example, the reticular cells of the hematopoietic organs give rise to the blood cells or to the various cellular elements of connective tissue. From these examples it becomes evident that as the cell differentiates, its developmental potency becomes restricted. Later we shall see the importance this has in the senescence of the cell.

In the course of differentiation, the behavior of the nucleus and the cytoplasm differs markedly. The nucleus does not undergo such definite modifications as the cytoplasm, and at times nuclei of completely different types of cells appear similar. Just as the nucleus has a dominant role in *heredity,* assuring the maintenance of general hereditary characters, the cytoplasm has a dominant role in *differentiation,* exhibiting the specific qualities of the cells. Nevertheless, the nucleus shows some kind of functional differentiation with loss of potentialities in the somatic cells, as was demonstrated by the experiment of nuclear transplantation at different stages of embryonic development in the amphibian.

Specific Differentiation of the Cytoplasm

The detailed study of cytoplasmic differentiation is carried out in the field of histology, the science of tissues, since the various types of cells that constitute the tissues and organs of higher animals and plants are distinguished chiefly by the structural and physiological characteristics of their cytoplasm. In some epithelial cells and in some connective tissue elements, the cytoplasm retains characteristics similar to those of embryonic tissue and appears to lose only a part of its water content and to increase in viscosity. In other cell types, differentiation may be more developed, leading to profound changes in the structure and chemical organization of the cytoplasm. These changes are adapted to the special function of the cell and are generally permanent, lasting throughout the life of the cell, and permit one to recognize cytoplasmic differentiations from the inclusions or paraplasm.

Differentiations can be considered as derivations of special adaptations or modifications of some of the main cellular components, such as the plasma membrane or the cell matrix, or of the cellular organoids. A number of these derivatives have already been studied in different parts of this book. For example, in Chapter 12 we discussed the differentiations of the cell surface in plant cells; in Chapter 8, the complex modifications that the *plasma membrane* of animal cells may undergo in adapting to special functions; and in Chapter 10, some special differentiations of the *vacuolar system*. In Chapter 21 we will refer to some products of the activity of the *centrioles* forming cilia (Fig. 21–11), flagella and the rod

and cone outer segment (Fig. 21–17). Most cytoplasmic differentiations take place in the cytoplasmic matrix. For example, the *myofibrils* and *myofilaments* found in muscle cells (Chap. 21) and the *neurotubules* and *neurofilaments* observed in neurons (Chap. 22) are produced in this region of the cytoplasm. Here as an example we will refer to the epitheliofibrils.

Epitheliofibrils (Tonofibrils). To this type of differentiation belong a number of fibrillar structures found in epithelial cells that are especially adapted to maintain the cohesive and mechanical properties of the tissue. These *epitheliofibrils*, or *tonofibrils*, are made of *keratin*, a fibrillar protein that has special mechanical properties and that forms the main bulk of some epithelial derivatives, such as hair, wool and nails.

As shown in Figure 19–1, the main portion of the cytoplasmic matrix is composed of the fine filamentous component represented by the keratin fibrils. The rest of the ground cytoplasm is reduced to a few membranes of the endoplasmic reticulum and ribosomes. This process of differentiation, called *keratinization*, advances from the deeper layers of the tissue toward the most peripheral cells and is accompanied by a progressive reduction of the active cytoplasm represented by few mitochondria and the endoplasmic reticulum.

Figure 19–1 shows that the keratin fibrils are distributed along special lines that are related to the mechanical forces acting on the tissue. This is particularly evident at the base of the cell, where there are dense spots called "anchoring attachments," which are comparable to the desmosomes described in Chapter 8. Also at the base of the cell keratin fibers converge toward a denser spot on the surface membrane. These attachment points maintain the adhesion of the epithelial cell to the subjacent connective tissue. This adhesion may change drastically in some experimental or pathologic conditions. If, for example, a wound is produced, the attachment points disappear, and the cell may become motile on the subjacent tissue. When cicatrization of the wound is completed, the attachment points reappear.[4]

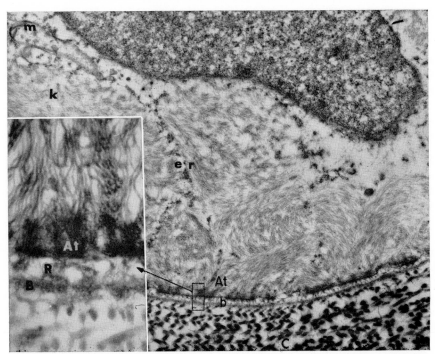

Figure 19–1. Electron micrograph of a basal epithelial cell of the tadpole. The cytoplasm is filled with keratin fibrils (*k*). *At,* anchoring attachments; *b,* basement membrane; *C,* collagen fibrils; *er,* endoplasmic reticulum; *m,* mitochondrion. ×40,000. **Inset:** Portion of the cell magnified to 150,000×. (Courtesy of K. Hama.)

GROWTH AND RENEWAL OF CELL POPULATIONS

The preceding section stated the commonly accepted opinion that as cells become differentiated they lose the capacity of cell division. According to this view, the cells that divide actively in an adult organism must be undifferentiated. In this respect they would have the same properties as the unicellular organisms that divide continuously as long as nutritive material is available. However, in multicellular complex organisms, either plants or animals, most tissues undergo a differentiation process of varying degree and some of them may lose the ability to divide and may undergo, later on, senescence and death.

At the beginning of this century, Bizzozero classified tissues from this viewpoint into *labile, stable* and *perennial,* and in later times more precise classifications have been proposed.[5, 6] In *labile tissues,* division and cell renewal may take place rapidly. One striking example is the red blood cell, which spends an average time of only 120 days in the blood stream before being destroyed. It can be easily calculated that in man, to replace the cells destroyed, two million new red blood cells per second must enter the circulation. Assuming that the mitosis of precursor cells lasts for one hour, in the bone marrow there should be about 8000 million cells undergoing mitosis at any given moment to maintain the stock of blood cells. Remember that bone marrow is much used for study of mitosis and chromosomes in the human (see Chap. 13).

At the other extreme are some *perennial cells,* such as the *neurons,* which multiply only during the embryonic period and then differentiate, remaining constant in number throughout the life of the organism.

New Methods for Investigation of Cell Renewal

In recent years new and more precise methods have been introduced into cell biology for the study of the proliferative behavior of cell populations. One approach, essentially biochemical, consists of determining the DNA content of the entire animal or of the different organs and from this calculating the number of nuclei and how this changes with age. The other approach, more cytologic, consists of determining the mitotic rate or the number of cell nuclei that incorporate radioactive DNA precursors.

Estimation of the Number of Nuclei from DNA Determination. Numerous investigators[7, 8] have used the measurement of total DNA to estimate the number of nuclei in tissues. This is based on the fact that with few exceptions (e.g., some liver nuclei) the DNA content per nucleus is constant for the species (see Chap. 17). If in a rat one determines the DNA content of an organ and divides by 6.2 mμg, which is the DNA content of a single nucleus, one obtains the *total number of nuclei.* Since in most tissues of young rats each cell has only

one nucleus, this determination is also the *total number of cells.*

Figure 19–2 shows the possibilities of this method. Analyzing the DNA content of a whole rat from the embryo to the adult, one can calculate that: at 10 days before birth there are 50 million cells, at birth 3000 million and at 90 days 67,000 million.[7] With this method one can also calculate the *increase in number of nuclei per day* and the amount of material that is associated with one nucleus. This index, called the *weight per nucleus* (organ weight divided by the number of nuclei), increases with enlargement of the cell or with accumulation of intercellular material (see Fig. 19–2).

Determination of the Mitotic Rate. This can be determined after the injection of *colchicine* or some derivative (e.g., Colcemid) that arrests cell divi-

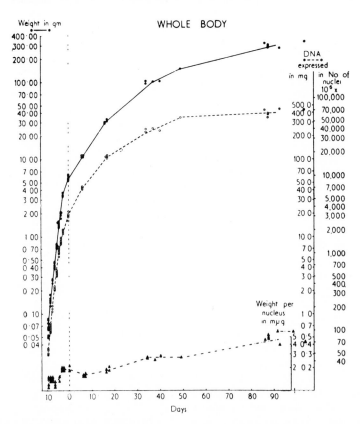

Figure 19–2. Semilogarithmic plot of the weight in grams (dots), DNA in milligrams (circles) of the whole body of the rat and weight per nucleus in mμg (triangles), versus the age in days of the rat. DNA is expressed both in milligrams and in number of nuclei. Time 0 corresponds to the time of birth of the rat. Notice that in the prenatal period there is a steep rise in weight and DNA content. (From M. Enesco and C. P. Leblond.)

sion at metaphase. In general, colchicine is administered during the day to four groups of animals at six-hour intervals and then they are sacrificed and the tissues fixed six hours after the injection. The total percentage of cells that enter in mitosis over a 24 hour period constitutes the *daily mitotic rate*.

Determination of Cell Division by Radioautography. A great advance has been introduced with the use of methods for labeling cells with radioisotopes and tracing them by autoradiography. This labeling technique is based on the fact that DNA synthesis generally takes place at a stage prior to cell division (Chap. 17). In the past, P^{32}-phosphate and C^{14}-adenine were used, but apparently these DNA components produced considerable radiation damage to the cell, and the resolution of the autographs was poor with P^{32} and only fair with C^{14} (see Chap. 6).

The introduction of thymidine labeled with tritium (H^3)[9] has overcome these difficulties; cells can be traced for months without apparent signs of radiation damage. Furthermore, DNA is the only compound marked with thymidine, and, as explained in Chapter 5, the resolution is excellent.

If radioautographs are prepared a short time after administering H^3-thymidine, the nuclei that were passing through the *synthetic* or *S-period* are marked and are still single at the G_2 phase (Fig. 17–5). If the study is made at a later time, G_2 cells divide and the two daughter cells are in turn labeled. Thus with this method dividing cells may be identified before and after division.

CELL POPULATION IN EMBRYONIC LIFE. The rat embryo contains 50 million cells 10 days prior to birth, i.e., at 12 to 13 days of embryonic life. (The total embryonic life of the rat is 22 to 23 days.) Assuming that the egg divisions are regular and without cell loss, one can calculate that at 10 days prior to birth there have been 25 to 26 cell generations with a half day division time. In other words, in the early embryo the number of cells should double every half day. In the last 10 days of embryonic life the doubling time has increased to 1.7 days and growth is slower. There are 6000

million cells at birth (Fig. 19–2). The study with H^3-thymidine in a 16 day old rat embryo reveals that most cells are dividing and only some nerve cells have stopped dividing at that time.

Classification of Cell Populations

The application of the methods just mentioned to the study of growth and renewal of cell populations during the postnatal life has led to the classification of the different cell types into three groups designated as: *static, expanding* and *renewing* cell populations (see reference 10).

Static Cell Populations. These are *homogeneous groups of cells in which no mitotic activity can be detected* and in which *the total DNA content remains constant*. Only the nerve cells, either central or peripheral, were found not to divide after the age of seven days. The striated muscle cells, which were believed to belong in this group, show mitosis and should be classified in the second group. In the nervous system not all the cells belong to the static population. In fact, some neuroglia cells and subependymal cells of young animals may be labeled with thymidine. One of the most important characteristics of perennial cells is the constant increase in cell volume that runs parallel to the growth of the organism and is proportional to the total volume of the body.[11] These cells persist until the death of the organism, undergoing senescent changes linked to the senescence of the individual.

Expanding Cell Populations. These are *homogeneous groups of cells showing scattered mitosis in numbers that account for the increase in the total DNA content*. This implies that the life of each cell extends for as long as that of the individual and that new cells are produced by division only to cover the growth of the tissue. In these cells the DNA content test shows a progressive increase in number of nuclei, but the rate slows down with age in a way that is more pronounced than for the whole body (Fig. 19–2). By labeling the cells with colchicine and H^3-thymidine, it can be observed that a few scattered cells are undergoing mitosis. Contrary to the former belief, the dividing cells that are observed are fully differentiated. For example, a secretory cell of the pancreatic acinus may undergo mitosis.

Examples of expanding cells are: the pancreas, the thyroid gland, the kidney and the adrenal and salivary glands. Skeletal and cardiac muscle tissues, believed by Bizzozero and others to be perennial cells, show also scattered divisions throughout life and should be considered as expanding cell populations.

One impressive characteristic of expanding cells is that the mitotic index, which is normally slow, increases dramatically with adequate stimuli. For example, after partial extirpation of the liver, or unilateral nephrectomy, there is a rapid regeneration and hypertrophy. In the thyroid gland the injection of thyroid-stimulating hormone of the hypophysis produces a wave of mitotic activity.

It can be assumed that normally the liver produces a substance that inhibits its own growth. Partial extirpation would reduce the amount of circulating inhibitors, thus allowing for more cell divisions.[12, 13]

Renewing Cell Populations. These are *homogeneous groups of cells in which mitosis is abundant and exceeds that required for the total increase in DNA content.* In other words, in renewing populations the high production of cells is balanced by a corresponding cell loss. Red blood cells, which have an average life of 120 days, are examples. In higher animals there are other examples that are even more extraordinary. In a 90 day old rat it has been calculated that about 3000 million cells are released daily from the digestive tract! Since in the entire animal there are about 67,000 million cells (Fig. 19–2), it thus seems that the digestive tract produces daily $\frac{1}{22}$ of this entire number. The rapid renewal of cells in the intestine can be demonstrated clearly with H^3-thymidine (see Fig. 6–17). Also, in the epidermis cells are renewed rapidly to replace the dead ones that are shed at the surface. It can be assumed that this supply of new cells is abundant in order to replace

automatically any damaged cell. This process is even more marked in regeneration during wound healing.

Other renewing populations are the testis (which continuously sheds spermatozoa), the lung (which produces "dust cells"), the thymus, the lymph ganglia and the bone marrow and all hematopoietic organs in general. Also, in the sebaceous glands cell renovation is continuous.

The duration of life in labile cells is regulated by complex factors. In some cases external mechanical and chemical factors can be of some importance. In others, such as vaginal epithelium, hormonal factors have a major role. The number of circulating blood cells is kept constant by a balance between the number of cells destroyed and the number produced by the hematopoietic organs. In renewing cell systems there should be an outlet to eliminate the cells produced. Thus the cells lining the outer or inner surfaces are cast off and those of the hematopoietic organs pass into the circulation.

Neoplastic Cell Populations

It is interesting to compare the different cell populations of a normal individual with that found in a cancerous tissue. We have seen above that whereas embryonic cells grow exponentially, soon after birth cell populations become either *static, expanding* or *renewing.* In static cells division has ceased entirely, whereas in expanding cells division continues at a decreasing rate and in *renewing cells* the mitotic index is maintained, to insure replacement of cells. In neoplastic tissue the cell population increases considerably by mitosis, which varies from one type of tumor to another, but, in contrast with an expanding normal population, the rate does not decrease with age. For example, in kidney or adrenal cells the mitotic rate slows down and eventually tends to stabilize, whereas *neoplastic cells* divide indefinitely at the same rate.

Compared to normal renewing cells, neoplastic cells have in common the high mitotic index, but whereas normal renewing cells give rise to cells that lose the ability to divide and eventually die, neoplastic cells retain the capacity of division. Another difference is that renewing systems have an outlet for the cells, whereas cancer systems seldom do. Furthermore, renewing cells do not have the invasive properties that are characteristic of some neoplasms. (For literature, see reference 10.)

SENESCENCE AND DEATH OF THE CELL

After an initial undifferentiated phase in which differentiation occurs, most cells pass finally into a terminal period of senescence, which ends in death. These last phases of cell life are still little understood, and have not been completely studied with all the cytologic and cytochemical methods at our disposal. Relatively more is known of *cellular pathology,* which is the study of abnormal processes that take place in the cell under the action of various agents or by metabolic, genetic or other alterations. This study is not, strictly speaking, cytology, for which reason we shall consider here only those modifications that characterize senescence and death when these processes occur normally, without the addition of extraneous factors or perturbations.

In studying these problems in cells and tissues we must not confuse them with those of senility and death of the entire organism, although they are intimately related. Indeed, even in the embryo some cell populations continually undergo senescence and dying; and the entire individual is enveloped by dead cells (external layers of the epidermis) that serve for protection. On the other hand, the death of the individual does not imply the immediate cessation of vital phenomena in all cells. For example, the ciliary movement of the cells of the trachea and bronchi continues long after the heart has ceased to beat, and the ameboid activity of leukocytes continues. In laboratory animals that have been killed, certain cells survive as long as 120 hours after death.[14] Furthermore, many cells transplanted at the time of the death of the individual continue to live in other individuals or in tissue cultures. Nevertheless, it is evident that the death of cells of vital importance to the organism, such as those of the nervous tissue, finally causes the death of all the remaining cells.

The study of senescence in various cells and tissues demonstrates that elements that retain the capacity of dividing continuously do not grow old. Division and growth of cells apparently involve a physicochemical renewal of the cell and prevent senescence. This is true in unicellular organisms, which generally reproduce continuously and therefore are potentially immortal. This also happens in certain cells cultivated in vitro. The famous culture, begun by Carrel, of cells from a fragment of chicken heart continues to grow after more than 50 years! These cells require only the renewal of the nutritive fluids to continue to live an apparently endless existence. However, the concept of the "potential immortality" of the cell should not be taken too strictly. In fact, nerve cells, although they cease to divide early in life, do not age faster than the basal cells of the skin, which undergo continuous renewal during the lifetime of the individual. (For a discussion of this concept of immortality and cellular life see reference 15.)

Cytologic and Cytochemical Changes in Senescence

When a cell senesces, a series of morphologic and physicochemical changes takes place. One of the most characteristic is the accumulation of the "exhaustion" pigment (sometimes also called "wear and tear" pigment or "abnutzungs" pigment), which is observed particularly in the nerve cell and myocardial tissue and to a lesser degree in the cells of the liver, kidney, testis, ovary, thyroid and so on. This senility pigment is somewhat related to the so-called "ceroid pigments," a name first applied to a yellow or orange-yellow pigment that does not dissolve in fat solvents and can be stained with Sudan.[16] This type of pigment has been found in nerve cells and also in liver and atheromatous arteries. From the chemical viewpoint the pigment is considered to be derived from the oxidation of unsaturated lipids.[17, 18]

Recently the value of pigmentation as a constant sign of the aging of nerve cells has been discussed. It is believed, in general, that the accumulation of pigment in senile cells is due to the progressive difficulty the cells have in excreting poorly soluble products and that this functional alteration is an important factor in senescence. (In Chapter 20 we will mention that the lack of lipolytic enzymes in lysosomes makes the disposal of lipoid materials more difficult.)

Other common cytologic changes in aging cells are: the accumulation of small lipid droplets, a decrease of the basophil substance (in the nerve cells) and a decrease of the cell volume (hypotrophy). Hypotrophy is considerable in striated muscle fibers, but it is difficult in this case to decide whether it is due exclusively to senescence or also to lack of activity.

The process of senescence in the epidermal cells has been studied with numerous histologic and cytochemical techniques. The changes in the viscosity of the cell protoplasm have been studied also by means of ultracentrifugation.

Tissue culture techniques permit favorable studies of senescence because aging processes and death can occur in the course of a single cultivation. Cultured cells, like the whole organism, pass through a series of stages, but at a much faster rate. The stages might be listed as follows: "(1) increase in mass, (2) differentiation and organization, (3) equilibrium, (4) senility, and (5) death and dissolution."[19] Aging starts "by a remission of growth and adjustment to a minimum activity, the formation of intercellular substance, increase in the death quota of the cells, reduction in residual growth energy" and finally morphologic cell changes.[19] These changes are first seen at the periphery of the culture and are generally characterized by vacuolization and infiltration of the cytoplasm with fat; they are followed by cell disintegration.

In senescence the nucleus often stains more intensely and is shrunken; simultaneously, its structural details are progressively lost. This process, which is called *nuclear pyknosis* (Gr. *pyknos* dense), leads to cell death (Fig. 19–3).

Senescence in Nerve Cells. Cell senescence has been studied in great detail, particularly in nerve cells. In normal senility the following take place constantly: a retraction of the cell boundaries, "a change in the nucleus, consisting in the loss of transparency of the nucleus sap, a notable diminution of the chromidial substance of Nissl and a fragmentation of the Golgi complex (golgiorrhexis). Furthermore, in some species, a tendency is seen for the nucleus to divide by amitotic division (for example, division of the nucleolus, globulation of the nucleus and even a true division)."[20]

In ganglion cells of young and adult dogs, glycogen is found in the cytoplasm. In senile dogs this is replaced by a mucoprotein. The ascorbic acid content of the nerve cell decreases with senility, and a pigment with high alkaline phosphatase activity is deposited.[21]

Great differences are observed in the time of onset and speed of aging among the different cell types of the nervous system. In some cells only shrinkage is found. In most cells, however, large vacuoles containing fat or minute droplets of lipofuscin are found.[22] A degeneration of neurofibrils in relation to the accumulation of lipofuscin has been described.[23]

Several studies tend to show that the histologic and cytologic picture of old age in individual organs is not the result of "simple" processes of degeneration and atrophy. The changes seem to be relatively complex and to depend not only on cellular atrophy, but on interactions among the different cell types under the conditions of senescence of the organism.

For example, in the nervous system, while the nerve cells show a series of degenerative changes and many of them actually die and disappear, some neuroglial cells (particularly the oligodendroglia and microglia perineuronal satellites) actually increase in number and appear to participate in the removal of dead nerve cells. Furthermore, a marked proliferation of the relatively

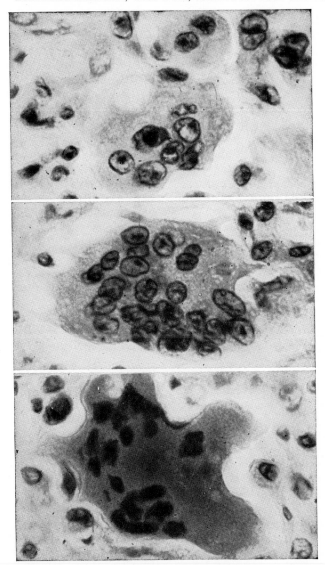

FIGURE 19–3.   Life cycle of myeloplax (polykaryocyte) in a benign myeloplaxoma. **Above,** young cell. **Center,** adult cell. **Below,** senile phase. Pyknotic nuclei with their irregular outlines are visible. The cytoplasm has become darkened and retracted. (Courtesy of D. Brachetto-Brian.)

undifferentiated cells of the intralobular ducts has been observed in the pancreas. This process results in numerous cystlike spaces formed by the multiplying duct cells.[20] Whereas fibrosis is a conspicuous feature of senility in some organs, as in the thyroid gland, it is almost nonexistent in others, as in the liver. In the liver, giant nuclei and intranuclear inclusions are often seen. (The varied and complicated senile changes occurring in the different organs necessitate a detailed histologic and cytologic study of the process in each type of tissue. This is beyond the limits of this book. See references 14 and 24.)

Biochemical Changes in Senescence

From the biochemical viewpoint, aside from the infiltration by pigments and lipids as just mentioned, changes in both the organic and inorganic cell components have been observed. One of the most remarkable is an increase in the calcium content of the blood and several tissues. On the other hand, decalcification takes place in bones. An increase in the calcium content of the peripheral zone (cortex) of the cytoplasm has been observed in plant cells, the sea urchin, Rotifera ova and other tissues. These changes have been demonstrated by cytochemical methods, such as microincineration (Chap. 6). They are probably related to a decrease in cell permeability. In Rotifera the experimental reduction of calcium increases longevity. It has been suggested that Ca is bound to ribonucleoprotein at all the surfaces and that age changes are reflected in Ca binding.[25] Little data has been obtained about other inorganic compounds, but an increase in iron and potassium and a decrease in magnesium are indicated.

Cholesterol and insoluble proteins, especially globulins, increase. Several enzymatic systems decrease with advanced age, such as acid and alkaline phosphatase and esterase in general. Tissue respiration decreases and protein synthesis is inhibited. Histochemically a decrease in "carbonyl groups" as revealed by the plasmal and other reactions has been observed in aging tissues.[26] The reaction is given mainly by the "plasmalogens" and particularly by the acetylphosphatides (Chap. 6).

Recently these studies of changes in senescence have reached the field of molecular biology. Some of the molecules of cells and tissues may age because they are not renewed as the others. Changes in the DNA molecule could be of great importance. It is thought that with age there is an increase in cross linkages in the nucleoproteins with an increase in stability. This would reduce the action of DNA on the synthetic processes of the cell. This increased stability of DNA would be related to its relationship with the histones.[27]

The best known molecular model of aging is that of collagen. This constitutes about 30 per cent of the protein of the human body and is present in large amounts in the dermis, tendons, cartilage, bone and several parenchymal tissues. Once it is formed (see Chap. 7), the collagen molecule remains basically unchanged throughout the life of the individual.

With age covalent cross linkages increase continuously, and reduce the solubility of the molecule and produce other mechanical and physicochemical changes in collagen that can be analyzed quantitatively. Certain aldehydes (such as formaldehyde) can produce cross linkages in collagen, such as those that take place in leather tanning. (Leather is essentially the skin corion or dermis submitted to a tanning procedure.)

It has been thought that in the metabolism of aging individuals and in certain pathologic conditions some aldehydes are produced. In certain cases of arthrosis and arthritis the cross linkages between collagen molecules increase. One interesting case is that of the eye lens, which becomes harder and harder with age. This is apparently due to an increase in —S—S— linkages in the protein. These molecular changes may be due to extrinsic factors, and one way of treating them could be to avoid the action of such factors or to revert the process of protein denaturation (i.e., solubilize the protein).[28]

Theories of Cell Senescence

We are still a long way from knowing the causes that determine the aging of the cell. Various theories have been elaborated, which in general deal only with partial aspects of the problem. Some of these theories stress the role of *endogenous factors,* by which we mean the progressive and irreversible alterations of the protoplasm. Other theories emphasize *exogenous factors,* or modifications of the surrounding medium. Finally, others state that the cell has in itself the *genetic factors* that limit the duration of its life.

Endogenous Factors. Among the theories that stress endogenous factors is one that suggests that senescence is due to an alteration of the *colloidal state* of the protoplasm. According to this theory, the protoplasmic colloid becomes less dispersed, with loss of water and of electrical charge. This process as a whole is called *protoplasmic hysteresis.* Other conspicuous colloidal modifications are: an increase in protein substances that, like keratin, are resistant to digestion and dissolution by enzymes; a decrease in water content; and an increase in cellular consistency. Cornification, which takes place in certain stratified epithelia, can be considered as a rapid phenomenon of this type. This starts at the basal cells, which divide by mitosis, and continues toward the surface, where cornification and death ensue. Simultaneously, the protein content of the cells increases and the isoelectric point of the proteins is displaced from the acid toward the neutral point.

Other investigators give considerable importance to the accumulation of residues that, along with condensation of colloids and diminution of cell permeability, might disturb the total metabolism of the cell. However, one may raise the question whether the accumulation of pigment is the cause of senescence or simply one of its manifestations.

Exogenous Factors. The medium in which the cell lives also seems to have considerable importance, and changes in its composition may influence cell development and senescence. For example, with aging, the regulatory mechanisms that maintain the uniformity of the blood are disturbed. At the same time, the various tissue fluids are altered, and the changes may not be the same in every case. Thus cell senescence is accompanied by a senescence of the internal medium, and these two processes not only appear to be correlated but also interdependent.

The importance of the hormonal control of these processes has been emphasized. Low molecular weight substances such as coenzymes, vitamins and some hormones, influence growth, but, because their formation and function depend on other governing regulators, they cannot be directly connected with the primary cause of aging. The governing hormones, such as those of the pituitary gland (e.g., growth and gonadotropic hormones), are substances of higher molecular weight. It has been suggested that a decrease in the synthesis of these governing hormones could be the primary cause of aging.[29]

In cells that are cultured in vitro, senility is primarily due to external factors, such as the accumulation of metabolic products or lack of foodstuffs. When these causes are eliminated by transfer or change of the medium, the cells are rejuvenated. However, in the plasma of

senile individuals there are other factors that may affect the life history of cultured cells.

The studies of Carrel and his collaborators have shown that blood plasma not only contains growth-promoting substances that stimulate the growth of a tissue culture, but also inhibitory substances. The latter increase with the age of the animal and reach a maximum concentration in old age. The inhibitory substances could be considered as the cause of cell senescence. However, it must not be forgotten that tissue fluids are produced by the cells, so that these inhibitory substances may be the consequence and not the cause of senescence. Although this problem has not been completely solved, it is evident that the internal media contain at least some of the factors that limit proliferation.[19]

Genetic Factors. Some investigators postulate that factors that lie in the cell itself determine irreversible vital cycles. According to this view, certain cells of the organism not only have a fixed determination of their specific functional and morphologic differentiation but also a genetic predetermined limit of their potential life.

Cell Death

The senescence of the cell leads finally to catabiosis (Gr. *kata* down + *bios* life) and to death. The histopathologic literature on cell death is abundant, but precise definitions and a clear understanding of the purely cytophysiologic alterations are lacking. In dealing with cell death it is at times difficult to separate the strictly physiologic from the pathologic processes.

Cell death is generally defined as the *irreversible cessation of vital phenomena*. Nevertheless, it is at times difficult to determine the instant at which a cell ceases to live. Except when death is produced rapidly by agents that cause the protoplasm to coagulate or precipitate quickly (as in fixation, heating, or the use of various toxic agents), cellular processes cease gradually. A cell may be injured irreparably, and nevertheless some of its functions may persist for a certain length of time. If a tissue is ground until all of the cell boundaries are destroyed (brei), several metabolic activities, such as oxygen consumption, fermentation and glycolysis, may persist. Nevertheless, when these processes are studied in relation to time, appreciable differences are noticed. In the brei the majority of metabolic processes decrease relatively rapidly and disappear, whereas in the intact cell these are maintained at the same level as long as cell vitality is conserved.

Cytologically, a retraction of the cytoplasm or a characteristic alteration of the nucleus may often be noted in dying cells, but these changes are found only when the process is far advanced. In some cells, the lack of reproduction, growth or movement may be important criteria of death. However, they do not have a general value, because in many cells and tissues these processes are not observed even in the living state. Variations in the oxidation-reduction potential or pH also have no value, although acidosis is generally found in dying cells. With the ultramicroscope it is often possible to see brownian movement. However, this phenomenon may be apparent in living cells. Dead cells seem to absorb ultraviolet light more intensely.

A cytologic criterion of cell death that is usually considered reliable is the diffuse staining of the cytoplasm and of the nucleus by vital dyes (neutral red, methylene blue and so forth). In a living cell these stains are accumulated in circumscribed granules or vacuoles in the cytoplasm, but after death the cytoplasm and the nucleus stain intensely and diffusely.

The following have been considered as criteria of cell death by means of supravital staining with neutral red: "(1) loss of color of the granules and vacuoles, (2) diffuse staining of the cytoplasm and nucleus, (3) the appearance of a sharp and distinct nuclear membrane and a change in the texture of the cytoplasm and nucleus."[14]

In cultured cells the following changes are ordinarily considered as signs of death: (1) retraction of pseudopodia and rounded cell, (2) coagulation and shriveling of the nucleus, (3) dissolution of mitochondria and (4) diffuse vital staining of the cytoplasm and nucleus.[24]

Postmortem Modification of the Cell. Necrobiosis

When cell death occurs rapidly and all enzymatic activity ceases simultaneously (as in fixation, heating and so on), cell structure is not altered after death. Otherwise, however, a cell seldom dies rapidly, and, in general, autolytic "postmortem" phenomena occur.

In studying the modifications that take place when the cell dies, modifications that precede and lead to such a death must be distinguished from those that occur after death. The former are grouped generally under the name *necrobiosis* (Gr. *nekros* death + *bios* life) when death is slow and gradual. Some necrobiotic changes were described in our discussion of cell senescence. It was said at that time that these changes vary from one type of cell to another. In certain cases the viscosity of the cytoplasm is diminished, as evidenced by the appearance of brownian movement. Finally, liquefaction occurs (*necrobiosis by liquefaction*). In other cases the viscosity increases and the protoplasm gels (*gelation*) or coagulates (*necrobiosis by coagulation*).

In many cells, death is preceded by a shorter or longer period characterized by an alteration of the normal metabolism and by degenerative changes, such as fatty, waxy, hydropic, pigmentary or other types of degeneration. Since these processes are more frequently due to external factors (toxic, infectious and the like), they are studied in detail in general pathology.

The *postmortem modifications* generally result from the activity of intracellular enzymes that begin their action after death. These are hydrolytic enzymes that attack and break down the large molecules of the cell, particularly protein molecules (proteolysis). At the same time, the lack of oxygen favors anaerobic fermentation and the formation of various acids, especially lactic acid. The accumulation of small molecules and ions resulting from autolysis increases the osmotic pressure and causes water to enter the cell and thus the cell swells.

It is generally admitted that one of the phenomena following death is the irreversible coagulation of protoplasm. This may persist for a long time, but is generally followed by the digestion and liquefaction of the cell. Frequently liquefaction is preceded by the swelling of the cell and by the appearance of protein granules in the midst of the cytoplasm, which give it a turbid and characteristic dusty aspect (cloudy swelling). This process may occur also in living cells altered by the influence of toxins, infectious diseases and so on. In this case we are dealing with a degenerative change that may be reversible.

The cloudy swelling of the cell is preceded by the accumulation of acids in the protoplasm and by the lowering of the pH (acidosis). This accumulation of ions increases the imbibition of water and at the same time brings about precipitation of the proteins of the cytoplasmic matrix in the form of fine granules. It is also common to find that minute lipid droplets appear, produced by the dissociation of the lipoprotein complexes (*lipophanerosis*). The cloudy swelling may be reversed when it is due to degeneration. When the alteration occurs after cell death, it is generally followed by a progressive imbibition of water and finally by the disintegration and dissolution of the cell.

Cloudy swelling should not be confused with a similar appearance of the cytoplasm that may be produced by the alteration of mitochondria. We know that the mitochondrion (Chap. 11) is one of the most sensitive parts of the cell, and that after death it rapidly fragments into granules that swell. In cloudy swelling the granules apparently result from the separation of the phases and the precipitation of the proteins of the ground cytoplasm.

In postmortem alteration the *behavior of the nucleus* differs from that of the cytoplasm. In general, the structure and stainability of the nucleus resist the autolytic phenomena for a longer time than that of the cytoplasm, and in many cases, the stainability may even increase.

This process, called *pyknosis*, is generally accompanied by a shrinkage of the nucleus and the disappearance of its structural details (perhaps due to dissolution of nucleic acid to nuclear sap). Cytochemical studies of pyknosis made with cytophotometric methods have shown that the increase in basophilia is not real because it does not correspond to an increase of absorbing material but to the diminution in nuclear volume. A sequence of three decreasing sizes of pyknotic nuclei (stages I, II, III) have been recognized. In the first stage, the deoxyribonucleic acid content does not decrease significantly but the protein content diminishes to nearly half normal. Later, deoxyribonucleic acid is lost progressively. This has been interpreted as an indication that proteolysis takes place first. Nucleases come into action later and break down the nucleic acid molecules. The nucleus then loses its stainability and dissolves (*karyolysis*), either with or without previous nuclear fragmentation (*karyorrhexis*). The nucleohistone complex of pyknotic nuclei has been studied cytochemically.[28]

GENERAL REFERENCES

Bloom, W. (1937) Cellular differentiation and tissue culture. *Physiol. Rev.*, 17:589.

Bourne, G. H. (1957) Aging from a biological and cellular point of view. In: *Modern trends in geriatrics*. Butterworth & Co., London.

Cowdry, E. V. (1952) *Problems of aging.* (Revised by A. Lansing.) The Williams & Wilkins Co., Baltimore.

Kunz, A., ed. (1952) Aging of the nervous system. *J. Geront.*, 7:439.

Leblond, C. P. (1964) Classification of cell populations on the basis of their proliferative behavior. *J. Nat. Cancer Inst.*, 14:119.

Leblond, C. P., and Walker, B. E. (1956) Renewal of cell populations. *Physiol. Rev.*, 36: 255.

Levi, G. (1934) Explanation. *Ergebn. Anat. Entwickl.-Gesch.*, 31:398.

Levi, G. (1946) *Accrescimento et senescenza.* "La Nuova Italia" Editrice, Florence.

Needham, J. (1942) *Biochemistry and morphogenesis.* Cambridge University Press, London.

Nowinski, W. W., ed. (1960) *Fundamental aspects of normal and malignant growth.* Elsevier Pub. Co., Amsterdam.

Spemann, H. (1938) *Embryonic development and induction.* Yale University Press, New Haven.

CITED REFERENCES

1. Spemann, H. (1938) *Embryonic development and induction.* Yale University Press, New Haven.
2. Needham, J. (1942) *Biochemistry and morphogenesis.* Cambridge University Press, London.
3. Bloom, W. (1937) *Physiol. Rev., 17:*589.
4. Weiss, P., and Ferris, W. (1954) *Exp. Cell Res., 6:*546.
5. Cowdry, E. V. (1952) *Problems of aging.* (Revised by A. Lansing.) The Williams & Wilkins Co., Baltimore.
6. Leblond, C. P., and Walker, B. E. (1956) *Physiol. Rev., 36:*255.
7. Enesco, M., and Leblond, C. P. (1962) *J. Embryol. Exp. Morphol., 10:*530.
8. Nowinski, W. W., ed. (1960) *Fundamental aspects of normal and malignant growth.* Elsevier Pub. Co., Amsterdam.
9. Hughes, W. L., Bond, V. P., Brecher, G., Cronkite, E. P., Painter, R. B., Quaster, H., and Sherman, F. G. (1958) *Proc. Nat. Acad. Sci., 44:*476.
10. Leblond, C. P. (1964) *J. Nat. Cancer Inst. 14:*119.
11. Levi, G. (1934) *Ergebn. Anat. Entwickl.-Gesch., 31:*398.
12. Glinos, A. D., and Gey, G. O. (1952) *Proc. Soc. Exp. Biol. Med., 80:*421.
13. Stich, H. F., and Florian, M. L., (1958) *Canad. J. Biochem. Physiol., 36:*855.
14. Lewis, W. H., and McCoy, C. C. (1922) *Bull. Johns Hopkins Hosp., 33:*284.
15. Bourne, G. H. (1957) Aging from a biological and cellular point of view. In *Modern trends in geriatrics.* Butterworth & Co., London.
16. Lillie, R. D. (1942) *Publ. Hlth. Rep (Wash.), 57:*502.
17. Casselman, W. G. B. (1951) *J. Exp. Med. 94:*549.
18. Hartfort, W. S. (1953) *J. Geront., 8:*158.
19. Fischer, A. (1946) *Biology of tissue cells* Cambridge University Press, London.
20. Andrew, W. (1941) *J. Anat., 75:*406.
21. Sulkin, N. M., and Kuntz, A. (1952) *J Geront., 7:*533.
22. Vogt, O. (1951) *J. Geront., 6,* suppl.: 164.
23. Sosa, J. M. (1952) *J. Geront., 7:*191.
24. Levi, G. (1946) *Accrescimento et senescenza.* "La Nuovo Italia" Editrice Florence.
25. Lansing, A. I. (1951) *J. Geront., 6,* suppl. 177.
26. Albert, S., and Leblond, C. P. (1949) *J Anat., 83:*183.
27. Von Euler, H. (1951) *J. Geront., 6,* suppl.: 84.
28. Vendrely, R., Alfert, M., Matsudaira, H., and Knobloch, A. (1958) *Exp. Cell Res., 14:* 295.

PART SEVEN

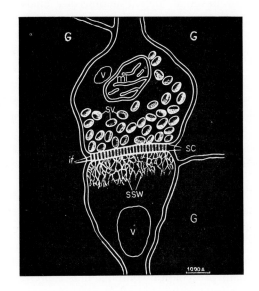

CELL

PHYSIOLOGY

The following chapters group some of the most important functions of the cell that were not discussed in previous chapters. These physiological processes are studied in intimate relationship with the structure and chemical organization of the cell.

First studied are all the processes grouped under cell permeability by which the cell regulates the entrance and exit of different ions and molecules. The important concepts of passive diffusion and active transport are introduced as well as their relationship to the osmotic and ionic concentration of the cell and the membrane potentials. The existence of noncharged and charged pores in the membrane is postulated, as well as the concept of permease systems that may serve for the specific chemical transport through the membrane.

In addition to the entrance of molecular material are less specific mechanisms of bulk ingestion of solids and fluids called phagocytosis and pinocytosis. These processes are intimately related to those of digestion, as well as to the lysosome, a particle that contains hydrolytic enzymes.

Because of these correlations all the above processes and structures will be studied in an integrated way.

Chapter 21 is a discussion of the different manifestations of mechanical activity and cell movement, such as cyclosis or cytoplasmic streaming, ameboid and ciliary movement and muscular contraction. The structural and biochemical aspects of all these functional processes are emphasized.

Muscle is an extraordinary example of macromolecular "machinery" adapted to the work of contraction. This can be explained as resulting from the interaction of fibrous protein molecules—actin and myosin—which can be recognized with the electron microscope in the intimate structure of the muscle fiber. Also, on the structural base of the sarcoplasmic reticulum it is possible to explain the conduction of the action potential to the interior of the muscle fiber and the functional synchronization of the myofibrils.

Muscle is an admirable example of physiological and structural integration, comparable only to mitochondria and chloroplasts. Both muscle and nerve tissues conduct impulses by way of action potentials, but nerve tissue is specially adapted to receive stimuli, to transmit impulses across the synapse and to induce a response at the effectors. The cellular bases of these functions are analyzed; special emphasis is placed on nerve conduction and synaptic transmission. In the nerve fiber the structural-functional relationship is related to the diameter of the nerve fiber, the presence and thickness of the myelin sheath and the internode length. In unmyelinated fibers, conduction implies a change in membrane potential which produces the nerve impulse. This is conducted without decrement in an *all-or-none* fashion. In myelinated fibers the action potential apparently jumps from one node to the next (saltatory conduction) and is conducted electronically along the internode. The ultrastructure of the axon, with the neurotubules and mitochondria, is probably related to the trophic function of the nerve fiber, including its continuous growth and the synthesis of material at the level of the nerve ending.

Synaptic transmission can be electrical but more frequently it is chemical and implies a neurochemical mechanism with the production of transmitter substances at the nerve ending. Both types of transmission have a structural foundation. Electrical synapses show a tight junction of the membranes without intermediary cleft. Chemical synapses have a complex structure both at the membranes and at the ending. The main presynaptic component is represented by the synaptic vesicles that are true quantal units of the transmitter.

With the electron microscope it is possible to distinguish the adrenergic synapses and to follow the changes induced by pharmacological agents that deplete or increase the amount of catecholamines. At present, by cell fractionation techniques the nerve endings and synaptic vesicles have been isolated, as well as the study of their content in transmitters and related enzymes. In general terms in chemical synapses a localized process of neurosecretion takes place, which is similar to the production of other neurohumors.

The last chapter is a discussion of cell secretion. This process is highly developed in numerous cells. The study of the secretory cycle is interesting, because it implies the coordinated intervention of all cellular components both in time and in space. This chapter is a review of the numerous processes and structures that have been studied in previous chapters.

It will be shown that cell fractionation techniques, the use of labeled substances and the electron microscope are permitting an integrated study of the synthesis of the secretion products and of their passage through the vacuolar system to be finally expelled from the cell.

The pancreatic cell is taken as a central example because in it the several stages of the secretory cycle are most characteristic and best studied.

CHAPTER 20

CELL

PERMEABILITY,

PHAGOCYTOSIS,

PINOCYTOSIS

AND THE

LYSOSOME

In Chapter 8 the chemical and molecular organization of the cell membrane were studied. The cell membrane is a thin layer (less than 100 Å) made of lipids and proteins with a compact molecular structure. Most of our knowledge about this membrane is indirect and based on its different properties. Although it can be visualized with the electron microscope, its detailed molecular organization cannot be detected, owing to its thinness. In this chapter we will consider several of the properties of the cell membrane that are related to its role in cell physiology. This is generally known as *cell permeability* but comprises a variety of important functions.

Permeability is fundamental to the functioning of the living cell and maintenance of satisfactory intracellular physiologic conditions. This function deter-

mines which substances can enter the cell, many of which may be necessary to maintain its vital processes and the synthesis of living substances. It also regulates the outflow of excretory material and water from the cell.

The presence of a membrane establishes a net difference between the *intracellular* fluid and the *extracellular* fluid in which the cell is bathed. This may be fresh or salt water in unicellular organisms grown in ponds or the sea, but in multicellular organisms the internal fluid, i.e., the blood, the lymph and especially the *interstitial* fluid, is in contact with the outer surface of the cell membrane. Thus the interchanges across the membrane are generally between this interstitial, or extracellular, fluid and that contained within the cell, or intracellular fluid.

Osmotic Pressure and
Physiological Solutions

One of the functions of the cell membrane is to maintain a balance between the osmotic pressure of the intracellular fluid and that of the interstitial fluid. In plant cells the osmotic pressure, which depends mainly on the concentration of small molecules and ions, maintains turgidity. When these cells are placed in a solution that has an osmotic pressure similar to that of the intracellular fluid (isotonic solution), the cytoplasm remains adherent to the cellulose wall and is not changed. When the solution of the medium is more concentrated (hypertonic solution), the cell loses water and the cytoplasm retracts from the rigid cell wall. On the other hand, when the solution of the medium is less concentrated than the intracellular fluid (hypotonic solution), the cell swells and eventually bursts. Since the plasma membrane of the cell is permeable to water and to certain solutes, the osmotic pressure is maintained by a mechanism that regulates the concentration of the dissolved substances within the cell.

At the end of the last century, Hamburger demonstrated that maintenance of osmotic pressure plays an important role in the life of the cell. He found that the cell membrane behaves like an

357

osmotic membrane and that a solution of 0.9 per cent sodium chloride maintains mammalian erythrocytes intact, whereas in less concentrated solutions they are hemolyzed. In a medium of higher concentration, the erythrocytes retract, owing to loss of water. These experiments are applicable to all animal cells.

From the biologic viewpoint, solutions can be grouped into three classes: *Isotonic* solutions have the same osmotic pressure as that of the cells. For example, 0.3 M solutions of nonelectrolytes are isotonic in relation to mammalian cells. *Hypotonic* solutions have a lower osmotic pressure than that of the cells. For example, a 0.66 per cent solution of sodium chloride, which is isotonic for amphibian erythrocytes, is hypotonic for mammalian cells. *Hypertonic* solutions have a higher osmotic pressure than that of the cells.

These findings led to the adoption of *physiologic solutions,* which have a total osmotic pressure the same as the blood of animals, and a balanced concentration of different ions. Examples of physiologic solutions are Ringer's and Tyrode's solutions.

In higher organisms, the osmotic pressure of the body as a whole is regulated principally by the kidneys, and the osmotic pressure of the interstitial fluid is about the same as that of the intracellular fluid.

In plants, the intracellular fluid has a higher osmotic pressure than the extracellular fluid. The cell is protected from bursting by a rigid cellulose wall. In general, the intracellular osmotic pressure is about 10 atmospheres, but in some special cases, such as in *Penicillium,* it may be as high as 100 atmospheres. Animal cells generally lack the turgidity that characterizes plant cells, although there are exceptions, such as *Tubularia.* On the other hand, the unfertilized eggs of some marine animals, such as the sea urchin, behave like genuine osmometers. Since they are spheroid, one can, by measuring the diameter, determine the volume and the changes that the egg undergoes with changes in the osmotic pressure of the medium. In this material it can be dem-

onstrated that the velocity of osmosis increases with temperature. Many bacteria behave in the same manner. Thus their internal osmotic pressure can be determined by finding the concentration at which their volume does not change.[1]

In many unicellular organisms the osmotic equilibrium is maintained by means of a contractile vacuole. This "organoid" extracts the water from the protoplasm and contracts, eliminating its contents into the external medium. The unicellular organisms that lack contractile vacuoles eliminate their excess water across the cell membrane.

Ionic Concentration and Electrical Potentials Across Membranes

In addition to differences in osmotic pressure between the intra- and extracellular fluids in certain organisms, in all of these there is: (a) a difference in ionic concentration and (b) an electrical potential across the membrane. These two properties are intimately related, since the electrical potential depends on an unequal distribution of the ions on both sides of the membrane.

Using fine microelectrodes with a tip of 1μ or less it is possible to penetrate through the membrane into a cell and also into the cell nucleus (Fig. 10–8) and to detect an *electrical potential* (also called the *resting,* or *steady,* potential), which is always negative inside. The values of this steady potential vary in different tissues between —20 and —100 millivolts (mv).

In studying the ionic concentration

TABLE 20–1.   IONIC CONCENTRATION AND STEADY POTENTIAL IN MUSCLE[*]

INTERSTITIAL FLUID		INTRACELLULAR FLUID
Cations { Na+	145	12
K+	4	155
Anions { Cl−	120	3.8
HCO$_3^-$	27	8
A− and others	7	155
Potential	0	−90 mv

* Modified from Woodbury.[2]

inside a muscle cell and in the interstitial fluid, one is struck by the great difference between the different ions. As shown in Table 20–1, the interstitial fluid has a high concentration of Na$^+$ and Cl$^-$ and the intracellular fluid a high concentration of K$^+$ and of larger organic anions (A$^-$).

DIFFUSION OR PASSIVE PERMEABILITY

In the absence of an intervening membrane, when two solutions of different concentration are mixed a process of intermixing called *diffusion* occurs. For example, if a concentrated solution of a sugar (e.g., saccharose) is put in contact with water, there will be a net movement (also called flux:M) of the solute from the region of higher concentration to that of a lower concentration. This flux is similar to the flow of water in a river, which is proportional to the depth of the stream. In this case the higher the difference in concentration between the two solutions (i.e., the *concentration gradient*), the more rapid the rate of diffusion.

The presence of a lipoprotein membrane, such as the plasma membrane, greatly modifies this diffusion or passive permeability. The passage across the membrane is very slow because this membrane cannot be permeated easily and is a formidable barrier to most types of molecules. Taking into account the current concepts on the molecular structure of the membrane (lipid in the middle and the two protein layers outside and inside, Fig. 8–2), the passing of molecules differs, depending on whether they are hydrophilic or lipophilic.

At the end of the last century, Overton demonstrated that substances that dissolve in lipids pass more easily into the cell, and Collander and Bärlund,[3] in their classic experiments with the cells of *Chara*, demonstrated that the rate at which substances penetrate depends on their solubility in lipids and the size of the molecule. The more soluble they are, the more rapidly they penetrate, and with equal solubility in lipids the smaller molecules penetrate at a faster rate (Fig. 20–1).

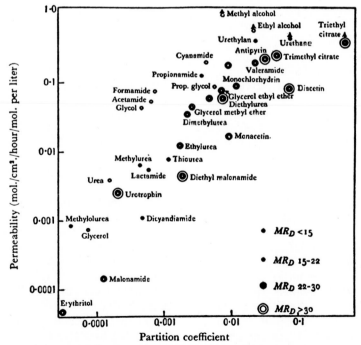

FIGURE 20–1.   Rate of penetration (permeability) in cells of *Chara ceratophylla* in relation to molecular volume (measured by molecular refraction, MR_D), and to the partition coefficient of the different molecules between oil and water. (After Collander and Bärlund.)

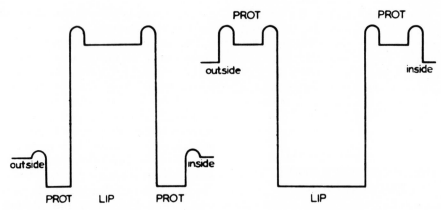

FIGURE 20–2. Diagram representing the potential barriers that hydrophilic (**left**) and lipophilic molecules (**right**) must overcome in order to go across the different components (proteins [*PROT*] and lipids [*LIP*]) of the cell membrane. The height of the barriers have no real values. (From C. M. A. Kuyper.)

As shown in Figure 20–2, in the passage of molecules through the lipoprotein membrane there are several transitions or energy barriers, which favor or make difficult the passage of a molecule. A lipophilic molecule will have a short transition between the protein outside and the lipid and then between this and the protein inside. The molecule is "dissolved" in the lipid layer and passes easily. For a hydrophilic molecule the situation is different. It will penetrate the protein "pulled" by the polar groups present in these layers, but then it will encounter the strong barrier created by the nonpolar lipids. This reasoning explains why polar substances (i.e., hydrophilic) penetrate with great difficulty.

As indicated below, some of these molecules, particularly the ions, penetrate by special mechanisms of *active transport*.

CELL PERMEABILITY AND ACTIVE TRANSPORT

In addition to the diffusion or passive passage of substances across membranes, cell permeability includes a series of mechanisms that involve the use of energy. These mechanisms are generally described as *active transport*, which indicates that an actual amount of work must be done in order that the molecules or ions can penetrate. Adenosine triphosphate (ATP), which is mainly produced by oxidative phosphorylation in mitochondria, is generally used as the source of energy (see Chap. 11). For this reason, active transport is generally related or coupled to cell respiration.

Every time that a molecule must be moved against a concentration gradient active transport takes place. (Remember the hydrostatic example given above: to move the water of a river uphill requires work against gravity (Fig. 20–3). In another case of active transport a charged molecule (i.e., an ion) has to cross through an electrochemical gradient or barrier. For example, in order to maintain a low intracellular concentration of Na^+, the cell must extrude sodium against a gradient (i.e., higher Na^+ concentration outside). In addition it must do this against an electrochemical barrier; the membrane is negative inside and positive outside.

Properties of Active Transport

To understand better the criteria that determine whether a substance moves across the cell membrane by active transport, let us take an example from the kidney. If isolated kidney tubules are immersed in a solution of phenol red, after a certain time the dye passes through the cells and becomes concentrated in the lumen (Fig. 20–4). That this is due to active transport is demonstrated by the fact that the concentration in the lumen becomes much greater than that of the original solution bath-

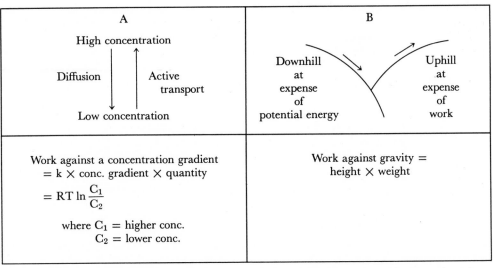

A	B
High concentration Diffusion Active transport Low concentration	Downhill at expense of potential energy Uphill at expense of work
Work against a concentration gradient $= k \times$ conc. gradient $\times$ quantity $= RT \ln \dfrac{C_1}{C_2}$ where $C_1 =$ higher conc. $C_2 =$ lower conc.	Work against gravity $=$ height $\times$ weight

FIGURE 20–3.   Analogy between concentration gradient (left half of **A**) and potential gradient (left half of **B**) and between movement against a concentration gradient (right half of **A**) and work done in moving uphill (right half of **B**). Equations for work against a concentration gradient (osmotic work) and for work in lifting a weight up a height are given at the bottom of the figure. (From A. C. Giese.)

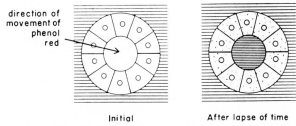

direction of movement of phenol red

Initial   After lapse of time

FIGURE 20–4.   Accumulation of phenol red in sections of proximal kidney tubules of the chick embryo (diagrammatic). Phenol red moves inward until it becomes more concentrated in the inside of the vesicle than on the outside. (From A. C. Giese.)

ing the tubule. Thus the cells are extruding or secreting the dye against a concentration gradient. Several other experiments carried out with phenol red demonstrate that active transport depends on the energy produced by the cell: By cooling the tissue with ice (in other words, by inhibiting cell metabolism), the dye is not concentrated. Certain metabolic poisons that inhibit cell respiration (e.g., cyanide and azide) have the same effect.

The work done by the cell against the concentration gradient can be calculated, since it is proportional to a constant multiplied by the natural logarithm of the ratio of the concentration of the dye inside and outside the tubule. Figure 20–3 shows that this phenomenon is similar to a hydrostatic model.

In order to consider that a transport is active it is necessary to prove that it is metabolically coupled. Sometimes the blocking of respiration by cyanide is not sufficient, because energy (i.e., ATP) can be supplied by anaerobic metabolism.[4] In this case the addition of iodoacetate, which blocks anaerobic metabolism, will stop active transport.

Active Transport of Ions and Membrane Potentials

When an ion is transported the work done against the electrochemical gradient should be taken into account, and this requires an extra consumption of oxygen. It is calculated that 10 per cent of the resting metabolism of a frog muscle is required for transport of sodium ions. This consumption may increase to 50 per cent in some experimental conditions in which the secretion of sodium by the muscle is stimulated.

An interesting example of active transport has been provided by the use of isolated frog skin. This epithelium is specialized to transport Na^+ from the pond water to the interstitial fluids. By this mechanism the frog can trap this essential ion for use in different tissues. The isolated skin can be kept alive for many hours and used as a wall between two chambers in which the ionic concentration and other factors are changed experimentally (see reference 5). By means of this preparation, a potential difference across the skin has been demonstrated: the inside surface is positive with respect to the outside. The sodium ions are transported from the outer toward the inner surface, and it can be demonstrated that the current produced between both surfaces is due to the flux of sodium. In this preparation it was also observed that the antidiuretic hormone of the neurohypophysis stimulates the transport of sodium and water (see reference 5). Similar findings have been observed in other complex membranes, such as the isolated toad bladder (see reference 6) and the kidney tubules of *Necturus*.[7]

Ionic transport is marked in various secretory cells, such as those of the salivary and sweat-producing glands, and even more in the glands of the stomach that produce a great deal of H^+ and Cl^- that must be replaced by the blood. This ionic transfer is very marked in the salt-secreting glands of certain marine birds (e.g., albatross) that feed on sea water.

The active transport of ions is fundamental to maintenance of the osmotic equilibrium of the cell, the required concentration of anions and cations and the special ions needed for the functioning of the cell (see Table 20–1). Ions are required in a number of enzymatic reactions and also to regulate the exchange of water molecules between the cell and the environment. Together with the extrusion of Na^+, which is continuously pumped out by the cell, there is an exit of water molecules. In this way the cell keeps its osmotic pressure constant in spite of the many large molecules that constitute the protoplasm and that cannot be exchanged with the medium.

Potassium ions, which are concentrated inside the cell (Table 20–1), must pass against a concentration gradient. This can be achieved by a "pumping" mechanism at the expense of energy. As explained before, Na^+ also may be transported by an active process, which is sometimes called the "sodium pump." Because there is good evidence that other ions can be transported by a similar mechanism we can speak in general terms of an "ion pump."

The diagram of Figure 20–5 summarizes the relationship existing between the transfer of K^+ and Na^+ (i.e., ionic fluxes) by passive and active mechanisms and the resulting steady state potential. The passive (downhill) fluxes are distinguished from the active (uphill) fluxes. Notice that the active pumping out of Na^+ is the main mechanism for maintaining a negative potential inside the membrane of -50 mv.[2, 8]

Another important function of ions is related to the special properties of certain excitable membranes (e.g., muscle and neuronal membranes). In this case the *action potential* that propagates the impulse is also directly connected with the movements of Na^+, K^+, and Cl^- (see Chap. 22).

Mechanism of Ionic Transport. Pores in the Cell Membrane

It can now be ascertained that the molecular machinery involved in ionic transport is located within the cell membrane. This has been demonstrated in two key materials. For example, if hemolyzed red blood cells are emptied of their contents so that only the cell membrane remains (i.e., a red cell ghost), they can be filled again with appropriate solutions containing ions and ATP, and Na^+ is transported and K^+ is taken up as in a normal cell.

The giant axon of the squid, which has a diameter of about 0.5 mm, can be emptied of the axoplasm and then refilled with solutions of different electrolytes. The transport of ions against a concentration gradient, steady poten-

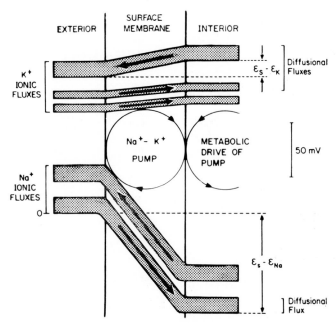

FIGURE 20–5. Active and passive Na^+ and K^+ fluxes through the membrane in the steady state. The ordinate is the electrochemical potential of the ion ($\epsilon_s - \epsilon_k$ for K^+, $\epsilon_s - \epsilon_{Na}$ for Na^+). The abscissa is the distance in the vicinity of the membrane. The width of the band indicates the size of that particular one-way flux. Passive efflux of Na^+ is negligible and is not shown. (After Eccles, J. C., 1957: *The physiology of nerve cells.* The Johns Hopkins Press.)

tials and even action potentials with the conduction of impulses can be obtained in this preparation in which most of the axoplasm is lacking and the excitable membrane left alone.

Other supporting evidence is provided by the action of a glucoside—ouabain—also used as a cardiotonic, which does not penetrate into the cell but reduces markedly the exit of Na^+ from the cell, thus inducing swelling.

Knowledge about the diameter of the different molecules and ions in the hydrated state is particularly pertinent. In this respect it is interesting to remember that the sodium ion, although smaller than K^+ and Cl^- in weight, is large in the hydrated condition and enters with more difficulty into the cell (see Fig. 20–7).

The use of radioisotopes demonstrated that ions can enter into the cell rapidly without obvious osmotic effects.[9] It was then suggested that an ionic interchange across the membrane could take place through electrically charged pores. According to this view, which has been substantiated by several experiments, there could be in the membrane, in addition to noncharged pores, other

pores that have a *positive* or a *negative* net charge. These pores could be located principally in protein molecules and in some hydrophilic lipids (e.g., phosphatidic acid), which can bind Na^+ and polar molecules.[10] The sign of the charge of these water-filled pores could depend on the proportion between the number of positive charges (e.g., amino groups) and negative charges (e.g., carboxylic groups).

Figure 20–6 depicts a pore lined with

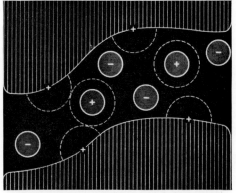

FIGURE 20–6. Pore in a cell membrane lined with molecules bearing a positive charge which hinder the passage of positive ions, but do not retard negative ions. (From A. K. Solomon, 1960: *J. Gen. Physiol., 43,* 5, part 2.)

molecules bearing positive charges. Notice that these can hinder the passage of cations ($^+$) but have no effect on anions ($^-$).

In recent years the theory of the existence of pores in the membrane has been strengthened by the study of the penetration of noncharged molecules, which are insoluble in the lipid phase (e.g., urea, formamide and glycerol). The rate of passage of these substances is related to the size of the molecule and to the area occupied by the pores on the membrane. The equivalent pore radius in different biologic membranes has been estimated to range between 8 and 3.5 Å (Fig. 20–7).

The total area of the pores in the red blood cell has been estimated to be in the order of 0.06 per cent of the surface area. This means that a 7 Å pore would be surrounded by a nonporous square of 200 × 200 Å. These findings indicate that the cell uses only a minute fraction of its surface area for ionic interchange (see reference 11).

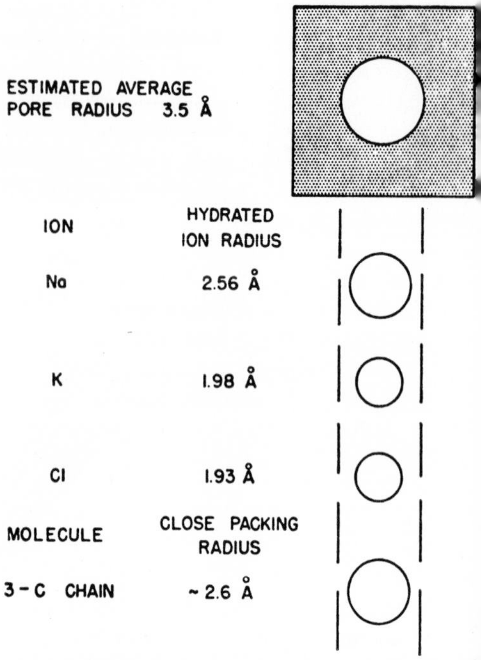

Permease Systems

The existence of such small pores in the cell membrane would prevent the penetration of some essential molecules. To incorporate them the membrane must develop a specific chemical transport system. In Chapter 18 we described the so-called *permease system for β-galactosidase,* which is found in *Escherichia coli* and which determines the penetration of permease into the bacterium. This permaese system, that is genetically determined, is an enzyme system specialized for transport and located at the cell membrane. The passage of amino acids would also be controlled by special permeases. *E. coli* are thought to have 30 to 60 such systems specialized in the transport of different molecules.[12]

Penetration of Larger Molecules

What has been said demonstrates that under the general name of cell permeability are a variety of different mechanisms, some known and others probably still unknown. In addition to certain

FIGURE 20–7. Schematic representation of the red cell pore. Notice that the hydrated ion radius is larger for Na$^+$ than for K$^+$. (From A. K. Solomon, 1960: *J. Gen. Physiol., 43,* 5, part 2.)

foreign substances that can penetrate the cell because they are lipid-soluble (e.g., anesthetics), generally ions penetrate through charged pores and other molecules penetrate by permease systems.

There is no doubt that under certain conditions large molecules, such as certain proteins, penetrate the cell. This is the case of ribonuclease, a protein that penetrates living plant cells readily (Fig. 17–18) and also eggs, flagellates, ascitic tumors, and so forth.[13]

Basic proteins of the protamine and histone type have been reported to enter into living cells.[14] In Chapter 18 we mentioned that DNA penetrates certain bacteria and produces a genetic change known as *transformation.*

Later on in this chapter we discuss *phagocytosis* and *pinocytosis,* by which solid or fluid material in bulk can be ingested by the cell.

Mechanism of Active Transport

Several hypotheses have been advanced to explain the mechanism of active transport across membranes.[15, 16]

An important point refers to the coupling of energy of cell metabolism with the transport of ions and other molecules. In Chapter 11 we mentioned the problem of swelling and contraction of mitochondria as related to the mechanism of oxidative phosphorylation. In this case it is evident that factors that uncouple this process (e.g., dinitrophenol and thyroxin) produce entrance of water and ions, while ATP produces the opposite effect (Fig. 11–16).

The basic theory of active transport involves the attachment of the transported substance to a component of the membrane. This may be a protein, a lipid or, frequently, an enzyme that is supposed to pick up the substance and transfer it toward the other side of the membrane. This has often been called the "carrier" hypothesis because it implies the existence of a carrier molecule that can form a complex with the substance.

The above observations on the permease systems suggest that the enzyme present in the cell membrane may also be the transporting mechanism. It has been thought that if the enzyme is spatially oriented within the membrane (i.e., in a direction perpendicular to the surface) an important vectorial factor would be involved. In this case the enzyme will be able to form a complex with the molecule and at the same time orient its penetration through the cell membrane.[17–19]

There are many indications that enzymes may be located in the membrane. This is, for instance, the case of cholinesterase[20] and proteolytic enzymes in the erythrocyte.[21] Phosphatases present in certain membranes may be related to the permeability of phosphate and glucose.[22] With histochemical methods at the electron microscope level, adenosine triphosphatase and 5-nucleotidase have been found in the plasma membrane of liver cells.[23] (For further readings, see the general references.)

INGESTION OF BULK SOLID AND FLUID MATERIAL

Intimately related to the activity of the plasma membrane are *phagocytosis* and *pinocytosis,* the processes by which solid or fluid material is directly ingested by the cell. With the introduction of electron microscopy, it has become apparent that these active processes of penetration are much more developed than was previously thought. These findings had a profound impact on the classic concepts of cell permeability by demonstrating that solutes, proteins and even particulate material can penetrate the cell by the activity of the plasma membrane without requiring the existence of preformed pores. This type of active transport is less general than the passive and active permeability described above, since it is observed only in certain cell types and in some of them only during certain periods of cellular life. As will be mentioned later, it does not replace but supplements the other types of permeability that are of more general use to the cell.

The problem of the entrance of solids and fluids in bulk is also related to the formation of digestive vacuoles and granules within the cell and to the more general phenomena of *defense and disposal of ingested material* by the cell. These processes and others lead to the formation of a special particle rich in hydrolytic enzymes, which is called the *lysosome.*

Because of this relationship the concept of lysosome and related *microbodies* is incorporated in this chapter and not in the chapter on the cell organoids as is generally done. As mentioned by de Duve:[24] "This small particle acts as the digestive tract of the living cell. Its enzymes dissolve the substances ingested by the cell and under certain circumstances can dissolve the cell itself."

Phagocytosis

Most cells, either free or in tissues, receive their food in a state of solution. In the complex Metazoa, substances are digested by enzymes in the interior of the digestive tube and, after absorption, pass to the internal fluids in molecular dimensions. The passage of these molecules across the plasma membrane cannot be detected with the optical microscope, and has been discussed above under the more general subject of passive and active permeability. In some cases, nevertheless, the cell may actively ingest large, solid particles, and then the process of penetration generally is visible with the light microscope. This activity, called phagocytosis (Gr. *phagein* to eat), is found in a large number of Protozoa and among certain cells of the Metazoa. In Metazoa, however, rather than serving for cell nutrition, phagocytosis is, in general, a means of defense, in which particles that are foreign to the organism, such as bacteria, dust and various colloids, are injected. In some cases phagocytosis is a means of reabsorbing portions of an organism, e.g., the process of disappearance of the tail of amphibian larvae during metamorphosis or the destruction of cellular elements that must be renewed, such as erythrocytes in the spleen.

Among mammals, phagocytosis is highly developed in granular leukocytes (which was first described by Metschnikoff at the end of the last century), and also in the cells of mesoblastic origin ordinarily grouped under the common term *macrophagic* or *reticuloendothelial system*. The cells belonging to this group include the histiocytes of connective tissue, the reticular cells of the hematopoietic organs (bone marrow, lymph nodes, spleen), and those endothelial cells lining the capillary sinusoids of the liver, adrenal gland and hyophysis. All these cells can ingest not only bacteria, protozoa, and cell debris, but also smaller colloidal particles. In this case, phagocytosis is called *ultraphagocytosis*, or *colloidopexy*. When the absorbed colloid is a chromogen, the name of *chromopexy* can be used. An example of chromopexy is the capacity of mesoblastic cells to ingest and store vital colloidal dyes.

Among Protozoa, phagocytosis is intimately linked to ameboid motion. An ameba ingests large particles, including microorganisms by surrounding them with pseudopodia to form a food vacuole within which the digestion of food takes place. Nevertheless, small particles may be ingested without the formation of vacuoles. In leukocytes and other phagocytic cells of multicellular animals, phagocytosis may be carried out by immobile cells.

Phagocytosis has a great importance in pathologic conditions as a general defense mechanism of the organism. This aspect is dealt with extensively in textbooks on microbiology and general pathology. Here we shall refer more particularly to the cytologic and physicochemical aspects of this cellular function.

In analyzing the process of phagocytosis one may distinguish two distinct phenomena. First the particle *adheres* (is *absorbed*) to the mass of the protoplasm, and then the particle actually penetrates the cell. In some cases it has been possible to dissociate these two phases of phagocytosis. For example, at low temperature, bacteria may adhere to the cytoplasm of the leukocyte without being ingested. This phase of absorption, which is comparable to a process of agglutination, seems to obey physicochemical factors, such as electrostatic surface charges. However, it is also likely that phenomena of chemical interaction may play a role. The ingestion of the particle may be considered as the result of the extension of the superficial cytoplasm or ectoplasm upon the interface. For example, macrophages put out hyaline, thin (about 0.25 μ), lamellar pseudopodia, which adhere to and extend over the surface of the particle until it is completely surrounded. This phenomenon is comparable to that occurring when a liquid "wets" and extends over a solid surface.

Ultraphagocytosis, or the ingestion of particles of submicroscopic dimensions, takes place not only through the intervention of similar mechanisms, but also of others of a more complex nature. Among them are the electric charge of the particles, the degree of dispersion of the colloid and the way of introduction. Macrophages accumulate the negatively charged acid vital dyes, such as pyrrole blue, trypan blue and lithium carmine, and other negatively charged colloidal substances, such as colloidal silver, iron saccharate and India ink.

The degree of dispersion of the substance, which depends on the size of the particle, also is important.

Vital acid dyes have a very small particle size and consequently a great power of diffusion. Nevertheless, in order to be ultraphagocytized, they must be previously attached to a protein, which acts as "vector." Vital acid dyes or negatively charged colloids, when injected into an animal, accumulate progressively in all the cells of the macrophage system. If the process is followed in vivo, it is seen that these substances are deposited at first as small granules, which increase in size until they constitute true intracellular precipitates. The fundamental characteristic of this system is that it accumulates and concentrates these dyes and colloids even when administered in dilute solutions. With massive injections, other cells that do not belong to this system may also ingest such substances.

Pinocytosis

In addition to the ingestion of solid particles, the uptake of fluid vesicles by the living cell has been observed. This process, first revealed by Lewis[25] in cultured cells, has been called *pinocytosis* (Gr. *pinein* to drink). As can be readily seen in Lewis' motion pictures, the uptake of fluids is accompanied by vigorous cytoplasmic motion at the edge of the cell, as if vesicles of fluid are being surrounded and engulfed by clasping folds of cytoplasm. Vacuoles taken up at the edge of the cell are then transported to other portions of the cell several microns away.

The possibility that pinocytosis is involved in the penetration of proteins into amebae was first suggested by Mast and Doyle in 1934. This was actually demonstrated by using a protein labeled with fluorescein and observing pinocytosis by means of the fluorescence microscope (see Chap. 6).[26] The presence of the protein seems to act as a stimulus to pinocytosis and the uptake of protein is surprisingly high. During the "feeding period," the ameba ingests approximately one-third of its volume of the protein solution. This material is then eliminated in five to six days. The ameba practically "drinks" the protein solution, and with it may absorb other substances that normally do not penetrate. For example C^{14}-glucose, if dissolved in the protein solution, can enter the ameba in considerable amounts. Therefore, pinocytosis supplies these organisms not only with water but also with solutes in physiologically significant amounts.[27]

By simple experiments it is possible to demonstrate that pinocytosis is induced by certain substances. If an ameba is placed in water, pinocytosis does not take place; if some carbohydrate is added nothing happens; but if certain amino acids, proteins and salts are added, pinocytosis begins with the formation of small pseudopodia and convoluted channels that penetrate and disintegrate into vacuoles or droplets at the inner end, as can be observed under the light microscope. Finally these vacuoles, together with the substance contained, may be incorporated into the cytoplasm.

It has been found that under the action of the inducer the pinocytic activity once started is kept going for about 30 minutes, during which time some 100 channels are formed. Then the process comes to a stop and the ameba has to wait for two to three hours before starting another pinocytotic cycle. This has been interpreted as an indication that the surface membrane available for invagination is exhausted in the 30-minute period.

That phagocytosis and pinocytosis are essentially similar phenomena can be demonstrated by allowing the ameba to phagocytose some ciliated cells first and then inducing pinocytosis. The number of channels formed is much less in these conditions. In the reverse experiment it has been found that an ameba can ingest much fewer ciliates for food.

Extraneous Coats and Pinocytosis

In Chapter 8 we mentioned the importance of the extraneous coats that cover the cell membrane. By using a fluorescent protein it was found that pinocytosis is produced in two stages: (a) Immediately after immersion, the cell surface of the ameba becomes covered by a thick layer of protein, the concentration of which may be 50 or more times that of the solution. (b) In the second stage the cell invaginates the membrane heavily encrusted with the protein.[28, 29]

If similar experiments are made with electron-opaque substances, such as ferritin molecules or a suspension of thorium oxide, it can be demonstrated that in the first stage of pinocytosis the concentration of large molecules occurs in the extraneous coats of the mucopolysaccharide that covers the plasma membrane of the ameba.[30]

Figure 20–8A shows the plasmalemma of an ameba with the membrane proper and the extraneous coat formed by filaments of about 60 Å in diameter and 1000 to 2000 Å in length. This coat gives a strong PAS positive reaction at the light microscope level. After electron-opaque material is added, it can be observed that this becomes heavily concentrated upon the filaments (Fig. 20–8B). These findings demonstrate the importance of the extraneous coats in phagocytosis and pinocytosis.

Micropinocytosis

The use of the electron microscope demonstrated that the plasma membrane of numerous cells could invagi-

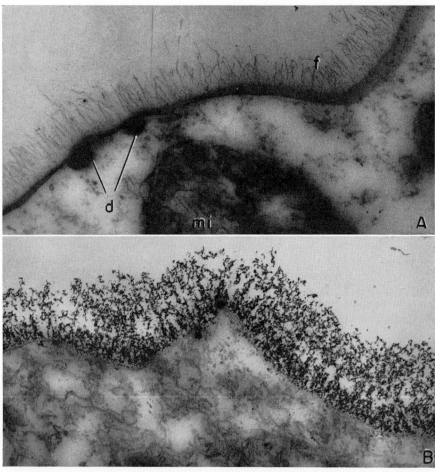

Figure 20–8. **A,** electron micrograph of the cell membrane of the ameba *Chaos Chaos*, showing the extraneous coat formed by fine filaments of 50 to 80 Å in diameter and 1000 to 2000 Å long. *d*, dense bodies; *f*, filaments; *mi*, mitochondrion. ×55,000. **B,** same, but after the addition of thorium dioxide particles. These particles are attached to the filaments prior to the formation of channels and penetration of this material into the ameba. ×38,000. (Courtesy of P. W. Brandt and G. D. Pappas.)

nate, forming small vesicles of about 650 Å and that this process could be related to pinocytosis but at a submicroscopic level. These vesicles were first found in endothelial cells lining capillaries in which they concentrate in the region adjacent to the inner and outer membranes. The presence of vesicles opening on both surfaces and of others traversing the cytoplasm suggested a possible transfer of fluid across the cell.[31] A similar component was then observed in Schwann in satellite cells of nerve ganglions[32] and in numerous cell types, particularly in: macrophages, muscle cells, reticular cells, etc.

An interesting example of the physiological importance of pinocytosis is found in the bone marrow. In the so-called erythroblastic islands, where red blood cells are formed and mature, it is possible to observe reticular cells filled with iron-containing macromolecules of ferritin. The electron microscope has shown that these molecules leave the reticular cells and enter in the erythroblast to be used in the manufacturing of hemoglobin by a process very similar to pinocytosis.[33]

As shown in Figure 20–9, the ferritin molecules that leave the reticular cell are adsorbed to the surface of the erythroblast. Then invagination takes place, with the formation of a micropinocytotic vesicle, and finally the membrane dissolves and the ferritin is incorporated in the cytoplasm. These findings show how cells can utilize again and again the iron resulting from the destruction of old red blood cells to form new erythrocytes.

Pinocytosis and Fat Absorption. The electron microscope study of fat absorption by the intestinal epithelium has demonstrated that this process is esentially a special type of micropinocytosis.

In animals fed with corn oil, after a few minutes, fine lipid droplets are observed in between the microvilli of the striated border of the intestinal cells. At the same time other droplets are seen within pinocytic vesicles in the apical cytoplasm (Fig. 20–10A, B). In later stages the droplets become larger and more abundant. All of them are enveloped by a thin membrane, which corresponds to the vacuolar system of the cytoplasm. Many droplets accumulate within the dilated cisternae of the Golgi complex. Later, fat droplets devoid of the membranous envelope can be seen in the extracellular space between the epithelial cells, in the connective tissue space of the lamina propia and in the lumen of the lacteals.

These observations can be interpreted as indicating that the striated border acts as a filter for the finely emulsified fat. Then the fat droplets enter the apical edge of the cell by a mechanism of pinocytosis and go across the cell cytoplasm by way of the endoplasmic reticulum and Golgi complex. Finally they are moved toward the sides of the cell into the extracellular spaces. The mechanism of fat absorption is thus another excellent example of pinocytotic activity related to the cytoplasmic vacuolar system of the cell.

Pinocytosis and Active Transport

Phagocytosis and pinocytosis are active mechanisms in the sense that the cell uses energy to carry them out, but compared with the above mentioned type of active transport, they lack specificity. The engulfment of the absorbed material is rather indiscriminating and sometimes even noxious substances are ingested. We shall see later on that the content of the phagocytosed material may be digested by enzymes present in the membrane or added to the ingested vacuole. The bodies thus formed belong to the so called *lysosomes*.

Pinocytosis is not an alternative process of active transport, but rather a supporting one. By means of pinocytosis the cell is provided with a much larger interior interface where passive and active transport are carried out more efficiently than at the surface membrane. In Chapter 10 we mentioned the relationship that pinocytosis may have with the flow of membranes of the vacuolar system of the cell. All these processes and those that are described below can now be interpreted within a general mechanism for the ingestion, digestion and disposal of bulk material by the cell.

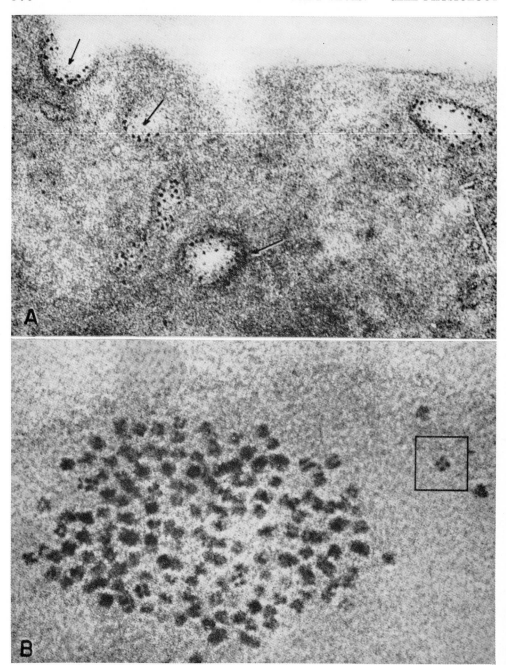

FIGURE 20–9. **A,** electron micrograph of the peripheral region of an erythroblast, showing the penetration of ferritin molecules by micropinocytosis. The arrows indicate several phases of the process starting at the surface. ×180,000. **B,** molecules of ferritin inside the cytoplasm of a reticular cell. Inset: one molecule with four dense points of about 15 Å, each of which contains about 300 atoms of iron. ×850,000. (Courtesy of M. Bessis.)

THE LYSOSOME

The concept of the lysosome originated from the development of cell fractionation techniques, by which different subcellular components are isolated (see Chap. 6). By 1949 a class of particles having centrifugal properties somewhat intermediary between those of mitochondria and microsomes was isolated and found to have a high content of acid phosphatase and other hydrolytic enzymes. By centrifugation it was calculated that the size of these particles

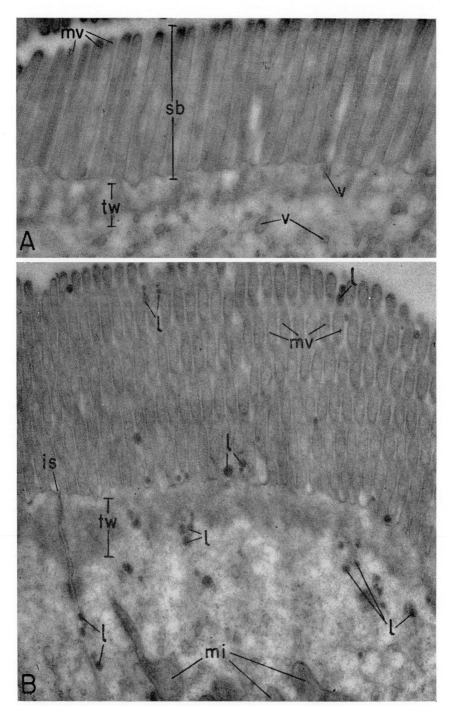

FIGURE 20–10. A, electron micrograph of the apical region of an intestinal cell of a fasting rat, showing the striated border (*sb*) and the subjacent terminal web (*tw*). The microvilli (*mv*) and the spaces between can be seen clearly; at the base of the intermicrovillous space one pinocytotic vesicle is being formed. Other vesicles (*v*) can be seen below. ×47,000. B, same, but after 22 minutes of feeding the rat with corn oil (see the description in the text). *is*, intercellular space; *l*, lipid droplets; *mi*, mitochondria, *mv*, microvilli. ×49,000. (Courtesy of S. L. Palay and L. J. Karlin, 1959.)

ranges from 0.2 to 0.8 μ, and because of their enzymatic properties they were named lysosomes (Gr. *lytic* body).[24]

Stability of the Lysosome and Enzymatic Content

One important property of the lysosome is its stability in the living cell. The enzymes are enclosed by a membrane and are not readily available to the substrate. After isolation with mild methods of homogenation, the amount of enzyme that can be measured by adding the molecules of phosphate ester is small. This increases considerably if the particles are treated with hypotonic solutions or surface active agents (e.g., *triton*) (see Fig. 20–11).

More than a dozen hydrolytic enzymes are recognized as being present in lysosomes. All of them share with acid phosphatase the property of splitting biologic compounds in a mild acid medium. In the living cell these enzymes, e.g., phosphatase, glucuronidase, sulfatase, catepsin, etc., are confined within the particle and can act only on material taken along within it, e.g., on phagocytosed material. If the lysosome is injured (e.g., by a toxic agent), these enzymes can be re-leased and digest the entire cell. In an isolated lysosome, rupture of the membrane will make the enzymatic content of the lysosome available to the different substrates (Fig. 20–11).

Polymorphism of the Lysosome

Observation of the lysosome fraction of the liver under the electron microscope led to the recognition, among typical mitochondria and contaminating microsomes, of dense bodies about 0.4 μ in diameter, having a single outer membrane and small granules of high electron opacity similar to the ferritin molecules.[34] Recently rather pure fractions of liver lysosomes have been obtained (Fig. 20–12). Bodies with similar morphologic characteristics were observed in intact liver cells and named "pericanalicular dense bodies" because of their preferential location along the fine bile canaliculi (Fig. 20–13).

Identification of these particles was made easier when the histochemical techniques for acid phosphatase were carried out at the electron microscope level (Fig. 20–14). (See reference 35.) However, the considerable polymorphism shown by these particles in different

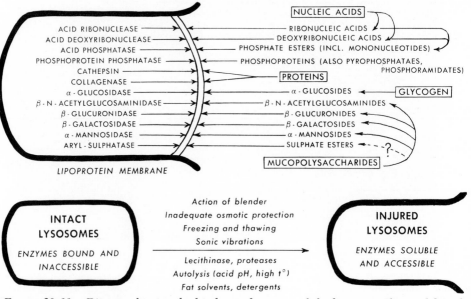

FIGURE 20–11.   Diagram showing the biochemical concept of the lysosome. This model applies mainly to lysosomes of rat liver. **Above**, different hydrolytic enzymes and substrates on which they act. **Below**, indicating the intact lysosomes and the effect of different agents that disrupt the membrane of the lysosomes. (From C. de Duve.)

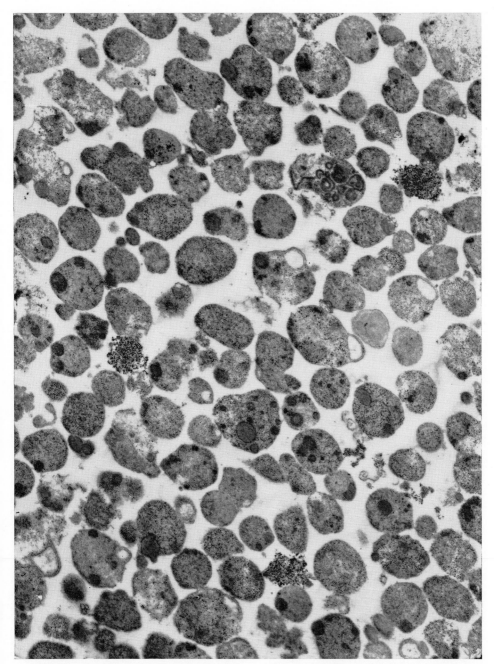

FIGURE 20–12. Lysosomes isolated by differential centrifugation from rat liver, showing the very dense particles and the variety of other dense material contained within the single membrane of the lysosome. ×60,000. (Courtesy of C. de Duve.)

cell types and even within a single cell remained as an obstacle to its identification.

According to the current interpretation the polymorphism is the result of the association of ribosomes with the different materials that are phagocytized by the cell. A summary of these concepts is presented in Figure 20–15. According to them there are four types of lysosomes:[24]

(a) The *original lysosome*, or *storage granule*, is a small body whose enzymatic content is synthesized by the ribosomes. In Chapter 10 we mentioned some histochemical results that pointed

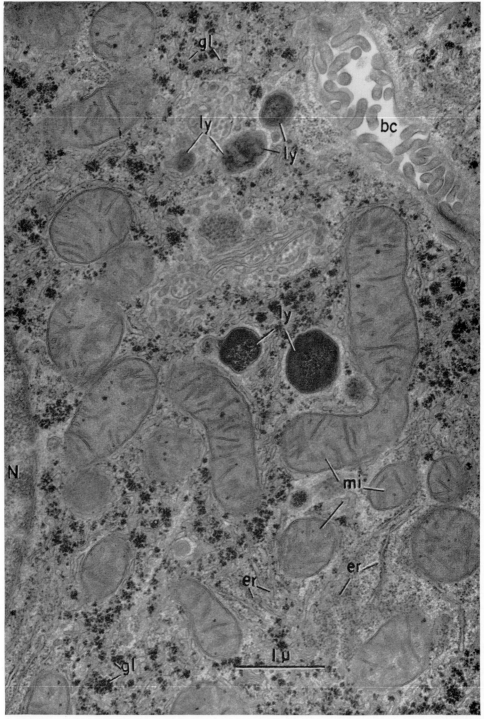

FIGURE 20–13. Peripheral region of a liver cell, showing a biliary capillary (*bc*) and several bodies interpreted as lysosomes (*ly*). *er*, endoplasmic reticulum; *gl*, glycogen; *mi*, mitochondria; *N*, nucleus. ×31,000. (Courtesy of K. R. Porter.)

toward a relationship of the endoplasmic reticulum and Golgi bodies with the formation of vesicles giving a strong acid phosphatase reaction[36] (Fig. 10–14).

(b) The *phagosome*, or *digestive vacuole*, results from the phagocytosis or pinocytosis of foreign material by the cell. This body, which contains the en-

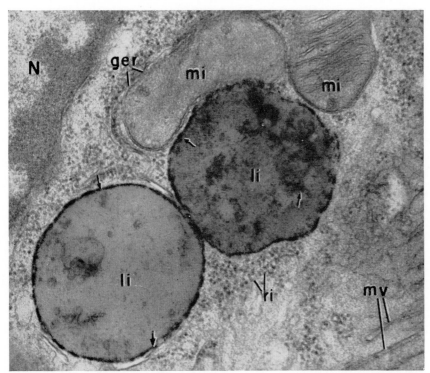

FIGURE 20–14. Electron micrograph of a proximal convoluted tubule cell of mouse kidney, two hours after injection of crystalline ox hemoglobin. Two absorption droplets (phagosomes, lysosomes) have formed at the apical region and the acid phosphatase reaction becomes positive at the surface (arrows) and penetrate inside the lysosome. *ger,* granular endoplasmic reticulum; *li,* lysosomes; *mi,* mitochondria; *mv,* microvilli; *N,* nucleus; *ri,* ribosomes. ✕60,000. (Courtesy of F. Miller.)

gulfed material within a membrane, shows a positive phosphatase reaction, which may be due to the association with a storage granule. There is however some evidence that at the sites in which the membrane invaginates to form a pinocytotic vesicle a positive reaction has already begun. Under the action of the hydrolytic enzymes, the material is progressively digested, giving rise to the residual body.

(c) The *residual body* is the final particle containing the material that cannot be digested. In some cells, such as ameba and other protozoa, these residual bodies are eliminated by *defecation.* In other cells they may remain for a long time and may be important in the aging process. For example, the pigment inclusions found in nerve cells of old animals may be a result of this type of process.

(d) The *autophagic vacuole* is a special case in which the lysosome contains part of the cell in a process of digestion (e.g., a mitochondrion or portions of the endoplasmic reticulum). A large number of these vacuoles are formed in certain physiological and pathological processes. For example, during starvation the liver cell shows numerous autophagic vacuoles in some of which mitochondrial remnants can be found. This is a mechanism by which the cell can feed upon its own substance without irreparable damage.

Lysosomes and Phagocytosis

Numerous examples can be given of the relationship of lysosomes to phagocytosis and pinocytosis. An interesting case is observed in the kidney tubules when the animal is injected with some foreign material. For example, by injecting the enzyme peroxidase into an animal, phagosomes are produced and their fate within the cell can be followed by the peroxidase reaction.[37] Injected hemoglobin is engulfed by the kidney tubular cells and the phagosome shows a positive phosphatase reaction, which starts at the periphery and with time "penetrates" to the interior (Fig. 20–14).

INTRACELLULAR DIGESTIVE TRACT

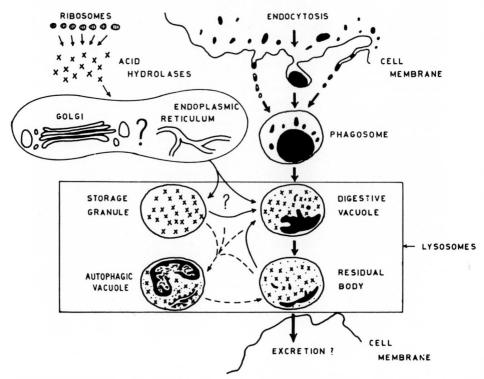

FIGURE 20–15.   Diagram representing four functional forms of lysosomes and their possible inter-relationships. (Courtesy of C. de Duve.)

Autophagic vacuoles having mitochondrial remnants and residual bodies with a layered structure containing undigested material (probably of lipid nature) can also be observed after hemoglobin is injected.

One interesting example is provided by the leukocytes that contain specific granules, particularly the neutrophils. Electron microscope and experimental studies on these cells have shown that these granules are really packages of digestive enzymes corresponding to the lysosomes. If these leukocytes are put in contact with bacteria, the bacteria are engulfed and the granules become incorporated and dissolved in the digestive vacuoles. Eventually most granules may be lost by the cell in this process and in some virulent infections the cell may die.[38]

Lysosomes and Cell Autophagy

There is considerable evidence that lysosomes play a role in the removal of parts of cells, whole cells and even of extracellular material. We mentioned above the case of starvation in the liver cell. During metamorphosis of amphibia there is considerable remodeling of tissues with destruction of numerous cells, and this is accomplished by lysosomal enzymes. For example, the degeneration of the tadpole tail is produced by the action of catepsins (i.e., proteolytic enzymes) contained in the lysosomes. It has been found that with the regression of the tail the concentration of catepsin increases progressively while the total amount of enzyme remains constant.[39]

Evidence indicates that lysosomal enzymes may be discharged outside the cell to produce lytic effects. This may be the mechanism by which *osteoclasts* remove bone. Then the broken parts of the bone may be engulfed and digested by these cells.

In cultured bone tissue receiving an excess of vitamin A bone absorption increases, which is apparently due to the "activation" of the lysosomes. This may be the cause of spontaneous fractures in animals that have vitamin A intoxication.

The opposite effect is observed with cortisone and hydrocortisone. These steroids which have a well known antiinflammatory action, also have a stabilizing effect on the membrane of the lysosome.

For further readings see references 35 and 40.

In summary, at present lysosomes are considered as cell particles containing hydrolytic enzymes that are involved in the digestion of material incorporated into the cell and in the removal of intracellular or extracellular materials. These concepts explain the polymorphism shown by these subcellular particles in different cells.

A word of caution should be introduced in the case of some tissues. For example, in nerve cells the particles that contain hydrolytic enzymes may be more complex. It is possible that different "lysosomal" enzymes may be carried by particles having different sedimentation properties and also a different stability regarding the penetration of substrates (see reference 41).

MICROBODIES

With improved cell fractionation methods a second and more rare group of particles, in addition to lysosomes, has been isolated from liver cells. These particles are rich in the enzymes catalase, D-amino acid oxidase and, to a lesser extent, urate oxidase.[42] In the past these enzymes were thought to be associated with the lysosomes but with the use of gradients containing heavy water or glycogen, in addition to sucrose, it has been shown that these enzymes can be separated almost completely from the lysosomal hydrolases.

The morphological representative of this group of particles has not been discovered. Some preliminary electron microscope observations suggest that they correspond to the so-called "microbodies" found in kidney and liver cells.[43, 44]

These microbodies are ovoid granules of 0.1 to 0.5 μ that are much less numerous than mitochondria and lysosomes. They are limited by a single membrane and contain a finely granular substance that may condense in the center forming an opaque and homogeneous core.

GENERAL REFERENCES

Anderson, B., and Ussing, H. H. (1960) Active transport. *Comp. Biochem. Physiol.*, 2:371.

Ciba Foundation Symposium (1963) *Lysosomes.* J. & A. Churchill, London.

Clark, H. T., ed. (1954) *Ion transport across membranes.* Academic Press, New York.

Conway, E. J. (1955) Evidence for a redox pump in active transport of cations. *Internat. Rev. Cytol.*, 4:377.

Danielli, J. F., ed. (1954) Active transport and secretion. *Symp. Soc. Exp. Biol.* No. 8. Academic Press, New York.

Davson, H. (1959) *A textbook of general physiology.* 2nd Ed. Little, Brown and Co., Boston, Chaps. 10 to 14.

Fuhrman, F. (1959) Transport through biological membranes. *Ann. Rev. Physiol.*, 21:19.

Harris, E. J., ed. (1956) *Transport and accumulation in biological systems.* Academic Press, New York.

Holter, H. (1960) Pinocytosis. *Internat. Rev. Cytol.*, 8:481.

Mitchell, P. (1959) Biochemistry of microorganisms. *Ann. Rev. Microbiol.*, 13:407.

Physiology of the cell membrane (1960). Symposium held at the Instituto Venezolano de Investigaciones Científicas. Caracas, July 31–Aug. 3, *J. Gen. Physiol.*, 43,5, part 2, suppl. 1.

Ponder, E. (1961) The cell membrane and its properties. In: *The cell*, Vol. 2, p. 1. (Brachet, J., and Mirsky, A. E., eds.) Academic Press, New York.

Robertson, R. N. (1960) Ion transport and respiration. *Biol. Rev.*, 35:231.

Robinson, J. R. (1953) The active transport of water in living systems. *Biol. Rev.*, 28:158; (1960) Metabolism of intracellular water. *Biol. Rev.*, 40:112.

Roche, M., ed. (1960) Symposium on active transport. *J. Gen. Physiol.*, 43:5, Part 2.

Rustad, R. C. (1961) Pinocytosis. *Scient. Amer.*, 204(Apr.):121.

Symposium on the plasma membrane. (1962) New York Heart Association, Inc.

CITED REFERENCES

1. Knaysi, G. A. (1951) *Elements of bacterial cytology.* 2nd Ed. Comstock Pub. Associates, Ithaca, N. Y.

2. Woodbury, J. W. (1961) The cell membrane: ionic and potential gradients and active transport. In: *Neurophysiology.*

(Ruch, T. C., Patton, H. D., Woodbury, J. W., and Towe, A. L.) W. B. Saunders Co., Philadelphia, p. 2.

3. Collander, R., and Bärlund, H. (1933) *Acta bot. fenn., 11*:1.

4. Harris, E. J., and Mezels, M. (1951) *J. Physiol., 113*:506.

5. Ussing, H. H. (1960) Physiology of the cell membrane. *J. Gen. Physiol., 43,*5, part 2, suppl. 1, p. 135.

6. Leaf, A. (1960) Physiology of the cell membrane. *J. Gen. Physiol., 43,*5, part 2, suppl. 1, p. 175.

7. Wittembury, G. (1960) Physiology of the cell membrane. *J. Gen. Physiol., 43,*5, part 2, suppl. 1, p. 43.

8. Eccles, J. C. (1957) *Physiology of nerve cells.* Johns Hopkins Press, Baltimore.

9. Brooks, S. C., and Brooks, M. M. (1941) *The permeability of living cells.* Gebr. Borntraeger, Berlin.

10. Hokin, L. E., and Hokin, M. R. (1959) *Nature, 184*:1068.

11. Solomon, A. K. (1960) Physiology of the cell membrane. *J. Gen. Physiol., 43*:5, part 2, suppl. 1, p. 1.

12. Cohen, G., and Monod, J. (1957) *Bact. Rev., 21*:169.

13. Brachet, J. (1957) *Biochemical cytology.* Academic Press, New York.

14. Fischer, H., and Wagner, N. I. (1954) *Naturwissenschaften, 41*:532.

15. Giese, A. C. (1963) *Cell physiology.* 2nd Ed. W. B. Saunders Co., Philadelphia.

16. Physiology of the cell membrane (1960) *J. Gen. Physiol., 43,*5, part 2, suppl. 1.

17. Mitchell, P. D. (1959) *Biochem. Soc. Symp., 16*:73.

18. Mitchell, P. (1961) *Nature, 191*:144.

19. Danielli, J. F. (1962) Structure of the cell surface. *Symposium on the plasma membrane.* New York Heart Association, Inc., p. 1163.

20. Koelle, G. B., and Friedenwald, J. S. (1949) *Proc. Soc. Exp. Biol. Med., 70*:617.

21. Morrison, W. L., and Neurath, H. (1953) *J. Biol. Chem., 200*:39.

22. Rothstein, A. (1954) *Protoplasmatologia, II*:E4.

23. Essner, E., Novikoff, A. B., and Massek, B. (1958) *J. Biophys. Biochem. Cytol., 4*: 711.

24. de Duve, C. (1963) General properties of lysosomes. In: *Lysosomes.* Ciba Founda-

tion Symp. J. & A. Churchill, London, p. 1.

25. Lewis, W. H. (1931) *Bull. Johns Hopkins Hosp., 49*:17.

26. Holter, H., and Marshall, J. M., Jr. (1954) *Comp. Rend. Lab. Carlsberg, série chim., 29*:7.

27. Chapman-Andresen, C., and Holter, H. (1955) *Exp. Cell Res.,* suppl. 3, 52.

28. Brandt, P. W. (1958) *Exp. Cell Res., 15*: 300.

29. Brandt, P. W. (1962) A consideration of the extraneous coats of the plasma membrane. In: *Symposium on the plasma membrane.* New York Heart Association, Inc. *Circulation, 26*:1075.

30. Brandt, P. W., and Pappas, G. D. (1960) *J. Biophys. Biochem. Cytol., 8*:675.

31. Palade, G. E. (1953) *J. Appl. Physiol., 24*: 1424.

32. De Robertis, E., and Bennett, H. S. (1954) *Exp. Cell Res., 6*:543.

33. Bessis, M., and Breton-Gorius, J. (1959) *J. Rev. Hémat., 14*:165.

34. Novikoff, A. B., Beaufay, H., and de Duve, C. (1956) *J. Biophys. Biochem. Cytol.,* suppl. 2:179.

35. Novikoff, A. B. (1961) In: *The cell.* Vol. 2, p. 423. (Brachet, J., and Mirsky, A. E., eds.) Academic Press, New York.

36. Essner, E., and Novikoff, A. B. (1962) *J. Cell Biol., 15*:289.

37. Straus, W. (1958) *J. Biophys. Biochem. Cytol., 4*:541.

38. Hirsch, J. G., and Cohn, Z. A. (1960) *J. Exp. Med., 112*:1005.

39. Weber, R., and Niehus, B. (1961) *Helv. Physiol. Pharmacol. Acta, 19*:103.

40. Ciba Foundation Symposium (1963) *Lysosomes.* J. & A. Churchill, London.

41. Conchie, J., and Levy, G. A. (1963) In: Methods of separation of subcellular structural components. *Biochem. Soc. Symp.,* No. 23. (Grant, J. K., ed.) Cambridge University Press, London, p. 86.

42. Beaufay, H., and Berther, J. (1963) In: Methods of separation of subcellular structural components. *Biochem. Soc. Symp.,* No. 23. (Grant, J. K., ed.) Cambridge University Press, London, p. 66.

43. Rodhin, J. (1954) Thesis. Karolinska Institutet, Stockholm.

44. Rouiller, C., and Bernhard, W. (1956) *J. Biophys. Biochem. Cytol., 2*:355.

CHAPTER 21

MECHANICAL ACTIVITY AND CELL MOTION

We have seen in previous chapters that the energy produced by the cell is stored in the form of adenosine triphosphate (ATP) and other energy-rich phosphates. This energy, in addition to being used in chemical transformations, such as protein synthesis, can be consumed in the *mechanical activity* of the cell. Several forms of energy can be included in this type, but the most important becomes apparent as *cell motion*. This is not only a manifestation of the mechanical energy of the cell, but one of the most objective signs of its activity. When we observe the displacement of a cell in a tissue culture, we have the impression that it is actually "living." Nevertheless, vital phenomena may occur without any apparent movement of the protoplasm. In certain cases cell movement occurs within the protoplasm and produces no exterior deformation of the cell. This type of motion is called *cytoplasmic streaming*, or *cyclosis*. In other cases, the movement is evidenced by the emission of pseudopodia, which leads to displacement of the cell (*ameboid movement*). Furthermore, movements may occur in specially differentiated appendices—*ciliary* and *flagellar*

motion—or in specific cytoplasmic fibrils —*muscular motion*.

Ameboid, ciliary and flagellar types of motion are the main means of locomotion in unicellular organisms. Plant cells are displaced mainly by growth and changes in water content (turgor). Some plant gametes have flagella. In animals, embryonic cells may move considerably during organogenesis (development of organs) and histogenesis (development of tissues). Also cells in tissue culture, healing wounds and cancer move freely. In mature animals only gametes, ciliated epithelia, wandering ameboid cells and the cells of different types of muscle tissue perform visible movements.

CYTOPLASMIC STREAMING

Cytoplasmic streaming, or *cyclosis*, is easily observed in numerous plant cells, in which the cytoplasm is generally reduced to a layer next to the cellulose wall and to fine trabeculae crossing the large central vacuole. In the peripheral cytoplasm as well as in the trabeculae. continuous currents can be seen that displace chloroplasts and other cytoplasmic granules. In ciliated protozoa—such as *Paramecium*—similar but slower movements are seen that displace the digestive vacuoles from the site of ingestion to that of excretion. In many cells of higher animals, particularly in tissue cultures, such intracellular movements can be seen. Observation is improved by using phase microscopy, a darkfield condenser or cinematography. Mitotic division, with the complex displacement of the cell center, the chromosomes and other cell organoids, also belongs to this type of intracellular movements.

The classic experimental work on cyclosis has utilized plant cells. Particularly appropriate are the cylindroid cells of *Nitella*, which have a thin protoplasmic layer of about 15 μ surrounding a central vacuole of 0.5 mm by 10 cm. Motion takes place in the inner, more liquid part of the protoplasmic layer along the longitudinal axis.

In some plant cells the protoplasmic current can be initiated by chemicals (*chemodynesis*) or by visible light (*photodynesis*). Cyclosis is modified by temperature (maximum activity is at some optimal temperature), by the action of ions or by changes in pH. It can continue in the absence of oxygen. Cyclosis is stopped by mechanical injuries, electric shock or some anesthetics. Some auxins (plant growth hormones) increase the rate of cyclosis when they act in low concentrations. In general, all the factors that decrease cell viscosity increase the speed of protoplasmic current and vice versa. However, some viscosity changes have the opposite effect. It has been observed that motion decreases progressively in cells submitted to increased hydrostatic pressure at the same time that the protoplasm becomes more liquid.

It is evident that viscosity is one of the most important factors in the intimate mechanism of cyclosis, since the protoplasmic colloid may pass by means of reversible sol-gel changes from a liquid or almost liquid state to an almost solid one. Nevertheless, the propulsive force of the movement is not well known.[1]

AMEBOID MOVEMENT

Whereas in cyclosis the protoplasmic components are simply displaced without any change in the shape of the cell, in ameboid movement the cell is deformed. The cell changes shape actively, sending forth cytoplasmic projections called *pseudopodia*, into which the protoplasm flows. This special form of locomotion is called *ameboid* movement because it can be observed easily in amebae. Nevertheless, it can be seen in numerous types of cells. One need only to place a drop of blood between a slide and coverglass, being careful to avoid drying it and to maintain a proper temperature, to see that the leukocytes, at first spheroidal, change their shape, emit pseudopodia and move about. In tissue cultures, all explanted elements, whether mesenchymal, endothelial, epithelial, etc., may free themselves from the rest of the tissue and move out actively, forming the zone of migration. In some cases, the cells must *"dedifferentiate"* in order to acquire this active ameboid form. This happens in epithelia in which the desmosomes connecting the cells disappear. These changes also occur in vivo. For example, in epithelial repair, the cells free themselves and slide along actively toward the depth of the wound. In an inflammatory process, leukocytes wander out of the blood vessels (*diapedesis*) by active ameboid motion and progress toward the focus of infection.

Ameboid motion generally occurs when the cells are attached to some substratum. In its simplest form there is an axial cytoplasmic streaming, which continuously displaces a tubular body. Some amebae are predominantly *monopodial* (one pseudopodium), but others may be temporarily or permanently *polypodial*. The shape of pseudopodia varies between a stout, almost cylindrical *lobo-*

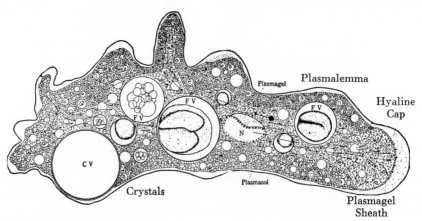

FIGURE 21–1. Structure of an ameba. *CV*, contractile vacuole; *FV*, food vacuoles; *N*, nucleus. (After a diagram from Mast.)

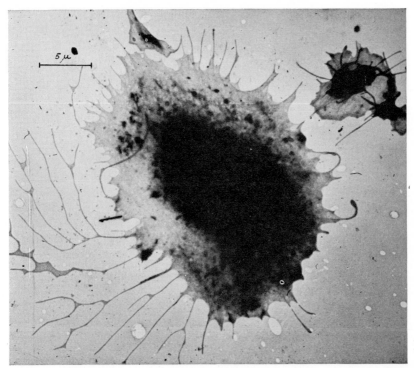

FIGURE 21–2.   Electron micrograph of a polymorphonuclear leukocyte. (See the description in the text.) ×3000. (De Robertis.)

podium and a fine filamentous (Fig. 21–1) or branching *filopodium* (see Fig. 21–2). Sometimes these fine processes may be anastomosing, i.e., *reticulopodia*, as in Foraminifera.

The ameba is the ideal cell in which to observe this type of motion. As shown by the classic studies of Mast, the protoplasm of the ameba has a clear ectoplasm, which expands considerably toward the end of the pseudopodium (hyaline cap), and agranular endoplasm, which constitutes the greater part of its mass (Fig. 21–1). More recent studies distinguish in amebae the organization shown in Figure 21–3. The axial endoplasm is surrounded by a "shear zone" where particles move more freely. At the advancing end is the hyaline cap and just posterior to it the "fountain zone," where the axial endoplasm appears to contract actively and flows below the ectoplasmic tube. At the opposite end is the tail process, also called the *uroid*, and near it the *recruitment zone*, where the endoplasm is recruited from the walls of the ectoplasm in the posterior third of the cell.[2, 3]

In slime molds several pseudopodia sometimes move in different directions (Fig. 21–4). There is a pulsating movement, the motive force of which can be measured and recorded as shown in Figure 21–5. By applying sufficient pressure with this apparatus, the movement can be prevented. A contractile protein on which ATP may be acting has been isolated from these organisms.[4]

The rate of progression varies among different amebae between 0.5 and 4.6 μ per second. In the neutrophil leukocytes it is approximately 0.58 μ per second. This rate is modified by temperature and other environmental factors. Insufficient oxygen supply does not stop the movement, but slows it. Calcium is required for this type of locomotion. If an ameba is placed in the presence of a substance that extracts calcium (such as an oxalate), motion is stopped. The effect of the potassium ion is antagonistic to that of the calcium ion. Severe mechanical injury, electric shock or ultraviolet radiation causes rigid retraction of the pseudopodia, and the cell becomes spheroidal.[3, 5, 6]

Another important factor in ameboid motion is *adhesion to a solid support*.

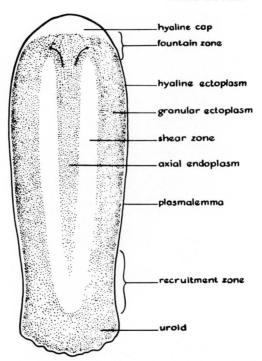

hyaline cap

fountain zone

hyaline ectoplasm

granular ectoplasm

shear zone

axial endoplasm

plasmalemma

recruitment zone

uroid

FIGURE 21–3. A new schema for ameboid structure and movement based on studies of cyto-plasmic flow. New terminology is proposed for different regions of the cytoplasm of the ameba. (From R. D. Allen.[3])

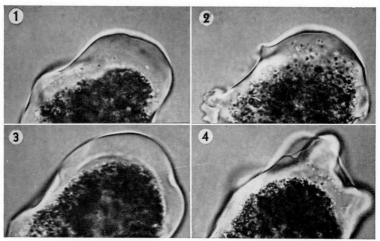

FIGURE 21–4. 1–4, advancing end of a slime mold. Microphotographs taken at 10-second inter-vals without moving the camera. The base line remained constant so that the advance and retraction could be measured. 1, hyaline cap at the tip of an advancing pseudopodium, showing the even, bulging contour of the granular gel layer. 2, same tip, 40 seconds later. The thin gel layer has disinte-grated and granules are filling the cap. 3, same tip, 20 seconds later. Gelation of the periphery of the granular protoplasm and the formation of a new hyaline cap. 4, same tip, 30 seconds later. Retraction of the pseudopodium and irregular hyaline cap. (Courtesy of W. L. Lewis and the Iowa State Col-lege Press. In: *Structure of protoplasm,* 1942.)

An ameba that floats freely in the liquid medium can emit pseudopodia, but does not progress; only when it adheres to a solid surface does it commence this type of locomotion. In tissue cultures the fibers of the coagulum serve as sup-port for the ameboid cells; in connective tissue the collagenous or reticular fibers may serve this purpose.

Cellular adhesiveness to a support or to other cells seems to be involved in histogenesis also. "The direction of cellu-

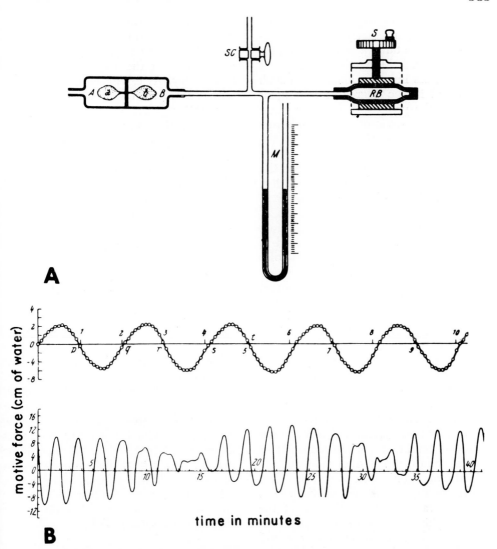

FIGURE 21–5. **A,** diagram showing the general arrangement for measuring the motive force of protoplasmic streaming in a myxomycete plasmodium. Note the double chamber (A, B) with myxomycete (a, b) connected through a small hole between the chambers. M, water-filled manometer; S, screw to control the pressure applied to the bulb (RB); SC, stopcock. **B,** a recording of the motive force in centimeters of water. Note the beatlike wave pattern under normal conditions. The upper line is a recording showing all the points recorded several times a minute. The lower line shows a record in which the points are left out and the abscissa is compressed in order to show the data for a longer period of time. Using this equipment, it is possible to study the effect of temperature, anesthetics and various injurious agents on the wave pattern. (From N. Kamiya.)

lar migration and the histotypical groupings and regroupings exhibited by the various types of cells in a developing organism appear to be controlled by a selective adhesiveness of the cell membrane."

In Chapter 8 we mentioned the influence of calcium and other ions on the cell membrane and the importance of proteins and glucoproteins as cementing substances between cells.

Substances that influence the motion by attracting or repelling the cells should be placed among the factors that determine ameboid motion. This property, which is called *chemotaxis*, has great importance in defense mechanisms, especially during inflammation.

Mechanisms of Ameboid Movement

Present theories on ameboid movement are based on modern knowledge of the structure of the cell matrix (see Chap. 9), and particularly on the hypothesis that it contains a network of protein molecules held together by different kinds of cross linkages. Changes in such forces and in the degree of folding or length of the protein chains may cause sol-gel transformations and protoplasmic contraction in a localized region of the protoplasm.[7]

In the gelled regions of the ameba the polypeptide chains would be unfolded, forming an interlocking network of fibers. As a result of the folding up of the molecules, the gel would contract and finally a sol would be produced in which the protein molecules are globular and no longer interlock.

This hypothesis gains some indirect support from observations of amebae in dilute solutions of a vital stain, such as neutral red. In an immobile ameba there is a peripheral stain that is similar all around. As soon as the ameba becomes mobile the staining decreases in the advancing pseudopodium and increases in the tail region, where it becomes accumulated. The interpretation is based on the fact that protein molecules in the unfolded condition (denatured) adsorb several times more dye than in the folded condition (native state). Thus the reasoning that there protein unfolds at the advancing end and folds at the tail. By this mechanism the dye molecules adsorbed at the periphery would be released in the region of folding at the tail. Injection of ATP causes the cortical gel to contract and liquefy. If the microinjection is in the tail, the ameba increases its speed of streaming;

if it is in the advancing pseudopodium, it reverses the direction of streaming.[8]

An interesting approach to this problem has been the use of interference microscopy. As explained in Chapter 5, with this method the concentration of dry matter (protein) and water can be measured, determining the refractive index and the phase changes. It has been found that in a motile ameba the protein concentration of the cytoplasm is significantly higher at the tail (Fig. 21–6). It can be demonstrated that this difference is not due to the activity of the contractile vacuole that removes water from the tail.[9]

In the mechanisms of ameboid motion the probable importance of surface tension has been discarded. The theory based on sol-gel changes, although it may interpret the variations in consistency that are involved in this type of motion, does not actually explain how the work involved in ameboid movement is performed.

Most data favor an active contraction as the motive force and some type of protoplasmic streaming as well. The views are divided regarding the most likely site of contraction. Whereas some investigators regard the posterior region of the ectoplasmic tube as more active, others give more importance to the "fountain zone" at the advancing end of the ameba (Fig. 21–3).[3]

CILIARY MOTION

In contrast to ameboid motion, which takes place on a solid substrate and in-

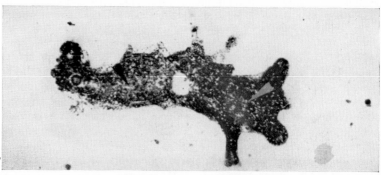

FIGURE 21–6.   Motile ameba observed under the interference microscope. The concentration of protein in the ground cytoplasm of the tail (*left*) is higher, as shown by its brighter appearance. (Courtesy of P. D. Allen and T. D. Roslansky, 1958.)

volves cellular deformation, ciliary movement is adapted to a liquid medium and is executed by minute, specially differentiated appendices. These are contractile filaments that vary in size and number. They are called *flagella* if they are few and long and *cilia* if short and numerous. Between the two extremes are intermediate forms, but in all cases the way of implantation and essential characteristics are similar.

These motile processes are relatively common in animal cells and are found also in some plant cells. In Protozoa, especially the Infusoria, each cell has hundreds or thousands of minute cilia, and their movement permits a rapid rotation and progression of the organism in the liquid medium. In some special regions of Infusoria, various cilia fuse and form larger conical appendices, *the cirri*, or membranes known as *undulating membranes*. Although the morphologic characteristics of these appendices are somewhat different, their function is similar to that of cilia and flagella.

Many bacteria have thin flagella visible only under the electron microscope. In Protozoa, one entire class, Flagellata, is characterized by the presence of these appendices. Among the Metazoa the spermatozoa have the property of progressing as isolated cells by means of flagella. On the other hand, epithelial cells that possess vibratile cilia and constitute true ciliated sheets are relatively common. These may cover large areas of the external surface of the body and determine the motion of the animal. Such is the case with some Platyhelminthes and Nemertea and also with larvae of Echinodermata, Mollusca, and Annelida. More often, the ciliated epithelial sheets line cavities or internal tubes of the multicellular animals, such as the air passages of the respiratory system or various parts of the genital tract. In these organs all the cilia move simultaneously in the same direction, and fluid currents are thus produced. In some cases the currents serve to eliminate solid particles in suspension that may damage the organism, e.g., the respiratory system. In others, the currents make it possible for solid particles to move along. A good example is that of the eggs of Amphibia or of mammals, which are driven along the oviduct with the aid of vibratile cilia. Some epithelial cells have a single central flagellum.

Structure of the Ciliary and Flagellar Apparatuses

The essential components of the ciliary apparatus are (a) the *cilium*, which is the slender cylindroid process that projects from the free surface of the cell, (b) the *basal body*, or granule, the intracellular organoid similar to the centriole (see Chap. 14) from which it originates and probably serves as a kinetic center, and (c) in some cells fine fibrils—called *ciliary rootlets*—that arise from the basal granule and converge into a conical bundle, the pointed extremity of which ends at one side of the nucleus (Fig. 21–7).

The basal bodies are embedded in the ectoplasmic layer beneath the cell surface. In general they are spaced uniformly and in parallel rows.

Cilia and flagella are extremely delicate filaments whose thickness is often at the limit of the resolving power of the light microscope. For this reason, they generally show no internal structure. Nevertheless, some flagella, such as spermatozoan tails, have an axial filament and a peripheral sheath.

Various epithelia have appendices similar in shape to cilia, but immobile; these are called *stereocilia*. Examples are the prolongations of the epithelial cells of the epididymis, which seem to intervene in the elimination of cellular secretion. In the macula and crista of the inner ear, there are stereocilia in addition to motile cilia, or *kynocilia*.

Ultrastructure of Cilia and Flagella

Some evidence that cilia and flagella were composed of finer fibrillar elements were obtained by early cytologists at the end of the last century. The spermatozoan tail was occasionally seen to fray into minute fibrils.[10] Later some evidence came from the use of polarization microscopy and the demonstration of a positive intrinsic and form birefringence

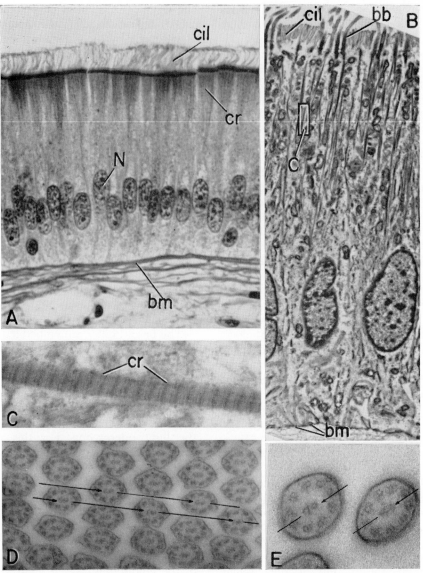

FIGURE 21-7. A, light microscope view of the ciliated epithelium of the intestine of the clam, showing cilia (*cil*), ciliary rootlets (*cr*), nuclei (*N*), and basement membrane (*bm*). B, the same material observed at low power under the electron microscope: *bb*, basal bodies; *c*, region enlarged in C. C, high power view of a ciliary rootlet, showing the periodic banding. D and E, cross section of cilia, showing 11 filaments and the orientation in a plane of the central pair. (Courtesy of D. W. Fawcett and K. R. Porter.)

(see Chap. 5). Direct evidence of the ultrastructure of the spermatozoan tail was obtained with the electron microscope. It was found to contain 11 fibrils, of which two are smaller (Fig. 21-8).[11]

In an extensive series of investigations in fern male gametes (antherozoids), it was found that cilia frayed into 11 fibrils.[12] This fundamental structure was universally confirmed for cilia and flagella, when the advances in techniques

made thin tissue sections possible.[13] In a cross section of a cilium, the total diameter of which is about 2000 Å, an outer ciliary membrane surrounds the ciliary matrix and is continuous with the plasma membrane. Embedded in this matrix are nine pairs of filaments, each about 80 Å in diameter, whereas two single filaments are at the center (Fig. 21-9). With special staining techniques some additional details have been de-

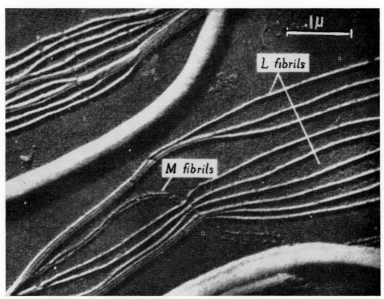

FIGURE 21–8. Electron micrograph of disintegrated tails of cock spermatozoa, showing the 11 fibrils. Two median fibrils (*M fibrils*) are more delicate than the nine larger and peripheral fibrils (*L fibrils*). (From Grigg and Hodge.)

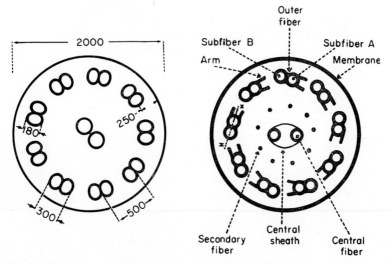

FIGURE 21–9. Left, diagram illustrating the disposition of fibrils in a cross section of a typical cilium and giving the approximate dimensions in Ångström units. (From D. W. Fawcett and K. R. Porter.) Right, diagram according to Gibbons and Grimstone, showing a set of secondary fibers interposed between the central and outer fibers. Notice that the arms are always associated with the same fiber and are consistent in direction.

scribed, such as radial projections or "arms" from each pair of peripheral filaments (Fig. 21–10).[14, 15] The arms are implanted in one of the fibers of the pair (subfiber A in Fig. 21–9). In the matrix nine dots corresponding to cross sections of fine longitudinal filaments have been described as well as a *central sheath,* which surrounds both central fibers. In all cilia of a given cell the central pair of fibers has the same orientation, lying in a plane perpendicular to that of the ciliary movement. At the tip of the flagellum or cilia the outer fibers converge and become single and finally all of them end independently and without contact with the membrane.[10] The fine structure of basal bodies, which is similar to that of centrioles, was studied in Chapter 14. The basal bodies do not have central fibers, but sometimes dense bodies can be observed (Fig. 21–11).[16]

The rootlets of cilia have a regular crossbanding with a period of 600 to 700 Å (Fig. 21–7). Five intraperiod subbands have been observed. The chemical or physiological significance of these rootlets, which are found only in certain materials, is unknown.

Spermatozoan flagella of mammals have an additional component not found in cilia. This is a helical fibril situated in the peripheral region, the so-called *cortical helix*[17] (see Fig. 21–12). Further

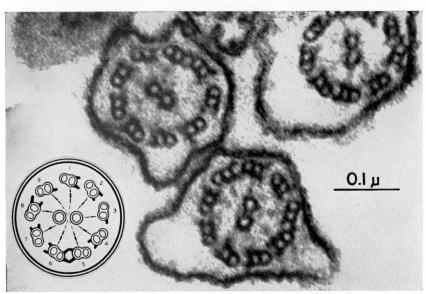

FIGURE 21–10. Electron micrograph of a cross section through the tail of three spermatozoa with an arrangement of the filaments similar to that indicated in the inset. The inset shows the radial projections and the "arms" that each pair of peripheral filaments has. An index number has been assigned to each filament. (Courtesy of B. Afzelius.)

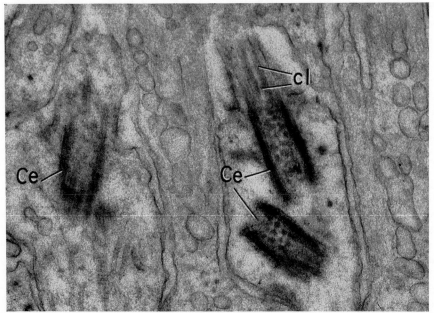

FIGURE 21–11. Electron micrograph of two basal bodies (centrioles) of a retinal rod, showing dense granules inside. Notice the connection of one centriole (*Ce*) with the cilium (*cl*). ×80,000. (Courtesy of A. Lasansky.)

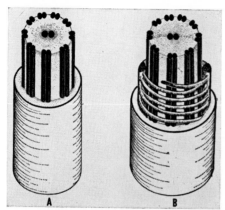

FIGURE 21–12. Diagram of the structure of a cilium (**A**) and (**B**) of the sperm flagellum. In **B** the bundle of filaments is wrapped by dense peripheral strands that are held laterally. (Courtesy of D. W. Fawcett.)

complexities are found in certain amphibian spermatozoa, which have a fin that is seen as a thin sheet projecting in the same plane to that of the central filaments.[18] (For further details on the structure of cilia and flagella, spermatozoa, undulating membranes, etc., in Protozoa and Metazoa see reference 10.)

Physiology of Ciliary Movement

Ciliary movement can be analyzed easily by scraping with a spatula the pharyngeal epithelium of a frog or toad and placing the scrapings in a drop of physiologic salt solution between a slide and a coverglass. On the free surface of the epithelial cell, the rapid motion of the vibratile cilia can be seen. If a row of cilia is observed during contraction, the contraction is *metachronic* in the plane of the direction of motion; that is, it starts before or after the contraction of the next cilium. In this way true waves of contraction are formed.

On the other hand, in a plane perpendicular to the direction of motion, the contraction is *isochronic*; all the cilia are found in the same phase of contraction at a given time. This coordination of the ciliary movement implies the existence of a regulatory mechanism, the nature of which is unknown. This mechanism evidently does not depend on the nervous system, since it persists after the epithelium has been separated from the rest of the organism. However,

cytoplasmic continuity is indispensable to its maintenance, for if a cut is made in the row of cilia the waves of contraction of the two isolated pieces become uncoordinated.

The direction of the effective ciliary beat appears to be a fixed characteristic that depends also on the underlying cytoplasm. If a piece of epithelium is removed from the pharynx of a frog and implanted with a reversed orientation, the movement is maintained but in a direction opposite to that on the remaining intact epithelium.

Ciliary contractions are generally rapid (10 to 17 per second in the pharynx of the frog); thus they are difficult to follow under the microscope. Analysis of the motion has been facilitated greatly by stroboscopic and ultrarapid cinematomicrography, which permits one to follow the various phases in the contraction of a cilium and to calculate the duration of each cycle.[19, 20]

Ciliary movement presents varying characteristics in different cells and, in general, may be pendulous, unciform (hooklike), infundibuliform or undulant. The first two are carried out in a single plane. In the pendulous movement, typical of the ciliated Protozoa, the cilium is rigid and the motion is carried out by a flexion at its base. On the other hand, in the unciform movement, the most common type in the Metazoa, the cilium upon contraction is doubled and takes the shape of a hook. In the infundibuliform movement, the cilium or flagellum rotates, passing through three mutually perpendicular planes in space, describing a conical or funnel-shaped figure. In the undulant motion, characteristic of the flagella and membranes, contraction waves proceed from the site of implantation and pass to the free border.

Mechanism of Ciliary Motion

Current hypotheses on the mechanism of ciliary motion are based on knowledge of the structure of cilia provided by electron microscopy. One ingenious hypothesis is that (1) the matrix of the cilium is stiff, (2) the nine peripheral pairs of fibers can contract and propa-

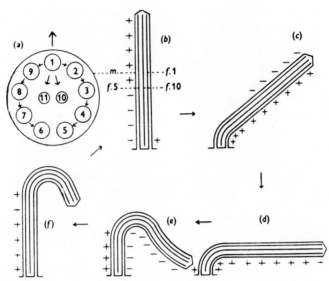

FIGURE 21–13. Hypothetical mechanism for ciliary movement proposed by Bradfield (1955). (a), transverse section of a cilium. It is assumed that the impulse causing contraction of the fibers originates under fiber 1 and spreads both around the ring of nine fibers and to the central pair, as indicated by arrows inside the cilium. (See the description in the text.)

gate waves of contraction from the base to the tip, (3) the central pair is not contractile, but specialized for rapid conduction, and (4) the impulse that initiates the beat arises rhythmically from the basal body and spreads sequentially to the different fibrils[21] (see Fig. 21–13). The shortening of fibrils 1, 2, 9, 3, 8 (Fig. 21–13a) causes the cilium to bend forward like a stiff rod (Fig. 21–13c). In the recovery phase these fibrils relax and a contraction is initiated in fibrils 4, 7, 5, and 6, which produces the recovery stroke (Fig. 21–13d–f). In this mechanism the effective or initial stroke would be helped by the rapid propagation of the signal by the central fibers, whereas the slower recovery stroke would be due to the slow propagation along the contracting fibers 4, 7, 5, 6 (Fig. 21–13).

Biochemistry of Ciliary Motion

Isolation of spermatozoan tails and algal flagella have permitted the isolation of a protein similar to myosin (found in muscle).[22, 23]

Several findings show the importance of ATP in cilia, flagella and spermatozoan tails. It has been shown that bacterial motility, which depends on submicroscopic, single, filamentous flagella, is stimulated by ATP, which also induces muscle contraction. Furthermore, as in muscle, the motion of bacteria is specifically inhibited by thiol inhibitors, which block the —SH groups present in the flagella.[24] In glycerin-extracted cilia, flagella and spermatozoan tails the addition of ATP produces rhythmic activity, which persists for a few minutes or even hours.[25, 26]

Coordination of the Ciliary Beat

The rhythmic contraction of cilia has been interpreted in different ways. A two-step process that involves *intraciliary* excitation followed by *interciliary* conduction has been proposed to explain the metachronal rhythm of the ciliary beat (Fig. 21–14).[27] According to this theory the frequency of beat is determined by the rate of contraction and excitation of the *pacemaker* cilium (as in the heartbeat, which is determined by the pacemaker region). The impulse would be conducted to the next cilium with a certain velocity and then to the following one and so forth (Fig. 21–14).

Ciliary Derivatives

Studies on the submicroscopic structure of retinal rods and cones have

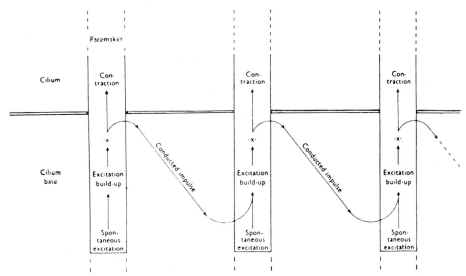

FIGURE 21–14.   Diagram showing the sequence of events in the metachromal rhythm of ciliary beat. (See the text.) (From Sleigh.[27])

shown that the short, fibrous connection found between the outer and inner segments is of a ciliary nature. Cross sections of this so-called "connecting cilium" have revealed nine pairs of filaments similar to those found in cilia[28] (Fig. 21–15). The filaments of the connecting cilium start from one of the centrioles, whereas the other centriole is arranged perpendicularly (see Chap. 14). The outer segment is composed of numerous double membrane rod sacs disposed like a pile of coins.

Classic studies on the histogenesis of the retina advanced the hypothesis that the differentiation of the rod and cone outer segments could develop from a cilium. This has been proved by studies with the electron microscope.[28] The first stage is the development of a primitive cilium projecting from the bulge of cytoplasm that constitutes the primordium of the inner segment (Figs. 21–16 and 21–17). This cilium contains the nine pairs of filaments and the two basal centrioles. The apical end is filled with a vesicular material. In the second stage the apical region of the primitive cilium enlarges greatly, owing to the rapid building up of the vesicles and cisternae that constitute the primitive rod sacs (Fig. 21–17). The surface membrane participates in the formation of these membranes, probably under the "inductive" influence of the cilium. This effect

is present only on one side of the cilium, resulting in an asymmetrical development of the outer segment. In the third stage the sacs are remodeled and reoriented into their permanent transverse position. The proximal part of the primitive cilium remains undifferentiated and constitutes the connecting cilium of the adult (Fig. 21–17).

Other structures have also been recognized as ciliary derivatives. For example, the so-called crown cells of the saccus vasculosus found in the third ventricle of fishes are modified cilia with swollen ends that are filled with vesicles.[29] Also, the primitive sensory cells of the pineal eye found in certain lizards have a ciliary structure.[30]

MUSCULAR MOVEMENT

Cell contractility reaches its highest development in the various types of muscular tissues. In muscle the structural organization is adapted to unidirectional shortening during contraction. Because of this, most muscle cells are elongate and spindle-shaped. The cytoplasmic matrix is considerably differentiated, and the major part of the cytoplasm is occupied by contractile fibrils. In smooth muscle these *myofibrils* are homogeneous and birefringent. In contrast, in cardiac and skeletal muscle the

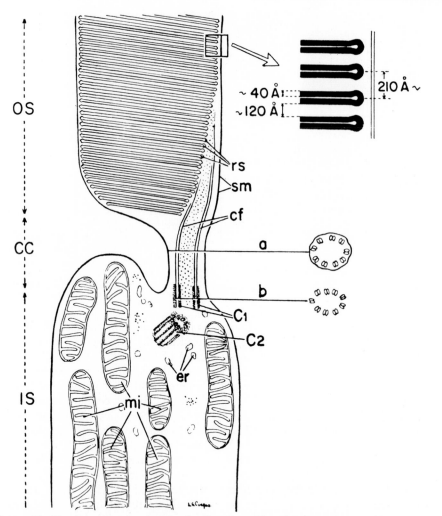

Figure 21–15. Diagram of a retinal rod cell in the rabbit: the outer segment (*OS*) with the rod sacs (*rs*); the connecting cilium (*CC*) and the inner segment (*IS*) are shown. *a* and *b* correspond to a cross section through the connecting cilium and the centriole (*C₁*). *C₁* and *C₂*, centrioles; *cf*, ciliary filaments; *er*, endoplasmic reticulum; *mi*, mitochondria; *sm*, surface membrane.

myofibrils are striated and have dark, birefringent (anisotropic) zones alternating with clear isotropic zones (Fig. 21–18). In muscle cells only a small part of the cytoplasm—the *sarcoplasm*—retains its embryonic characteristics. It lies between the myofibrils, particularly around the nucleus.

Some muscle cells are so highly differentiated that they are adapted to produce mechanical work equivalent to 1000 times their own weight and to contract 100 or more times per second.

The different types of muscle cells are studied in histology textbooks and the special types of contraction in physiology

textbooks. We are emphasizing here the macromolecular organization of the striated skeletal muscle and its relation to the work of contraction.

Striated skeletal muscles are composed of multinucleate cylindrical fibers, 10 to 100 μ in diameter and several millimeters or centimeters long. The entire fiber is surrounded by an electrically polarized membrane with an electrical potential of about −0.1 volt; the inner surface is negative with respect to the outer surface. This membrane, called the *sarcolemma*, becomes depolarized physiologically each time a nerve impulse that reaches the motor innervation of the

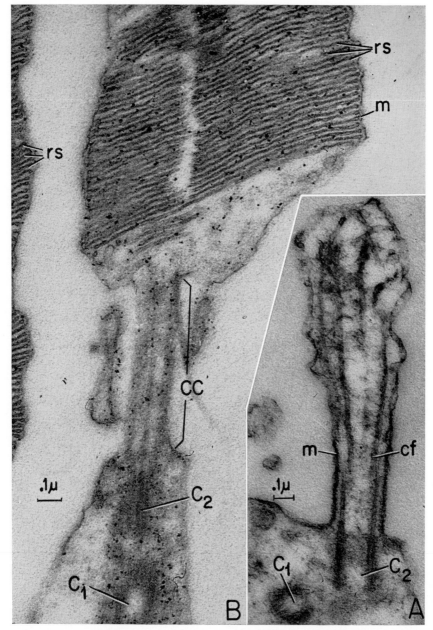

FIGURE 21-16. A, electron micrograph of a primitive cilium in the retina of an eight day old mouse. C_1 and C_2, centrioles; *cf*, ciliary fibrils; *m*, ciliary membrane. ×72,000. B, electron micrograph of an adult rod, showing the outer segment with the rod sacs (*rs*) and the outer membrane (*m*); the connecting cilium (*CC*) and the basal centrioles (C_1 and C_2). ×62,000. (De Robertis and Lasansky.)

muscle (*end plate*) activates the membrane. The final result is a coordinated contraction of the entire muscle fiber.

Two cytoplasmic components are highly differentiated in the muscle fiber. One is represented by the contractile machinery of the myofibrils, which is essentially made of proteins and is formed embryonically within the cyto-plasmic matrix. The second is a special differentiation of the vacuolar system, the so-called *sarcoplasmic reticulum,* which is thought to be involved with conduction inside the fiber and with co-ordination of the contractions of different myofibrils, in addition to being related to the relaxation of the muscle after a contraction.

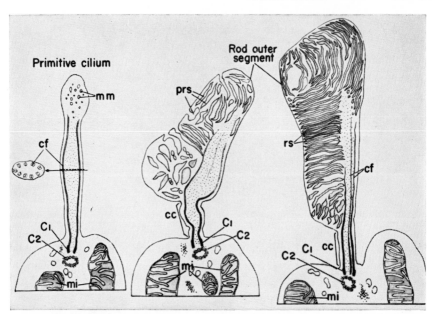

FIGURE 21–17. Diagram of the differentiation of the rod outer segment from the primitive cilium (see the description in the text).

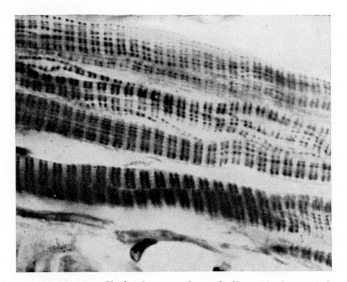

FIGURE 21–18. Myofibrils of a striated muscle fiber. Iron hematoxylin.

Myofibrils. Macromolecular Organization

Myofibrils are large subcellular structures about 1 μ in diameter. The striations that are characteristic of the entire fiber can be seen under the light microscope. These striations consist of the repetition of a fundamental unit, or *sarcomere*, limited by a dense band called the *telophragma*, or Z-line. This line is located in the center of the less dense zone known as the *I-band*, which

corresponds to the relatively isotropic disk (Fig. 21–19). The A-*band* which is anisotropic with polarized light, has a greater density than the I-band. Under certain conditions, a less dense zone may be observed in the center of the A-band, subdividing it into two dark semidisks (Fig. 21–19). This zone constitutes the *H-disk* (Hensen's disk).

In a relaxed mammalian muscle, the A-band is about 1.5 μ long and the I-band 0.8 μ. The striations of the myofibrils result from periodic variations in

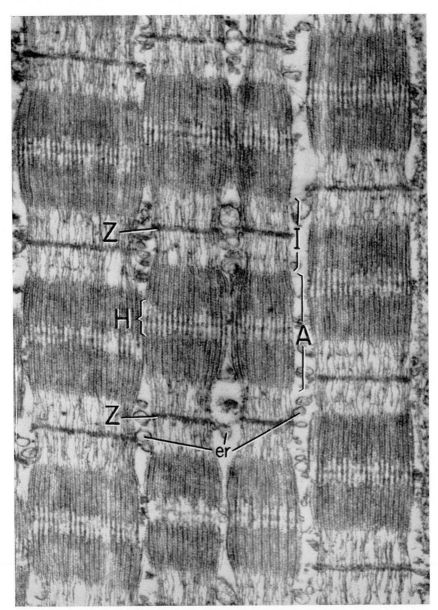

FIGURE 21–19. Electron micrograph of four myofibrils, showing the alternating sarcomeres with the Z-lines and the H-, A- and I-bands. *er*, sarcoplasmic reticulum situated between the myofibrils. The finer structure of the myofibril represented by the thin and thick myofilaments is also observed. ×60,000. (Courtesy of H. Huxley.)

density, i.e., in concentration of material along the axis. These striations are in register in the different myofibrils, thus giving rise to the striation of the entire fiber.

When myofibrils are examined under the electron microscope, new and finer structures become apparent. *Myofilaments* 50 to 100 Å in diameter form the main bulk of the sarcomere.[31] These myofilaments have now been extensively studied in vertebrate material and also

in insects. There are essentially two kinds: one 100 Å thick and about 1.5 μ long and the other 50 Å thick and about 2 μ long. As shown in the diagram of Figure 21–20, these two types of filaments are disposed in register and overlap to an extent that depends on the degree of contraction of the sarcomere. In a relaxed condition, the I-band contains only thin filaments, the H-band contains only thick filaments, and within the A-band the thick and thin filaments overlap. In a cross section through the A-band, the regular disposition of the two types of filaments can be observed best (Figs. 21–20 and 21–21). In vertebrate muscle each thick filament is seen to be surrounded by six thin filaments and each thin filament lies symmetrically among three thick ones (Fig. 21–21). Figures 21–19 and 21–22 show that the thin filament of one sarcomere apparently goes across the Z-line to the next sarcomere, but this is not entirely true, as will be shown later.

Another interesting detail revealed by the electron microscope is that the two sets of filaments are linked together by a system of cross bridges believed to play an important role in muscle contraction[32] (Fig. 21–22). They arise from the thick filaments at intervals of 60 to 70 Å. Each bridge is situated along the axis with a 60 degree angular difference. This means that they describe a helix about every 400 Å. By this arrangement one thick filament joins the six adjacent thin ones every 400 Å (Fig. 21–23). This

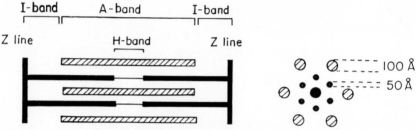

FIGURE 21–20.   Left, diagram showing the disposition of the thick and thin filaments within the sarcomere (see text). **Right,** cross section through the A-band, showing the hexagonal pattern formed by the thick and thin filaments. (From H. Huxley.)

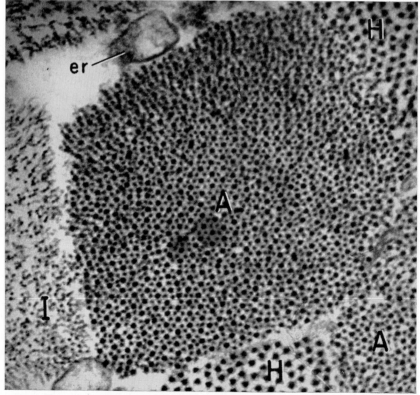

FIGURE 21–21.   Electron micrograph of cross sections passing through different levels of the sarcomere. The A-bands show the thick and thin filaments, the I-band only thin and the H-band only thick ones. *er,* sarcoplasmic reticulum. ×120,000. (Courtesy of H. Huxley.)

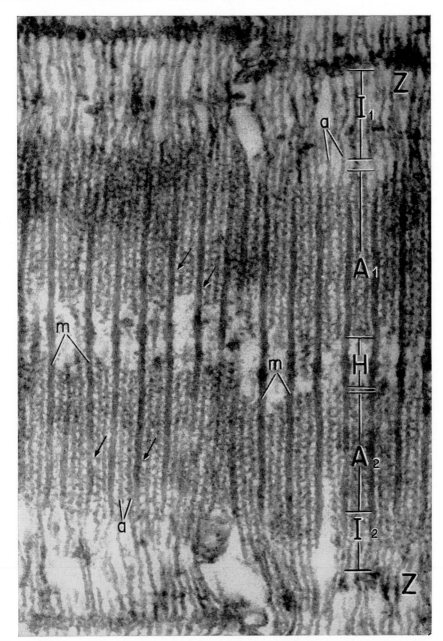

FIGURE 21–22.   Electron micrograph of two sarcomeres in the adjacent myofibrils: Z-lines. A_1 and A_2, anisotropic half bands; H, Hensen's band; I_1 and I_2, isotropic half bands; m, thick and a thin filaments. The cross band between both types of filaments can be clearly seen. Some of them are indicated by arrows. ×175,000 (Courtesy of H. Huxley.)

period had previously been observed in isolated myofibrils and was attributed to the myofilaments.[33]

Macromolecular Changes during Contraction

Changes in the myofibril during contraction are of considerable interest, and leave no doubt that contraction takes place at the level of the myofilaments. The observation made in classic histology of a reversal of banding during contraction has been confirmed with modern techniques. These changes can now be studied in the living fiber by means of the phase contrast and interference microscopes. One striking observation is that the A-band remains constant in a wide range of muscle lengths, whereas the I-band changes in accordance with the contraction. At the same time, the length of the H-band varies with contraction. However, the distance between the end of the H-band of one sarcomere and the beginning of the H-band of the other remains constant. These findings have been interpreted in the so-called *sliding filament theory* of contraction (see below). According to this concept, the two sets of filaments maintain their length but slide one with respect to the other. This is shown clearly in Figure 21–24, in which the degree of contraction or relaxation of the sarcomere is given in percentage figures. When the contraction is strong enough, the ends of the thin filaments will meet, closing the H-band, and then the thick ones also will come in contact at the Z-lines. Under these conditions new bands can be observed (inversion of the banding), suggesting a certain degree of crumpling and overlapping of the myofilaments.

Structural Proteins of Muscle

A striated skeletal muscle fiber contains about 20 per cent proteins by weight. The contractile portion of it consists almost exclusively of structural proteins, about 90 per cent of which is comprised of *myosin, actin* and, to a much lesser extent, *tropomyosin.*[34, 35]

Myosin. If a muscle is extracted with a 0.3 M solution of KCl, myosin solubilizes first and can be separated and purified by precipitation at a lower ionic strength. Myosin comprises about half the total protein and has a molecular weight of about 450,000. Under the electron microscope it appears to be composed of spindle-shaped elements about 2,000 Å long, which are remarkably similar to the thick filaments found in the A-band.[36] Along the length of these myosin filaments are numerous side projections, which probably correspond to the above-mentioned cross bridges (Fig. 21–23).

Myosin is presumably present as a magnesium salt. It binds sodium and

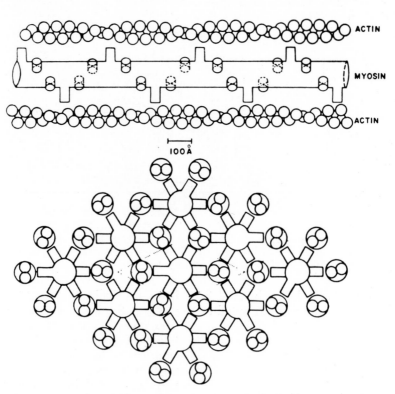

Figure 21–23. Spatial arrangement of myosin and actin filaments in striated muscle. (See the description in the text.) (From R. E. Davies, 1963, *Nature, 199:*1068.)

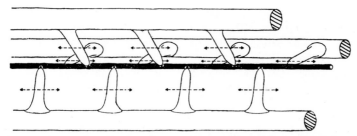

Figure 21–24.   Diagram of H. Huxley, showing the possible mechanism of sliding between thick and thin filaments. One thin filament lies among three thick ones. Each bridge is a part of a thick filament, but it is able to hook onto a thin filament at an active site (dot). Presumably the bridges can bend back and forth (arrows). A single bridge might thus hook onto an active site, pull the thin filament a short distance, then release it and hook onto the next active site.

potassium ions as well as divalent ions. Practically all the ATP present in muscle is bound to myosin.[37–40] This protein has been fragmented into two fractions called meromyosins, of which one is *heavy* and the other is *light*. Together they make up the myosin unit.[37] The cross bridges observed in myosin are associated with heavy meromyosin, whereas the light component is present in the backbone of these thick filaments.[36]

Actin.   The other major structural protein, actin, is less soluble in KCl solutions and dissolves in a 0.6 M concentration.[34] In the absence of salts actin becomes globular (G-actin) with a molecular weight of about 70,000, but in the presence of KCl and ATP it polymerizes, forming long fibers (F-actin). This change, which is reversible, is called a globular-fibrillar transformation. When the two isolated proteins are put together in a test tube they form the complex called *actomyosin*, which contracts in the presence of ATP.[41] This in vitro experiment indicates that interaction between actin and myosin is essential for contraction to take place.

When only myosin is removed from muscle, the light microscope shows that the A-bands disappear and the electron microscope indicates that the thick filaments are removed and the thin ones are maintained.[42] Myosin in the A-bands and actin in the I-bands have also been localized histochemically by means of the fluorescent antibody technique (see Fig. 6–16).[43]

When actin is extracted, a large part of the material of the I-band is removed. These and other observations indicate

that the *thick filaments are made of myosin* and the *thin of actin,* and that the interaction between actin and myosin observed in the test tube occurs in nature between the actin (thin) and the myosin (thick) filaments.

Tropomyosin.   About 2.5 per cent of the muscle fiber protein is tropomyosin. It can be extracted in solutions of 1 M KCl or weak acids. It has a low molecular weight (about 60,000) and crystallizes readily. It has not been localized in the muscle fiber, but is probably associated with the Z-lines. Under the electron microscope the crystals have a lattice structure that is similar to the system of interconnecting filaments found at the Z-lines.[36]

The Sliding Filament Theory of Muscular Contraction

The above-mentioned concepts on the macromolecular organization of the myofibril have given rise to the sliding filament theory of muscular contraction. It is postulated that the thick myosin filaments are displaced with respect to the thin actin filaments during each cycle of contraction and relaxation (Fig. 21–25). This sliding model depends on short-range interactions between the protein molecules that form the two types of filaments. The thick myosin filaments have projections (or cross bridges), which extend sideways and touch the thin actin filaments.

Figure 21–23 indicates diagrammatically the relationship of the actin molecules forming a double helix with 13 subunits of G-actin per turn of each helix and the myosin molecules having the six helically oriented cross bridges of heavy meromyosin. In this diagram it is apparent that each F-actin molecule is related to three myosin molecules.[44]

It is assumed that the end of each projection contains an enzymic site capable of splitting ATP and another for combining with actin. These two sites may be able to interact with each other. According to this theory, there must be a slight movement of one filament relative to the other during each reaction in which an ATP is split. The cross bridges could oscillate and hook up to specific sites of the actin molecules.

Figure 21–24 is a schematic diagram of this mechanism of contraction in which the thin filaments of actin move along the channels in between the thick myosin filaments without overall changes in length but with the penetration of one system of filaments into the other as in a collapsing telescope.

Related to this sliding theory are the recent findings that both the myosin and actin filaments are polarized. The actin filaments are interrupted at the Z-line and are probably interconnected there by an elaborate structure of tropomyosin. In addition, from each Z-line the actin filaments are polarized toward the respective H-band. Evidence indicates that all actin monomers on one side of the Z-line point in one direction whereas on the other side they point in the reverse direction. Similarly, the thick myosin filaments have their polarity reversed in either half of the A-band. This molecular polarization of both interacting proteins seems to be an essential feature of this sliding model of muscle contraction.[36]

Energetics of Contraction

Whereas the microfibrils constitute the mechanical machinery of the muscle, the fuel needed is produced mainly in the sarcoplasm. In all types of muscle numerous mitochondria called *sarcosomes* provide the essential oxidative phosphorylation processes and the Krebs cycle system (see Chap. 4). These mitochondria are particularly prominent in

size and number in heart muscle and in the flight muscles of birds and insects.

The sarcoplasmic matrix contains the glycolytic enzymes as well as other globular proteins, such as myoglobin, salts and high phosphate compounds. Glycogen is present in the matrix as small granules observed under the electron microscope. There is about 1 per cent glycogen and 0.5 per cent creatine phosphate as sources of energy in muscle. Glycogen disappears with contraction through glycolysis, and lactic acid is formed, which can be transformed into pyruvic acid to enter the Krebs cycle (see Chap. 4).

The initial energy source for contraction is ATP. Then there is a delayed heat phase with two components: one anaerobic and the other aerobic.[45] The ADP produced after the initial contraction is again recharged to ATP by glycolysis or from creatine phosphate. Oxidative phosphorylation is the last and most important source of ATP.

Muscle extracted with glycerol leaches out ATP and is converted into a *model* for contraction which can be induced by adding fresh muscle juice or ATP. We have previously mentioned that several other types of contractile cells can be induced to contract by ATP, e.g., cilia, flagella, spermatozoan tails and also dividing cells (see Chap. 14). It is postulated that there is a similar molecular mechanism of contractility in all these cases.

Sarcoplasmic Reticulum. Activation of Myofibrils and Muscular Relaxation

The sarcoplasmic reticulum found in skeletal and cardiac muscle fibers is one of the most interesting specializations of the vacuolar system. It was discovered by Veratti in 1902 as a reticulum present in the sarcoplasm of the muscle fiber and extending in between the myofibrils. It was completely neglected until 1953 when the first electron micrographs of this structure were published.[46–48]

The sarcoplasmic reticulum can be considered as an especially differentiated vacuolar system for this cell type. It is a continuous, membrane-limited reticular system whose organization is superimposed on that of the myofibril. As shown in Figure 21–25, the organization of the vesicles and tubules of the sarcoplasmic reticulum is regular. Special *terminal cisternae* are found at the level of the I-band; between these is a row of small vesicles forming the *triad*.[49] Between the terminal cisternae the tubules are disposed longitudinally on the surface of the A-band of the sarcomere. This structure is repeated between all myofibrils and also is continuous across the muscle fiber, making connections with the surface membrane at the level of the Z-lines. Earlier, light microscopic findings indicated that the Z-lines, or telophragms, were continuous septa across the fiber reaching the sarcolemma; however, the electron microscope has now clearly demonstrated that their continuity is established by way of the sarcoplasmic reticulum.

More recent investigations have emphasized that the sarcoplasmic reticulum can be divided into two parts. One is longitudinally oriented along the myofibril and would be the equivalent of the endoplasmic reticulum of the cells. The other part is a transverse component in between the terminal cisternae, which together with the cisternae constitutes the so-called *triad*. This transverse component is apparently continuous at certain points with the plasma membrane of the sarcolemma and would be the structure best fitted to conduct impulses from the fiber surface into the deepest portions of the muscle fiber.

The possible role of the sarcoplasmic reticulum in the physiology of the muscle fiber has been suggested by an experiment with microelectrodes in which the stimulation of the sarcolemma at the level of the Z-band produces a localized contraction of the adjacent sarcomeres. This is then transmitted into the fiber.[50]

It has been hypothesized that the sarcoplasmic reticulum serves to transmit the excitatory impulse intracellularly (see references 48 and 51). It has been postulated that the membrane of the sarcoplasmic reticulum, separating two different compartments within the cell (see Chap. 10), is electrically polarized in the same way as the surface membrane of muscle. It has been further assumed that this membrane is capable of conducting impulses inside the muscle fiber in order to activate the contractile elements. The presence of this intracellular conducting system may explain the physiologic paradox that a fiber 50 to 100 μ in diameter may contract quickly once the activating action potential has passed over the surface.

Another interesting approach to the study of the sarcoplasmic reticulum has been provided by its isolation and electron microscope identification.[52] This fraction has been found to contain the relaxing factor, which by inhibiting ATPase activity of the myofibril produces relaxation after contraction. This property is also produced by the binding of Ca^{++}. Apparently the sarcoplasmic reticulum and especially the membranes of the triad can fix Ca^{++}.

These findings suggest that the sarcoplasmic reticulum also has an important role in returning the fiber to the relaxed state after contraction.

The series of events produced after the arrival of the electrical signal that travels along the plasma membrane of the muscle fiber may be the following: the signal "is received at the individual Z band or A-I junction by the way of the intermediary vesicles or transverse system. This sets in motion a series of events which may include the release of Ca^{++} in the vicinity of the triad, the activation of the myofibril by ATP, the uptake of Ca^{++} by the elements of the reticulum and the release of the relaxing factor which inhibits the ATPase action of the myofibrils."[47]

All these data as well as those related to the sliding mechanism of contraction can be put together in a molecular theory of muscular contraction.[45] This is one of the best examples, so far studied, of a tight coupling between the energetic processes and the actual machinery involved in contraction. In this case, structure and function are so intimately related in the realm of molecular organization that they are an unseparable unit.

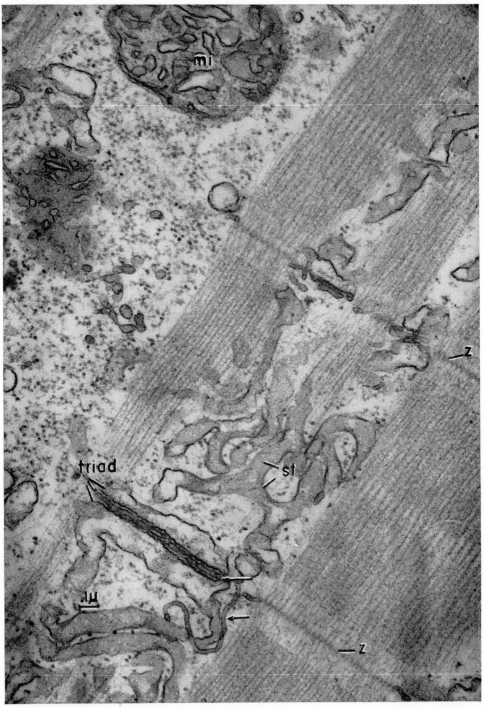

Figure 21–25. Electron micrograph of striated muscle, showing two myofibrils, one of which is tangentially cut and shows better the disposition of the sarcoplasmic reticulum. The two components of this system can be seen clearly. The transverse component is represented by the *triad* and especially by the central cisternae of the triad which continues in special tubules (arrows). Notice the relationship of the triad to the Z-line. The longitudinal component of the sarcoplasmic reticulum forms anastomosing tubules (*st*) on the surface of the sarcomere. *mi*, mitochondrion. (Courtesy of K. R. Porter.)

GENERAL REFERENCES

Allen, R. D. (1961) Ameboid movement. In: *The cell*, Vol. 2, p. 135. (Brachet, J., and Mirsky, A. E., eds.) Academic Press, New York.

Allen, R. D. (1962) Ameboid movement. *Scient. Amer., 206* (Feb.):112.

Bourne, C., ed. (1960) *Structure and function of muscles.* 2 volumes. Academic Press, New York.

Fawcett, D. (1961) Cilia and flagella. In: *The cell*, Vol. 2, p. 217. (Brachet, J., and Mirsky, A. E., eds.) Academic Press, New York.

Hanson, J., and Huxley, H. E. (1955) The structural basis of contraction in striated muscle. In: Fibrous proteins and their biological significance. *Symp. Soc. Exp. Biol., 9:228.*

Hayashi, T. (1961) How cells move. *Scient. Amer., 205* (Sept.):184.

Huxley, H. E. (1958) The contraction of muscle. *Scient. Amer., 199* (Nov.):67.

Huxley, H. E. (1960) Muscle cells. In: *The cell,* Vol. 4, p. 365. (Brachet, J., and Mirsky, A. E., eds.) Academic Press, New York.

Kamiya, N. (1960) Physics and chemistry of protoplasmic streaming. *Ann. Rev. Plant Physiol., 11:323.*

Marsland, D. (1956) Protoplasmic contractility in relation to gel structure: temperature and pressure experiments on cytokinesis and ameboid movement. *Internat. Rev. Cytol., 5: 199.*

Mommaerts, W. (1950) *Muscular contraction.* Interscience Publishers, New York.

Peachey, L. D., and Porter, K. R. (1959) Intracellular impulse conduction in muscle cells. *Science, 129:721.*

Perry, S. V. (1956) Relation between chemical and contractile function and structure of the skeletal muscle cell. *Physiol. Rev., 36:1.*

Physiology of voluntary muscle. (1956) *British Med. Bull., 12:* No. 3.

Szent-Györgyi, A. (1947) *Chemistry of muscular contraction.* Academic Press, New York.

CITED REFERENCES

1. Osterhout, W. J. V. (1951) *J. Gen. Physiol., 34:519.*
2. Allen, R. D. (1960) *J. Biophys. Biochem. Cytol., 8:379.*
3. Allen, R. D. (1961) Ameboid movement. In: *The cell,* Vol. 2, p. 135. (Brachet, J., and Mirsky, A. E., eds.) Academic Press, New York.
4. Loewy, A. G. (1952) *J. Cell. Comp. Physiol., 40:127.*
5. Heilbrunn, L. V. (1952) *An outline of general physiology.* 3rd Ed. W. B. Saunders Co., Philadelphia.
6. Heilbrunn, L. V. (1956) *The dynamics of living protoplasm.* Academic Press, New York.
7. De Bruynn, P. P. H. (1947) *Quart. Rev. Biol., 22:1.*
8. Goldacre, R. J., and Lorch, I. J. (1950) *Nature, 166:497.*
9. Allen, R. D., and Rolansky, J. D. (1958) *J. Biophys. Biochem. Cytol., 4:517.*
10. Fawcett, D. (1961) Cilia and flagella. In: *The cell,* Vol. 2, p. 217. (Brachet, J., and Mirsky, A. E., eds.) Academic Press, New York.
11. Grigg, G. W., and Hodge, A. J. (1949) *Australian J. Sci. Res., ser. B, 2:271.*
12. Manton, I., Clarke, B., Greenwood, A. E., and Flint, E. A. (1952) *J. Exp. Bot., 3:204.*
13. Fawcett, D. W., and Porter, K. R. (1954) *J. Morphol., 94:221.*
14. Afzelius, B. (1959) *J. Biophys. Biochem. Cytol., 5:269.*
15. Gibbons, I. R., and Grimstone, A. V. (1960) *J. Biophys. Biochem. Cytol., 7:679.*
16. Noirot-Timothée, C. (1959) *C. R. Acad. Sci., 246:2293.*
17. Randall, J. T., and Friedlander, M. (1950) *Exp. Cell Res., 1:1.*
18. Burgos, M. H., and Fawcett, D. W. (1956) *J. Biophys. Biochem. Cytol., 2:223.*
19. Dalhamn, T. (1956) *Acta Physiol. Scand., 36,* suppl. 123, 1.
20. Gray, J. (1958) *J. Exp. Biol., 35:96.*
21. Bradfield, J. R. G. (1955) *Symp. Soc. Exp. Biol., 9:306.*
22. Tibbs, J. (1957) *Biochim. Biophys. Acta, 23:275.*
23. Tibbs, J. (1958) *Biochim. Biophys. Acta, 28:636.*
24. De Robertis, E., and Peluffo, C. A. (1951) *Proc. Soc. Exp. Biol. Med., 78:584.*
25. Hoffmann-Berling, H. (1956) In: *Cell, organism and milieu.* (Rudnick, D., ed.) The Ronald Press Co., New York, p. 45.
26. Bishop, D. W. (1958) *Nature, 182:1638.*
27. Sleigh, M. A. (1957) *J. Exp. Biol., 34:106.*
28. De Robertis, E. (1956) *J. Biophys. Biochem. Cytol., 2:319.*
29. Porter, K. R. (1957) *Harvey Lect.* ser. 51 (1955–1956), p. 175.
30. Steyn, W. (1959) *Nature, 183:764.*
31. Hall, C. E., Jakus, M. A., and Schmitt, F. O. (1946) *Biol. Bull., 90:32.*
32. Huxley, H. E. (1958) *Scient. Amer., 199* (Nov.):67.
33. Draper, M. H., and Hodge, A. J. (1950) *Aust. J. Exp. Biol. Med. Sci., 28:549.*
34. Straub, F. B. (1942) *Stud. Inst. M. Chem. Univ. Szeged, 2:3.*
35. Mommaerts, W. (1950) *Muscular contraction.* Interscience Publishers, New York.
36. Huxley, H. E. (1963) *J. Molec. Biol., 7:281.*
37. Szent-Györgyi, A. (1953) *Chemical physiology of contraction in body and heart muscle.* Academic Press, New York.
38. Szent-Györgyi, A. (1955) *Advanc. Enzymol., 16:313.*
39. Sandow, A. (1949) *Ann. Rev. Physiol., 11: 297.*
40. Dubiusson, M. (1952) *Ann. Rev. Biochem., 21:387.*
41. Szent-Györgyi, A. (1957) *Chemistry of*

muscular contraction. Academic Press, New York.

42. Hanson, J., and Huxley, H. E. (1957) *Biochim. Biophys. Acta,* 23:250, 260.

43. Marshall, J. M., Jr., Holtzer, H., Finck, H., and Pepe, F. (1959) *Exp. Cell Res.,* suppl. 7:219.

44. Davies, R. E. (1963) *Nature,* 199:1068.

45. Ruch, T. C., and Fulton, J. F. (1960) *Medical physiology and biophysics.* W. B. Saunders Co., Philadelphia, Chap. 4.

46. Bennett, H. S., and Porter, K. R. (1953) *Amer. J. Anat.,* 93:1.

47. Porter, K. R. (1961) *J. Biophys. Biochem. Cytol.,* 10,suppl. 219.

48. Porter, K. R. (1956) *J. Biophys. Biochem. Cytol.,* 2,suppl. 163.

49. Huxley, A. F., and Taylor, R. E. (1955) *J. Physiol.,* 130:46.

50. Peachey, L. D., and Porter, K. R. (1959) *Science,* 129:721.

51. Muscatello, U., Andersson-Cedergren, E., Azzone, G. F., and von Der Decken, A. (1961) *J. Biophys. Biochem. Cytol.,* 10, suppl. 201.

CHAPTER 22

CELLULAR BASES

OF

NERVE CONDUCTION

AND

SYNAPTIC

TRANSMISSION

One of the most important functions of living organisms is reacting to an environmental change. Such a change, which is called a *stimulus,* generally elicits a *response.* In its most basic sense this general property of cells and multicellular organisms is called *irritability.* For example, a unicellular protozoon may react to different stimuli, such as changes in heat or light or the presence of a food particle, by a mechanical response, such as ciliary motion, ameboid movement, etc. (Chap. 21). *Plants* also may react to the environment by slow responses, which produce differential growth, also called a *tropism.* For example, the responses to the gravitational field, temperature, light, touch and chemicals are referred to respectively as *geotropism, thermotropism, phototropism, thigmotropism* and *chemotropism.*

Irritability reaches its maximal development in animals, and special cells forming the nerve tissue are differentiated to respond rapidly and specifically to the different stimuli originated in the outer and inner environment.

In these organisms special *receptors* adapted to "receive" the different types of stimuli are differentiated. Receptors are made of special cells or of the distal endings of neurons, which are specialized to receive a particular stimulus. For example, the receptors of light, touch, taste, pressure, heat, cold, etc., are characterized by their great sensitivity to the specific stimulus. Even a slight stimulus can elicit a response. This means that at the receptor the *threshold of excitation* is much lower than in any part of the nerve cell.

In an animal, the response to the stimulus may be of a varied nature. Most frequently the animal reacts with a rapid movement by contraction of muscle tissue (see Chap. 21). However, other types of reaction may be elicited. For example, a hungry dog in the presence of food reacts by secreting saliva; an electric fish, upon being touched, may produce an electrical discharge; and a firefly may give off light quantas. These different types of responses are produced in special tissue (e.g., muscles, glands, electric plates, luminous organs), called *effectors,* that are controlled by efferent neurons.

The Reflex Arc. Action Potentials

In an animal the simplest mechanism of nerve action is represented by the so-called monosynaptic reflex. This consists of a neuronal circuit formed by two *neurons* (nerve cells). One neuron is *sensorial* (afferent) and has a receptor at one end to receive the stimulus. At the other end the sensory neuron makes a special contact, also called a *synapsis,* with a *motor* (efferent) neuron, which in turn acts on the effector (i.e., muscle).

Figure 22–1 is a simplified diagram of the way in which the information *received* at the receptor is *conducted* along the sensory neuron and then

405

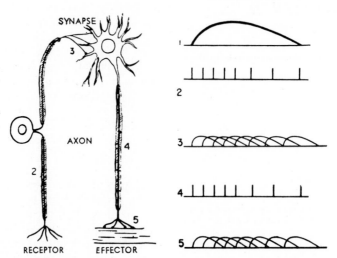

FIGURE 22–1. Diagram showing the monosynaptic reflex arc. **Left,** one sensory and one motor neuron with the synaptic junction. Notice the receptor and the effector. **Right,** different types of potentials produced at the different portions of the reflex arc (1–5), indicated in the figure. (Modified from Bishop.)

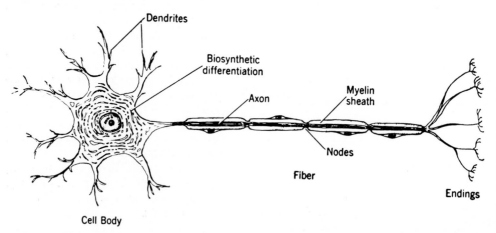

FIGURE 22–2. Diagram of a neuron. The myelinated nerve fiber shows one Schwann nucleus per internode. (From Schmitt, F. O., 1959. In *Biophysical science.* [J. L. Oncley et al., eds.] John Wiley & Sons.)

transmitted at the synapse. Notice that a new wave of information starts in the second neuron, which finally reaches the effector, where the final response is elicited.

As we shall see below, in nerves and muscle information is propagated by temporary changes in the *resting* or *steady potential* at the surface membrane. (For the concept of resting potential, see Chapter 20.) This change originates a *wave of excitation,* which moves along the surface of the cell from one end to the other. In the nerve cell this *propagated* or *action potential* is also known as a *nerve impulse.*

Nerve impulses are *conducted* along the elongated parts of neurons (i.e., the nerve fibers) by way of action potentials. At the receptors, the synapse and the effectors, other electrical potentials having different characteristics are produced. We shall concentrate in this chapter on the *cellular bases* of *nerve conduction* and *synaptic transmission.*

General Organization of a Neuron

The nerve cell (neuron) is the most differentiated cell in the organism. After embryonic life neurons do not divide, and remain in a permanent interphase throughout the postnatal growth period and the entire life of the organism (see Chap. 19). During this time a neuron may undergo changes in volume and in the number and complexity of its processes and functional contacts, but the number of neurons is not increased by cell division. This fact may be of paramount significance, since, in addition to conducting and transmitting impulses, nerve cells store instinctive and learned *information* (e.g., conditioned reflexes, memory), a property that would be best served by a more permanent system of structures.

The different types of neurons and neuronal interconnections are discussed in the histology and neuroanatomy textbooks. Only a few general considerations will be made here.

Neurons are adapted to the specialized functions by means of different types of outgrowths. As shown in Figure 22–2, the cell body (perikaryon) may emit one or more short outgrowths, or *dendrites,* which carry nerve impulses centripetally, and a longer one, the *axon,* which carries the impulse centrifugally to the next neuron or the effector. An axon is also called a *nerve fiber* when, after emerging from the neuron, it is wrapped in the different sheaths. The axon terminates, ramifying in the *telodendrons,* or endings. Some neurons have only one dendrite and the axon (i.e., *bipolars*) and others have only the axon (i.e., *monopolars*), in addition to the most common *multipolars.* In invertebrates most neurons are monopolar.

As we shall see below, nerve fibers are parts of the neuron that are adapted to conducting signals rapidly over long distances without losses. The perikaryon is characterized by the presence of considerable amounts of basophilic material—the Nissl substance—which, as in other cells, is composed of ribosomes and endoplasmic reticulum. A well developed Golgi complex is also characteristic of the neuron. The immature neuron, or *neuroblast,* has a considerable number of free ribosomes. In later stages, the vacuolar system develops (see Fig. 9–1). The great abundance of ribosomes is related to the biosynthetic functions of the perikaryon, which has a volume of cytoplasm in its outgrowths that may

be considerably greater than its own. (It will be recalled that in mammals axons may be 1 meter or longer.)

The entire territory of the neuron with all its expansions is maintained by the synthetic processes that are controlled by the nucleus (Fig. 22–2). If a nerve fiber is cut, the distal part degenerates (wallerian degeneration), and the proximal stump may regenerate later on by a growing process that is dependent on the perikaryon. There is also experimental evidence that the axon is continuously growing and being used at the endings.[1] (For further details on the structure of the neuron, see reference 2.)

Nerve Fibers: Diameter and Conduction Velocity

Nerve fibers are *nonmyelinated* when wrapped only in Schwann cells. *Myelinated* nerve fibers have in addition a myelin sheath, which consists of a multilayer lipoprotein system (Chap. 8, see Fig. 8–5). In the autonomic system of vertebrates most nerve fibers are unmyelinated and are contained within invaginations of the plasma membrane of the Schwann cells. The myelin sheath is interrupted at the *nodes of Ranvier* (Fig. 22–2). The distance between nodes varies with the diameter of the fiber. The *internode,* i.e., the distance between successive nodes, is the segment of myelin that is produced and contained within a single Schwann cell. The internode is 0.2 mm in a bull frog fiber of 4 μ, about 1.5 mm in a fiber of 12 μ and 2.5 mm in one of 15 μ.[3] Later we shall discuss the importance of this in the so-called saltatory conduction of the myelinated nerve fibers.

Within the internode, obliquitous (conic) *incisures* go across the myelin sheath and where the myelin leaflets have a looser disposition. At the node the myelin lamellae are loosely arranged, and a small zone of axon is in direct contact with the extracellular fluid. The myelin sheath acts as an insulator and, as a consequence, myelinated fibers conduct nerve impulses at a much faster rate than unmyelinated fibers. The diameter of the fiber also influences the conduction rate. As shown in Table 22–1,

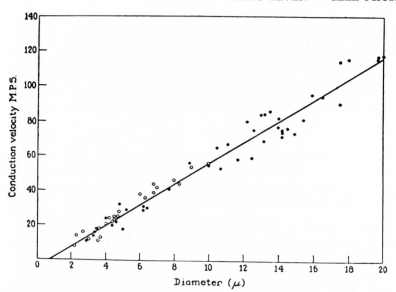

FIGURE 22–3. The linear relation between diameter and conduction velocity in meters per second (*M.P.S.*) of mammalian myelinated nerve fibers. The dots represent adult nerves; the circles represent immature nerves. (After Hursh, from Gasser, 1941, *Ohio J. Sci.*, 41:145.)

fibers can be classified according to the diameter into groups A, B and C. C-fibers are unmyelinated. The diameter may vary from 20 μ in A-fibers to less than 1 μ in C-fibers, and the conduction velocity from 100 to 2 meters or less per second. As shown in Figure 22–3, the rate of conduction of the nerve impulse follows a linear relationship with fiber diameter in mammalian myelinated fibers.

Structure of the Axoplasm. Neurofibrils and Neurotubules

In fixed and stained preparations observed under the light microscope fine

TABLE 22–1. PROPERTIES OF NEURONS OF DIFFERENT SIZES (Cat and Rabbit Saphenous Nerves)*

PROPERTIES	GROUP		
	A	B	C
Diameter of fiber (μ)	20–1	3	—
Conduction velocity (m/sec)	100–5	14–3	2
Duration of action potential (msec)	0.4–0.5	1.2	2.0
Absolute refractory period (msec)	0.4–1.0	1.2	2.0

* After Grundfest (1940), *Ann. Rev. Physiol.*, 2.

filaments called *neurofibrils* can be demonstrated in the cytoplasm of the cell. These *neurofibrils* run in all directions and continue into the dendrites, axon and nerve fiber (Fig. 22–4). Although fibrils have been observed in living ganglion cells cultured in vitro, they are generally invisible in living cells even under darkfield illumination. This fact gave rise to a controversy concerning the significance of neurofibrils, and led some investigators to consider these structures as fixation artifacts. This controversy has only historical interest now.

Observation of the living axoplasm of the giant nerve fibers of the squid with polarization microscopy has revealed a weak positive birefringence indicative of an elongated submicroscopic material oriented along the axis.[4] The axoplasm of myelinated nerve fibers has been extruded and separated from the myelin sheath, and this has made possible studies with the electron microscope and with polarization microscopy[5, 6] (Fig. 22–5A). In these studies the partial volume occupied by the axially oriented material has been found to be less than 1 per cent by analysis of the form birefringence and by electron microscopy (0.7 and 0.6 per cent, respectively).

In the extruded axoplasm observed under the electron microscope a fibril-

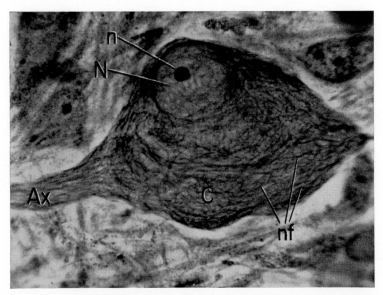

Figure 22–4. Nerve cell showing the neurofibrils (*nf*) within the perikaryon and the axon (*Ax*). *C*, cytoplasm; *n*, nucleolus; *N*, nucleus. Silver staining; light microscopy. (Courtesy of W. Hild.)

lar material has been found that is formed by fibrils of indefinite length, smooth contour and a diameter of 100 to 400 Å (Fig. 22–5B).[5] In sections of myelinated and unmyelinated peripheral nerve fibers, in addition to the fibrillar material, mitochondria, strands of canaliculi, vesicles of the endoplasmic reticulum and a few ribosomes have been observed.[6]

In the last few years the study of thin sections of nerve tissue has demonstrated that the fibrillar material present in the axon, dendrites and perikaryon is formed by long tubular elements of 200 to 300 Å in diameter—the *neurotubules*—which correspond to the neuroprotofibrils found in extruded axoplasm and previously in nerve homogenates.[5, 7] The tubular nature of this component is ascertained by the observation of cross and oblique sections (Figs. 22–5C and 22–6). In addition to the neurotubules, which are the most conspicuous axial components, some finer *neurofilaments* of about 100 Å can be observed (Fig. 22–6). There is now no doubt that neurotubules and neurofilaments, which are much beyond the resolving power of the light microscope, when clumping under the action of the fixatives and with the addition of colloid silver form the neurofibrils of classic histology (Fig. 22–4).

Although neurofibrils were described more than a century ago, their signifi-

cance remained practically unknown. The hypothesis that they are involved in nerve conduction has been disproved. In fact, neurotubules are sensitive to wallerian degeneration[7] and are destroyed prior to the disappearance of nerve conduction.[8] In Chapter 20 we mentioned the experiments of axoplasm extrusion and replacement by a saline solution with normal conduction of nerve impulses. There is now no doubt that nerve conduction takes place at the surface membrane of the axon (see below). The hypothesis that the neurofibrils are trophic elements of the axon[9] might have some meaning if translated into modern terms of axon growth and synthesis of essential materials for trophic action or synaptic transmission at the endings.

There is now experimental evidence that the axoplasm is produced continually by the perikaryon of the nerve cell.[1] It is possible that this process of axon growth involves the formation and migration of neurotubules. It can also be postulated that this tubular material carries essential enzyme systems or other components used at the nerve ending for the formation of synaptic vesicles and transmission of the nerve impulse.[10]

Conduction of the Nerve Impulse

For the study of the physicochemical

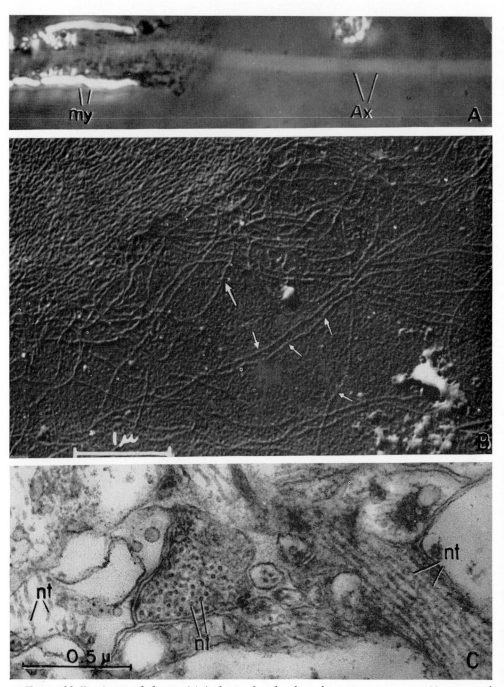

FIGURE 22–5.   A, extruded axon (*Ax*) observed under the polarization microscope. Note its weak positive birefringence. With appropriate treatment it can be demonstrated that the birefringence is both of form and intrinsic. *My*, myelin with a strong birefringence. In the normal fiber the axon birefringence is obscured by that of the myelin sheath. (From W. Thornburg and E. De Robertis, 1956). ×26,000. **B**, fibrillar material (neurotubules and neurofilaments) observed under the electron microscope in an axon extruded from the myelin fibers and compressed. Preparation shadow-cast with chromium. The arrows indicate some neurotubules. ×26,000. (From E. De Robertis and C. M. Franchi, 1953.) **C**, electron micrograph of a section of the cortex of the frog brain. Neurotubules (*nt*) can be seen in longitudinal, cross and oblique sections of axons. Note the annular aspect in cross section. ×60,000.

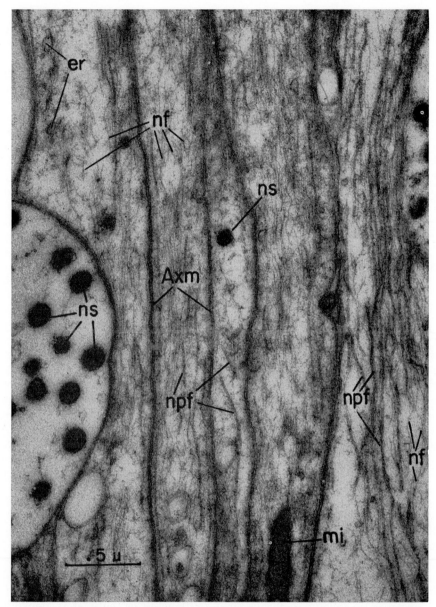

FIGURE 22–6. Electron micrograph of unmyelinated nerve fibers of the neurohypophysis of the toad, showing the fibrillar substance which is formed by thick (200 to 300 Å) neurotubules (*npf*) and thin (>100 Å) neurofilaments (*nf*); *er*, endoplasmic reticulum; *mi*, mitochondrion. Some axons show granules of neurosecretion (*ns*). *Axm*, axon membrane. ×48,000. (Gerschenfeld and De Robertis.)

phenomena underlying the conduction of the nerve impulse, consult general physiology textbooks.[11–14] Here the subject is discussed briefly and superficially as a continuation of the discussion of *active transport* and *membrane potentials* in Chapter 20. Remember what was said then about the *steady (resting) potential* and the ionic fluxes of Na^+ and K^+. As shown in Figure 20–5, the pump-

ing out of Na^+ (the so-called sodium pump) is the main mechanism to maintain a negative steady potential inside the membrane (see also Table 20–1).

When a muscle or a nerve fiber is stimulated, a profound change is produced in the electrical properties of the surface membrane and in the steady potential. For example, the electrical resistance in the squid axon falls from

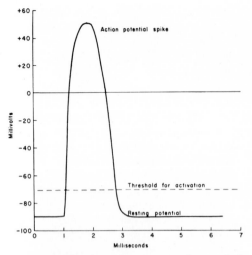

FIGURE 22–7. Action potential recorded from a single electroplax of the electric fish (*Electrophorus electricus*). In this case the action potential is similar but higher than in most axons. (From Gerebtzoff and Schoffeniels.)

1000 to 25 ohms per cm², which indicates an increased ionic permeability.[15]

As shown in Figure 22–7, with an intracellular recording, it can be demonstrated that with excitation, the resting potential is suddenly changed. At the point of stimulation there is not only a depolarization with loss of its charge, but an overshoot and the potential becomes positive inside. In the special case of Figure 22–7 the total amplitude of the action potential is 140 mv. With radioactive tracers it has been found that at the point of stimulation there is a sudden and several hundred-fold increase in permeability to Na⁺, which reaches its peak in 100 microseconds.[16] At the end of this period the membrane again becomes essentially impermeable to Na⁺, but the K⁺ permeability increases and this ion leaks out of the cell, repolarizing the nerve fiber. In other words, during the rising phase of the spike Na⁺ enters and in the descending phase K⁺ is extruded. Whereas the events occurring at the spike are extremely rapid, complete restoration of the ionic balance takes a longer time after the electrical event.

The action potential that develops in the nerve fiber has several other characteristics: (a) The stimulus produces a slight local depolarization in the fiber, which, after reaching a certain *threshold*

of *activation* (Fig. 22–7), produces spikes of the same amplitude. If the sensitivity of the stimulus is increased, the height of the spike always remains the same. This is called an *all-or-none response*. A similar type of response is produced in muscle fibers and in the electroplax, which is a modified muscle fiber. (b) The nerve impulse is *nondecremental*; i.e., the amplitude of the spike does not decrease and is the same all along the course of the nerve fiber. This type of action potential is thus well adapted to conduction over long distances without losses (see Fig. 22–1). (c) Once a nerve impulse has passed over any point of the fiber, there is a *refractory period* during which it cannot react to another stimulus. Corresponding to the height of the spike is an *absolute refractory period*, during which a stimulus cannot elicit a response, regardless of the strength of the stimulus. (d) During the tail of the spike there is a *relative refractory period*, during which a stimulus much stronger than normal can excite the neuron.

The *propagation* of the nerve impulse is generally explained by the so-called *local circuit theory* (Fig. 22–8). At the point of stimulation the area becomes depolarized (or negative outside) and acts as a sink toward which the current flows from the adjacent areas (Fig. 22–8B, C). This wave of depolarization advances along the nerve fiber at the rate of conduction that is characteristic for each fiber (Table 22–1 and Fig. 22–3). While this wave of depolarization advances, repolarization is so rapid that only a fraction of the nerve fiber (a few millimeters or centimeters, depending on the conduction rate) is depolarized at a time. In the recovery period, sodium leaves the cell by the action of the sodium pump and potassium reenters to restore the steady state. This recovery is most likely produced at the expense of high energy phosphate bonds. However, impulses continue to discharge for some time in the absence of oxygen and even when glycolysis is inhibited, which indicates that high energy bonds are stored at the membrane.

An all-or-none response with conduction without decrement would be expected if the membrane of the entire

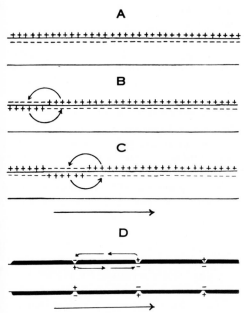

A

B

C

D

FIGURE 22–8. Diagram illustrating the local circuit theory of propagation of the action potential (**A, B, C**) in unmyelinated neurons and muscle fibers as compared to saltatory conduction in myelinated neurons (**D**). **A,** the membrane of an unexcited nerve (or muscle) fiber; **B,** the cell membrane excited at one end; **C,** the movement of the action potential, followed by recovery; **D,** node-to-node saltatory conduction. In large nerve fibers less than one hundredth as much ionic exchange occurs during an impulse in saltatory conduction as compared to conduction in an unmyelinated nerve fiber. The arrows in **C** and **D** show the direction of impulse propagation. (After Hodgkin, 1957, *Proc. Roy. Soc. London*, ser. B, *148:1.*)

fiber is initially equally polarized. While the action potential advances, the reaction of the membrane is self-regenerating. It is thought that the absolute refractory period is the time during which the membrane is no longer permeable to sodium. During the following period, when potassium leaks out, the fiber starts to be excitable but at a higher threshold (relative refractory period).

Saltatory Conduction

Whereas the preceding theory of nerve conduction applies to unmyelinated nerve fibers, in myelinated fibers it is thought that the local circuits occur only at the nodes (Fig. 22–8D). According to this so-called *saltatory theory*, at the internode, the impulse is conducted electrotonically and at each node

the action potential is boosted to the same height by ionic mechanisms. In this way the amount of Na^+ and K^+ exchanged is greatly reduced and the net work required is much less.

We have mentioned above that the velocity of conduction is related to the internode distance, and this in turn to the fiber diameter. Stimulation of myelinated nerve fibers with fine electrodes has shown that at the nodes the threshold of stimulation is much lower (i.e., the sensitivity is greater) than at the internode.[3] It has been found that the nerve impulse can jump across one anesthetized node, but not two of them. In this case the third node is beyond the operation of the electric field. In the squid axon that has a dead segment, the impulse cannot cross, but this property is regained if a metal wire is laid across, bridging this position. These findings indicate that at the internode the potential is conducted electrotonically.

Graded Responses in the Neuron. Generator and Synaptic Potentials

Physiological studies have demonstrated that in addition to the all-or-none response, with absolute refractoriness, constant maximal and nondecremental amplitude, variable frequency and electrical excitability, which we have just studied, in nervous tissue there is another type of electrical activity. This is by far the most frequent in the central nervous system and is referred to as a *graded response*. In the graded response the impulse is not *propagated* and the *amplitude* varies with the intensity of the stimulus. This type of response is characteristic of the receptors and synapses (see Fig. 22–1). Both the *generator potentials* found at the receptors and the *synaptic potentials* are graded responses.

If a peripheral receptor, such as a Paccini corpuscle or a stretch receptor (neuromuscular spindle), is mechanically stimulated—at the distal ending of the sensory fiber—a local, graded and decremental potential is recorded, the amplitude and duration of which depends on the intensity and duration of the stimulus.[17] In the case of the Paccini corpuscle it is possible to remove most of the connective lamellae that surround the nerve ending without impairing the generator potential (Fig. 22–9). It appears that in this case the *biological transducer* capable of transforming the mechanical energy (pressure) into the electrical energy (generator potential) is localized at the sensory part of the ending (Fig. 22–9). Probably the mechanical deformation of the ending produces a change in permeability with entrance of ions and partial depolarization. The local electrical change is often called the *generator potential,* because if it reaches a certain threshold, it can determine the further depolarization of the fiber and the starting of a propagated action potential (Fig. 22–9). In the case of the Paccini corpuscle it has been observed that the nerve impulse

starts at the first node of Ranvier (Fig. 22–9).[18]

The intensity of the sensory stimulus is reflected in the amplitude of the generator potential and this in turn in the *frequency* of the propagated signal. (The stronger the generator potential, the higher the frequency.) In this way the information received is coded for conduction along the nerve fiber in the form of a train or volley of impulses (see Fig. 22–1).

For a discussion of the structural organization of the different receptors, refer to histology and neuroanatomy textbooks.

SYNAPTIC TRANSMISSION

The earliest knowledge of *synapses,* or *synaptic junctions,* came from the

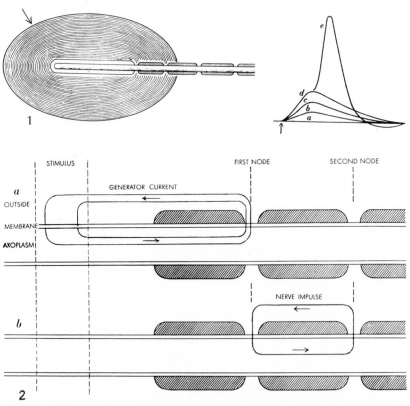

Figure 22–9. **1,** Paccini corpuscle with the nerve ending surrounded by multiple layers. Stimulation at the point marked by the arrow produces a generator potential (**right**) which increases in amplitude (*a–d*) until it fires an all-or-none nerve impulse (*e*). **2,** mechanism of the transducer. The stimulus produces a drop in the resistance of the membrane with ion transfer. Notice the generator current induced by the stimulus (*a*) and the nerve impulse (*b*) originated at the first node. (Courtesy of W. R. Loewenstein.)

discoveries at the turn of the last cen- tury of the morphologic and physiologi- cal organization of the nervous system. The so-called *neuron theory* established mainly by Cajal led to the assumption that the functional interactions between nerve cells was by way of contiguities or *functional contacts*. Different types of nerve terminals on dendrites or perikarya were described by the use of silver staining methods such as the characteristic boutons, the club endings, the so-called baskets or the contacts *en passant*.[19]

In 1897, Sherrington coined the name *synapse* to explain the special properties of the reflex arc, which he considered to be dependent on the functional contact between neurons. He attributed to the synapse a valve-like action, such as to transmit the impulses in only one direc- tion (see Fig. 22–1). In his studies on reflex transmission he discovered some of the fundamental properties of syn- apses, such as *synaptic delay* (the delay as the impulse experiments in traversing the junction), the fatigability of the synapse and the greater sensitivity to reduced oxygen and anesthetics. He also pointed out that the many synapses situ- ated on the surface of a motoneuron could interact, and that some would have an additive excitatory action, whereas others would be inhibitory and antagonize the excitatory ones. In view of these concepts, the synaptic junction was considered by Sherrington as a spe- cialized locus of contact at which ex- citatory or inhibitory influences are transmitted and act on other cells.[20]

As synaptic regions, we shall con- sider the special zones of contact be- tween two neurons, or between a neuron and a non-neuronal element, such as the junctions between some receptors and neurons or with an effector cell, i.e., a myoneural junction. Synapses thus em- body all the regions "anatomically dif- ferentiated and functionally specialized for the transmission of liminal excitations and inhibitions from one element to the following in an irreciprocal direction."[21] These typical polarized synapses com- prise the great majority in the nervous system of both vertebrates and inverte- brates, but a more modern definition of

the synapse should also include the ex- istence of a complex submicroscopic organization in both the pre- and post- synaptic parts of the junction and of the specific neurochemical mechanism in which transmitter, receptor substances, synthetic and hydrolytic enzymes and so forth are involved.

Referring back to the diagram of Figure 22–1, it is clear that the main problem in synaptic transmission con- sists in finding out by which mechanism the information brought forward by one neuron is transferred to the following. In other terms, how the code of frequency conducted by one neuron originates a new code of frequency in the following neuron.

Chemical and Electrical Transmission

DuBois-Reymond (1877) was the first to suggest that transmission could be either *chemical* or *electrical*. These two types of mechanisms have been ob- served. However, so far chemical syn- apses seem to be by far the most fre- quent in the peripheral and central nervous system.

Chemical transmission presupposes that a specific chemical transmitter is synthesized and stored at the nerve terminal and is liberated by the nerve impulse. The transmitter produces a change in ionic permeability at the post- synaptic component with a bioelectrical change *(synaptic potential)*. In 1904, Elliot suggested that sympathetic nerves act by liberating adrenalin at the junc- tions with smooth muscle. Later on it was demonstrated that *noradrenalin* was the true adrenergic transmitter. The studies of Dixon (1906) and particu- larly of Dale (1914) strongly supported the chemical transmission in the para- sympathetic system. This was finally proved on the heart by Loewi (1921). Since then *acetylcholine* has been demonstrated to act in sympathetic ganglia, neuromuscular junctions and in many central synapses.

Electrical transmission was first dem- onstrated in a giant synapse of the ab- dominal ganglion of the crayfish cord and since then in several other cases.[22]

In this type of synapse the membrane contact acts as an efficient electric rectifier, allowing current to pass relatively easily from the pre- to the postsynaptic element, but not in the reverse direction. In this case the action current, of the arriving nerve impulse, is passed without delay and can depolarize directly and excite the postsynaptic neuron. Here the one-way transmission is due to the valve-like resistance of the contacting synaptic membranes.

Excitatory and Inhibitory Synapses. Synaptic Potentials

Physiological studies on synaptic transmission were greatly improved by the use of microelectrodes which could be implanted near the synaptic region or intracellularly in the pre- and post-synaptic neuron.[23] The first synaptic potential to be recorded directly was the *end plate potential* of the myoneural junction.[24–27]

With intracellular recordings in large nerve cells (e.g., motoneurons, pyramidal cells, invertebrate ganglion cells, etc.),[20, 28] it has been observed that the arrival of the presynaptic nerve impulse produces a local synaptic potential. *Synaptic potentials,* as the generator potentials studied above, are graded and decremental and do not propagate. They extend electrotonically only for a short distance with reduction in amplitude.

A typical experiment is shown in Figure 22–10, which involves two ganglion cells of *Aplysia* (a marine mollusc), one of which (*P*) acts synaptically with the other (*F*). Neuron P is impaled with two microelectrodes, one of which is used for stimulation (*St*) and the other for recording (*R*). Neuron F is impaled with one microelectrode (*R*) to register the synaptic potential. Two types of P cells can be found, one of which produces an excitatory synaptic potential in F (1) and the other an inhibitory postsynaptic potential in F (2).[29]

Excitatory synapses induce a depolarization of the postsynaptic membrane, which upon reaching a certain critical level causes the neuron to discharge an impulse. The *excitatory postsynaptic potential* (EPSP) is due to the action of the transmitter released by the ending (Fig. 22–10,1). This causes a change in permeability of the subsynaptic membrane, allowing the free passage of small ions, such as Na^+, K^+ and Cl^- (see also Chap. 20).

Similarly, *inhibitory synapses* affect the subsynaptic membrane. In this case the transmitter causes a transient increase in membrane potential, the so-called *inhib-*

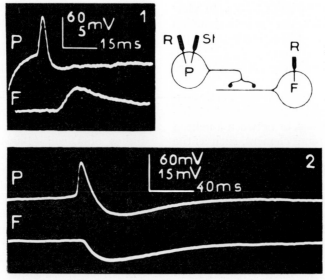

FIGURE 22–10.   Diagram of the experiment in two ganglion cells of *Aplysia* that are related synaptically (see the description in the text). **1,** excitatory response. Depolarization of the membrane at *F* after arrival of the action potential from *P*. **2,** inhibitory response. Hyperpolarization of the membrane at *F* after arrival of the action potential from *P*. (Courtesy of L. Tauc and H. M. Gerschenfeld.)

itory postsynaptic potential (IPSP) (Fig. 22–10,2). This hyperpolarizing effect induces a depression of the neuronal excitability and an inhibitory action.

The excitatory or inhibitory action is not dependent exclusively on the type of transmitter substance. For example, acetylcholine is excitatory in the myoneural junction, sympathetic ganglia and so forth, but inhibitory in the vertebrate heart, in which it reduces the frequency of contraction.

Figure 22–11 shows that also in the ganglion cells of *Aplysia* the injection of acetylcholine may have an excitatory synaptic effect in certain cells producing depolarization and increased frequency of discharges (1) or only a depolarization without firing (2). In other cells the same treatment provokes a hyperpolarization and inhibition of spontaneous discharges (3).

These facts indicate that the nature of

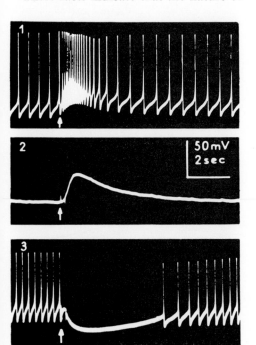

Figure 22–11. 1, intracellular recording in a neuron of *Aplysia* (see Fig. 22–10) that is firing spontaneously. At the point marked by arrow acetylcholine is added, producing depolarization and increase in the frequency of discharges (excitatory synapse). 2, same experiment on a neuron without firing. Only depolarization is produced. 3, in this neuron the action of acetylcholine induces hyperpolarization and inhibition of spontaneous discharges. (Courtesy of L. Tauc and H. M. Gerschenfeld.)

a synapse depends in particular on the chemical reactivity of the membrane in the postsynaptic neuron. The use of intracellular recording has greatly contributed to delineating some of the basic mechanisms by which the code of signals is transmitted from one cell to the other. All the synaptic potentials from the different excitatory and inhibitory endings impinging upon a neuron are algebraically added and act upon a region of the cell where the new spikes originate. Both types of input will change the electrical properties of the membrane at this critical zone of the cell of low excitatory threshold, which is called the "pacemaker." In this region, which in the motoneurons is located at the initial segment of the axon, new impulses are fired.[20]

Structure of the Synaptic Region. The Synaptic Vesicles

The classical morphologic studies with the light microscope revealed that the size, shape and distribution of synapses of different regions of the central and peripheral nervous tissue vary considerably. Synapses are classified into *axo-dendritic*, *axo-somatic* and *axo-axonic*, according to the relationship of the ending to the postsynaptic component. The endings may have different sizes and shapes, e.g., bud, foot or button ending, club ending, calix (cup) ending.

In a motoneuron several thousand nerve endings can be observed to terminate on the surface of the perikaryon and dendrites and a few at the beginning of the axon (Fig. 22–12). As many as 10,000 synapses have been calculated to impinge on a single pyramidal cell of the cortex. This gives one an idea of the extraordinary complexity of the nervous system. This immense number of synapses carry information from numerous other neurons, some of which may have an excitatory and others an inhibitory effect. Thus the neuron is a real center where all this information is integrated and sent as new nerve impulses along the axon.

With the increased resolution of the electron microscope new structural details became apparent (Fig. 22–12). At

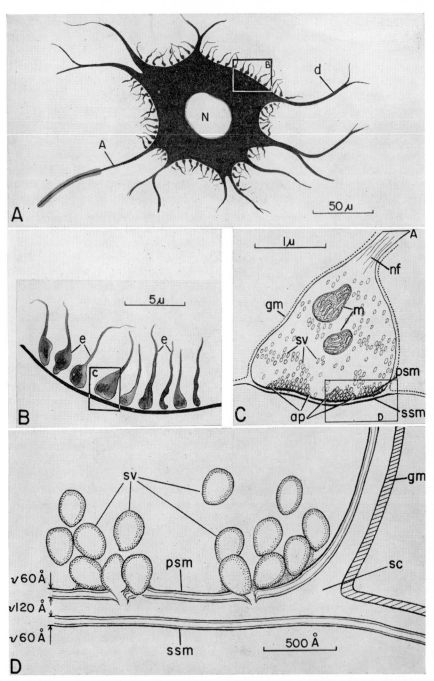

FIGURE 22–12.   Diagram showing button-like synaptic junctions at different magnifications under light and electron microscopes.

A, a motoneuron as seen at medium power under the light microscope. The nucleus (*N*), axon (*A*), and dendrites (*d*) are indicated. Numerous button-like endings make synaptic contact with the surface of the perikaryon (axosomatic junctions) and of the dendrites (axodendritic junctions). Enclosure *B* is magnified ten times in **B.**

B, end-feet (*e*) as seen at high magnification with the light microscope. The afferent axons are enlarged at the endings. The presence of mitochondria is indicated. Enclosure *C* is magnified about six times, with the electron microscope, in **C.**

C, diagram of an end-foot as observed with the electron microscope. Mitochondria (*m*), neurotubules (*nf*), and synaptic vesicles (*sv*) are shown within the ending. Three clusters of synaptic vesicles become attached to the presynaptic membrane (*psm*); these are probably active points (*ap*) of the synapse. Both the presynaptic membrane and the subsynaptic membrane (*ssm*) show higher

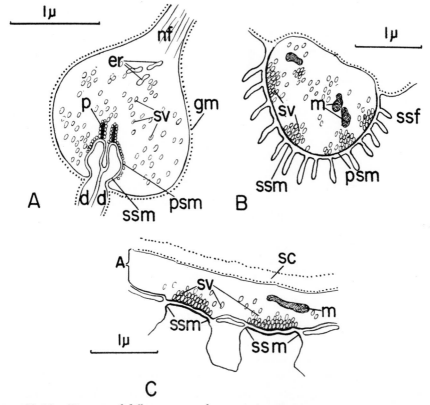

FIGURE 22–13.   Diagram of different types of synaptic junctions.

A, synapse between a rod and a bipolar cell of the retina. *d,* dendrites of the bipolar cell; *er,* endoplasmic reticulum; *gm,* glial membrane; *nf,* neurotubules; *p,* a blind projection of the presynaptic membrane (*psm*); *ssm,* subsynaptic membrane; *sv,* synaptic vesicles.

B, ending of a myoneural junction. Several active points on the presynaptic membrane are indicated. The main difference from other synapses is the folding of the subsynaptic membrane, forming the subsynaptic or postjunctional folds, *ssf. m,* mitochondria.

C, type of lateral junction between an axon (*A*) and an electroplaque of the electric organ of the eel. Synaptic vesicles are present along the axon at synaptic contacts. *sc,* Schwann cell. (De Robertis, 1959.)

the synaptic junction the membranes of the two neurons were seen in direct opposition, separated only by a synaptic cleft. Of great physiologic and biochemical interest was the demonstration of a special vesicular component—the *synaptic vesicles*—at the presynaptic endings.[30, 31]

The general disposition of the synaptic vesicles and their relationship to the synaptic membrane in different types of synapses are illustrated in Figures 22–12 and 22–13. The synaptic vesicles have a diameter of 400 to 500 Å and a limiting membrane of 40 to 50 Å. They are distributed throughout the ending but tend to collect and to make close contact with the presynaptic membrane at certain points that are probably the *active points* of the synapse.[32–35]

When the synaptic vesicles were first observed, it was suggested that they could be the storage sites of acetylcholine and other transmitters. This has been proved recently by isolation of the synaptic vesicles.[36, 37] It was also sug-

electron density. The glial membrane is shown by dotted lines (*gm*). Enclosure *D* is magnified about 20 times in **D.**

D, diagram of the synaptic membrane as observed with high resolution electron microscopy (see the description in the text). Some synaptic vesicles (*sv*) can be seen attached to the presynaptic membrane and opening into the synaptic cleft (*sc*). (De Robertis, 1959.)

gested that they could flow and perforate the presynaptic membrane, discharging their contents in the synaptic cleft.[10, 38]

Figure 22–13 shows three other types of synapses observed with the electron microscope that differ from the one just described in the relationship of the synaptic membranes.

The Synaptic Membranes

At the junction both synaptic membranes appear to be thicker and denser in addition to showing the above-mentioned "active points." Further complexities of this contact region are shown in Figures 22–14 and 22–15. The synaptic cleft in most cortical synapses is larger than the spaces between other membranes and may show a system of fine *intersynaptic* filaments of about 50 Å that join both synaptic membranes (Fig. 22–14).

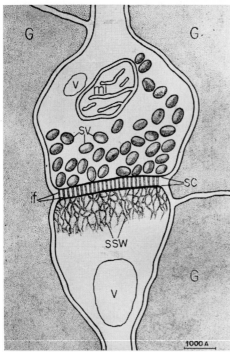

Figure 22–14. New diagram of the synapse based on studies on the brain. **Above,** the presynaptic component with a mitochondrion (*mi*), a vacuole (*v*), and numerous synaptic vesicles (*sv*). The synaptic cleft (*sc*) is crossed by parallel intersynaptic filaments (*if*). Notice the subsynaptic web (*ssw*) in the postsynaptic component. *G,* glial processes. (De Robertis et al., 1961.)

Another system of filaments or fine canaliculi has been observed to penetrate at a varying distance into the postsynaptic cell. This is the so-called *subsynaptic web*.[39] The demonstration of intersynaptic filaments in between the membranes confirms that there is greater adhesion at the junction, which was demonstrated by microdissection experiments. In fact, in an isolated cell the endings break the connection with the axons, but remain attached to the cell.

At the *electrical synapses* studied so far under the electron microscope it has been observed that the cleft is much smaller than in the other synapses and probably is nonexistent.[40, 41] It is now thought that *tight junctions* are the structural bases of electrical synapses[42] (see Chap. 8).

Adrenergic Synaptic Vesicles

In sympathetic axons and endings in the pineal gland and in the splenic nerve a special type of synaptic vesicle has been described.[43] These vesicles contain a dense granule formed by a deposit of reduced osmium (Fig. 22–16). They resemble, but are much smaller than, the catechol-containing droplets of the adrenal medulla (see Fig. 23–4). Similar synaptic vesicles were found in the anterior hypothalamus of the rat in a region rich in noradrenalin.[44]

Using pharmacological agents that release catecholamines, such as reserpine and aramine, a depletion of the granulated vesicles is observed. These vesicles increase in concentration with inhibitors of the enzyme monamine oxidase (e.g., iproniazid), or when the animal is given precursors of catecholamine (e.g., dopa, dopamine).[45] All these results indicate that granulated vesicles contain the adrenergic transmitter.

Synaptic Vesicles and Quantal Units in Transmission

Several experiments have been carried out to demonstrate the possible role of synaptic vesicles in transmission. In central synapses, cutting the nerve results in early degeneration with clumping and

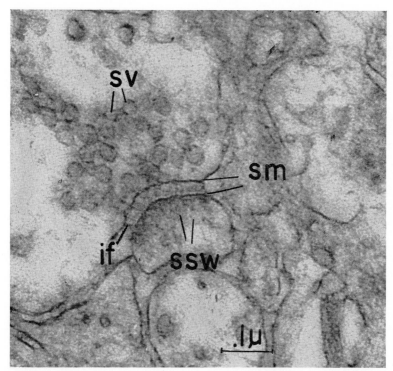

FIGURE 22–15. Electron micrograph of a synapse of the amygdaloid nucleus of the rat, showing the components described in Figure 22–14. *sm*, synaptic membranes. ×140,000. (From E. De Robertis and A. Pellegrino de Iraldi.)

lysis of the vesicles.[38] Similar observations have been made in the degenerating myoneural junctions.[46, 47]

Electrical stimulation of the nerve endings of the adrenal medulla (Fig. 22–17) showed that with certain frequencies of stimuli known to produce maximal output of catecholamines (see Chap. 23 and Fig. 23–5), the number of vesicles increased. With much higher frequencies the vesicles tended to disappear (Fig. 22–18). All these results indicate that synaptic vesicles play a role in the transmission of the nerve impulse and that a balance exists between the formation of vesicles and their discharge at the synapse.

Physiological studies have revealed that the two essential types of synaptic actions—excitatory and inhibitory—are produced by a flux of ions across the synaptic cleft that leads respectively to depolarization or to hyperpolarization of the synaptic membrane. This ionic flux is preceded by the discharge of the chemical transmitter at the synaptic cleft.[20]

The myoneural junction shows a spontaneous electrical activity in the form of *miniature end-plate potentials* that are more than a hundred times smaller than the synaptic potential.[48] It was suggested that these miniature potentials are produced by the spontaneous release of multimolecular (or quantal) units of acetylcholine on the synaptic membrane. With the discovery of the synaptic vesicles it became probable that acetylcholine and other transmitters could be segregated into packets surrounded by a membrane and that *each synaptic vesicle could represent a quantal unit of transmitter.* According to this theory, at the arrival of the nerve impulse a synchronized release of several hundred synaptic vesicles would liberate acetylcholine producing the synaptic potential (end-plate potential).[10]

Isolation of Nerve Endings and Synaptic Vesicles. Acetylcholine System

Owing to the extraordinary complexity of the central nervous system, our knowledge of the mechanisms of chem-

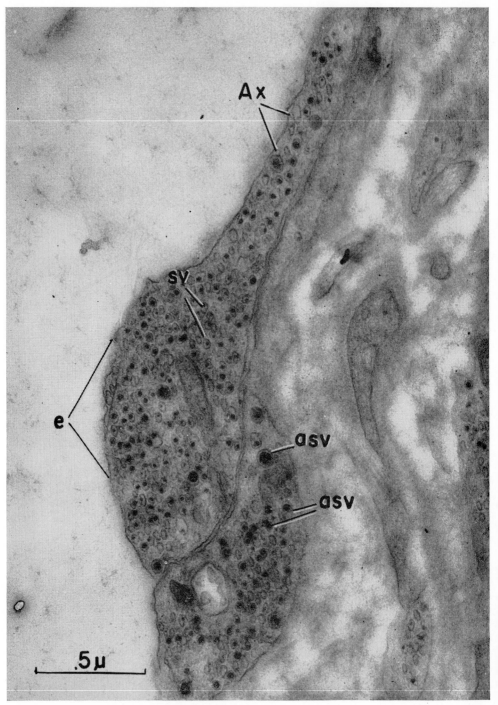

Figure 22–16. Electron micrograph of an adrenergic axon (*Ax*) and nerve ending (*e*) in the pineal gland of a rat. Both are filled with vesicles (*sv*), many of which contain a deposit of reduced osmium (*asv*). These are the adrenergic vesicles. ×60,000. (From A. Pellegrino de Iraldi and E. De Robertis.)

ical transmission is much more scanty. In recent years, owing to the development of cell fractionation methods, new information has been gathered on the intracellular localization of acetylcholine and other active substances in the brain.[49] Techniques for isolating a pure preparation of nerve endings are now

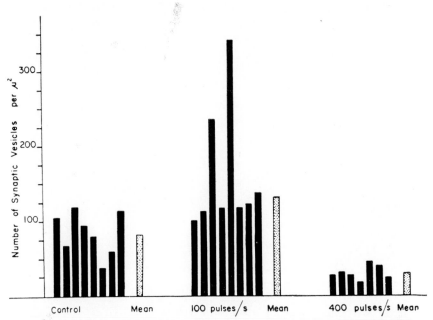

FIGURE 22–17. Diagram showing the results of measurements of synaptic vesicles per square micron of synaptic ending in control specimens and in rabbits, with stimulation of the splanchnic nerve at 100 and 400 pulses per second for ten minutes. (See the description in the text.) (De Robertis, 1959.)

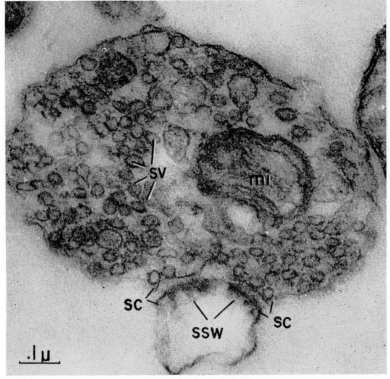

FIGURE 22–18. Isolated nerve ending in the mitochondrial fraction of the brain with the same components as in Figure 22–14. ×110,000. (From De Robertis et al.[36])

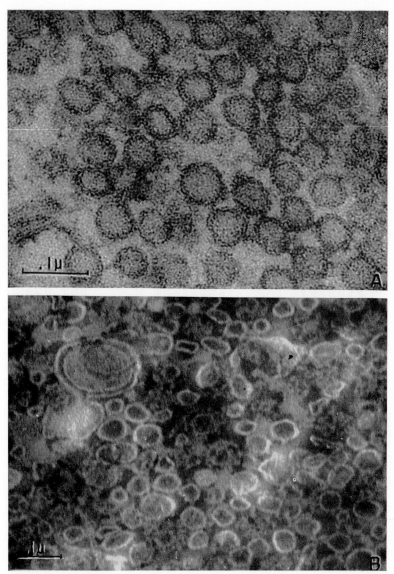

FIGURE 22–19. **A,** high resolution electron micrograph of synaptic vesicles in the hypothalamus of a rat, showing the fine structure of the vesicular membrane. ×180,000. **B,** isolated synaptic vesicles from rat brain after osmotic shock of the mitochondrial fraction. Negative staining with phosphotungstate. ×120,000. (From De Robertis et al., 1963.[87])

available[36] (Fig. 22–18). In addition, after disruption of the nerve ending complex the synaptic vesicles can be isolated (Fig. 22–19) and their content studied biochemically.

It is impossible to summarize here all the findings regarding the localization of the acetylcholine and other systems in synapses of the central nervous system.

The acetylcholine system is composed of: (a) the transmitter represented by the choline ester *acetylcholine;* (b) *choline acetylase,* the enzyme directly

involved in the synthesis; and (c) *cholinesterase,* the enzyme that hydrolyzes acetylcholine after this has been liberated.

All three components of the acetylcholine system were found to be localized in a special fraction of nerve endings. In the rat, the isolated synaptic vesicles showed a concentration of acetylcholine and choline acetylase. These findings are proof that the synaptic vesicles are the carriers of acetylcholine and that they also contain the enzyme directly in-

TABLE 22–2. SUBCELLULAR LOCALIZATION OF THE ACETYLCHOLINE SYSTEM, AND ITS RELATIONSHIP WITH SYNAPTIC VESICLES

FRACTION	M_1	M_2	M_3
SDH	2.7	0.3	0.0
AchE	1.2	2.3	0.0
Ach	0.7	3.6	1.5
ChAc	0.7	5.6	0.9
Ultra-structure	Myelin Mitochondria Nerve ending ghosts	Synaptic vesicles and membranes	Soluble

Ach, acetylcholine; AchE, acetylcholinesterase; ChAc, cholineacetylase; SDH, succinic dehydrogenase. All the results are expressed by the *relative specific activity:* $RSA = \dfrac{\% \text{ recovered activity}}{\% \text{ recovered protein}}$. Note that both Ach and ChAc are concentrated in fraction M_2 which contains the synaptic vesicles. (From De Robertis et al., 1963.[37])

volved in its synthesis (Table 22–2). Acetylcholinesterase is probably concentrated in the synaptic membrane and not in the vesicles. Other interesting results have been obtained on the localization of noncholinergic systems.[10]

In summary: From the viewpoint of cell biology the transmission of the nerve impulse is another excellent example of an intimate structural-functional relationship.

In nerve transmission the concepts of transmitters, ion fluxes and synaptic potentials should be closely correlated with those of synaptic vesicles, specializations of the synaptic membrane or tight junctions. In fact, in this fundamental process there occurs a series of biochemical, ionic and electrical events that are admirably integrated within the macromolecular and chemical organization of the synaptic region.

GENERAL REFERENCES

Davson, H. (1959) *A textbook of general physiology.* 2nd Ed. Little, Brown and Co., Boston.
De Robertis, E. (1959) Submicroscopic morphology of the synapse. *Internat. Rev. Cytol.,* 8:61.
De Robertis, E. (1964) *Histophysiology of syn-apses and neurosecretion.* Pergamon Press, Oxford.
Eccles, J. C. (1957) *The physiology of nerve cells.* Johns Hopkins Press, Baltimore.
Eccles, J. C. (1964) *The physiology of synapses.* Springer-Verlag, Berlin.
Flore, E. (1961) Transmitter substances. *Ann. Rev. Physiol.,* 23:501.
Hamburger, V. (1957) The life history of a nerve cell. *Am. Sci.,* 45:263.
Hodgkin, A. L. (1958) Ionic movements and electrical activity in giant nerve fibers. *Proc. Roy. Soc. London,* ser. B, 148:1.
Hydén, H. (1960) The neuron. In: *The cell,* Vol. 4, p. 215. (Brachet, J., and Mirsky, A. E., eds.) Academic Press, New York.
Katz, B. (1961) How cells communicate. *Scient. Amer.,* 205(Sept.):209.
Loewenstein, W. R. (1960) Biological transducers. *Scient. Amer.,* 203(Aug.):99.
Ruch, T. C., and Fulton, J. F. (1960) *Medical physiology and biophysics.* 18th Ed. W. B. Saunders Co., Philadelphia.
von Euler, U. S. (1961) Neurotransmission in the adrenergic nervous system. *Harvey Lect.,* ser. 55 (1959–1960), p. 43.

CITED REFERENCES

1. Weiss, P., and Hiscoe, H. B. (1948) *J. Exp. Zool.,* 107:315.
2. Hydén, H. (1960) The neuron. In: *The cell,* Vol. 4, p. 215. (Brachet, J., and Mirsky, A. E., eds.) Academic Press, New York.
3. Tasaki, I. (1953) *Nervous transmission.* Charles C Thomas, Springfield, Ill.
4. Bear, R. S., Schmitt, F. O., and Young, J. Z. (1937) *Proc. Roy. Soc. London,* ser. B, 123:505.
5. De Robertis, E., and Franchi, C. M. (1953) *J. Exp. Med.,* 98:269.
6. Thornburg, W., and De Robertis, E. (1956) *J. Biophys. Biochem. Cytol.,* 2:475.
7. De Robertis, E., and Schmitt, F. O. (1948) *J. Cell. Comp. Physiol.,* 31:1.
8. Vial, J. D. (1958) *J. Biophys. Biochem. Cytol.,* 4:551.
9. Parker, G. H. (1929) *Quart. Rev. Biol.,* 4:155.
10. De Robertis, E. (1964) *Histophysiology of synapses and neurosecretion.* Pergamon Press, Oxford.
11. Davson, H. (1959) *A textbook of general physiology.* 2nd Ed. Little, Brown and Co., Boston.
12. Heilbrunn, L. V. (1952) *An outline of general physiology.* 3rd Ed. W. B. Saunders Co., Philadelphia.
13. Giese, A. C. (1962) *Cell physiology.* 2nd Ed. W. B. Saunders Co., Philadelphia.
14. Ruch, T. C., and Fulton, J. F. (1960) *Medical physiology and biophysics.* 18th Ed. W. B. Saunders Co., Philadelphia, Chap. 4.
15. Hodgkin, A. L. (1951) *Biol. Rev.,* 26:339.
16. Hodgkin, A. L., and Huxley, A. F. (1952)

Cold Spr. Harb. Symp. Quant. Biol., 17: 43.

17. Davis, H. (1961) *Physiol. Rev., 41:*391.
18. Loewenstein, W. R. (1960) *Scient. Amer., 203*(Aug.):98.
19. Cajal, S. R. (1934) *Trab. Inst. Invest. Biol.* (*Madrid*), *24:*1.
20. Eccles, J. C. (1957) *Physiology of nerve cells.* Johns Hopkins Press, Baltimore.
21. Arvanitaki, A. (1942) *J. Neurophysiol., 5:* 108.
22. Furshpan, E. J., and Potter, D. D. (1957) *Nature, 180:*342.
23. Ling, G., and Gerard, R. W. (1949) *J. Cell. Comp. Physiol., 34:*383.
24. Fatt, P., and Katz, B. (1950) *J. Physiol., 111:*46.
25. Fatt, P., and Katz, B. (1951) *J. Physiol., 115:*320.
26. Nastuck, W. L. (1950) *Fed. Proc., 9:*94.
27. Nastuck, W. L. (1953) *J. Cell. Comp. Physiol., 42:*249.
28. Eccles, J. C. (1964) *The physiology of synapses.* Springer-Verlag, Berlin.
29. Tauc, L., and Gerschenfeld, H. M. (1960) *C. R. Acad. Sci.* (*Paris*), *257:*3076.
30. De Robertis, E., and Bennett, H. S. (1954) *Fed. Proc., 13:*35.
31. De Robertis, E., and Bennett, H. S. (1955) *J. Biophys. Biochem. Cytol., 2:*307.
32. De Robertis, E. (1955) *Acta Neurol. Lat.-Amer., 1:*1.
33. De Robertis, E. (1955) *Anat. Rec., 121:*284.
34. De Robertis, E. (1958) *Exp. Cell Res.,* suppl. 5:347.

35. Palay, S. L. (1958) *Exp. Cell Res.,* suppl. 5: 275.
36. De Robertis, E., Rodriquez de Lores Arnaiz, G., and Pellegrino de Iraldi, A. (1962) *Nature, 194:*794.
37. De Robertis, E., Rodriguez de Lores Arnaiz, G., Salganicoff, L., Pellegrino de Iraldi, A., and Zieher, L. M. (1963) *J. Neurochem., 10:*225.
38. De Robertis, E. (1959) *Internat. Rev. Cytol., 8:*61.
39. De Robertis, E., Pellegrino de Iraldi, A., Rodriguez de Lores Arnaiz, G., and Salganicoff, L. (1961) *Anat. Rec., 139:*220.
40. De Lorenzo, A. J. (1960) *Biol. Bull., 119:* 325.
41. Hama, K. (1961) *Anat. Rec., 141:*275.
42. Bennett, M. U. L., Aljure, E., Nakajima, Y., and Pappas, G. D. (1963) *Science, 141:* 262.
43. De Robertis, E., and Pellegrino de Iraldi, A. (1961) *Anat. Rec., 139:*298.
44. Pellegrino de Iraldi, A., Farini Duggan, H., and De Robertis, E. (1963) *Anat. Rec., 145:*521.
45. Pellegrino de Iraldi, A., and De Robertis, E. (1963) *Internat. J. Neuropharm., 2:*231.
46. Birks, R. I., Huxley, H. E., and Katz, B. (1960) *J. Physiol., 150:*134.
47. Birks, R. I., Katz, B., and Miledi, R. (1960) *J. Physiol., 150:*145.
48. Fatt, P., and Katz, B. (1952) *J. Physiol., 117:*109.
49. Whittaker, V. P. (1959) *Biochem. J., 72:* 694.

CHAPTER 23

CELL SECRETION

Secretion is one of the most common cellular functions. It can be defined as the process by which cells synthesize products that will be utilized by other cells or eliminated from the organism. In a multicellular individual secretions are (1) *external*, or *exocrine*, i.e., expelled into the outer environment or more frequently into natural cavities (e.g., the digestive or respiratory tract), or (2) *internal*, or *endocrine*, i.e., enter directly into the circulation to act on another organ or part. Internal secretion is characteristic of the endocrine glands, such as the thyroid, parathyroid and adrenal glands, the hypophysis, and the islets of the pancreas. Typical exocrine secretion is that of the pancreatic acinus, the salivary glands and the numerous small glands that are related to the digestive, respiratory and genital tracts. (For further details, consult histology textbooks.)

The basic concept of secretion, in most general terms, implies a *chemical transformation*. The cell absorbs small molecules by passive or active transport and so forth (studied in Chapter 20 under Cell Permeability). These molecules can be concentrated or, more frequently, transformed into products of a different chemical structure and molecular weight. In both cases the cell must utilize energy to carry the chemical transformation or the fluid transfers against a concentra-

tion gradient. Work is required for secretion, which implies that it is definitely different from the simple *excretion* of a nonmodified substance which is expelled along a favorable concentration gradient without expenditure of energy by the cell. For example, the passage of oxygen through the respiratory epithelium or the urine filtrated at the kidney glomerulus can be considered as a kind of excretion. However, both secretion and excretion are more or less intermingled and sometimes it is difficult to separate them clearly.

A secretory cell can be compared to a factory in which raw materials *come in* and products *go out*. Between these two events all the intracellular mechanisms by which the particular product is manufactured take place. The entire process resembles a modern "assembly line" in which the product flows along while being assembled piece by piece. Movement from one cell structure to another carries the secretion product along (see reference 1).

Secretion is a complex function of the cell involving all the parts and organoids which we have studied in previous chapters. The nucleus and the nucleolus, the ribosomes, the vacuolar system with the endoplasmic reticulum and the Golgi complex and also the mitochondria all participate directly or indirectly in this "assembly line," which will put out the final secretion product. In the cytologic study of secretion the main interest is in these coordinated series of physiological events in which each part of the machinery of the cell is involved at one point or another. This is a good time to recall some of the fundamental functions studied earlier, such as: (a) the production of the different RNA molecules by structural and other genes present in the DNA of the chromosomes, (b) the function of the nucleolus in concentrating ribosomal RNA, (c) the ribosome and especially the polyribosome as the site of protein synthesis, through the interaction of messenger RNA with the complex formed by the amino acids and different transfer RNAs, (d) the role of the endoplasmic reticulum of circulating proteins for export and (e) the role of the Golgi complex of concentrating the

427

secretion product and of providing a packing membrane. The study of secretion is thus a recapitulation of many chapters of cell biology.

The Secretory Cycle. Methods of Study

What has been said so far implies that in secretion there is a continuous change that can be best interpreted by studying the cell throughout the different stages of cellular activity.

If fixed and stained secretory cells are studied under the microscope, the image obtained represents only a single stage of cell work. In cell secretion, more than in any other process, the *time factor* must be taken into account in order to interpret the results of cytomorphologic analysis.

In some secretory cells secretion is *continuous* and in others it is *discontinuous*. In the former case the secretion product is discharged as soon as it is elaborated. In these cells all the phases of the secretory process (i.e., absorption of material, intracellular synthesis and elimination of the product) take place simultaneously. Under the microscope striking differences cannot be seen from one cell to another. This happens, for example, in some endocrine glands (e.g., thyroid, parathyroid and adrenal cortex) and in the muciparous cells of the gastric epithelium. In discontinuous secretion the secretory cycle has a special timing in which absorption is followed by elaboration and this in turn by accumulation of the product. This discontinuous type of activity is also called *rhythmic*. In this case there are considerable differences in morphologic characteristics as well as in metabolism from one cell to another. Examples of rhythmic secretory cells are the goblet cells of the intestine and to some extent the pancreatic acini. The best technique for the study of secretion is biomicroscopy or vital observation when this can be sufficiently prolonged in time. However, this is not always feasible and often offers technical difficulties.

In some glands, even if the activity is continuous, the different cells may be in different stages of the secretory cycle.

For example, the salivary glands of the rat and mouse are active continuously, whereas the individual acini show a rhythmic function. In such cases one may have to observe numerous sections through the gland in order to see the different stages. In other glands periods of almost complete inactivity may be followed by others of intense activity. To overcome these difficulties of observing the different stages of the secretory cycle, special stimuli can be used that rapidly modify the activity of the cells (which normally would be asynchronic or semisynchronic) and drive them in a given direction, thus establishing functional synchronization. If, for example, one wishes to study the secretion of the exocrine pancreatic cells, the animal is first fasted in order to bring about a resting state of the gland. The cells are stimulated by feeding the animals or with *pilocarpine*, whose action brings about the rapid excretion of the secretion products. In this way the various phases of cellular activity are synchronized, and practically all the cells expel their contents and then recover gradually (Fig. 23–1). In some cases, as in the submaxillary gland of the rat, the sexual differences that are under hormone control can be used for the cytologic and cytochemical study of secretion.[2]

The cytologic study is carried out at various times after the application of the stimulus and can be done in a purely qualitative or in a quantitative way, applying a statistical method (see reference 3). In the latter, an attempt is made to find any particular stage of the cell (for example, mitosis) and to count the cells in this stage to see in what proportion they appear at different times following the stimulus.

The methods for studying secretion are at present numerous, and involve not only the observation of living secretory cells for long periods of time or at different time intervals after fixation, but also cell fractionation methods to separate different parts of the secretory cell, the cannulation or fistula of the excretory ducts of the gland to analyze the products that are eliminated after the application of the stimulus, and es-

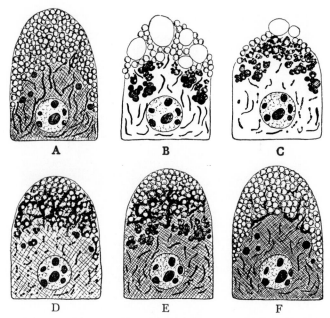

FIGURE 23–1.   Secretory cycle of the pancreatic cell of the white mouse. **A,** cell from a fasting animal. Zymogen granules and mitochondria; abundant chromidial substance. **B,** same, a half hour after injection of pilocarpine. Vacuolization and excretion of the zymogen; Golgi apparatus increased in size, disappearance of the chromidial substance. **C,** one hour later, excretion almost complete. Great osmiophilia of the Golgi apparatus. **D,** after four hours. Typical Golgi net with newly formed granules. **E,** after seven hours, the process of recovery continuing. **F,** after 14 hours. Recovery completed. (After Ries.)

pecially the use of radioactive precursors of the secretion. This last technique, when used on radioautographs at the light and electron microscope level, gives important information about the dynamics of the secretion process within the cell structure.

In studying the secretory cycle, fixation by freezing and drying (Chap. 6) is advantageous, since it stops the cellular processes rapidly and thus their different stages can be determined. In addition, it permits one to observe, under the best conditions and without changes, the soluble products and protein secretion when present in high dilution. In the case of the thyroid, this method demonstrates an intracellular colloid that is not readily observable by other methods and makes it possible to follow the different stages of its formation and excretion. Thus if an animal is injected with thyrotropic hormone, at the end of a few minutes numerous colloid droplets appear at the apical pole of the cell. These are then excreted into the thyroid follicle. The exit of these droplets is by evagination of the cyto-

plasm and rupture of the cell membrane at certain points. After this first step of apical excretion, the reabsorption of the follicular colloid begins. This colloid passes through the cell toward the blood capillaries. These changes can also be observed with the electron microscope (Fig. 23–2).

Some Cytologic Aspects of the Secretory Cycle

The secretory cycle has extremely variable cytologic expressions, but it is generally characterized by products visible with the microscope that accumulate in the cell and then are eliminated. These may be dense and refractile granules, vacuoles, droplets, etc., having a definite location in the cell and at times characteristic histochemical reactions.

In some glands, nevertheless, it is not possible to demonstrate by cytologic methods any secretion product, even when the physiological data indicate that secretion is active. A typical example is the parathyroid, a gland that secretes a powerful hormone that reg-

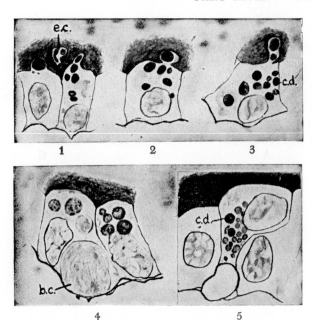

FIGURE 23–2.   Process of secretion in the thyroid gland, studied by the freezing-drying technique. 1, 2, and 3, thyroid cells, 30 to 60 minutes after the injection of the thyrotropic hormone of the hypophysis. The formation of colloid droplets and their secretion into the cavity of the follicle can be seen. *c.d.*, colloid droplets; *e.c.*, excreted droplet. 4, Thyroid cells, three hours after the injection. Reabsorption of the colloid predominates. *b.c.*, basal colloid. 5, thyroid cell 22 hours after the injection. The inversion of the secretory polarity can be seen. Fixation by the freezing-drying method. Stain: aniline blue and orange G.

ulates calcium metabolism. Parathyroid cells observed under the optical microscope do not reveal a product that can be considered as a pre-secretion or an intracellular precursor of the secretion. In such a case the existence of the secretory cycle can be demonstrated by taking into account the modifications produced in the nucleus and in the cytoplasmic components when the normal activity of the gland is modified. In the parathyroid, for example, the injection of a single large dose of parathyroid extract brings about a decrease in function, followed by a slow recuperation. Cytologically it is observed that in the first stage the dark, osmiophilic cells disappear and all the cells acquire a homogeneous cytologic aspect with a simple reticular Golgi apparatus (Fig. 23–3). In the state of recuperation the cells show a functional asynchronism by their cytomorphologic heterogeneity. There are certain larger cells with a fragmented and vacuolized Golgi apparatus and vesicular mitochondria. The dark, osmiophilic elements reappear. In the same gland, the functional hyperactivity, which occurs when the animals are placed on certain diets, exaggerates the cytologic heterogeneity and increases the number of osmiophilic cells. From these experimental studies one can infer approximately which is the normal cytomorphologic cycle of secretion even though the product elaborated is not visible (Fig. 23–3).[4, 5]

Submicroscopic Morphology of Secretion in Different Gland Cells

The introduction of electron microscopy has helped to clarify the relationship between the fine structure of the cytoplasm and the secretion products. Several studies of this kind were mentioned in Chapters 8 and 9, in which we considered the function of the ribosomes in processes of protein synthesis and mentioned the vacuolar system and the Golgi complex as sites in which the products could be segregated and stored, to be extruded later from the cytoplasm.

A detailed study of the "morphology of secretion" with electron microscopic

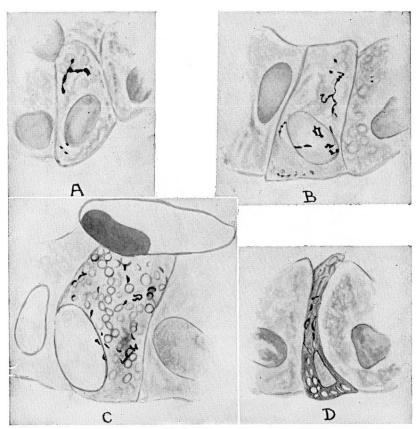

FIGURE 23–3. Parathyroid cells in various stages of their secretory activity. **A,** cell in repose, with a simple Golgi apparatus. **B,** hypertrophy and fragmentation of the Golgi apparatus. **C,** cell apparently accumulating the secretion; vacuoles with osmiophilic borders; Golgi apparatus completely fragmented. **D,** dark cell in stage of excretion. Osmic impregnation.

techniques in the different holocrine, apocrine and merocrine glands and also in the endocrine gland cells is presented in Palay's *Frontiers in cytology.*[6] Only a few more examples and remarks will be made here.

Particularly favorable material for the study of the secretory process are the cells of the adrenal medulla that produce and secrete catecholamines (epinephrine and norepinephrine). As shown by Plenick in 1902, catecholamines reduce osmium tetroxide intensely, and by this reaction they can be detected in minute amounts within the structure of the cell.

As can be observed in Figures 23–4 and 23–5, the first and smallest secretion droplets that appear are in the deepest region of the cytoplasm near the nuclear membrane. Some of the small vesicles belonging to the Golgi complex become filled with the dense material of the catecholamines. These droplets, always surrounded by the membrane, migrate toward the surface of the cell while increasing in size and density. As a result of this process of elaboration, the cytoplasm of the cell becomes filled with catechol-containing droplets about 160 $m\mu$ in diameter (Fig. 23–4).

The expulsion of the secretory material is mediated in this gland through the splanchnic nerves that innervate the cell by terminal endings filled with synaptic vesicles (see Chap. 22). These endings are cholinergic, which means that stimulation of the nerve releases acetylcholine, thus activating the excretion of catecholamines. It has been observed that an electrical stimulation that produces the maximum expulsion of the catechol secretion also increases the number of synaptic vesicles in the ending and the amount of acetylcholine released.[7]

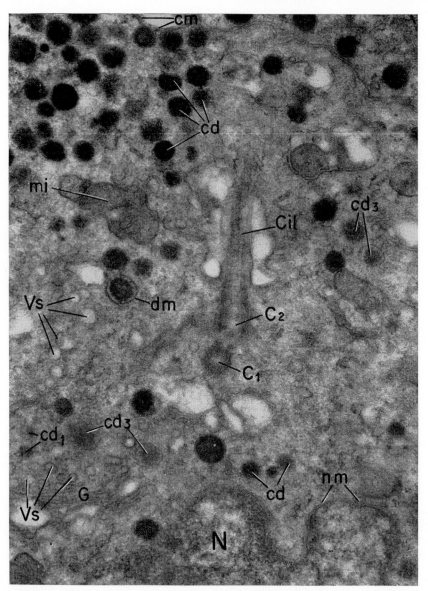

FIGURE 23–4. Electron micrograph of a chromaffin cell from the adrenal gland of the hamster. At the bottom, the nucleus (*N*) with the folded nuclear membrane (*nm*) can be seen. The supranuclear portion of the cytoplasm shows the Golgi complex (*G*), two centrioles (C_1, C_2) with a cilium (*Cil*) arising from one of them, several mitochondria (*mi*) and the catechol-containing droplets (*cd*). The smaller catechol droplets (cd_1, cd_2) appear in the Golgi zone. Within some of the small Golgi vesicles (*Vs*) the dense deposit is first observed. As the vesicles enlarge and the content increases (cd_2, cd_3), the clear space under the droplet membrane (*dm*) narrows. Completely formed catechol-containing droplets occupy the peripheral part of the cytoplasm near the cell membrane, (*cm*). ×51,500. (De Robertis and Sabatini.)

From the morphologic viewpoint the mechanism of the actual expulsion of the secretory product into the intercellular spaces is of considerable interest. As is indicated in the diagram of Figure 23–5, the catechol-containing droplets first become attached to the surface membrane. In a second stage they increase in size and become less dense (swelling). In a final stage the dense material is evacuated, leaving empty membranes that probably "disappear" within the surface membrane. At the same time, new droplets are being formed actively in the Golgi region (Fig. 23–5).[8]

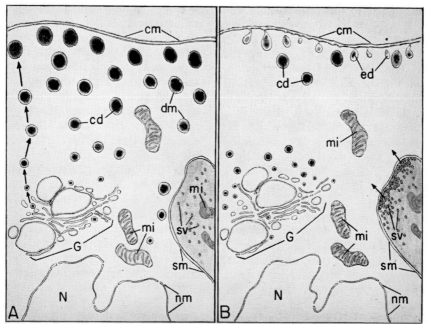

FIGURE 23–5. Diagrammatic interpretation of the mechanism of secretion in the chromaffin cell. **A,** Cell in the resting stage, showing the storage of mature catechol droplets in the outer cytoplasm. Near the nucleus within the Golgi complex new secretion is being formed at a slow rate. At the right, a portion of a nerve terminal, showing the synaptic vesicles (*sv*) and mitochondria (*mi*). *cd,* catechol droplets; *cm,* cell membrane; *dm,* droplet membrane; *G,* Golgi complex; *N,* nucleus; *nm,* nuclear membrane; *sm,* surface membrane. **B,** cell after strong electrical stimulation by way of the splanchnic nerve. Most of the catechol droplets have disappeared; the few that remain can be seen in different stages of excretion into the intercellular cleft. The Golgi complex is now forming new droplets at a higher rate. The nerve ending shows an increase of synaptic vesicles with accumulation at "active points" on the synaptic membrane. (De Robertis and Sabatini.)

This is a striking example of the process of vesiculation and membrane flow for active transport within the cell that was described in Chapter 10 (Fig. 10–18).[9] A similar mechanism for the excretion of synaptic vesicles at the synaptic endings was previously postulated.[10] By this mechanism, acetylcholine, epinephrine, norepinephrine or other active humoral agents may be synthesized by the cell, stored within a membrane and then moved and discharged instantly at the surface membrane, when the appropriate stimulus is acting.

An Example of a Secretory Process: The Pancreatic Cell

An example of a secretory cycle in which the secretion products are readily visible is that of the exocrine pancreatic cell, in which the cycle has been carefully studied (see reference 11). These cells belong to the groups of cells with serous or zymogenic secretion, so-called because they secrete a protein rich in enzymes.

The structure of a pancreatic cell has been described elsewhere in this book. In the resting state it presents a typical polarization of its components, which can be observed under the light microscope. The base of the cell is occupied by the nucleus, the basophilic substance containing ribonucleoproteins (Fig. 23–1), and elongate mitochondria oriented in the apicobasal direction. The apical or excretory region is occupied by refractile granules with a high protein concentration (Fig. 23–1). In the supranuclear zone and among the zymogen granules is a Golgi complex with a reticular appearance.

Under the electron microscope the great development of the endoplasmic reticulum with large cisternae oriented parallel to the cell axis is observed in the basal region (Fig. 10–3). These cisternae are covered by numerous ribosomes attached to the membrane while a smaller number of ribosomes are free in the cytoplasmic matrix (Fig. 10–3). The supranuclear region contains the cisternae and vesicles of the Golgi complex with their characteristic lack of ribosomes. Some of the vesicles contain a clear material; in others there is a more concentrated material, which by progressive condensation is transformed into the zymogen granules at the apex of the cell. Each one of these granules is bound by a membrane provided by the Golgi complex.

Injection of pilocarpine brings about a liquefaction of the zymogen granules and the rapid expulsion of their contents (Fig. 23–1B, C). By means of biomicroscopy the secretion products have been observed to pass directly through the cell membrane at the luminal surface.

Later, the cells elaborate more secretory granules, which accumulate at the apical pole. After several hours the cells regain the same appearance they had at the beginning of the cycle (Fig. 23–1F). During this stage the Golgi apparatus hypertrophies and becomes intensely osmiophilic and the basophilic substance shows a decrease in ribonucleic acid content.[12]

Isolation and Significance of Zymogen Granules

Since first postulated by Heidenhain in 1883, one of the most firmly supported views in cytology is that the granules observed in the majority of gland cells are secretion products. There are several evidences that this is the case, but until recently none of them were based on direct cytochemical evidence. In recent years by combining cell fractionation methods and electron microscopy of the pancreas it has been possible to confirm in a more direct way the correlation between zymogen granules and enzymic content.[13] This study has been facilitated by the extensive information available on the physical, biochemical, chemical and enzymic properties of the pancreatic juice and the use of suitable chromatographic procedures that permit the isolation of most of the proteins present in it.[14] A rather homogeneous and pure zymogen granule fraction has thus been isolated and studied under the electron microscope. This has been found to contain about 94 per cent protein and only 5 per cent phospholipid and 1 per cent nucleic acid. At pH 8 the granules are soluble and a membrane fraction remains, which represents the surface membranes that cover the zymogen granules within the cell. In the lysate of the granules and also in the pancreatic juice the following enzymes could be isolated by column chromatography: trypsinogen, chymotrypsinogen A, ribonuclease, amylase, chymotrypsinogen B, procarboxypeptidase B, deoxyribonuclease and procarboxypeptidase A.

The identity in enzyme composition between the zymogen granules and the pancreatic juice obtained by cannulation of the duct is direct evidence that both are related, and that, as postulated by Heidenhain, the granules are the secretion products.[13]

Ultrastructure of Pancreatic Secretion

The study under the electron microscope of the secretory process of the pancreas has confirmed and extended the observation of a functional relationship between the endoplasmic reticulum and the Golgi complex in secretion. The material synthesized by the ribosomes may sometimes be observed within the cavities of the endoplasmic reticulum, forming the so-called intracisternal granules.[15, 16] This material then passes into the Golgi complex and finally is concentrated and packed into the zymogen granules. The use of amino acids marked with radioisotopes, such as tritiated leucine (H^3-leucine) has confirmed the time and structural sequence: endoplasmic reticulum → Golgi complex → zymogen granules.

Guinea pigs are starved for several hours and then fed while H^3-leucine is given intravenously. In the fixed tissue, by radioautography at the electron microscope level, it is possible to observe that after a few minutes the isotope is localized in the endoplasmic reticulum of the basal region. Later it can be observed that the newly synthesized protein passes into the Golgi complex. In this region it apparently undergoes a two-step process: (1) it is diluted and may appear within large, clear vesicles, and (2) it becomes progressively concentrated into prozymogen granules surrounded by a membrane (Fig. 10–3). If the animal is sacrificed after a longer time, the label is found mainly in the zymogen granules and in the lumen of the acinus.[17] The discharge of the zymogen granules is produced by fusion of their limiting membrane with the cell membrane at the luminal surface.[18] These autoradiographic studies have clearly demonstrated that neither the nucleus nor the mitochondria participate directly in the secretory process. However, remember that the nucleus contributes the different RNA molecules, and mitochondria the energy (i.e., ATP) for the biochemical transformations.

Time Sequence in the Intracellular Secretion Process

In a study of the synthesis and migration of proteins in the pancreas of the rat similar results have been obtained. Owing to the feeding habits of these rodents, both synthesis and secretion in the pancreas are continuous. After the precursor is injected, the *radioactive concentration* (i.e., number of silver grains per unit area in the light microscope radioautograph) and the *protein concentration* were measured.[19] (The Millon reaction and an absorption cytophotometric method were employed. See Chap. 6.)

As shown in Figure 23–6, the radioactivity rapidly increased in the basal zone containing the endoplasmic reticulum (or ergastoplasm). Within two to five minutes protein containing H^3-leucine was found in this region. This increased for 30 minutes and then decreased. Measurements were also made in two other zones of the acinus. As shown in the diagram of Figure 23–6, these corresponded to the proximal zone of the zymogen granules containing also the Golgi complex and to the distal portion of the zymogen near the lumen.

Analysis of the time course in these three portions of the cell indicates that the protein migrates, and that in 30 minutes it reaches the proximal zymogen region and later on the distal one (Fig. 23–6), before being secreted into the duct system.

Figure 23–7 indicates the estimated

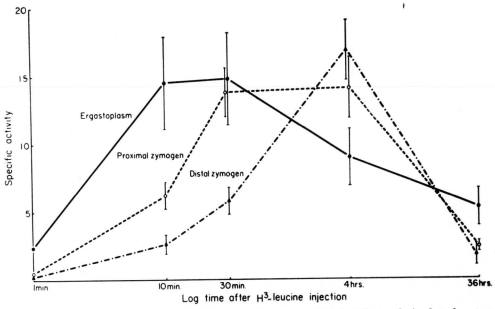

FIGURE 23–6.   Specific activity of the proteins in the ergastoplasm (solid triangles), plotted against the log of the time after injection of H^3-leucine into rats. The peak of specific activity is reached first in the ergastoplasm, then in the proximal and, finally, in the distal zymogen regions. (From Warshawsky et al., 1963.)

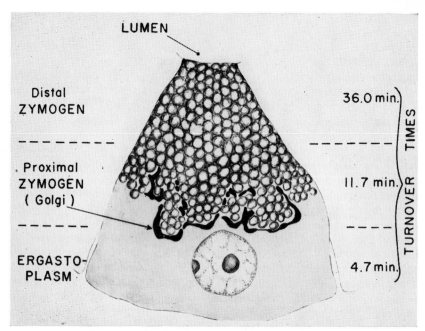

FIGURE 23–7. Diagram of a pancreatic acinar cell of the rat, showing the Golgi complex, ergasto-plasm and zymogen granules. **Right,** the turnover times of the proteins in each of the regions of the cell after the injection of H³-leucine. (From Warshawsky et al., 1963.)

turnover time of the radioactivity in the three regions of the cell: 4.7 minutes for the synthesis at the basal ergastoplasm, 11.7 minutes in the proximal zymogen (Golgi) region and 36 minutes in the distal zymogen region. The sum of these last two figures (i.e., 47.7 minutes) is the mean life span of a zymogen granule. Adding all the turnover times, the total life span of the proteins produced for export (i.e., zymogen granule) is of 52.4 minutes.

In addition to the *exportable proteins* with the rapid turnover of 4.7 minutes, the ergastoplasm apparently synthesizes other proteins of slow turnover (mean of 62.5 hours), which remain in the cell and are not used for export (i.e., *sedentary proteins*).

Mechanisms of Protein Synthesis and Secretion in the Pancreas

It is now possible to summarize all the available data in a coherent theory of protein secretion for the pancreas, which will probably apply for other protein secreting cells. The following sequential stages of secretion can be recognized (Fig. 23–8):

Ribosomal Stage. Proteins are synthesized in direct contact with polyribosomes present on the surface of the vacuolar system of the endoplasmic reticulum (Fig. 18–10). As indicated in Chapters 8 and 18, this is done by the interaction of messenger RNA (mRNA), which carries the genetic information from the DNA molecule contained in the chromosome and the aminoacyl-transfer RNA complex, which attaches in the proper sequence, with subsequent polymerization of the amino acids. This first stage takes place in seconds or a few minutes. Short experiments with labeled H³-leucine followed by cell fractionation have shown that in only three minutes the maximal activity is found in the ribosomes that are attached to the membranes of the vacuolar system. The disposition of the ribosomes on these membranes probably facilitates the interaction with mRNA and also the rapid passage of the exportable protein into the endoplasmic reticulum system.

Endoplasmic Reticulum Stage. The new synthesized proteins (i.e., enzymes) rapidly penetrate into the cisternae of the endoplasmic reticulum and migrate toward the apical zone of the cell. Some-

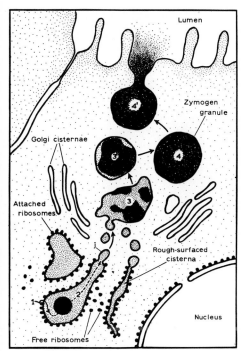

FIGURE 23–8. Diagram of the secretory process in the pancreatic acinus, showing the different stages described in the text. *1*, ribosomal stage; *2*, endoplasmic reticulum stage; *3,3'*, Golgi complex stage; *4*, zymogen stage; *4'*, release of zymogen into the lumen, (intraluminal stage). (Courtesy of G. E. Palade.)

times this material appears as small intercisternal granules, but in most cases it is a dilute solution of protein.

Golgi Complex Stage. After a few minutes the secreted protein reaches the Golgi zone, probably by way of continuities with the endoplasmic reticulum, which may be permanent or, more probably, transient. In this region a two-fold process may occur. The protein may be first diluted, filling large vacuoles of the Golgi complex and at a second stage concentrated progressively, forming *pro-zymogen granules* surrounded by a Golgi membrane.

Zymogen Stage. By progressive condensation, the enzymes migrate into the apical portion of the cell where they will be delivered by previous attachment of the surface membrane of the granule with the cell membrane at the luminal surface.

Intraluminal Stage. The enzymes progress slowly through the lumen of the acinus and ducts and then are di-

luted by other secretions prior to entering the intestinal cavity.

GENERAL REFERENCES

Bennett, H. S. (1941) Cytological manifestations of secretion in the adrenal medulla of the cat. *Amer. J. Anat.*, 69:333.

Caro, L. G., and Palade, G. E. (1961) Le role de l'appareil de Golgi dans le processus sécrétoire. Étude autoradiographique. *C. R. Soc. Biol.*, 155:1750.

Dawson, A. B. (1942) Some morphological aspects of the secretory process. *Fed. Proc.*, 1:233.

De Robertis, E. (1942) Citofisiologia de la glándula paratiroides. *Rev. Med. Lat. Amer.*, 27:118.

De Robertis, E. (1949) Cytological and cytochemical bases of thyroid function. *Ann. N.Y. Acad. Sci.*, 50:317.

De Robertis, E., and Sabatini, D. D. (1960) Submicroscopic analysis of the secretory process in the adrenal medulla. *Fed. Proc.*, 19:70.

Gabe, M., and Arvy, L. (1961) Gland cells. In: *The cell.* Vol. 5, p. 1. (Brachet, J., and Mirsky, A. E., eds.) Academic Press, New York.

Hirsch, G. C. (1955) Allgemeine Stoffwechselphysiologie des Cytoplasmas. *Hb. Allg. Pathol.*, Bd. 11.

Hirsch, G. C. (1961) The external secretion of the pancreas as a whole and the communication between the endoplasmic reticulum and the Golgi bodies. In: *Biological structure and function*, Vol. 1, p. 195. (Goodwin, T. W., and Lindberg, O., eds.) Academic Press, New York.

Junqueira, L. C. (1955) Aspects of the biochemistry of cell secretion. In: *Symposium on cell secretion.* Bello Horizonte.

Junqueira, L. C., and Hirsch, G. C. (1956) Cell secretion: a study of pancreas and salivary glands. *Internat. Rev. Cytol.*, 5:323.

Kurosumi, K. (1961) Electron microscopic analysis of the secretion mechanism. *Internat. Rev. Cytol.*, 11:1.

Palay, S. L. (1958) The morphology of secretion. In: *Frontiers in cytology.* (Palay, S. L., ed.) Yale University Press, New Haven.

Ries, E. (1938) *Grundriss der Histophysiologie.* Akademische Verlagsgesellschaft, Leipzig.

CITED REFERENCES

1. Hirsch, G. C. (1961) The external secretion of the pancreas as a whole and the communication between the endoplasmic reticulum and the Golgi bodies. In: *Biological structure and function*, Vol. 1,

p. 195. (Goodwin, T. W., and Lindberg, O., eds.) Academic Press, New York.

2. Junqueira, L. C., et al. (1949) *J. Cell. Comp. Physiol., 34:*129.

3. Hirsch, G. C. (1955) Allgemeine Stoffwechselphysiologie des Cytoplasmas. *Hb. Allg. Pathol.,* Bd. *11.*

4. De Robertis, E. (1940) *Anat. Rec., 78:*473.

5. De Robertis, E. (1941) *Anat. Rec., 80:*219.

6. Palay, S. L. (1958) The morphology of secretion. In: *Frontiers in cytology.* Yale University Press, New Haven.

7. De Robertis, E., and Vaz Ferreira, A. (1957) *J. Biophys. Biochem. Cytol., 3:*611.

8. De Robertis, E., and Sabatini, D. D. (1960) *Fed. Proc., 19:*70.

9. Bennett, H. S. (1956) *J. Biophys. Biochem. Cytol., 2,* part 4, suppl. 99.

10. De Robertis, E., and Bennett, H. S. (1955) *J. Biophys. Biochem. Cytol., 1:*47.

11. Ries, E. (1938) *Grundriss der Histophysiologie.* Akademische Verlagsgesellschaft, Leipzig.

12. Caspersson, T., Landstrom-Hyden, H., and Aquilonius, L. (1941) *Chromosoma, 2:* 127.

13. Greene, L. J., Hirs, C. H. W., and Palade, G. E. (1963) *J. Biol. Chem., 238:*2054.

14. Keller, P. J., Cohen, E., and Neurath, J. (1958) *J. Biol. Chem., 230:*905.

15. Palade, G. E.(1956) *J. Biophys. Biochem. Cytol., 2:*417.

16. Siekevitz, P., and Palade, G. E. (1958) *J. Biophys. Biochem. Cytol., 4:*203.

17. Caro, L., and Palade, G. E. (1964) *J. Cell Biol., 20:*473.

18. Palade, G. E. (1959) In: *Subcellular particles.* (Hayashi, T., ed.) The Ronald Press Co., New York, p. 64.

19. Warshawsky, H., Leblond, C. P., and Droz, B. (1963) *J. Cell Biol., 16:*1.

20. Siekevitz, P., and Palade, G. E. (1959) *J. Biophys. Biochem. Cytol., 5:*1.

INDEX

Page numbers in *italics* refer to illustrations and tables.